TRANSCRIPTIONAL REGULATION

TRANSCRIPTIONAL REGULATION

Edited by

Steven L. McKnight
Carnegie Institution of Washington

Keith R. Yamamoto
University of California, San Francisco

COLD SPRING HARBOR LABORATORY PRESS
1992

TRANSCRIPTIONAL REGULATION

Monograph 22
Copyright 1992 by Cold Spring Harbor Laboratory Press
All rights reserved
Printed in the United States of America
Book design by Emily Harste

Library of Congress Cataloging-in-Publication Data

Transcriptional Regulation / edited by Steven L. McKnight and Keith R. Yamamoto.
   p. cm. -- (Cold Spring Harbor monograph series; 22)
   Includes bibliographical references and index.
   ISBN 0-87969-410-6
   ISBN 0-87969-425-4 (pbk.)
   1. Genetic transcription--Regulation   2. Genetic regulation.
I. McKnight, Steven L.   II. Yamamoto, Keith R.   III. Series.
QH450.2.T695   1992   92-31461
574.87'322--dc20   CIP

All Cold Spring Harbor Laboratory Press publications may be ordered directly from Cold Spring Harbor Laboratory Press, 10 Skyline Drive, Plainview, New York 11803-2500. Phone: 1-800-843-4388 in Continental U.S. and Canada. All other locations (516) 349-1930. FAX: (516) 349-1946.

Contents

Chromatin/DNA Topology

Contents of companion volume

BOOK 1

Preface

Termination/Attenuation

Structural Studies

TRANSCRIPTIONAL
REGULATION

Regulatory Factors

23

lac Repressor

Jay D. Gralla
Department of Chemistry and Biochemistry and
The Molecular Biology Institute
University of California
Los Angeles, California 90024-1569

OVERVIEW

Physiological repression of the *lac* operon involves a DNA loop stabilized by the interaction of two pairs of DNA-recognition domains with two separated DNA sequence elements. The critical roles of DNA sequences, repressor protein domains, and the competition between RNA polymerase and repressor are discussed in this review.

INTRODUCTION

"The reports of my death are greatly exaggerated," said Mark Twain, and so has it been with study of the *lac* operon. The 1990s mark the sixth decade in which *lac* has been studied as a genetic system (Monod and Audureau 1946), and such work continues to serve both as a model for comparison and as an engine for change. Although some interest in the *lac* operon is mere idle curiosity about the way that blue colonies appear, much more is centered on how *lac* repressor binds simultaneously to two remote operators and what it does there in cooperation with RNA polymerase to accomplish regulation.

Over the years, the *lac* system has been a proving ground for testing new concepts and developing new techniques. The intensity of investigation is staggering; thousands of point mutations have been introduced into the protein (see Kleina and Miller 1990 and references therein) and bases in the operator have not only been mutated extensively (see Lehming et al. 1990 and references therein), but have even been changed to specifically modified nucleotides to test groups involved in recognition (see Goeddel et al. 1978). Such essential techniques as footprinting, chemical probing, gel shift analysis, and blue colony assays were all tried first on *lac* and extended subsequently to other systems. For a while it seemed that *lac* would be left behind in the age of regulation from distant sites, but here, too, the unexpected involvement of remote operators has made *lac* studies appropriate to such systems (for review, see Gralla 1989a,b). Because of the historical availability of techniques and strains, we now know precisely how the distant sites communicate and even what sites on the protein as well as the DNA are important for this. We know the molecular step at which repressor acts during transcription and the role of sequence context in altering its ability to function. The point of this brief review is to present the detailed action of *lac* repressor in the hope of making the core of this vast body of knowledge accessible to researchers working on other regulatory systems.

STRUCTURE OF THE REPRESSOR/O_1 COMPLEX

Although the *lac* operon has three repressor binding sites, most studies have focused on the role of the O_1 operator. This is the sequence that was first isolated as the primary *lac* operator and that overlaps the start point of transcription (Gilbert and Maxam 1973). It is also the DNA element that is of dominant importance in repression and that binds repressor most tightly (see below). In this section, I discuss what is known about the repression complex consisting of *lac* repressor tetramer and O_1 operator. The influence of the other operators on the functional and structural aspects of this complex are considered later.

Since this structure has not yet been solved by crystallographic methods, a combination of genetic, biochemical, and biophysical studies has been used to infer it. As most regulatory proteins suffer from the same status, *lac* studies continue to be adapted to other proteins. The basic features of the protein are well known from these studies. It is a tetramer with four identical subunits; it binds DNA tightly only in the absence of inducing sugars; the amino-terminal region of the protein is the part that mediates DNA binding; and the carboxy-terminal region is important in determining its aggregation state.

Symmetry is known to play a key role in operator recognition by the protein (see Gilbert et al. 1975; Ogata and Gilbert 1979; Betz et al. 1986; Lehming et al. 1987). The *lac* O_1 operator (as well as the auxiliary operators) is pseudo-symmetric, with each half forming a similar binding site but in opposite orientation. Each half-operator is believed to be recognized by a repressor subunit. That is, two identical subunits of the tetramer appear to be oriented head-to-head, and this dimer surface interacts with the two head-to-head half-operators within the overall symmetric operator. The importance of this symmetry is probably that it allows the complex to be stabilized by the simultaneous interactions of two DNA-binding domains from the same protein complex. Very substantial evidence, cited below, indicates that the interaction of a single DNA-binding domain is insufficient to allow tight binding. Thus, the binding energy resulting from interaction between a single DNA-binding domain and the operator is inadequate. The symmetry allows this binding energy to be increased by specifying the simultaneous interaction of two DNA-binding domains with the symmetric element.

Although the operator is symmetric, there are some differences in how the left and right halves are bound by repressor. This may be due in part to their slightly different sequences and in part to the suboptimal spacing between the halves. Point mutations that increase operator symmetry lead to lesser rather than greater binding. However, one of these fully symmetric operators does direct greater affinity than wild type if the spacing between the two halves is reduced by one base pair. These observations (Lehming et al. 1987; Sasmor and Betz 1990) may suggest that the natural spacing specifies DNA surfaces of the half-operators that are mutually oriented so as to prevent the simultaneous insertion of the repressor subunits in an optimal manner. The halves may need to be of slightly different sequence to accommodate this suboptimal orientation of the repressor on the full operator.

The specificity for operator recognition resides in the amino terminus of the protein. Many mutations in this region show reduced ability to function (Miller et al. 1979; Gordon et al. 1988; Kleina and Miller 1990 and references therein) without obviously affecting the ability of the protein to form tetramers (Müller-Hill et al. 1968). This amino terminus appears to constitute a separate protein domain (Adler et al. 1972; Platt et al. 1973), since mild proteolytic digestion separates it from the remainder of the protein. The separated amino-terminal headpiece binds operator using contacts common to the whole protein (Ogata and Gilbert 1978) but with much reduced affinity.

The reason that the isolated headpiece alone binds operator weakly is probably that it cannot dimerize due to missing residues elsewhere in the protein. This means that a complex with only one headpiece is missing half its stabilizing interactions. Although a complex with two separate headpieces bound to DNA does form, its pathway involves a less favorable three-component interaction. In contrast, nonproteolyzed *lac* repressors that form dimers rather than tetramers do bind *lac* O_1 DNA tightly (Oehler et al. 1990), which emphasizes the importance of delivering two but not four domains to the O_1 operator DNA (Kania and Müller-Hill 1977). Most bacterial DNA-binding proteins form complexes involving the simultaneous presence of two DNA-binding domains, presumably because a single domain provides insufficient energy. This is reflected in the symmetry of most bacterial operators and the presence of two separated elements bound simultaneously in bacterial promoters (for review, see Gralla 1989a,1990).

The structure of the DNA-binding domain was predicted to be a helix-turn-helix (HTH) (Matthews et al. 1982), and this general idea was confirmed by nuclear magnetic resonance (NMR) studies of the headpiece (Lamerichs et al. 1989) and is supported by genetic studies (Gordon et al. 1988; Kleina and Miller, 1990 and references therein). The actual DNA-binding domain, however, extends beyond the HTH region, which ends near residue 25 and continues to near residue 60. The NMR model suggests that a third helix forms within this region, completing a DNA-binding domain held together by a hydrophobic core common to all three helices. The major contacts to DNA are believed to be from the central "recognition" helix of the HTH part of the structure, but the other helices also make contact with the DNA. The orientation of the HTH with respect to *lac* DNA is opposite from that observed with the regulatory proteins that bind the operators of lambdoid phages (Lehming et al. 1988; Lamerichs et al. 1989).

Although the orientation of the HTH within the recognition domain structure differs, it is still presumed to promote DNA recognition by penetrating the major groove of the DNA. Both the protein and DNA components have been mutated extensively in attempts to deduce the details of recognition. Some of the interactions appear to be simple recognition between single amino acids and nucleotides (see Lehming et al. 1990). Although simple interactions with bases in the major groove are important, chemical probing and synthesis studies (see Goeddel et al. 1978; Ogata and Gilbert 1979) indicate that other interactions are important as well. These include minor groove and backbone contacts.

The sequences of the repressor DNA "recognition" helix and of the operator are similar to a number of other repressors and operators. Thus, just a few changes in gal DNA can cause the *lac* repressor to recognize the operators of the gal operon (Haber and Adhya 1988). Similarly, a few changes in the gal repressor protein cause it to recognize a *lac* operator (Lehming et al. 1990). These similarities suggest that common means of recognition are used by a family of bacterial repressors.

Mutations in the DNA-binding domain are generally negative dominant; that is, when coexpressed with wild-type proteins, they interfere with the function of the wild-type proteins. This occurs in part because of subunit mixing with the mixed tetramers containing both wild-type and mutant DNA-binding domains (Müller-Hill et al. 1968). The mixed tetramers bind DNA poorly because, as just discussed, they have only one optimal DNA-binding domain rather than the two that are required to bind tightly to DNA. Some repressors with mutations in this region have an increased susceptibility to intracellular degradation.

Repressor binding to operator is accompanied by modest conformational changes. The DNA remains in B-form (Lamerichs et al. 1989) and is unwound slightly (Douc-Rasy et al. 1989), and strong bending has not been detected. As the protein binds, it displaces cations from the DNA (Ha et al. 1989). Point mutations in either half of the operator disrupt DNA binding to the O_1 operator as a whole (Jobe et al. 1974). This dominance is formally analogous to having mixed wild-type and defective repressor subunits; mutating either the protein or the DNA component to inactivate interactions at just one half of the operator is sufficient to prevent function.

The carboxy-terminal region of the repressor is important in determining the aggregation state of the protein (Platt et al. 1973; Schmitz et at. 1976). Some of the mutants in this region form dimeric proteins that nevertheless can repress *lac* transcription, although not fully (see below). Other mutations promote dissociation to monomers and do not repress well. These monomers have the intact amino-terminal DNA-binding domain and bind inducing sugars (Daly and Matthews 1986). That they are ineffective is again likely related to the inability of monomeric DNA-binding domains to interact tightly with DNA.

Inducing sugars reduce the affinity of repressor for operator (Gilbert and Müller-Hill 1966; Riggs et al. 1968) so that the two come apart to allow induction when necessary. The residues important for induction have been mapped genetically. They cluster just after the amino-terminal DNA-binding domain and then occur in patches elsewhere in the protein with an approximate periodicity of 26 residues (Miller 1979). There have been proposals for mechanisms of sugar binding, but these have remained largely untested (Sams et at. 1984). It is also not known how sugar binding prevents DNA binding. Since the DNA-binding region seems to form a separate domain, one possibility would be that the sugar causes a change in the relative orientation of the DNA-binding domains in the tetramer; this could prevent the simultaneous delivery of two domains and reduce affinity drastically. This idea has not been tested.

In the most simple view, *lac* repressor consists of two complex domains. The induction domain is clearly noncontiguous in the linear amino acid sequence but has been suggested to form a compact sugar-binding structure in three dimensions. The repression domain consists at least of an amino-terminal DNA-binding subdomain and a carboxy-terminal multimerization subdomain. These structures cooperate to form a surface capable of binding simultaneously to the two very similar halves of the *lac* operator. What happens when this binding occurs in vivo is the subject of the next section.

WHAT HAPPENS AT THE O_1 OPERATOR TO ACCOMPLISH REPRESSION

When repressor is bound to the O_1 operator, it covers the start point of transcription and part of the binding site for RNA polymerase (Gilbert et al. 1975). It has been known for some time that bound repressor prevents initiation of transcription by interfering with the function of RNA polymerase. This was demonstrated using order of addition experiments where conditions were set up so that the DNA template could be transcribed only a single time. Repressor was effective if added to DNA before the addition of RNA polymerase, but ineffective if the DNA was first allowed to form open complexes with the polymerase. Thus, prebound repressor prevents polymerase from functioning, but repressor cannot inactivate open or initiated transcription complexes (Majors 1975).

Initially, it was thought that the bound repressor sterically blocked the binding of polymerase, thereby preventing its functioning. However, it is now known that repressor and polymerase can bind the *lac* promoter-operator simultaneously, as shown by the isolation of complexes containing the two proteins and DNA (Straney and Crothers 1987). Footprinting shows that the polymerase does not make the usual downstream DNA contacts in this complex; it is this region that is covered by bound repressor. The polymerase presumably uses the upstream transcription elements, not covered by repressor, to make some stabilizing contacts. Such contacts are normally insufficient to hold polymerase at the promoter (Gralla 1990), and the evidence suggests that the DNA-bound repressor provides additional elements of stabilization for the polymerase (Straney and Crothers 1987). Nevertheless, the bound polymerase is prevented from functioning, either because it cannot melt the DNA or because repressor interferes with initiated polymerase and prevents it from leaving the promoter.

A key determinant of the effectiveness of repression is the lifetime of the repressor-operator complex. The repressor binds very tightly to DNA, but the half-life of the complex in vitro is typically just a few minutes. Although the complex reforms extremely rapidly after dissociating, during the very brief time that the DNA is free there is theoretically a window of opportunity for polymerase to initiate transcription. In studies of mutant operators, it was found that as the lifetime of the repressor-DNA complex decreased there was a commensurate increase in the level of constitutive transcription under repression conditions (Jobe et al. 1974). This observation supports the idea that during the cycling of repressor on and off the operator, polymerase can occasionally transcribe. During repression conditions there would be a small but finite probability of this happening each time repressor dissociated.

The effect of transient dissociation of repressor is probably amplified since, as cited above, the polymerase can be bound to DNA during repression in vitro, albeit in a nonfunctional complex. In this context, when the repressor is released transiently during the normal course of equilibrium dissociation and association, the bound polymerase might initiate rapidly, leading to an inappropriate round of transcription. If the polymerase were not prebound, this would likely occur less frequently. This is because in a functional competition between the two proteins from free solution, repressor wins (Majors 1975), probably because open promoter complexes form only after a series of slow conformational changes (Gralla 1990). As just mentioned, there is a secondary consequence of repressor binding which is to actually increase the occupancy of the promoter by assisting the association of polymerase with the transcriptionally inactive complex (Straney and Crothers 1987). This may position the polymerase to initiate a rapid round of transcription upon physiological induction.

This kinetic competition between polymerase and repressor is of critical importance in understanding the effectiveness of repression (Lanzer and Bujard 1988). With some exceptions, repressor is less effective as the nearby promoter sequence is changed to increase the rate at which RNA polymerase can become associated with the DNA in a stable manner. This is interpreted to mean that although repressor normally wins the competition, polymerase can do so with finite probability. The repressor is also more effective when the operator is artificially moved upstream to the spacer region that separates the two transcription elements of the typical *Escherichia coli* promoter. This may be because in that position it occludes both elements, interfering with even the nonproductive binding of RNA polymerase. Thus, when repressor dissociates, there is likely not a prebound polymerase present that can win the subsequent round of kinetic competition.

A key property associated with tight *lac* repression is therefore the placement of repressor over a region that is also critically important for RNA polymerase binding and function. Once bound, the repressor's effectiveness appears to be determined by the lifetime of the protein-DNA complex. This lifetime is lengthened due to the presence of remote auxiliary *lac* operators, as I now discuss.

THE ROLE OF DISTANT OPERATORS

In addition to the O_1 operator, there are two auxiliary *lac* operators that are located at sites somewhat distant from the start point of transcription (Reznikoff et al. 1974; Gilbert et al. 1975). These sites bind repressor rather weakly on their own, and this, coupled with their remote location, caused their possible functional significance to be deemphasized. The stronger of the two sites (O_2) is located approximately 400 bp downstream within the coding region for β-galactosidase. The weaker (O_3) is located 93 bp upstream from O_1. It is now known that these sites have an important secondary influence on repression of the *lac* operon (Eismann et al. 1987; Flashner and Gralla 1988a; Gralla 1989a,b; Oehler et al. 1990).

When both of these auxiliary operators are inactivated by mutation (Oehler et al. 1990), *lac* repression drops to 18-fold from its full potential level of approximately 1300-fold, a factor of 70 loss of repressibility. Mutating either of the two auxiliary operators alone leads to only modest effects, a 3-fold loss with lack of O_2 and less than a 2-fold loss upon inactivation of O_3. In contrast, when both auxiliary operators are retained but the O_1 operator is mutated, repression is barely detectable, having dropped more than 600-fold. Thus, the O_1 operator is clearly of primary importance, since its inactivation is greater than 100-fold more deleterious than inactivation of either of the other operators. Nevertheless, the O_2 and O_3 operators are important, since the presence of at least one of them is necessary to bring repression near (within 2- or 3-fold of) the full potential level. Since the retention of either of the auxiliary operators is sufficient for this level of repression, they can be viewed as somewhat functionally redundant.

The causes of these various effects are now understood at the molecular level. Recall that the repressor is a tetramer, but only a dimer is sufficient to bind the O_1 operator properly. This leaves the other dimer within the DNA-bound tetramer free to interact with another free *lac* operator. Numerous studies have shown that artificial (Herrin and Bennett 1984; Besse et al. 1986; Mossing and Record 1986) and natural (Whitson and Matthews 1986; Betz 1987; Borowiec et al. 1987; Flashner and Gralla 1988a; Sasse-Dwight and Gralla 1988) *lac* operators can cooperate functionally over long distances. The form of this cooperativity was deduced to involve DNA loop formation from phasing, chemical probing, and most directly, observation using electronmicroscopy (Mossing and Record 1986; Borowiec et al. 1987; Krämer et al. 1987, 1988). Thus, when repressor is bound to O_1, it may also become bound to either O_2 or O_3 with the intervening DNA being looped out. Although the interaction with O_2 is of greater importance, the alternative

O_1/O_3 loop builds a functional redundancy into the repression system.

Binding studies in vivo (Flashner and Gralla 1988a; Sasse-Dwight and Gralla 1988) have shown that the three *lac* operators cooperate to bind repressor more tightly than would be allowed by noncooperative interactions. For example, when O_2 is inactivated, repressor binds approximately 3-fold less tightly to O_1. Inactivation of O_1 decreases affinity at the remote O_2 operator approximately 12-fold. Thus, the looped complex containing repressor, O_1, and O_2 is considerably more stable than a complex containing repressor and any single operator. As discussed in the previous section, complexes of greater stability would be expected to compete better with RNA polymerase, leading to more effective repression, as has been observed.

This general model is further supported by experiments showing that both loop formation and cooperative repression are nearly undetectable when a mutant *lac* repressor that forms dimers rather than tetramers is used (Oehler et al. 1990). Thus, in an experimental context where the auxiliary operators cause a nearly 500-fold increase in repression by the repressor tetramer, the dimeric mutant repressor is assisted only 2-fold by the presence of both O_2 and O_3. The molecular basis of this loss of ability to assist O_1 is likely to be inability to form a stable looped complex; the same mutant repressor dimer is also strongly inhibited from forming loops in vitro (Mandal et al. 1990). Taken together, these data confirm that one needs tetrameric repressor capable of interacting with O_1 and another remote operator to achieve very tight repression.

The primacy of the O_1 operator in repression is due to its position with respect to the start point of transcription, which allows it to interfere with transcription initiation. When it is artificially removed to a downstream position, it functions poorly (Reznikoff et al. 1969; Deuschle et al. 1986). It does, however, have residual function (Deuschle et al. 1986), suggesting that it can inhibit transcription elongation (Sellitti et al. 1987). The O_2 operator has a minor blocking effect of this type in accord with its position within the transcribed β-galactosidase gene (Flashner and Gralla 1988a). The blocking effect, however, depends on the presence of the upstream O_1 operator since, as discussed above, O_1 enhances binding to the weak O_2 operator by 12-fold. Without repressor binding to O_1, O_2 will not be strongly filled in vivo and will not repress. Thus, under strong repression conditions, an O_1/O_2 looped complex is believed to predominate in vivo and primarily block initiation but also interfere with elongation by any nonblocked polymerases. The role of the O_2 operator is to strengthen binding to O_1 assisting in the primary initiation control and to cooperate with O_1 in promoting the minor elongation control (Flashner and Gralla 1988a).

Since the *lac* repression looping system is so easy to manipulate in vitro, it has been used in model studies of the mechanisms involved in forming complexes involving looped DNA. The ability to form a looped complex varies with the relative position of two operators (Bellomy et al. 1988; Krämer et al. 1988). As has been inferred in other systems, loop formation (and repression) is maximal when the two operators are separated by an integral number of DNA helical turns. In this arrangement, the intervening DNA can loop out to touch the *lac* tetramer at two sites without needing to twist the helix of the DNA in between to bring the two sites to the same side of DNA. If the looped-out *lac* DNA is too short and therefore too stiff to bend around easily, then it becomes sharply bent (Krämer et al. 1987) at a preferred position within the loop (Borowiec et al. 1987). Such short loops are less stable than longer loops. *lac* loop formation can be assisted by DNA supercoiling (Borowiec et al. 1987; Whitson et al. 1987; Sasse-Dwight and Gralla 1988; Eismann and Müller-Hill 1990), which promotes the bending and untwisting of DNA. Repressor binding is also assisted by the chromosomal protein HU in vitro, which is believed to make the DNA more flexible by promoting bent conformations (Flashner and Gralla 1988b). Thus, the relative orientation of the two operators on the DNA helix circumference and the ability to distort the operators and intervening DNA are significant determinants in forming a looped *lac* repression complex.

A BRIEF PERSPECTIVE

Although the *lac* system is often described as simple in comparison to eukaryotic systems, it is revealing to analyze the *lac* system as eukaryotic systems are commonly analyzed. Consider a thought experiment where a series of linker scans and deletions are made in the *lac* regulatory region. Beginning upstream, one would first encounter a site (O_3) where deletions lead to a 2-fold loss of repression control. Next, one would encounter a region where there would be a 50-fold loss of promoter function (the site for binding catabolite activator protein). This effect would be much less if the cells were grown in rich media where CRP activation is weak. Next would come another site required for high-level promoter function (the –35 polymerase element). After a short spacer, one would encounter yet a third element required for full promoter activity (the –10 region, which is a TATA-like element). Deletion of this element not only reduces transcription drastically, but also can activate minor cryptic promoter elements leading to new mRNA start sites (see Karls et al. 1989). Just adjacent, one would find an element required for strong repression (O_1). Finally, some 0.4 kb downstream, one would encounter the third element of the repression apparatus (O_2). In this analysis, six elements would be encountered: three for positive regulation and three for negative regulation. Five would be closely clustered, and in some cases overlapping, and one would be 0.4 kb removed. One of the positive elements would be inducible by general changes in media. All the negative elements would show properties that were dependent on the presence of certain sugars. If analysis of a eukaryotic regulatory region showed six transcription elements with such properties, it would undoubtedly seem complicated, yet in the *lac* case it seems simple because we know the detailed role of each. One hopes that such studies of *lac* regulation will ultimately contribute to making the eukaryotic systems appear to be more simple.

ACKNOWLEDGMENTS

Preparation of this article was supported by U.S. Public Health Service grant GM-35754.

REFERENCES

Adler, K., K. Beyreuther, E. Fanning, N. Geisler, B. Gronenborn, A. Klemm, B. Müller-Hill, M. Pfahl, and A. Schmitz. 1972. How *lac* repressor binds to DNA. *Nature* **237:** 322–327.

Bellomy, G.R., M.C. Mossing, and M.T. Record, Jr. 1988. Physical properties of DNA *in vivo* as probed by the length dependence of the *lac* operator looping process. *Biochemistry* **27:** 3900–3906.

Besse, M., B. von Wilcken-Bergmann, and B. Müller-Hill. 1986. Synthetic *lac* operator mediates repression through *lac* repressor when introduced upstream and downstream from *lac* promoter. *EMBO J.* **5:** 1377–1381.

Betz, J. 1987. Affinities of tight-binding lactose repressors for wild-type and pseudo-operators. *J. Mol. Biol.* **195:** 495–504.

Betz, J.L., H.M. Sasmor, F. Buck, M.Y. Insley, and M.N. Caruthers. 1986. Base substitution mutants of the *lac* operator: In vivo and in vitro affinities for *lac* repressor. *Gene* **50:** 123–132.

Borowiec, J.A., L. Zhang, S. Sasse-Dwight, and J.D. Gralla. 1987. DNA supercoiling promotes formation of a bent repression loop in *lac* DNA. *J. Mol. Biol.* **196:** 101–111.

Daly, T.J. and K.S. Matthews. 1986. Characterization and modification of a monomeric mutant of the lactose repressor protein. *Biochemistry* **25:** 5474–5478.

Deuschle, U., R. Gentz, and H. Bujard. 1986. *lac* repressor blocks transcribing RNA polymerase and terminates transcription. *Proc. Natl. Acad. Sci.* **83:** 4134–4137.

Douc-Rasy, S., A. Kolb, and A. Prunell. 1989. Protein-induced unwinding of DNA: Measurement by gel electrophoresis of complexes with DNA minicircles. Application to restriction endonuclease EcoRI, catabolite gene activator protein and *lac* repressor. *Nucleic Acids Res.* **17:** 5173–5189.

Eismann, E.R. and B. Müller-Hill. 1990. *lac* repressor forms stable loops *in vitro* with supercoiled wild-type *lac* DNA containing all three natural *lac* operators. *J. Mol. Biol.* **213:** 763–775.

Eismann, E.R., B. von Wilcken-Bergmann, and B. Müller-Hill. 1987. Specific destruction of the second *lac* operator decreases repression of the *lac* operon in *Escherichia coli* five-fold. *J. Mol. Biol.* **195:** 949–952.

Flashner, Y. and J.D. Gralla. 1988a. Dual mechanism of repression at a distance in the *lac* operon. *Proc. Natl. Acad. Sci.* **85:** 8968–8972.

————. 1988b. DNA dynamic flexibility and protein recognition: Differential stimulation by bacterial histone-like protein HU. *Cell* **54:** 713–721.

Gilbert, W. and A. Maxam. 1973. The nucleotide sequence of the *lac* operator. *Proc. Natl. Acad. Sci.* **70:** 3581–3584.

Gilbert, W. and B. Müller-Hill. 1966. Isolation of the *lac* repressor. *Proc. Natl. Acad. Sci.* **56:** 1891–1898.

Gilbert, W., J. Gralla, J. Majors, and A. Maxam. 1975. Lactose operator sequences and the action of *lac* repressor. In *Protein ligand interactions* (ed. H. Sund and G. Blauer), pp. 193–210. de Gruyter, Berlin.

Goeddel, D., D. Yansura, and M. Carruthers. 1978. How *lac* repressor recognizes *lac* operator. *Proc. Natl. Acad. Sci.* **75:** 3578–3582.

Gordon, A.J.E., P.A. Burns, D.F. Fix, F. Yatagai, F.L. Allen, M.J. Horsfall, J.A. Halliday, J. Gray, C. Bernelot-Moens, and B.W. Glickman. 1988. Missense mutation in the *lacI* gene of *Escherichia coli.* Inferences on the structure of the repressor protein. *J. Mol. Biol.* **200:** 239–251.

Gralla, J.D. 1989a. Bacterial gene regulation from distant DNA sites. *Cell* **57:** 193–195.

————. 1989b. Specific repression in the *lac* operon. *UCLA Symp. Mol. Cell. Biol.* **95:** 3–10.

————. 1990. Promoter recognition and mRNA initiation by *E. coli* Eσ^{70}. *Methods Enzymol.* **185:** 37–54.

Ha, J.-H., R.S. Spolar, and M.T. Record, Jr. 1989. Role of the hydrophobic effect in stability of site-specific protein-DNA complexes. *J. Mol. Biol.* **209:** 801–816.

Haber, R. and S. Adhya. 1988. Interaction of spatially separated protein-DNA complexes for control of gene expression: Operator conversion. *Proc. Natl. Acad. Sci.* **85:** 9683–9687.

Herrin, G.L. and G.N. Bennett. 1984. Role of DNA regions flanking the tryptophan promoter of *Escherichia coli.* II. Insertion of *lac* operator fragments. *Gene* **32:** 349–356.

Jobe, A., J.R. Sadler, and S. Bourgeois. 1974. *Lac* repressor-operator interaction. *J. Mol. Biol.* **85:** 231–248.

Kania, J. and B. Müller-Hill. 1977. Construction, isolation and implications of repressor-galactosidase •β-galactosidase hybrid molecules. *Eur. J. Biochem.* **79:** 381–386.

Karls, R., V. Schulz, S. Jovanovich, S. Flynn, A. Pak, and W. Reznikoff. 1989. Pseudorevertants of a *lac* promoter mutation reveal overlapping nascent promoters. *Nucleic Acids Res.* **17:** 3927–3949.

Kleina, L.G. and J.H. Miller. 1990. Genetic studies of the *lac* repressor. XIII. Extensive amino acid replacements generated by the use of natural and synthetic nonsense suppressors. *J. Mol. Biol.* **212:** 295–318.

Krämer, H., M. Amouyal, A. Nordheim, and B. Müller-Hill. 1988. DNA supercoiling changes the spacing requirement of two *lac* operators for DNA loop formation with *lac* repressor. *EMBO J.* **7:** 547–556.

Krämer, H., M. Niemöller, M. Amouyal, B. Revet, B. von Wilcken-Bergmann, and B. Müller-Hill. 1987. *lac* repressor forms loops with linear DNA carrying two suitably spaced *lac* operators. *EMBO J.* **6:** 1481–1491.

Lamerichs, R.M.I.N., R. Boelens, G.A. van der Marel, J.H. van Boom, R. Kaptein, F.

Buck. B. Fera, and H. Rüterjans. 1989. ^{3}H NMR study of a complex between the *lac* repressor headpiece of a 22 base pair symmetric *lac* operator. *Biochemistry* **28:** 2985–2991.

Lanzer, M. and H. Bujard. 1988. Promoters largely determine the efficiency of repressor action. *Proc. Natl. Acad. Sci.* **85:** 8973–8977.

Lehming, N., J. Sartorius, B. Kisters-Woike, B. von Wilcken-Bergmann, and B. Müller-Hill. 1990. Mutant *lac* repressors with new specificities hint at rules for protein-DNA recognition. *EMBO J.* **9:** 615–621.

Lehming, N., J. Sartorius, S. Oehler, B. von Wilcken-Bergmann, and B. Müller-Hill. 1988. Recognition helices of *lac* and λ repressor are oriented in opposite directions and recognize similar DNA sequences. *Proc. Natl. Acad. Sci.* **85:** 7947–7951.

Lehming, N., J. Sartorius, M.Neimoller, G. Genenger, B. von Wilcken-Bergmann, and B. Müller-Hill. 1987. The interaction of the recognition helix of *lac* repressor with *lac* operator. *EMBO J.* **6:** 3145–3153.

Majors, J. 1975. Initiation of in vitro mRNA synthesis from the wild-type *lac* promoter. *Proc. Natl. Acad. Sci.* **72:** 4394–4398.

Mandal, N., W. Su, R. Haber, S. Adhya, and H. Echols. 1990. DNA looping in cellular repression of transcription of the galactose operon. *Genes Dev.* **4:** 410–418.

Matthews, B.W., D.H. Ohlendorf, W.F. Anderson, and Y. Takeda. 1982. Structure of the DNA-binding region of *lac* repressor inferred from its homology with *cro* repressor. . *Proc. Natl. Acad. Sci.* **79:** 1428–1432.

Miller, J.H. 1979. Genetic studies of the *lac* repressor. XI. On aspects of *lac* repressor structure suggested by genetic experiments. *J. Mol. Biol.* **131:** 249–258.

Miller, J.H., C. Coulondre, M. Hofer, U. Schmeissner, H. Sommer, A. Schmitz, and P. Lu. 1979. Genetic studies of the *lac* repressor. IX. Generation of altered proteins by the suppression of nonsense mutations. *J. Mol. Biol.* **131:** 191–222.

Monod, J. and A. Audureau. 1946. Mutation et adaptation enzymatique chez *Escherichia coli*-mutable. *Ann. Inst. Pasteur* **72:** 868.

Mossing, M.C. and M.T. Record, Jr. 1986. Upstream operators enhance repression of the *lac* promoter. *Science* **223:** 889–892.

Müller-Hill, B., L. Crapo, and W. Gilbert. 1968. Mutants that make more *lac* repressor. *Proc. Natl. Acad. Sci.* **59:** 1259–1264.

Oehler, S., E.R. Eismann, H. Kramer, and B. Müller-Hill. 1990. The three operators of the *lac* operon cooperate in repression. *EMBO J.* **9:** 973–979.

Ogata, R.T. and W. Gilbert. 1978. An amino-terminal fragment of *lac* repressor binds specifically to *lac* operator. *Proc. Natl. Acad. Sci.* **75:** 5851–5854.

———. 1979. DNA binding site of *lac* repressor probed by dimethylsulfate methylation of *lac* operator. *J. Mol. Biol.* **132:** 709–728.

Platt, T., J.G. Files, and K. Weber. 1973. *Lac* repressor: Specific proteolytic destruction of the NH_2-terminal region and loss of the deoxyribonucleic acid-binding activity. *J. Biol. Chem.* **248:** 110–121.

Reznikoff, W.S., R.B. Winter, and C.K. Hurley. 1974. The location of the repressor binding sites in the *lac* operon. *Proc. Natl. Acad. Sci.* **71:** 2314–2318.

Reznikoff, W., J.H. Miller, J. Scaife, and J. Beckwith. 1969. A mechanism for repressor action. *J. Mol. Biol.* **43:** 201–213.

Riggs, A.D., S. Bourgeois, R.F. Newby, and M. Cohn. 1968. DNA binding of the *lac* repressor. *J. Mol. Biol.* **34:** 365–368.

Sams, C.F., N.K. Vyas, F.A. Quiocho, and K.S. Matthews. 1984. Predicted structure of the sugar-binding site of the *lac* repressor. *Nature* **310:** 429–430.

Sasmor, H.M. and J.L. Betz. 1990. Symmetric *lac* operator derivatives: Effects of half-operator sequence and spacing on repressor affinity. *Gene* **89:** 1–6.

Sasse-Dwight, S. and J.D. Gralla. 1988. Probing cooperative DNA-binding *in vivo*: The *lac* O$_1$:O$_3$ interaction. *J. Mol. Biol.* **202:** 107–119.

Schmitz, A., U. Schmeissner, J.H. Miller, and P. Lu. 1976. Mutations affecting the quaternary structure of the *lac* repressor. *J. Biol. Chem.* **251:** 3359–3366.

Sellitti, M., P. Pavco, and D. Steege. 1987. *Lac* repressor blocks *in vivo* transcription of *lac* control region DNA. *Proc. Natl. Acad. Sci.* **84:** 3199–3203.

Straney, S.B. and D.M. Crothers. 1987. Lac repressor is a transient gene-activating protein. *Cell* **51:** 699–707.

Whitson, P.A. and K.S. Matthews. 1986. Dissociation of the lactose repressor-operator DNA complex: Effects of size and sequence context of operator-containing DNA. *Biochemistry* **25:** 3845–3852.

Whitson, P.A., W.T. Hsieh, R.D. Wells, and K.S. Matthews. 1987. Supercoiling facilitates *lac* operator-repressor-pseudooperator interaction. *J. Biol. Chem.* **262:** 4943–4946.

24
Regulation of the L-Arabinose Catabolic Operon *araBAD*

Robert Schleif
Biology Department
Johns Hopkins University
Baltimore, Maryland 21218

OVERVIEW

Regulation of the L-arabinose operon began as an exercise in genetics in *Escherichia coli* many years ago. This led to the discovery of positive regulation, which, in turn, awakened researchers to the possibility of many modes of gene regulation, as are now known. DNA looping was first discovered and demonstrated in the arabinose operon. In this chapter, both the regulation of the arabinose operon and DNA looping are discussed. The discussion includes biological and physical reasons that DNA looping is sensible. Yet to be learned in the system is how the protein can possess the flexibility necessary to participate in the known DNA-binding structures, the structure of the protein, and the actual mechanism of transcription activation.

INTRODUCTION

The Arabinose Operon

Genes of the L-arabinose operon of *E. coli* enable the cells to take up and catabolize the pentose sugar L-arabinose. Arabinose is found naturally in polysaccharides of plant cell walls. Since humans cannot take up or catabolize arabinose, a meal with vegetables provides our guests (*E. coli*) with a free lunch. Likely then, the mechanisms for regulation of the arabinose operons in *E. coli* reflect the value of being able to respond rapidly to the periodic pulses of arabinose seen by the bacterium. The regulatory protein, AraC, of the arabinose system senses the presence of arabinose and induces synthesis of proteins that transport arabinose into cells and then catabolize the intracellular arabinose.

The arabinose catabolic operon consists of three genes that code for the enzymes necessary to convert L-arabinose to D-xylulose-5-phosphate:

araB, araA, and *araD* (Englesberg and Wilcox 1974; Lee 1978). The xylulose phosphate enters the pentose phosphate shunt, the genes of which do not respond to the presence or absence of arabinose. Arabinose is concentrated within the cells by at least four other proteins that are encoded by two other arabinose-responsive operons (Fig. 1). These are AraE, which is the only known component of a low-affinity uptake system, and AraF, AraG, and AraH, which are components of a high-affinity uptake system (Kolodrubetz and Schleif 1981a,b; Lee et al. 1981; Stoner and Schleif 1983; Horazdovsky and Hogg 1989; Hendrickson et al. 1990). A final arabinose-responsive promoter directs synthesis of a protein named AraJ of unknown function (Kosiba and Schleif 1982; Reeder and R. Schleif, in prep.)

Historical Background

Work on the arabinose operon began as a genetic mapping exercise (Gross and Englesberg 1959). Soon it was discovered that one of the genes, *araC*, was required for activity of the other arabinose-inducible genes (Englesberg et al. 1965). Among the possible explanations were

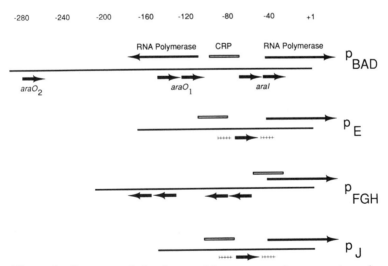

Figure 1 Structure of the four arabinose-responsive promoters showing the binding locations of RNA polymerase, cAMP receptor protein CRP, and AraC protein. The orientations of the AraC-binding sites are indicated. The dotted extensions represent areas in which binding is less certain because footprinting data have not been confirmed by other means and the fit to consensus sequence is not high.

that the *araC* gene product was a subunit common to the enzymes of the arabinose catabolic pathway, that the protein was required for transport of arabinose into the cells, or that the protein was required for inducing synthesis of the arabinose genes. This latter possibility was strongly resisted by most in the field because at that time only the negative regulatory system of the *lac* operon was known, and there seemed no need for a positive regulation scheme.

Genetic experiments provided strong, but not definitive, proof that AraC protein is a positive activator of the expression of the other genes induced by arabinose (Sheppard and Englesberg 1967). For example, the genetic experiments showing that AraC protein was required for induction of the other *ara* genes could have been explained by the existence of genes as yet undiscovered. AraC could have been the repressor of a gene that itself repressed synthesis of the other *ara* genes (Schleif 1985).

In vitro experiments definitively proved that AraC was a positive activator (Greenblatt and Schleif 1971). Only when AraC protein was added to a coupled in vitro transcription-translation system was the gene product AraB synthesized. This type of experiment permitted the assay and hence purification of AraC. As expected for a regulatory protein, very low levels of the protein are normally synthesized, only 20–40 monomers per cell (Kolodrubetz and Schleif 1981a), and purification was most difficult. Once AraC assays could be conducted, various tricks were used to increase synthesis of the protein, and finally, with the development of genetic engineering, much higher levels of AraC could be obtained (Steffen and Schleif 1977a,b; Schleif and Favreau 1982).

The coupled transcription-translation assay which showed that AraC is a positive activator (Greenblatt and Schleif 1971) could not establish that AraC is the *only* regulatory protein required for control of the arabinose operon. Other essential proteins could have been present in the crude extracts used for the assay. Such other proteins could be required for the initiation of transcription from other operons or from essential genes and therefore would not have been detected in genetic screens for mutants incapable of growing on arabinose. A transcription system containing purified components (DNA, RNA polymerase, cAMP receptor protein, and AraC) proved that these components are sufficient to activate transcription from the promoter of the *araBAD* operon, p_{BAD} (Lee et al. 1974). Unfortunately, the ratio of expression in the absence and the presence of arabinose in this in vitro transcription system is only 10- to 50-fold, whereas the in vivo induction ratio is on the order of 200-fold. Therefore, it remains possible that other proteins or components in addition to AraC protein and the cAMP receptor protein stimulate transcription or modulate expression.

Why Study the Arabinose Operon?

In the context of biological regulation, there are a number of biochemically important questions that can be addressed by studying the arabinose
operon. For example, how does a protein recognize and bind to a small
molecule substrate? How is a small molecule transported across a membrane, and how is energy coupled to the process so that concentration
gradients can be developed? How are specific DNA sequences recognized by proteins? How can a protein activate transcription? From my
own perspective, the most interesting and most approachable of these
questions over the past 20 years have been those related to recognition of
specific DNA sequences and regulation of transcription initiation. These
form the central focus of this review.

Studying regulation of the *ara* system was attractive for three reasons.
First was the initial uniqueness of positive regulation by AraC, in which
the protein acts positively to induce gene expression in the presence of
arabinose. At the time when data supporting positive regulation in the
arabinose operon became reasonably convincing, only negative regulation mechanisms were well established. The mechanism of negative
regulation by steric hindrance of RNA polymerase binding or movement
was simple, and there seemed no need for nature to have evolved another
mechanism of gene regulation. Consequently, it was of interest to establish convincingly that the *ara* operon did possess a positive regulatory
scheme and then to learn its mechanism.

A second reason for interest in regulation of the arabinose operon was
a second type of regulation exerted on the activity of p_{BAD}. This is a negative regulatory effect exerted by AraC protein in the absence of
arabinose. Although the magnitude of this negative regulation was only
about 15-fold compared to the 300-fold positive activity of AraC in the
presence of arabinose, it was sufficiently large to permit definitive study
of its mechanism. On the basis of genetic studies, it appeared that *cis*-
acting DNA sequences upstream of the promoter, in conjunction with
AraC protein, acted to repress the promoter for *araB*, *araA*, and *araD* in
the absence of arabinose (Sheppard and Englesberg 1967; Englesberg et
al. 1969).

The third reason for studying the arabinose system was that because it
is bacterial and contains a small number of regulatory proteins, it has
been possible to study in depth its mechanisms of action. On the other
hand, the system contains elements common to much more complicated
eukaryotic systems. Thus, what we have learned about the arabinose system has been of use in understanding more complicated systems.

Two aspects of the arabinose operon of *E. coli* simplify its study.
First, activity of the *ara* genes is nonessential. This means that expres-

sion of the genes can easily be turned on or off or damaged genetically without significantly altering other aspects of the cellular physiology. This is in contrast to many eukaryotic systems in which many regulatory signals are unknown and dramatic developmental changes often are required to alter expression of a gene.

The biological simplicity of *E. coli* also permits a wide range of research techniques to be applied to studying the system. Genetic, physiological, biochemical, and physicochemical experiments can easily and inexpensively be performed. The consequences of any specific alteration, whether it be a specific amino acid or nucleotide alteration or a more dramatic modification in the system, can be examined at all levels. Thus, the regulatory consequences can be determined in vivo and ultimately understood biochemically and physically from in vitro studies. It is this interplay between in vivo and in vitro experiments that has permitted rapid and decisive progress in understanding many aspects of the *ara* regulatory system.

ARAC PROTEIN

AraC protein activates transcription of the *araBAD*, *araE*, *araFGH*, and *araJ* genes in the presence of arabinose. To accomplish this, in addition to binding arabinose, it also binds to specific DNA sequences. How does the protein recognize these sequences, and more importantly, how does the DNA-bound protein activate transcription from the *ara* promoters?

AraC protein is a dimer of identical 30,500 molecular-weight monomers (Wilcox and Meuris 1976; Steffen and Schleif 1977a). No posttranslational modifications in the protein have been noticed, and no data hint at the presence of such modifications. Dimerization of the protein is tight, with more than half the protein remaining in dimeric form even at concentrations as low as 1 μg/ml. In the days before genetic engineering, slight overproduction of the protein was achieved by infecting cells with a λ-*ara* transducing phage (Steffen and Schleif 1977a). Protein from such a source was highly unstable until it was nearly pure. More recently, genetic engineering techniques have facilitated significant overproduction of the protein (Schleif and Favreau 1982). Purification of the protein has been difficult. The protein does not elute from most chromatography columns, and resuspension following other precipitation steps gives very low yields. Despite only 5% recoveries, a purification scheme based on polymin P precipitation of DNA, a precipitation and resuspension step, and chromatography on phosphocellulose gives yields of 25–100 mg per 100 g of cells. The purity of this protein ranges from 90% to 95%.

AraC protein loses activity in typical buffers at about 45°C, but the protein is significantly stabilized when bound to DNA or arabinose (R.F. Schleif, unpubl.). Its pI is 6.9 (Wilcox and Meuris 1976). Its full amino acid sequence does not show notable homologies with proteins of known three-dimensional structure (Miyada et al. 1980; Wallace et al. 1980; Stoner and Schleif 1982). Of the readily recognizable secondary structure motifs known to contact DNA, AraC possesses two possible helix-turn-helix regions (Brunelle and Schleif 1989). The potential roles of these regions are discussed below.

DNA Binding by AraC Protein

The dimeric AraC protein usually contacts four major groove regions on its DNA substrate. One subunit appears to contact the first two, and the second contacts the third and fourth major groove regions. Two adjacent major groove regions contacted by a single subunit are defined as one binding site. The binding sites contacted and utilized by AraC protein in regulating the arabinose operons can be immediately adjacent to one another, as they are at $araO_1$ (Ogden et al. 1980; Hendrickson and Schleif 1985), or they can be separated by several hundred nucleotides. In the latter case, the protein will bridge the gap and form a loop with the intervening DNA. Such a loop occurs when the protein binds simultaneously to half of $araI$ and $araO_2$ (Dunn et al. 1984; Lee et al. 1987; Brunelle and Schleif 1989; Lobell and Schleif 1990).

Surprisingly, the AraC-binding sites do not form a good inverted repeat sequence typical of most binding sites for bacterial regulatory proteins. The consensus of the binding sites more closely forms a direct repeat (Lee et al. 1987). Definitive biochemical data supporting the direct repeat organization have been obtained from missing contact experiments (Brunelle and Schleif 1989). In missing contact experiments, each nucleotide that contributes to binding by a protein is detected. This is achieved by randomly removing nucleotides from the DNA, then separating out of this population of DNA molecules a subpopulation which still binds to the protein with normal affinity and a subpopulation containing modifications that reduce the protein's binding affinity. The two populations are cleaved at the positions of missing bases and run on sequencing gels. The positions where missing nucleotides affect binding are enhanced in the DNA that bound weakly or not at all, and the positions where missing bases have no effect on binding are enhanced in the DNA that bound normally. This experiment is repeated with AraC protein possessing various amino residues substituted by alanine. Because alanine is a small amino acid, if the residue formerly touched DNA and now does not, at least one nucleotide of the binding site will shift from being contacted to not being contacted (Brunelle and Schleif 1989). The pattern of missing contacts found for various alanine-substituted AraC proteins showed that the protein binds to DNA as a direct repeat. If AraC protein binds to direct repeat DNA sequence, it would seem to follow that the basic structure of the protein is also a direct repeat. That is, the two dimers of the protein would interact in a head-to-tail configuration rather than in the more usual head-to-head configuration typical of many bacterial regulators like cAMP receptor protein or bacteriophage λ repressor and cro proteins. The problem introduced by head-to-tail interactions is that they are not self-limiting. Infinite head-to-tail polymers such as those formed in eukaryotic cells by actin and tubulin could form. Since AraC protein shows no evidence for formation of biologically significant large polymers, it seems more likely that AraC protein dimerizes in the more familiar head-to-head configuration typical of proteins that bind to inverted repeat sequences.

How might a direct repeat sequence on DNA be bound by a protein lacking a similar direct repeat structure? One possibility is that the protein could have two domains, one for dimerization and one for DNA binding. Dimerization could be via homotropic, head-to-head interactions between the dimerization domains. The DNA-binding domains, however, could be connected to the dimerization domains via arms that permit rotation (Fig. 2). Upon binding to a direct repeat sequence, one or both of the DNA-binding domains could rotate with respect to the dimerization domain. A no larger amount of rotation per subunit would also allow binding to sites in inverted repeat orientation or in "inside out" inverted repeat orientation.

Many questions about AraC protein would be answered if its three-dimensional structure were available. Therefore, it is not surprising that at least three different laboratories have attempted to crystallize the

  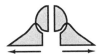

Figure 2 Contortions necessary for a protein to dimerize by homotropic interactions and then to bind to inverted, direct, or inside-out sequences. For ease in depicting, subunits are shown as twisting 180°. Twisting of the two subunits in the three cases is 0° and 0°, 0° and 180°, and 180° and 180°. If the subunits are naturally skewed 90°, then each individual subunit need rotate only 90°, and the rotations required for binding to the three different sequence symmetries are +90° and +90°, +90° and −90°, and −90° and −90°.

protein for X-ray diffraction studies. Unfortunately, these attempts have
all been unsuccessful. These failures suggest that the protein may be unusually flexible, heterogeneous, or prone to aggregate. The dimeric
protein of 60,000 kD is too large for two-dimensional nuclear magnetic
resonance (NMR) structure determination, greatly exceeding the current
upper limit of about 20 kD (Wüthrich and Gehring, this volume). Therefore, the most detailed structural information may require studies of isolated domains of the protein.

Encouraging data in this direction have recently appeared. Lee and
colleagues have reported that overexpression of the carboxy-terminal 137
amino acids of AraC yields a protein that can bind to DNA in vivo and
can partially activate transcription even in the absence of arabinose
(Menon and Lee 1990). This implies that both the DNA binding and the
transcription activation functions of the protein are present on a relatively
small domain.

DNA-binding Domain of AraC

Each subunit of the dimeric AraC protein contacts two adjacent major
groove regions of DNA. Therefore, each subunit must contain two DNA-
contacting regions. Within the carboxy-terminal third of the protein are
two stretches of amino acids with appreciable similarity to the consensus
helix-turn-helix sequence found in many DNA-contacting proteins (Fig.
3). The pattern of contacts made by several alanine substitutions in these
regions of the protein, as assayed by the missing contact method, show
that the first of these regions contacts DNA as though it is a helix-turn-
helix region, but the second does not (Brunelle and Schleif 1989). In
these experiments, different amino acids were changed to alanine, and
the missing contact experiments were used to locate the bases which
were now not contacted by the variant AraC protein. To confirm such as-
signments, the base in question was changed. Wild-type AraC protein,
which contacts the base, indeed was sensitive to the identity of the base.
The alanine variant, which did not contact the base, was insensitive to the
identity of the base. The second contacting region has not yet been identified.

The inability to crystallize AraC protein led us to investigate the possibility that other proteins similar to AraC might exist, and that one of
these might be easier to crystallize. The L-rhamnose operon was found to
possess two genes whose products possess significant similarity to AraC
protein (Tobin and Schleif 1987). At least eight additional proteins have
been discovered that possess significant sequence similarity to AraC
protein, of which seven are shown in Figure 4. Common to all is a

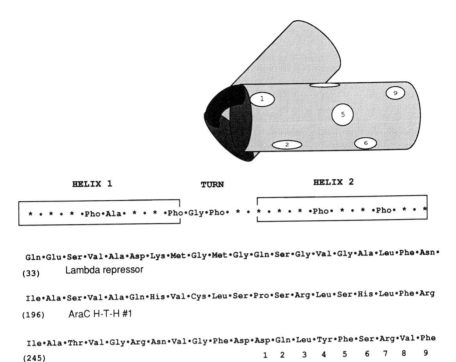

Figure 3 Helix-turn-helix structure as it would be seen from the DNA-binding site. Shown also is the consensus sequence, the λ repressor sequence, and the sequence of the two potential helix-turn-helix regions in AraC.

carboxy-terminal segment which corresponds to the region of AraC that contacts DNA and which is likely also to be involved in activation of transcription (Tobin and Schleif 1990b). As yet no structural information is available on any of these other proteins.

TRANSCRIPTION ACTIVATION

The basic mechanisms of transcription initiation are likely to be similar in prokaryotes and eukaryotes, since the problems confronted by the initiation reactions are the same. RNA polymerase must bind to the correct site, separate the DNA strands, and begin the polymerization process. Hints that the initiation mechanisms might be similar are that RNA polymerases from prokaryotes and eukaryotes possess many sizable regions of amino acid sequence similarity (see Allison et al. 1985; Broyles and Moss 1986; Sentenac et al. this volume).

Both prokaryotes and eukaryotes possess promoters that function with a minimum of auxiliary assistance, as well as promoters on which RNA

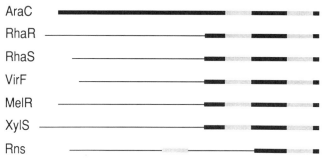

Figure 4 Seven members of the AraC family of related proteins. The heavy line shows high homology, and the two gray areas are the likely DNA-binding regions.

polymerase cannot initiate without the assistance of ancillary "activator" proteins. As is described in numerous other chapters in this volume, the initiation process can be experimentally subdivided into binding, isomerization, and initiation steps. Auxiliary proteins can activate any of these three steps.

Evidence has begun to indicate that transcription in some bacterial systems utilizes a bend in the DNA located somewhat upstream of RNA polymerase (Bracco et al. 1989; Rojo et al. 1990). Binding of cAMP receptor protein, CRP, which is also known as CAP for catabolite activator protein, bends DNA more than 90° (Liu-Johnson et al. 1986; Gartenberg and Crothers 1988). CRP binding beside RNA polymerase in some promoters stimulates activity by as much as 50-fold. Much of the activity of the *lac* operon promoter can be restored in the absence of CRP by replacing the CRP-binding site with a DNA sequence that bends in the same direction as the CRP-induced bend (Bracco et al. 1989). Whether the transcription activation results from an intrinsic property of bends, or whether bends facilitate the binding of other proteins, is unclear.

Although binding and bending may be sufficient for some proteins to activate transcription, these processes are clearly insufficient for other proteins and promoters. AraC protein remains bound at the *araI* site when arabinose is removed (Huo et al. 1988), yet activation of transcription falls by at least 200-fold. Similarly, in the rhamnose system, RhaR protein at the p_{SR} promoter binds, sharply bends the DNA, but only activates transcription in the presence of rhamnose (Tobin and Schleif 1990a,b). Precise measurements have not yet been done to test whether arabinose or rhamnose alters the bends induced by AraC or RhaR.

The regulatory protein of outer membrane porins, OmpR, is a transcriptional activator. It can activate transcription when placed in the appropriate position upstream of a wide variety of promoters that are either intrinsically weak or that require an auxiliary protein for maximal activity (Tsung et al. 1990). This result implies there need not be a special relationship between an activating protein and the promoter it activates. Such observations are reminiscent of the behavior of enhancers and promoters in eukaryotic cells.

If AraC does not activate transcription by a mechanism involving DNA bending, it might activate through direct and specific protein-protein interactions with RNA polymerase. Such an induction mechanism, however, is difficult to reconcile with the structure of the regulatory region of the *araFGH* promoter. In the p_{BAD} and p_E promoters, the direct repeats of the AraC-binding sites are oriented in the direction of transcription, and the binding sites themselves are immediately adjacent to RNA polymerase. At p_{FGH}, the orientation of the AraC-binding site is reversed (Fig. 1) from that seen in p_{BAD} and p_E. Additionally, at p_{FGH}, CRP binds next to RNA polymerase, and AraC binds beside CRP (Hendrickson et al. 1990).

DNA LOOPING BY ARAC PROTEIN

In this section, I first discuss why looping is biologically sensible, then explain how looping was discovered, and finally, discuss many of the looping results that have been obtained with the arabinose operon and explain how they pertain to regulation of initiation of transcription.

A transcription regulator must sense a signal such as the presence of a large or small molecule (like arabinose), or such as temperature, and then adjust transcription of the appropriate genes. How is the action of a regulatory protein restricted to the appropriate genes? The simplest way this can be accomplished is for the gene-specific or signal-specific regulatory protein to bind to a DNA sequence near the gene and regulate transcription through direct interactions with the initiation complex. Many examples are known in prokaryotic systems of such a close association between a regulatory protein and a transcription initiation complex.

The problem generated by transcription regulators binding close to RNA polymerase is that a limited number of such proteins may bind immediately adjacent to a bound RNA polymerase molecule. How could such a system work for a gene that has to respond to more than a few regulatory signals? The answer is DNA looping. In this case, certain proteins can bind immediately adjacent to RNA polymerase on a promoter, and additional regulator proteins can bind at some distance from the initiation complex but still interact with it via DNA looping. DNA looping permits almost endless variations on a theme. Additional proteins could bind in the looping region and could aid or hinder loop formation. Furthermore, any of the proteins required to form the loop could be regulated in level or capability to participate in loop formation.

A second merit of DNA loop formation in the context of genetic regulation is the cooperativity inherent in the process. Consider the binding of two subunits of a protein to two specific sequences located 200 bp apart, followed by the dimerization of the DNA-bound monomers and the consequent DNA loop formation. Because the two monomers are held within 200 bp of one another, the local concentration of one subunit in the presence of the other is increased, and dimerization is stimulated. Another pathway to loop formation is the binding of a dimer to one of the DNA sequences. This locates the other DNA recognition region of the protein in the vicinity, i.e., within 200 bp, of its binding sequence and, therefore, binding and hence looping are stimulated. That is, looping increases the local concentration of components and increases the rates of binding and/or the extent of binding. For example, faster rates of binding by *lac* repressor in the *lac* operon facilitate repression, for there a repressor molecule competes with RNA polymerase for binding at the promoter. The cooperativity inherent in the process reduces the individual affinities required of protein-binding sites. Weaker binding permits dissociation of an individual subunit from the DNA without total dissociation, as might be required during DNA replication or recombination.

It is important to understand the origin of the increase in local concentrations as discussed above. Such an increase absolutely requires DNA looping. A simple binding site on the DNA from which a protein might slide or diffuse to another site on the DNA cannot increase the concentration of the protein near the binding site unless the system is not at equilibrium and is consuming energy to remain at disequilibrium.

Background to the Discovery of DNA Looping

Early genetic experiments by Englesberg revealed an interesting deletion affecting regulation of the p_{BAD} promoter of the *araBAD* genes. The deletion left the promoter normally inducible by arabinose in the presence of AraC protein, but in the absence of arabinose, the deletion caused AraC protein to elevate the basal level of the promoter 10- to 30-fold above the normal wild-type levels (Englesberg et al. 1969). Importantly, AraC protein was required to maintain the anomalously high uninduced level of expression. The Englesberg deletion entered the *ara* regulatory region from upstream of p_{BAD} and extended toward the promoter but did not affect its ability to be induced by AraC in the presence of arabinose. These

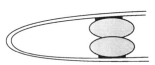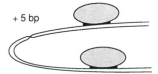

+ 5 bp

Figure 5 How insertion of 5 bp can rotate a site such that DNA looping becomes more difficult.

bility. On the other hand, the fact that spacings exist that block repression indicates that AraC protein is not completely flexible or is incapable of reaching around the DNA to contact a site on the back face of the helix.

As the spacing between $araO_2$ and $araI$ is changed, repressibility of p_{BAD} oscillates with a period of 11.1 bp (Fig. 6) (Lee and Schleif 1989). This indicates that the helical repeat of this region of DNA in vivo is 11.1 bp per turn. In contrast, linear DNA in vitro possesses a helical repeat of about 10.5 bp per turn. The difference between the in vivo and in vitro helicities is not surprising, for in vivo the DNA possesses a linking number deficit. This both generates supercoiling and unwinds the DNA, thereby reducing the helical twist (Bliska and Cozzarelli 1987; see also Wang, this volume).

Mutants Affecting Repression

Fusion of p_{BAD} to the *galK* gene yields a simple assay for repression of p_{BAD}. The normal uninduced or basal level of GalK driven by p_{BAD} produces white colonies on McConkey galactose indicating plates, whereas *ara* repression-deficient strains produce red colonies. This assay facilitated isolation of more than 70 repression-negative mutants of p_{BAD}. Many were found to lie in $araO_2$. As expected, these mutations reduced the affinity of AraC protein for the $araO_2$ site. In this class of mutant, the

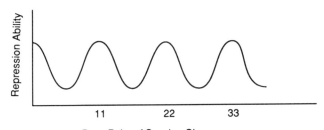

Base Pairs of Spacing Change

Figure 6 Idealized oscillatory behavior of repression, and looping ability as the distance between $araO_2$ and $araI$ is altered.

reduction in affinity of AraC protein for the $araO_2$ site typically was about 30-fold (Martin et al. 1986).

Mutations in the regulatory region that elevated the basal level of expression of p_{BAD} were also found in the RNA polymerase-binding site and the adjacent AraC protein-binding site. Those within the RNA polymerase-binding site permit the promoter to function, albeit weakly, on its own without activation by AraC protein. They appear to have little to do with repression or DNA looping. Those within the $araI$ site interfere with repression by AraC; i.e., they have little influence on the activity of the promoter in the absence of AraC protein, but they weakly stimulate p_{BAD} in the presence of AraC protein and the absence of arabinose. When arabinose is added to these mutants, p_{BAD} is fully induced. The affinity of AraC protein for these sites is increased only by about twofold (Lobell 1990). The existence of these mutations and their behavior indicate that the DNA sequence of $araI$ somehow can alter a property of the bound AraC protein to reduce its repressing activity.

In Vivo Footprinting

$araO_2$ and $araI$ cooperate in the repression of p_{BAD} so that deletion or mutation of $araO_2$ eliminates repression. Because both are required for repression, $araI$ must be occupied by AraC protein for repression to occur; i.e., $araI$ must be occupied in the absence of arabinose. Before the discovery of looping, the model for regulation of ara p_{BAD} was that upon arabinose addition, the affinity of AraC for $araI$ increased, the protein bound to $araI$ as a result, and induction somehow ensued. The looping hypothesis required a drastic change from the simple idea that gene induction or repression resulted from a protein binding to DNA or dissociating from DNA. The behavior of the ara system implied that alteration in gene expression could result from a change in the activity of a DNA-bound protein.

In vivo footprinting with dimethylsulfate offered a means of demonstrating that AraC protein is bound to the $araI$ site in the absence of arabinose (Martin et al. 1986). The techniques that were developed for assaying AraC occupancy of $araI$ were general and were used to show that AraC protein also occupies the $araO_2$ site. Occupancy of the sites thought to be involved in looping was fundamental to the looping mechanism. If looping occurred, the sites had to be occupied. The occupancy of the sites could not prove the existence of looping, however.

Another in vivo experiment provided independent and strong evidence for looping. This was a demonstration of the cooperativity provided by looping. Prior in vitro experiments had shown that $araO_2$ binds

AraC protein with about 1/50 the affinity of *araI*. In vivo footprinting experiments showed that the binding is sufficiently weak that at the normal in vivo concentrations of AraC, the $araO_2$ site is not occupied if *araI* and $araO_1$ are both deleted. Only when one of these other sites is present is $araO_2$ occupied by AraC protein; i.e., looping from *araI* to $araO_2$ or from $araO_1$ to $araO_2$ provides sufficient cooperativity that $araO_2$ can be occupied despite its low affinity for AraC protein. It is looping that generates this cooperativity.

Another discovery from the footprinting experiments was that looping is not fixed. Two different loops can form in the arabinose system. Either *araI* or $araO_1$ can loop to $araO_2$ (Huo et al. 1988). The biological consequences of such an alternative looping scheme are not yet fully understood in the *ara* system. Nonetheless, alternative looping appears to be a flexible control mechanism that could be used in many gene systems.

In Vitro Looping

It quickly became apparent that simple in vitro biochemical experiments for the study of looping could not be done in the *ara* system because the strengths of looping were too weak. The weakness was a mixed blessing. If the looping strengths had been stronger, as they are in many systems, then the energies available would have twisted the DNA when the protein-binding sites were misoriented, and the helical twist experiments would not have been instructive. On the other hand, the weakness of looping complicated the biochemical study of the *ara* system.

Weak binding reactions can be forced to occur by raising the concentrations of the reactants. In the case of looping, this is best accomplished by placing both DNA-binding sites on the same DNA molecule. This alone was not adequate for the *ara* system. Therefore, a means had to be found of forcing the AraC-binding sites still closer together or of reducing the energies required to position them appropriately for DNA looping. Placing two of the *lac* repressor-binding sites on a small supercoiled circle of about 400 bp permitted DNA looping to occur (Kramer et al. 1988). Furthermore, the looped species could be electrophoretically separated from naked circles as well as from circles containing a bound *lac* repressor. Such separations are essential for an electrophoretic assay of looping. Analogous conditions were found to yield a usable assay for DNA looping in the *ara* system (Lobell and Schleif 1990).

Using the minicircle looping assay, Lobell found that loops could be formed in vitro between an $araO_2$ site and an *araI* site and that arabinose opened the loop, just as occurs in vivo (Lobell and Schleif 1990). Because AraC protein is a dimer in solution and binds to *araI* on linear DNA as a dimer, it seemed most probable that loops would be formed between a dimer bound at *araI* and a dimer bound at *araO$_2$*. On the other hand, footprinting data obtained with linear DNA suggested that under certain conditions only half the *araI* site is occupied by AraC protein in the absence of arabinose and that the complete *araI* site is occupied in the presence of arabinose (Menon and Lee 1990). Such results suggested that a dimer of AraC might be capable of forming DNA loops.

In the in vitro system with small supercoiled DNA molecules, loops could be formed by binding a dimer at *araI* in the presence of arabinose (*araO$_2$* remained free of AraC protein at this point), removing all free AraC protein, and then removing arabinose (Lobell and Schleif 1990). This result implied that loops are formed by a dimer of the protein rather than a tetramer. If this were true, then not all the *araI* site would be required for looping. This possibility was examined by locating the bases which, when methylated, prevented loop formation. Methylation of a guanosine in the left half of *araI*, *araI$_1$*, blocked loop formation. In contrast, methylation of a guanosine in the right half, *araI$_2$*, did not affect loop formation. As expected, methylation of guanosines in the *araO$_2$* site blocked loop formation. These results show that AraC protein contacts only *araI$_1$* and *araO$_2$* when it is looping. Further data leading to the same conclusion were that alteration of the sequence of *araI$_2$* did not alter the dissociation rate of looped DNA but greatly decreased the affinity of AraC protein for the *araI* site under nonlooping conditions. Arabinose addition opens the loop despite the alteration of the sequence in *araI$_2$*. This means that AraC protein need not make contacts with the *araI$_2$* portion of the sequence in order that the loop open. Stoichiometry measurements completed the demonstration that looping is accomplished by a dimer of AraC protein rather than a tetramer (Lobell and Schleif 1990).

How does AraC know to open the loop in the presence of arabinose? The three relevant AraC-binding sites, *araI*, *araO$_1$*, and *araO$_2$* are similar, but each is unique. In principle, therefore, the protein could detect this difference in the various binding sites and associate most effectively to certain sites in the absence of arabinose and to different sites in its presence. Alternatively, the protein chooses to loop or not depending on the absence or presence of arabinose, and the precise sequences of the various sites may be unimportant. This latter possibility was found to be the case. Loops still formed when an *araI$_1$* site was substituted for the *araO$_2$* site. Moreover, arabinose addition opened this loop (Lobell and Schleif 1990).

One mechanism for loop opening is particularly simple. In the absence of arabinose, the two subunits of the dimeric AraC protein could be loosely connected and free to pick the tightest binding sites in the vicinity. In the native state, this would be the $araI_1$ and $araO_2$ sites, and looping would result. When arabinose is added, the protein might then become unable to contact these two nonadjacent sites. The loop would therefore be broken, and the protein would bind to the two adjacent $araI_1$ and $araI_2$ sites (Fig. 7). In addition to explaining all the looping data described above, this model also explains why AraC protein binds more tightly to $araI$ on linear DNA in the presence of arabinose. When arabinose is present, the subunits are more correctly aligned for binding to $araI_1$ and $araI_2$, and the protein binds more tightly than in the absence of arabinose.

CONCLUSIONS AND PERSPECTIVES

Many questions remain unanswered about the arabinose system. The most important is, How does AraC activate transcription? Because AraC protein is a member of a family of transcriptional activators including the two regulators of the rhamnose system, RhaR and RhaS, the mechanism of action used by the various family members is likely to be similar. Does it involve DNA bending, or direct protein-RNA polymerase interactions, or some other mechanism? Another major interest is determining the structure of AraC protein. This may then tell how the protein loops and how the presence of arabinose changes the protein so as to open the

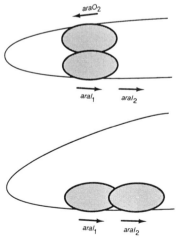

Figure 7 Current picture depicting formation of a dimer loop between $araO_2$ and $araI_1$, and then the shift to binding of the dimer to $araI_1$ and $araI_2$.

loop. Although the detailed mechanisms used by the arabinose system to regulate gene expression may appear quite baroque and unique, the conceptual strategy related to DNA looping likely represents a fundamental means of genetic regulation in all organisms.

ACKNOWLEDGMENTS

The work described in this chapter originating from our laboratory has been supported by National Institutes of Health grant 18277. I thank Steve McKnight, Thadd Reeder, and Susan Egan for comments on the manuscript.

REFERENCES

Allison, A., M. Moyle, M. Shales, and C. Ingles. 1985. Extensive homology among the largest subunits of eukaryotic and prokaryotic RNA polymerases. *Cell* **42**: 599–610.

Bliska, J. and N. Cozzarelli. 1987. Use of site-specific recombination as a probe of DNA structure and metabolism in vivo. *J. Mol. Biol.* **94**: 205–218.

Bracco, L., D. Kotlarz, A. Kolb, S. Diekmann, and H. Buc. 1989. Synthetic curved DNA sequences can act as transcriptional activators in *Escherichia coli*. *Eur. J. Mol. Biol.* **8**: 4289–4296.

Broyles, S. and B. Moss. 1986. Homology between RNA polymerases of poxviruses, prokaryotes, and eukaryotes: Nucleotide sequence and transcriptional analysis of vaccinia virus genes encoding 147-kDa and 22-kDa subunits. *Proc. Natl. Acad. Sci.* **83**: 3141–3145.

Brunelle, A. and R. Schleif. 1989. Determining residue-base interactions between AraC protein and *araI* DNA. *J. Mol. Biol.* **209**: 607–622.

Dunn, T. and R. Schleif. 1984. Deletion analysis of the *Escherichia coli* P_C and P_{BAD} promoters. *J. Mol. Biol.* **180**: 201–204.

Dunn, T., S. Hahn, S. Ogden, and R. Schleif. 1984. An operator at –280 base pairs that is required for repression of *araBAD* operon promoter: Addition of DNA helical turns between the operator and promoter cyclically hinders repression. *Proc. Natl Acad. Sci.* **81**: 5017–5020.

Englesberg, E. and G. Wilcox. 1974. Regulation: Positive control. *Annu. Rev. Genet.* **8**: 219–242.

Englesberg, E., C. Squires, and F. Meronk. 1969. The L-arabinose operon in *Escherichia coli* B/r: A genetic demonstration of two functional states of the product of a regulator gene. *Proc. Natl. Acad. Sci.* **62**: 1100–1107.

Englesberg, E., J. Irr, J. Power, and N. Lee. 1965. Positive control of enzyme synthesis by gene C in the L-arabinose system. *J. Bacteriol.* **90**: 946–957.

Gartenberg, M. and D. Crothers. 1988. DNA sequence determinants of CAP-induced bending and protein binding affinity. *Nature* **333**: 824–829.

Greenblatt, J. and R. Schleif. 1971. Arabinose C protein: Regulation of the arabinose operon in vitro. *Nat. New Biol.* **233**: 166–170.

Gross, J. and E. Englesberg. 1959. Determination of the order of mutational sites governing L-arabinose utilization in *Escherichia coli* B/r by transduction with phage P1bt. *Virology* **9**: 314–331.

Hahn, S., T. Dunn, and R. Schleif. 1984. Upstream repression and CRP stimulation of the *Escherichia coli* L-arabinose operon. *J. Mol. Biol.* **180:** 61–72.

Hendrickson, W. and R. Schleif. 1985. A dimer of AraC protein contacts three adjacent major groove regions of the *araI* DNA site. *Proc. Natl. Acad. Sci.* **82:** 3129–3133.

Hendrickson, W., C. Stoner, and R. Schleif. 1990. Characterization of the *Escherichia coli araFGH* and *araJ* promoters. *J. Mol. Biol.* **215:** 497–510.

Hirsh, J. and R. Schleif. 1976. Electron microscopy of gene regulation: The arabinose operon. *Proc. Natl. Acad. Sci.* **73:** 1518–1522.

Horazdovsky, B. and R. Hogg. 1989. Genetic reconstitution of the high-affinity L-arabinose transport system. *J. Bacteriol.* **171:** 3053–3059.

Huo, L., K. Martin, and R. Schleif. 1988. Alternative DNA loops regulate the arabinose operon in *Escherichia coli*. *Proc. Natl. Acad. Sci.* **85:** 5444–5448.

Kolodrubetz, D. and R. Schleif. 1981a. Identification of AraC protein on two-dimensional gels, its *in vivo* instability and normal level. *J. Mol. Biol.* **149:** 133–139.

———. 1981b. Regulation of the L-arabinose transport operons in *Escherichia coli*. *J. Mol. Biol.* **151:** 215–227.

Kosiba, B. and R. Schleif. 1982. Arabinose-inducible promoter from *Escherichia coli*, its cloning from chromosomal DNA, identification as the *araFG* promoter, and sequence. *J. Mol. Biol.* **156:** 53–66.

Kramer, H., M. Amouyal, A. Nordheim, and B. Müller-Hill. 1988. DNA supercoiling changes the spacing requirement of two *lac* operators for DNA loop formation with *lac* repressor. *Eur. J. Mol. Biol.* **7:** 547–556.

Lee, D. and R. Schleif. 1989. *In vitro* DNA loops in *araCBAD*: Size limits and helical repeat. *Proc. Natl. Acad. Sci.* **86:** 476–480.

Lee, J.-H., S. Al-Zarban, and G. Wilcox. 1981. Genetic characterization of the *araE* gene in *Salmonella typhimurium* LT2. *J. Bacteriol.* **146:** 298–304.

Lee., N. 1978. Molecular aspects of *ara* regulation. In *The operon* (ed. J.H. Miller and W. Reznikoff), pp. 389–409. Cold Spring Harbor Laboratory, Cold Spring Harbor, New York.

Lee, N., C. Francklyn, and E. Hamilton. 1987. Arabinose-induced binding of AraC protein to *araI₂* activates the *araBAD* operon promoter. *Proc. Natl. Acad. Sci.* **84:** 8814–8818.

Lee, N., G. Wilcox, W. Gielow, J. Arnold, P. Cleary, and E. Englesberg. 1974. *In vitro* activation of the transcription of *araBAD* operon by *araC* activator. *Proc. Natl. Acad. Sci.* **71:** 634–638.

Lis, J. and R. Schleif. 1975a. The isolation and characterization of plaque-forming arabinose transducing bacteriophage lambda. *J. Mol. Biol.* **95:** 395–407.

———. 1975b. The regulatory region of the L-arabinose operon: Its isolation on a 1000 base pair fragment from DNA heteroduplexes. *J. Mol. Biol.* **95:** 409–416.

———. 1975c. Size fractionation of double-stranded DNA by precipitation with polyethylene glycol. *Nucleic Acids Res.* **2:** 383–389.

Liu-Johnson, H., M. Gartenberg, and D. Crothers. 1986. The DNA binding domain and bending angle of *E. coli* CAP protein. *Cell* **47:** 995–1005.

Lobell, R. 1990. "DNA looping and loop breaking in the *araCBAD* operon of *Escherichia coli*." Ph.D. thesis, Brandeis University, Waltham, Massachusetts.

Lobell, R. and R. Schleif. 1990. DNA looping and unlooping by AraC protein. *Science* **250:** 528–532.

Martin, K., L. Huo, and R. Schleif. 1986. The DNA loop model for *ara* repression: AraC protein occupies the proposed loop sites in vivo and repression-negative mutations lie in these same sites. *Proc. Natl. Acad. Sci.* **83:** 3654–3658.

Menon, K. and N. Lee. 1990. Activation of *ara* operons by a truncated AraC protein does not require inducer. *Proc. Natl. Acad. Sci.* **87**: 3708–3712.

Miyada, C., A. Horwitz, L. Cass, J. Timko, and G. Wilcox. 1980. DNA sequence of the *araC* regulatory gene from *Escherichia coli* B/r. *Nucleic Acids Res.* **8**: 5267–5274.

Ogden, S., D. Haggerty, C. Stoner, D. Kolodrubetz, and R. Schleif. 1980. The *Escherichia coli* L-arabinose operon: Binding sites of the regulatory proteins and a mechanism of positive and negative regulation. *Proc. Natl. Acad. Sci.* **77**: 3346–3350.

Reeder, R.H. and R. Schleif. 1991. Mapping, sequence, and apparent lack of function of *araJ*, a gene of the *Escherichia coli* arabinose regulon. *J. Bacteriol.* **173**: 7765–7771.

Rojo, F., A. Zaballos, and M. Salas. 1990. Bend induced by phage Phi29 transcriptional activator in the late promoter is required for activation. *J. Mol. Biol.* **211**: 713–725.

Schleif, R. 1972. Fine-structure deletion map of the *Escherichia coli* L-arabinose operon. *Proc. Natl. Acad. Sci.* **69**: 3479–3484.

———. 1985. Induction and the *ara* operon. In *The arabinose operon, genetics and molecular biology*, pp. 347–371. Addison Wesley, Reading, Massachusetts.

Schleif, R. and M. Favreau. 1982. Hyperproduction of araC protein from *Escherichia coli*. *Biochemistry* **21**: 778–782.

Schleif, R. and J. Lis. 1975. The regulatory region of the L-arabinose operon: A physical, genetic and physiological study. *J. Mol. Biol.* **95**: 417–431.

Sheppard, D. and E. Englesberg. 1967. Further evidence for positive control of the L-arabinose system by gene *araC*. *J. Mol. Biol.* **25**: 443–454.

Shore, D. and R. Baldwin. 1983. Energetics of DNA twisting. *J. Mol. Biol.* **170**: 957–981.

Shore, D., J. Langowski, and R. Baldwin. 1981. DNA flexibility studied by covalent closure of short fragments into circles. *Proc. Natl. Acad. Sci.* **78**: 4833–4837.

Smith, B.R. and R. Schleif. 1978. Nucleotide sequence of the L-arabinose regulatory region of *Escherichia coli* K12. *J. Biol. Chem.* **253**: 6931–6933.

Steffen, D. and R. Schleif. 1977a. Overproducing *araC* protein with lambda-arabinose transducing phage. *Mol. Gen. Genet.* **157**: 333–339.

———. 1977b. *In vitro* construction of plasmids which result in overproduction of protein product of the *araC* gene of *E. coli*. *Mol. Gen. Genet.* **157**: 341–344.

Stoner, C. and R. Schleif. 1982. Is the amino acid but not the nucleotide sequence of the *Escherichia coli araC* gene conserved? *J. Mol. Biol.* **171**: 1049–1053.

———. 1983. The *araE* low affinity L-arabinose transport promoter: Cloning, sequence, transcription start site and DNA binding sites of regulatory proteins. *J. Mol. Biol.* **171**: 369–381.

Tobin, J. and R. Schleif. 1987. Positive regulation of the *Escherichia coli* L-rhamnose operon is mediated by the products of tandemly repeated regulatory genes. *J. Mol. Biol.* **196**: 789–799.

———. 1990a. Transcription from the *rha* operon p_{SR} promoter. *J. Mol. Biol.* **211**: 1–4.

———. 1990b. Purification and properties of RhaR, the positive regulator of the L-rhamnose operons of *Escherichia coli*. *J. Mol. Biol.* **211**: 75–89.

Tsung, K., R. Brissette, and M. Inouye. 1990. Enhancement of RNA polymerase binding to promoters by a transcription activator, OmpR, in *Escherichia coli*: Its positive and negative effects on transcription. *Proc. Natl. Acad. Sci.* **87**: 5940–5944.

Wallace, R., N. Lee, and A. Fowler. 1980. The *araC* gene of *Escherichia coli*, transcriptional and translational start-points and complete nucleotide sequence. *Gene* **12**: 179–190.

Wilcox, G. and P. Meuris. 1976. Stabilization and size of AraC protein. *Mol. Gen. Genet.* **145**: 97–100.

Wilcox, G., S. Al-Zarban, L. Cass, P. Clarke, L. Heffernan, A. Horwitz, and C. Miyada. 1982. DNA sequence analysis of mutants in the *araBAD* and *araC* promoters. In *Promoters: Structure and function* (ed. R. Rodriquez and M. Chamberlin), pp. 183–194. Praeger, New York.

Yamamoto, K., B. Alberts, R. Benzinger, L. Lawhorne, and G. Treiber. 1970. Rapid bacteriophage sedimentation in the presence of polyethylene glycol and its application to large-scale virus purification. *Virology* **40:** 734–744.

25
Prokaryotic Transcriptional Enhancers

David S. Weiss, Karl E. Klose, Timothy R. Hoover,[1]
Anne K. North, Susan C. Porter, Andrew B. Wedel,
and Sydney Kustu
Departments of Plant Pathology and Molecular and Cell Biology
University of California, Berkeley, California 94720

OVERVIEW

All known prokaryotic enhancer-binding proteins activate transcription by alternative holoenzyme forms of RNA polymerase, rather than σ^{70} holoenzyme. The enhancer-binding proteins activate transcription by stimulating a change in configuration of RNA polymerase at a promoter—specifically, the isomerization of a closed recognition complex to an open complex. To catalyze isomerization, the enhancer-binding proteins must hydrolyze ATP, making them the only transcriptional activators known to have a required enzymatic activity.

On the basis of their cognate RNA polymerases, prokaryotic enhancer-binding proteins can be divided into two classes. One class activates transcription by σ^{54} holoenzyme and has been shown to contact this polymerase by means of a DNA loop. At some, but not all, σ^{54}-dependent promoters, loop formation is assisted by a DNA-bending protein, IHF. The best-studied activator of σ^{54} holoenzyme is the NTRC protein; the ability of NTRC to activate transcription is regulated by phosphorylation, which controls its ATPase activity. The other class of prokaryotic enhancer-binding proteins, which is represented by a single member, activates transcription by a holoenzyme that contains both a sigma factor and an adapter protein encoded by phage T4. The T4 enhancer-binding protein is unusual in that it probably does not control the function of its cognate polymerase by a simple looping mechanism.

INTRODUCTION

Transcriptional enhancers play a critical role in the differentiation and development of eukaryotic organisms and in control of their metabolism

---

[1]Present address: Department of Microbiology, University of Georgia, Athens, Georgia 30602.

Transcriptional Regulation.
Copyright 1992 Cold Spring Harbor Laboratory Press 0-87969-410-6/92 $3 + 00

(Gehring 1987; Maniatis et al. 1987; Levine and Hoey 1988; Muller et al. 1988). Hence the mechanism(s) by which enhancers communicate with promoters and control their function has been a central issue in transcriptional regulation. Within the last few years, transcriptional enhancers have been found in prokaryotes (members of the eubacterial kingdom) and their viruses (Buck et al. 1986; Reitzer and Magasanik 1986; Herendeen et al. 1989). Because the function of prokaryotic enhancers is amenable to study in purified transcription systems, it has been possible to define precisely the means by which they influence promoter function and, in some cases, the means by which they communicate with promoters. It is our purpose to review what has been learned about prokaryotic enhancers, a term we restrict to elements that influence transcription positively. We also note a few similarities and differences between prokaryotic and eukaryotic enhancers.

One class of prokaryotic enhancers functions in conjunction with promoters recognized by σ^{54} holoenzyme, an alternative holoenzyme form of RNA polymerase that is the target of the enhancer-binding proteins (for review, see Kustu et al. 1989; Thony and Hennecke 1989). The best-studied enhancer-binding proteins of this class are the NTRC protein (*ni*trogen *r*egulatory protein *C*) and the NIFA protein (*ni*trogen *f*ixation protein *A*). The NTRC and NIFA proteins activate transcription by catalyzing isomerization of closed recognition complexes between σ^{54} holoenzyme and a promoter to open complexes (Sasse-Dwight and Gralla 1988; Morett and Buck 1989; Popham et al. 1989), a reaction that appears to require only transient contacts between activator and polymerase. For NTRC, which is better characterized, the isomerization is known to be ATP-dependent (Fig. 1) (Popham et al. 1989). Once open complexes have been formed, NTRC is no longer required to maintain them or to allow the initiation of transcription per se or the ensuing phases of elongation (Popham et al. 1989). Thus, NTRC activates transcription by stimulating a change in configuration of polymerase at the promoter. There is no evidence that it stimulates the initial binding of polymerase in closed complexes. This is in contrast to a role postulated for some eukaryotic enhancer-binding proteins, i.e., to stimulate or stabilize the binding of other transcription factors such as TFIID (for review, see Ptashne and Gann 1990). Whether stabilization requires persistent protein-protein contacts between activator and target remains to be determined; such persistent contacts have been postulated to explain the phenomenon of transcriptional interference or "squelching" (for review, see Ptashne 1988).

In the following sections, we consider the mechanism by which NTRC and NIFA stimulate open complex formation. First, we focus on

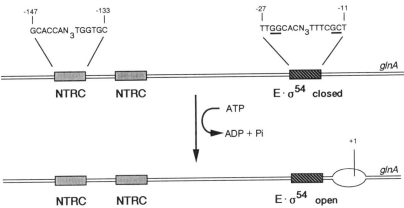

Figure 1 Diagram of the *glnA* promoter-regulatory region from *Salmonella typhimurium*. The upstream binding sites for NTRC, which are centered at −140 and −108, function as a transcriptional enhancer (Reitzer and Magasanik 1986; Ninfa et al. 1987); each site has twofold rotational symmetry. The promoter serves as a binding site for σ^{54} holoenzyme ($E \cdot \sigma^{54}$) The underlined GG and GC doublets, which must be separated by 10 bp, are conserved in σ^{54}-dependent promoters (Kustu et al. 1989; Thony and Hennecke 1989). Formation of open complexes requires ATP hydrolysis (see text).

the evidence that these proteins contact RNA polymerase from distant sites by means of DNA loop formation (Buck et al. 1987a; Minchin et al. 1989; Reitzer et al. 1989; Su et al. 1990; Wedel et al. 1990). Whereas contacts between NTRC and polymerase appear to be mediated by random and transient changes in the conformation of the DNA, NIFA is assisted in contacting polymerase by site-specific DNA bends that are induced by the integration host factor IHF (Hoover et al. 1990). After discussing loop formation, we summarize what is known about structure-function relationships for NTRC and NIFA, including the recent observation that NTRC has a required enzymatic activity (ATPase activity). Finally, we briefly discuss the only other prokaryotic enhancer that is well characterized, the enhancer of late transcription in the *Escherichia coli* virus T4. This enhancer appears to be very different from any other yet described (Herendeen et al. 1989, 1990).

MECHANISM OF ACTION OF THE NTRC PROTEIN

Background

The general nitrogen regulatory protein NTRC, which is found in a wide variety of gram-negative bacteria belonging to the phylum "Purple Bacteria," activates transcription in response to limitation of combined nitrogen (Kustu et al. 1989; Magasanik 1988). The protein from enteric bacteria (*E. coli, Salmonella typhimurium, Klebsiella pneumoniae*) has been studied intensively in the context of the promoter for the *glnA* gene (Fig. 1); this gene encodes glutamine synthetase, an enzyme with a major role in assimilation of ammonia. NTRC binds to five sites in the *glnA* promoter-regulatory region. The two upstream sites, which are centered at -140 and -108 with respect to the start site for transcription (Fig. 1), appear to mediate activation as efficiently as all five sites. These two sites were demonstrated by Reitzer and Magasanik (1986; see also Ninfa et al. 1987) to have properties of eukaryotic transcriptional enhancers: They function efficiently at large distances from the promoter, both downstream and upstream of it, and in either orientation. Although unmodified NTRC can bind to these sites with high affinity (Ninfa et al. 1987), the protein must be phosphorylated to activate transcription (not shown in Fig. 1). Phosphorylation of NTRC is catalyzed by the NTRB protein (Ninfa and Magasanik 1986). The sensing circuit that controls NTRC function in response to availability of combined nitrogen does so by controlling the degree of phosphorylation of the protein, which is increased under nitrogen-limiting conditions (Ninfa and Magasanik 1986; Keener et al. 1987; Magasanik 1988). Interestingly, differences in the degree of phosphorylation appear to be achieved not by regulating the phosphorylation reaction itself but by regulating the dephosphorylation of NTRC in a reaction that also requires NTRB (Keener and Kustu 1988).

To demonstrate that ATP is required directly for the formation of open complexes (Fig. 1), as well as for phosphorylation of NTRC, we used a mutant form of NTRC that bears a single amino acid substitution in its central domain (Ser-160→Phe; see Fig. 7C). This mutant form of NTRC, termed NTRC[constitutive], has some ability to activate transcription without being phosphorylated, although its activity is greatly increased by phosphorylation. When studied in the absence of NTRB, the NTRC[constitutive] protein still requires ATP to catalyze formation of open complexes (Popham et al. 1989). Since nonhydrolyzable analogs of ATP will not substitute, we infer that ATP hydrolysis is required for open complex formation (discussed below). We have used the NTRC[constitutive] protein in the absence of NTRB for many of the experiments reviewed here because phosphorylated NTRC has an autophosphatase activity (distinct from the regulated dephosphorylation reaction described above). The phospho-aspartate linkage in this protein (Weiss and Magasanik 1988) has a half-life of approximately 4 minutes at 37°C (Keener and Kustu 1988). It is therefore difficult to purify phosphorylated NTRC or to control its amount in transcription reactions.

NTRC Contacts RNA Polymerase (σ^{54} Holoenzyme) by Means of a DNA Loop

To ask how NTRC bound at its enhancer sites can stimulate formation of open complexes at a distant *glnA* promoter, we performed experiments to determine whether this reaction depends on an intact DNA pathway between the two (Wedel et al. 1990). We compared the ability of the enhancer sites to stimulate formation of open complexes when they are linked in *cis* to the *glnA* promoter (and at a distance of 3.0 kb from it) with their ability to do so when they are in *trans* to the promoter but tethered to it (Fig. 2A). In the *cis* configuration, the enhancer sites and the promoter were present on a supercoiled plasmid, whereas in the *trans* configuration, the enhancer and the promoter were present on different circles of a singly linked catenane. It is likely that the average distance between enhancer and promoter is similar in the two cases (Boles et al. 1990). We found that the sites work efficiently in both the catenated configuration and the *cis* configuration (Fig. 2B), congruent with the view that NTRC contacts polymerase by means of DNA loop formation. The results provide evidence against any mechanism of NTRC action that depends on an intact pathway between enhancer and promoter. In particular, they provide evidence against the plausible competing views that NTRC, which has an ATPase activity (see below), functions as a site-specific topoisomerase or a helicase.

Enhancer-like binding sites for NTRC are not stimulatory in *trans* once the circle carrying them has been decatenated from that carrying the *glnA* promoter. This finding provides evidence that one function of the enhancer sites is to tether NTRC near the *glnA* promoter (i.e., to increase its "local concentration") and thereby to increase the frequency with which it contacts σ^{54} holoenzyme. Failure of the enhancer sites to work in *trans* when they are decatenated from the promoter rules out the possibility that other hypothetical roles for these sites are sufficient in the absence of tethering; it does not rule out that such roles are required in addition to tethering (see below, Role of Enhancer-like Binding Sites for NTRC).

Together with Su and Echols (Su et al. 1990), we have visualized looped structures formed by contact between NTRC and σ^{54} holoenzyme in the electron microscope (Fig. 3b). To allow accurate measurement of loops, we increased the native distance from the enhancer to the *glnA* promoter by inserting 347 bp of DNA between them. The size of the loops we observed centered around the expected 390 bp, indicating that loops are formed by specific contacts between NTRC bound at its upstream sites and polymerase bound at the promoter. Moreover, it is possible to see directly that there are two different proteins at the base of

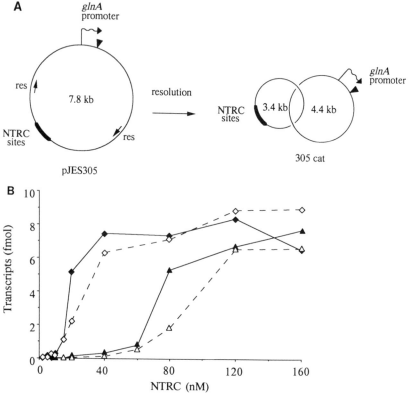

Figure 2 Function of the NTRC enhancer when catenated to the *glnA* promoter. (*A*) Diagram of templates. A plasmid containing NTRC sites in *cis* to the *glnA* promoter was resolved by the recombinase from transposon Tn3 to yield a singly linked catenane in which the NTRC sites and the promoter are on different circles. (*B*) Formation of open complexes on plasmids and their corresponding catenanes as a function of NTRC concentration. Open complexes were detected in a single-cycle transcription assay. (Closed diamonds) NTRC sites in *cis* to the *glnA* promoter; (open diamonds) NTRC sites in *trans* (catenated) to the promoter; (closed triangles) control template lacking specific NTRC sites (not shown in *A*); (open triangles) control catenane lacking NTRC sites. Plasmid pJES305 contains the NTRC-binding sites normally centered at −140 and −108 in the *glnA* promoter region, except that the site at −108 was inadvertently mutated; in pJES305 these sites are located 3.0 kb from the *glnA* promoter. Intact sites are stimulatory at even lower NTRC concentrations. (Reprinted, with permission, from Wedel et al. 1990 [copyright held by the AAAS].)

many loops because NTRC and polymerase look different after the tungsten shadowing necessary to visualize them by electron microscopy: NTRC appears gray and polymerase black.

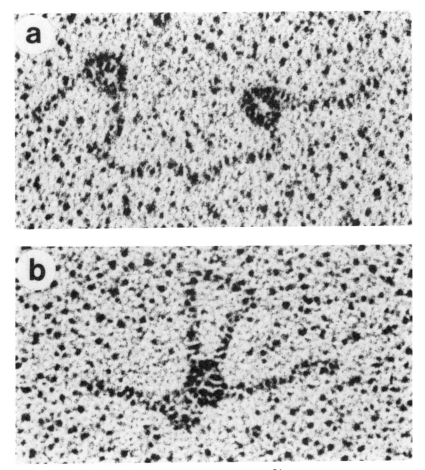

Figure 3 Electron micrographs of NTRC and E·σ^{54} on a DNA fragment carrying a modified *glnA* promoter-regulatory region (Su et al. 1990). (*a*) Linear; (*b*) looped. Measurements of the DNA segments indicate that NTRC (gray) is bound at the enhancer and that polymerase (black) is bound at the promoter. Protein-DNA complexes were formed in the presence of NTRB and ATP.

The demonstration of looped structures formed by contact between NTRC and σ^{54} holoenzyme provides another line of evidence that such structures function as intermediates in open complex formation. However, we infer that the loops are not bona fide kinetic intermediates. Rather, we think they are a form of the end product in which polymerase has completed the transition to an open complex. We reached this conclusion after considering four possibilities for the nature of looped species: (1) They are a form of the "reactant" in which polymerase is present in closed complexes, (2) they are a kinetic intermediate in which polymerase is in transition from closed to open complexes, (3) they are a form of the "product" in which polymerase has completed the transition to open complexes, and (4) they are a nonproductive by-product of open complex formation. We do not think that the loops are a form of the reactant because polymerase is not stable to spreading on the grids needed for electron microscopy when it is present in closed complexes. To observe RNA polymerase at the *glnA* promoter, it is necessary to allow the formation of open complexes by providing ATP in addition to the required proteins. Under these conditions approximately 15% of the molecules that carry polymerase are looped, whereas the remainder are linear (Fig. 3a). We doubt that the loops are intermediates in open complex formation because grids were prepared for electron microscopy long after the formation of open complexes had ceased (Popham 1989; Su et al. 1990). We excluded the only worrisome possibility, that loops are simply a nonproductive by-product of open complex formation, by showing that they are competent for transcription, as are linear molecules carrying polymerase. After addition of ribonucleotides, polymerase is not seen on the DNA, as expected if it has initiated transcription and run off the end of the DNA fragment. This result supports the view that both looped and linear species carry polymerase in open complexes.

Role(s) of Enhancer-like Binding Sites for NTRC

The aforementioned results indicate that a major role of the enhancer-like binding sites for NTRC in the *glnA* promoter-regulatory region is to maintain the activator in high concentration near the promoter. Since there are multiple sites, cooperative interactions between molecules of NTRC, which exists as a dimer in solution (Reitzer and Magasanik 1983), may be exploited to lower the dissociation rate of the protein. This would make the enhancer a more effective tether for NTRC. On the basis of the results of gel mobility shift assays, binding of NTRC to the two upstream-most sites in the *glnA* promoter-regulatory region appears to be cooperative. We infer cooperativity because binding of NTRC to a DNA fragment carrying the *glnA* promoter region (or to a fragment carrying only the two most upstream binding sites for NTRC) gives rise to only a single retarded species, which contains two dimers of NTRC as assessed with ^{35}S-labeled protein (S. Porter, unpubl.). If NTRC dimers bound independently, we would expect to see a second (intermediate) species that carries only one dimer. Such a hypothetical species has not been seen even at very low protein concentrations.

It is possible that binding sites for NTRC play roles in addition to tethering. Such hypothetical roles might include activating NTRC allosterically or directing assembly of a nucleoprotein structure that is required for efficient NTRC function. (As discussed above, a nucleoprotein structure would be expected to arise from cooperative binding of NTRC and to contribute to its slow dissociation rate. The issue here is whether such a structure might also have a more sophisticated and as yet undefined role in transcriptional activation.) In electron micrographs (Fig. 3), NTRC bound to the *glnA* promoter-regulatory region appears to form a structure that is comparable in size to RNA polymerase, which has a molecular mass of approximately 450 kD. This structure contains at least two dimers of NTRC (~105 kD each) and may also contain NTRB (a dimer of ~77 kD), which was present to increase the efficiency of open complex formation (S. Porter and D. Weiss, unpubl.).

If the only role of the enhancer is to tether NTRC near the *glnA* promoter, one might expect that high concentrations of NTRC will activate transcription from solution. (It has been calculated that a solution concentration of ~100 nM should compensate for the tethering effect of binding sites [Mossing and Record 1986].) Failure to satisfy this prediction would suggest that the NTRC binding sites serve additional roles of the sort postulated above. At concentrations well below 100 nM, NTRC can activate transcription on templates that lack specific binding sites for it (Fig. 2B). However, interpretation of this finding is complicated by the fact that activation appears to depend, at least in part, on binding to secondary or nonspecific sites on DNA and therefore to occur in *cis* (Popham et al. 1989). We are using two tools to test for activation from solution: (1) linear transcription templates that are too short to allow for looping and hence for activation in *cis* and (2) mutant forms of NTRC that lack the ability to bind DNA.

THE NIFA PROTEIN

Background

Like NTRC, NIFA is an activator of transcription for σ^{54} holoenzyme and is found widely among gram-negative bacteria of the "purple" group. NIFA activates transcription of genes whose products are required for biological nitrogen fixation—the reduction of dinitrogen to ammonia (Gussin et al. 1986; Kustu et al. 1989; Thony and Hennecke 1989). Unlike NTRC, NIFA does not require phosphorylation to function as a transcriptional activator. Rather, NIFA activity is regulated negatively in the presence of molecular oxygen by mechanisms that remain to be defined (Roberts and Brill 1980; Hill et al. 1981; Fischer et al. 1988). Inactivation of NIFA prevents the synthesis of nitrogen fixation proteins, several of which are oxygen labile, under conditions in which they could not function catalytically. The regulatory cascade that controls NIFA synthesis and activity in the enteric bacterium *K. pneumoniae* is diagramed in Figure 4. Note that synthesis of NIFA is activated by phosphorylated NTRC under nitrogen-limiting conditions and that NIFA activity is then controlled by molecular oxygen.

Function of the NIFA protein from *K. pneumoniae* has been studied in detail at the promoter for the *nifHDK* operon, which encodes nitrogenase. NIFA binds to a single upstream site that is centered at −132 with respect to the start site of transcription (Fig. 5) (Morett and Buck 1988). Like NTRC, it catalyzes isomerization of closed complexes between σ^{54} holoenzyme and the promoter to open complexes, identified as such because the region around the transcriptional start site shows chemical reactivity characteristic of single-stranded DNA (Morett and Buck 1989). Although both these properties have been demonstrated in vivo, they have not been demonstrated in vitro. Crude extracts containing the NIFA protein from *K. pneumoniae* have been shown to activate transcription from the *nifHDK* promoter in a coupled transcription-trans-

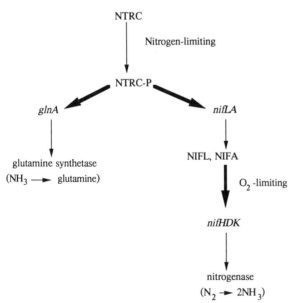

Figure 4 Regulatory cascade controlling the synthesis and activity of NIFA in *K. pneumoniae*. When combined nitrogen is limiting, NTRC is phosphorylated by NTRB and activates transcription of the *nifLA* operon (heavy arrow). In the absence of molecular oxygen, NIFA activates transcription of the *nifHDK* and other *nif* operons (heavy arrow). In the presence of oxygen or combined nitrogen, NIFA is inactivated by NIFL (mechanism unknown) (Roberts and Brill 1980; Hill et al. 1981; Buchanan-Wollaston et al. 1981; Gussin et al. 1986).

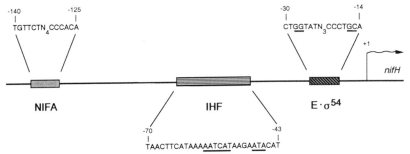

Figure 5 Diagram of the *nifHDK* promoter-regulatory region of *K. pneumoniae*. The upstream binding site for NIFA (Morett and Buck 1988), the promoter (Gussin et al. 1986), and the IHF-binding site (Santero et al. 1989; Hoover et al. 1990) are indicated. Bases corresponding to an IHF consensus sequence (Craig and Nash 1984; Leong et al. 1985) are underlined. Plasmid p318 (used in Fig. 6) carries a C→T transition at position –18 in the promoter, and plasmid p319 carries two C→T transitions at positions –18 and –20 (Ow et al. 1985). Note that the *glnA* promoter (Fig. 1) carries Ts rather than Cs at positions corresponding to –18, –19, and –20 of the *nifHDK* promoter. (This is true for the *glnA* promoter of *K. pneumoniae* as well as that of *S. typhimurium*.)

lation system (Fig. 6A) (Santero et al. 1989; Austin et al. 1990; Hoover et al. 1990), but it has not yet been possible to purify active NIFA.

**NIFA Appears to Contact RNA Polymerase by Means of
an IHF-induced DNA Bend**

In attempting to demonstrate DNA binding by NIFA in vitro, we found that another factor in crude extracts bound to the *nifHDK* promoter-regulatory region at a location between the upstream binding site for NIFA and the promoter (Fig. 5) (see also Beynon et al. 1983). We identified this factor as the integration host factor (IHF) and demonstrated that it bound in a similar location to many *nif* promoter-regulatory regions from several members of the phylum Purple Bacteria (Santero et al. 1989; Hoover et al. 1990). IHF is a small, site-specific DNA-binding protein that participates in several processes, including site-specific recombination, transposition, DNA replication, and transcription (for review, see Friedman 1988). The primary function of IHF is to bend DNA. This appears to be its only role at one of its binding sites in the attachment region for bacteriophage λ, the H2 site in *attP*, which can be replaced with a piece of DNA that is inherently bent (Goodman and Nash 1989). We have shown by electron microscopy that IHF sharply bends

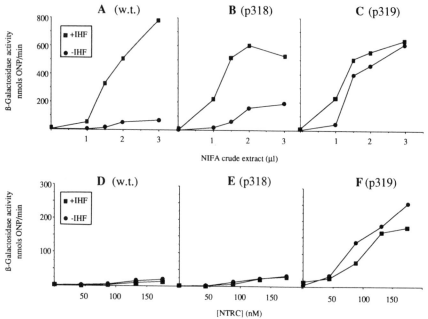

Figure 6 Effect of *nifHDK* promoter strength on activation by NIFA and NTRC and on stimulation of this activation by IHF (Reprinted, with permission, from Hoover et al. 1990 [copyright held by Cell Press].) Transcription of a *nifH-lacZ* fusion expressed from the wild-type *nifHDK* promoter or from the stronger mutant promoters p318 and p319 (see Fig. 5) was monitored in a coupled transcription-translation system. The coupled system was prepared from a strain that lacked IHF, and IHF (60 nM) was provided as indicated. In panels *A–C* the activator is NIFA (provided from a crude extract), and in panels *D–F* it is purified NTRC in the presence of NTRB.

the DNA in the *nifHDK* promoter-regulatory region of *K. pneumoniae* (Hoover et al. 1990).

Functionally, IHF stimulates the ability of NIFA to activate *nifHDK* expression by up to 20-fold in a coupled transcription-translation system (Fig. 6A) (Hoover et al. 1990). (Both the coupled system and the NIFA crude extract were prepared from strains that lack IHF, and purified IHF was added as indicated.) To demonstrate the IHF stimulation in a purified transcription system, we replaced the upstream binding site for NIFA in the *nifHDK* promoter-regulatory region with a single binding site for NTRC. On this template, IHF stimulates NTRC-mediated activation by up to 30-fold in a purified transcription system and by approximately 10-fold in the coupled system (T. Hoover, unpubl.). The fact that stimulation in the purified system is of the same order of magnitude as in the crude coupled system indicates that IHF is the only factor required. We infer that stimulation by IHF is due to the ability of the IHF-induced bend to increase contacts between the activator bound upstream and σ^{54} holoenzyme because IHF does not appear to stimulate binding of any of the individual components—NIFA, NTRC, or polymerase (Hoover et al. 1990; T. Hoover, unpubl.). Increased contacts between activator and polymerase at the promoter would, in turn, increase the efficiency of open complex formation.

IHF Is Employed Together with "Weak" *nif* Promoters to Achieve High Efficiency and High Fidelity of Activation by NIFA

We have been interested in the question of why IHF is employed at *nif* promoters and not at *glnA*. There appear to be two aspects to the answer (Morett and Buck 1989; Hoover et al. 1990). The first is that IHF is employed selectively at promoters that are "weak" in the sense that they constitute weak binding sites for σ^{54} holoenzyme in closed complexes; IHF stimulates activation only at such weak promoters. The second is that weak promoters can be used to prevent spurious activation by non-physiological activators—i.e., activators that do not have a specific binding site located near the promoter. Nonphysiological activators can activate transcription from strong promoters by binding to secondary or nonspecific sites anywhere in their vicinity and possibly also from solution (Fig. 2B). IHF selectively stimulates activation of transcription from a weak promoter by the physiological activator, which has a specific binding site that is appropriately placed with respect to the IHF-induced bend. These arguments are elaborated below with respect to the role of IHF at the *nifHDK* promoter of *K. pneumoniae*.

Both the *nifHDK* and *glnA* promoters of enteric bacteria are "strong" in the sense that they can be expressed at high levels under suitable physiological conditions. However, unlike the *glnA* promoter, the *nifHDK* promoter of *K. pneumoniae* is weak in the sense that σ^{54} holoenzyme does not form physically detectable closed complexes at *nifHDK* (Morett and Buck 1989; Hoover et al. 1990). Occupancy by polymerase is sufficient to yield a DNase I footprint at *glnA* but not at *nifHDK*. The strength of the *nifHDK* promoter as a binding site for σ^{54} holoenzyme is improved by mutations that bring its sequence closer to that at *glnA* (see legend to Fig. 5) (Morett and Buck 1989; Hoover et al. 1990). For such mutant promoters, NIFA works better as an activator in the absence of IHF, and IHF is less stimulatory (Fig. 6, compare panels B and C with panel A). In the presence of IHF, maximum activation by NIFA at the two "stronger" mutant promoters is the same as that at the weak wild-type promoter. Our interpretation of these results is as follows. As polymerase shows greater occupancy of a promoter in closed complexes, NIFA bound at its upstream site is better able to contact it by means of transient and random changes in the conformation of the DNA. The IHF-induced bend is less stimulatory because the DNA conformational change is no longer the rate-limiting step in open complex formation.

At the strongest of the mutant *nifHDK* promoters, there is little stimulation by IHF, and NIFA alone works almost as well at the mutant promoter as the combination of NIFA plus IHF at the wild-type promoter (Fig. 6, panel C vs. panel A). Why then doesn't the cell employ the strongest promoter and dispense with IHF? We think that the answer has to do with achieving high fidelity of activation by NIFA, i.e., preventing activation by other activators of σ^{54} holoenzyme such as NTRC. Panels D–F of Figure 6 illustrate the effects of NTRC as an activator at the wild-type and mutant *nifHDK* promoters. (Note that the templates for these experiments contain the normal region upstream of the promoter, i.e., a specific binding site for NIFA and no such site for NTRC.) For the weak wild-type promoter, NTRC shows little ability to activate. We think that residual activation by NTRC occurs from secondary or non-specific binding sites on the DNA, although we have not rigorously excluded the possibility that it occurs from solution. Like NIFA, NTRC is a better activator for the stronger mutant promoters than the wild-type promoter. Again, we attribute this to the fact that polymerase shows greater occupancy of the mutant promoters in closed complexes. As expected, IHF does not stimulate NTRC-mediated activation from any of the promoters, because NTRC does not occupy a specific binding site that is correctly placed with respect to the IHF-induced bend. From the point of view of cell physiology, a major problem in using the strongest mutant promoter is that NTRC has considerable ability to activate it not only in vitro (panel F) but also in vivo (Ow et al. 1985; Buck and Cannon 1989). In vivo, activation from the mutant promoter occurs under nitrogen-limiting conditions (which are appropriate physiologically), but it occurs in the presence of molecular oxygen as well as in its absence. Thus, NTRC can activate synthesis of nitrogenase under conditions in which this enzyme is needed but is catalytically inactive. Use of the weak wild-type *nifHDK* promoter makes the synthesis of nitrogenase dependent on NIFA and hence on the entire regulatory cascade illustrated in Figure 4. Use of IHF in conjunction with the weak promoter allows the cell to maintain high efficiency of activation by NIFA selectively, because only NIFA has a binding site that is appropriately placed with respect to the IHF-induced bend.

The strategy of using IHF in conjunction with a weak σ^{54}-dependent promoter is apparently employed in other cases for which high fidelity of activation by a particular activator is of selective advantage. Examples include the following: (1) promoters for the hook and flagellin genes of *Caulobacter crescentus*, which are expressed in a temporally and spatially discrete manner (Gober and Shapiro 1990), and (2) the promoter for a gene encoding a dicarboxylate transport component in *Rhizobium leguminosarum*, which is expressed only when dicarboxylic acids are present external to the cell (B. Gu and B. T. Nixon, pers. comm.).

The NIFA-binding Site Is an Upstream Activating Sequence

Unlike binding sites for NTRC at *glnA*, which are enhancer-like and function efficiently at distances of several kilobases from the promoter, the binding site for NIFA in the *nifHDK* promoter region functions as an upstream activating sequence (Buck et al. 1986, 1987b). The efficacy of the NIFA site falls off rapidly with distance, and it is not effective downstream from the promoter. We attribute this behavior primarily to the low occupancy of the *nifHDK* promoter by σ^{54} holoenzyme. Although the IHF-induced bend compensates for low promoter occupancy, it can do so only when the NIFA-binding site is positioned correctly. When the NIFA-binding site is moved away from the IHF site to a location downstream from the promoter or far upstream of it, the NIFA site presumably works as poorly as in the absence of a bend. We would predict that a strong *nifHDK* promoter, which is known to eliminate the need for a bend, would enable the NIFA-binding site to work more like an enhancer—i.e., with greater positional independence. Since activation of transcription is a function of the frequency with which an occupied NIFA-binding site interacts with an occupied promoter, we think it likely that the strength of the NIFA-binding site will also influence whether the site functions more like an enhancer or an upstream activating sequence.

The issue of why some binding sites for transcriptional activators are enhancer-like whereas others are upstream activating sequences is of general interest due to the observation that mammalian activator proteins function from either downstream or upstream of a promoter, but yeast activators function only from the upstream position (for review, see Guarente 1987). This difference does not appear to be intrinsic to the sites or the proteins that bind them, because an upstream activating sequence from yeast together with its cognate binding protein functions from downstream of mammalian promoters in mammalian cells (Webster et al. 1988). Thus, whether a binding site for a eukaryotic transcriptional activator is an enhancer or an upstream activating sequence depends on the context in which it is functioning. As discussed above, we think the same is true of the NIFA-binding site at *nifHDK*, where the strength of the promoter as a binding site for σ^{54} holoenzyme is likely to be the primary influence of context on function of the activator site.

DOMAIN STRUCTURE OF THE NTRC AND NIFA PROTEINS

Overview

The view emerging from studies of the structure and function of NTRC and, to a lesser extent, NIFA (which cannot yet be purified in an active form) is that activation of transcription is a complex process. We have recently found that NTRC catalyzes an enzymatic reaction, ATP hydrolysis, that appears to be required for its function as a transcriptional activator (Weiss et al. 1991). It is our working hypothesis that the ATPase activity of NTRC is required in addition to its ability to contact its target protein, σ^{54} holoenzyme, via DNA looping. However, we have not excluded the possibility that ATP hydrolysis is required for the formation of specific contacts per se. The ATPase activity of NTRC is dependent on phosphorylation: It is stimulated at least several hundred-fold when NTRC is phosphorylated by NTRB. The need to activate the ATPase may account for the fact that NTRC must be phosphorylated to activate transcription, although it can bind efficiently to the enhancer without being modified.

Another indication that transcriptional activation by NTRC is a complex process requiring a precise interaction with σ^{54} holoenzyme is that there are amino acid substitutions in NTRC which result in failure to activate transcription, even though they do not affect binding to the enhancer or phosphorylation (Wei and Kustu 1981; D. Weiss, unpubl.). This is in contrast to the case for a number of eukaryotic activators, which cannot be deprived entirely of their ability to activate transcription by means of a point mutation (see, e.g., Gill and Ptashne 1987; Johnston and Dover 1987). In the extreme examples, the latter can be reduced to a DNA-binding motif and an activating region whose composition and general structure (often acidic and α-helical) are important, but whose precise amino acid sequence is not (for review, see Ptashne 1988; Mitchell and Tjian 1989; Struhl 1989).

As is the case with a number of eukaryotic enhancer-binding proteins, the functional domains of NTRC and NIFA are physically separable. NTRC and NIFA are organized similarly. Each has a central activation domain, a carboxy-terminal DNA-binding domain, and an amino-terminal domain that is regulatory for NTRC and probably also for NIFA (Drummond et al. 1986, 1990; Nixon et al. 1986; Keener and Kustu

1988; Morrett et al. 1988; Buck and Cannon 1989; Huala and Ausubel 1989). The following sections discuss the means by which these domains and interactions between them contribute to transcriptional activation.

Central Activation Domain

The central domains of NTRC and NIFA (~240 amino acid residues) appear to be directly responsible for their ability to activate transcription by σ^{54} holoenzyme. Three lines of evidence support this conclusion. First, the central domain is shared by all the known activators of σ^{54} holoenzyme for which sequence information is available (Fig. 7A). Second, mutant forms of NTRC that fail to activate but are otherwise normal (see Overview) have lesions in the central domain in residues that are highly conserved among the activators (Fig. 7B; NTRC[repressor]; so named because they retain the ability to repress transcription from a secondary σ^{70}-dependent promoter in the enhancer region). Finally, and most convincing, the isolated central domain of the NIFA protein from *Rhizobium meliloti* is sufficient for transcriptional activation in vivo when it is overexpressed (Huala and Ausubel 1989).

The central domains of activators for σ^{54} holoenzyme contain a recognizable ATP-binding motif (Fig. 7A) (Ronson et al. 1987). The ATPase activity of phosphorylated NTRC is absent in several NTRC[repressor] proteins, including one that has a lesion in the ATP-binding motif. We infer from these results that the ATPase activity is essential for the ability of NTRC to activate transcription and that it is responsible for the ATP requirement in formation of open complexes by σ^{54} holoenzyme (see Fig. 1). Presumably, the central domain of NTRC (and other activators of σ^{54} holoenzyme) also contains determinants that mediate specific protein-protein contacts with RNA polymerase, the determinants responsible for the formation of looped structures. Although such determinants have not yet been defined, activators of σ^{54} holoenzyme do not contain sequence motifs thought to mediate protein-protein interaction of eukaryotic transcriptional activators: acidic regions, glutamine- or proline-rich regions, or leucine zippers. Curiously, several of these motifs seem to occur in σ^{54} (Sasse-Dwight and Gralla 1990; Gross et al., this volume).

Carboxy-terminal DNA-binding Domain

The carboxy-terminal regions of NTRC and NIFA (40–60 residues) are responsible for DNA binding (Morett et al. 1988; Drummond et al. 1990). These regions, which contain a helix-turn-helix DNA-binding

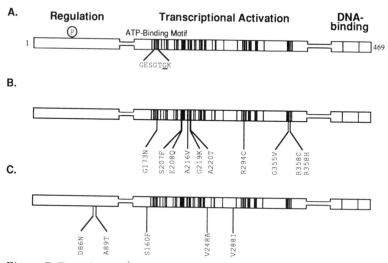

Figure 7 Domains of NTRC (*A*) and amino acid substitutions in NTRC[repressor] proteins (*B*) and NTRC[constitutive] proteins (*C*). (*A*) NTRC is 469 amino acids long and contains domains for regulation (~120 amino acids), transcriptional activation (~240 amino acids), and DNA binding (40–60 amino acids). The regulatory domain is phosphorylated at Asp-54 (circled P). The activation domain contains an ATP-binding motif (GESGTGK in one-letter amino acid code). The amino acids that are identical in all the activators of σ^{54} holoenzyme whose sequences are known are indicated in black. These activators are NTRC and NIFA of several organisms (for review, see Kustu et al. 1989; D. Weiss and P. Wong [unpubl.] for *S. typhimurium* NTRC), DCTD of *R. leguminosarum* (Ronson et al. 1987), FLBD of *C. crescentus* (Ramakrishnan and Newton 1990), XYLR of *Pseudomonas putida* (Inouye et al. 1988), and HRPS of *Pseudomonas syringae* pathovar *phaseolicola* (Grimm and Panopolous 1989). The underlined glycine in the ATP-binding motif is at position 173 and is mutated to asparagine in one of the NTRC[repressor] proteins (see below). (*B*) Location of NTRC[repressor] mutations. Note that all are in universally conserved residues of the transcriptional activation domain. (*C*) Location of NTRC[constitutive] mutations. Note that all are in nonconserved residues and occur in both the regulatory and activation domains.

motif, are both necessary and sufficient for binding to specific sites. When the DNA-binding region of NIFA is deleted, the remainder of the protein retains activity in vivo if it is overproduced, implying that the only role of a NIFA-binding site is to tether this protein near a promoter (Morett et al. 1988; Huala and Ausubel 1989). Since NIFA has not yet been purified, the deleted protein cannot be tested in vitro. When the DNA-binding region of NTRC is deleted, the remainder of the protein is inactive (Drummond et al. 1990; S. Shiau and L.R. Reitzer, pers. comm.;

A. North, unpubl.). However, we have found that at least one carboxy-terminal deletion of NTRC causes loss of ATPase activity as well as DNA binding (A. North, unpubl.). It remains to be determined whether point mutations that cause loss of DNA binding by NTRC will leave the protein active (see above, Role of Enhancer-like Binding Sites for NTRC). At this point it is not clear whether the difference between NIFA and NTRC with respect to the necessity for DNA binding is fundamental or is due to technical difficulties with NTRC.

Amino-terminal Regulatory Domain

The amino-terminal domain of NTRC (~120 residues) controls its function as a transcriptional activator. This domain must be phosphorylated on Asp-54 (D. Sanders and D. Koshland, pers. comm.) for the protein to be competent in transcriptional activation. The isolated domain contains not only the site of phosphorylation but all of the determinants required for phosphorylation by NTRB and for dephosphorylation (Keener and Kustu 1988). We have been interested in whether the amino-terminal domain of NTRC functions negatively or positively and in how it controls transcriptional activation. If the domain functioned negatively, removing it would be equivalent to phosphorylating it, in that either would allow high levels of transcriptional activation. However, this does not appear to be the case. Removal of this domain does not allow transcriptional activation by otherwise wild-type NTRC (Drummond et al. 1990; D. Weiss, unpubl.) and does not increase transcriptional activation by NTRC^{constitutive} proteins with lesions in the central domain (Ser-160→Phe and Val-288→Ile; Fig. 7C). Thus, the phosphorylated amino-terminal domain appears to play a positive role in function of the protein as a transcriptional activator. We note, however, that there appears to be more than one principle by which homologs of the amino-terminal domain of NTRC regulate the activity of proteins to which they are attached. Such homologs have been found on more than 20 bacterial regulatory proteins either known or thought to be activated by phosphorylation, so-called "receiver" proteins of "two-component" regulatory systems (Nixon et al. 1986; Kofoid and Parkinson 1988; Stock et al. 1989). The conserved regulatory domain plays a negative role in controlling the activity of several receiver proteins, including the transcriptional activators DCTD (B. Gu and B.T. Nixon, pers. comm.) and FIXJ (D. Kahn, pers. comm.) and the methylesterase, CHEB (Simms et al. 1985).

Phosphorylation of the amino-terminal domain of NTRC greatly stimulates the ATPase activity of the protein, which in turn appears to be required for its function as a transcriptional activator (Weiss et al. 1991). The phosphorylated amino-terminal domain itself does not exhibit ATPase activity; rather, this activity depends on phosphorylation of intact NTRC. These results support the view that phosphorylation of the amino-terminal domain of NTRC activates an enzymatic activity that is contained in the central domain, the location of the ATP-binding site. We postulate that control of the ATPase activity may be the primary means by which phosphorylation of NTRC controls its ability to activate transcription. We know that phosphorylation does not play either of two other plausible roles: Transfer of phosphate from the amino-terminal domain of NTRC to σ^{54} holoenzyme is not required for transcriptional activation, and phosphorylation does not directly create an acidic surface that interacts with this form of RNA polymerase. The evidence for both these conclusions derives from the properties of NTRC[constitutive] proteins, those that have some ability to activate transcription in the absence of NTRB. Two such proteins (Ser-160→Phe and Val-288→Ile) not only activate without being phosphorylated but do so when their amino-terminal domain is deleted. Furthermore, none of the amino acid substitutions in NTRC[constitutive] proteins results in an increase in acidity (Fig. 7C).

The amino-terminal domain of NIFA is not related to that of NTRC (Drummond et al. 1986) and is not required for NIFA activity (Beynon et al. 1988; Huala and Ausubel 1989, Drummond et al. 1990). Since posttranslational modification of the amino-terminal domain of NIFA does not appear to be required for its function as a transcriptional activator, we predict that NIFA will have constitutive ATPase activity.

ENHANCER OF LATE TRANSCRIPTION IN BACTERIOPHAGE T4

Expression of bacteriophage T4 late genes, which encode proteins found in the virion, is dependent on DNA replication (Epstein et al. 1964; Bolle et al. 1968). Geiduschek and co-workers have obtained evidence that the replication fork acts directly as an enhancer of transcription at T4 late promoters (Herendeen et al. 1989). In vitro the replication fork can be mimicked by a nick in the DNA. The fork (mimicked by the nick) serves as a site of assembly for the DNA replication apparatus of T4. A portion of this apparatus, which serves as a "sliding clamp" to increase the processivity of DNA replication (Piperno et al. 1978; Jarvis et al. 1989), is necessary and sufficient for enhancement of transcription in vitro: The products of T4 genes 44, 45, and 62 together function as the enhancer-binding protein (Herendeen et al. 1989). Like NTRC and NIFA, these proteins control the function of an alternative holoenzyme form of RNA polymerase, which carries the products of two T4 genes (55 and 33) associated with *E. coli* core polymerase. Whereas the product of gene 55 alone can serve as sigma factor—it is sufficient to allow the core polymerase to recognize T4 late promoters (Kassavetis et al. 1983)—the product of gene 33 is essential for communication with the enhancer (Herendeen et al. 1990). As is the case for activation of transcription by σ^{54} holoenzyme, activation of T4 late transcription is dependent on ATP hydrolysis, which stimulates the formation of open complexes (Herendeen et al. 1989). The enhancer-binding protein (sliding clamp) is known to have a DNA-dependent ATPase activity that is required for assembly of T4 DNA polymerase holoenzyme at the replication fork (Piperno et al. 1978; Jarvis et al. 1989, 1991).

The T4 replication fork (nick) behaves like an enhancer in that it functions efficiently at large and variable distances from a T4 late promoter (Herendeen et al. 1989). However, its properties differ from those of other enhancers in several ways (Herendeen et al. 1989). (1) It is not defined by base pair sequence. (2) Its effect is strictly dependent on orientation: Whether the nick is located upstream or downstream from the promoter on a linear template, it must be present on the non-transcribed strand of the DNA. This would correspond to a situation in which DNA replication and transcription were proceeding in the same direction. (3) In vivo, the replication fork is moving. Whether mobility of the enhancer-binding protein is integral or incidental to its function in activating transcription remains to be determined.

One of the most interesting issues regarding function of the T4 late enhancer is the means by which it communicates with its cognate promoters. The fact that the orientation dependence of this enhancer is maintained at distances many times that of the persistence length of the DNA argues strongly against a simple looping mechanism for enhancer-promoter interaction (Herendeen et al. 1989).

CONCLUSIONS

Communication between Enhancers and Promoters

We have obtained direct evidence that a bacterial enhancer to which the NTRC protein binds communicates with the *glnA* promoter by means of a DNA loop that brings the two sites together. Similar evidence has been obtained for the SV40 and cytomegalovirus enhancers (Mueller-Storm et al. 1989), which activate transcription from promoters recognized by eukaryotic RNA polymerase II, and for the *Xenopus laevis* ribosomal RNA enhancer, which activates transcription from a promoter recognized by RNA polymerase I (Dunaway and Droge 1989). (The latter evidence was obtained in vivo.) In agreement with a number of earlier experiments performed in vivo (Brent and Ptashne 1985; Plon and Wang 1986; Ptashne 1986; Guarente 1988; Muller et al. 1988), the recent evidence indicates that looping of DNA is a pervasive mechanism by which enhancers communicate with their cognate promoters. However, there is no a priori reason why this mechanism must pertain in all cases; in fact, the orientation dependence of the enhancer for T4 late transcription (the fork for DNA replication) argues against a simple looping mechanism for enhancer-promoter interaction in this case (Herendeen et al. 1989).

Where looping does pertain, it may involve embellishments. Both NTRC in the *glnA* promoter region and NIFA in the *nifHDK* promoter region contact polymerase (σ^{54} holoenzyme) by means of a DNA loop. Whereas loop formation at *glnA* appears to rely on random and transient changes in the conformation of the DNA, loop formation at *nifHDK* is directed by the IHF, which binds to a site between the enhancer and the promoter, inducing a sharp bend (Hoover et al. 1990). This bend serves to decrease the effective volume shared by the NIFA site and the *nifHDK* promoter, thereby raising the local concentration of NIFA in the promoter region above that achieved by the tethering effect of the enhancer alone. The increased local concentration of NIFA compensates for the fact that σ^{54} holoenzyme shows low occupancy of the *nifHDK* promoter in closed complexes relative to its occupancy of the *glnA* promoter. As discussed in the text, an advantage to lower promoter occupancy at *nifHDK* is that it decreases spurious activation by homologs of NIFA. The requirement for an IHF-induced bend seems likely to account for the fact that the NIFA-binding site at *nifHDK* shows properties of an upstream activating sequence rather than a true enhancer (Buck et al. 1986, 1987b): Presumably the NIFA-binding site must be an appropriate distance from the IHF-induced bend to function efficiently.

Binding of IHF and NIFA upstream of *nif* promoters in bacteria provides a possible parallel to binding of multiple factors upstream of promoters for eukaryotic RNA polymerase II. Introduction of a DNA bend is a mechanism by which one DNA-binding protein might work to allow both high efficiency and high fidelity of transcriptional activation by another. Interestingly, the yeast transcriptional regulator TUF is known to bend DNA (Vignais and Sentenac 1989).

Mechanisms by Which Enhancer-binding Proteins Control Promoter Function

Activators of σ^{54} holoenzyme catalyze a change in configuration of this polymerase at promoters to yield open complexes. Similarly, the activator of T4 late transcription catalyzes the formation of open complexes by its cognate polymerase (Herendeen et al. 1989). In both cases, formation of open complexes depends on ATP hydrolysis, which is catalyzed by the activator (enhancer-binding protein). It is our working hypothesis that hydrolysis of ATP by NTRC (and presumably other activators of σ^{54} holoenzyme) is used to provide energy for open complex formation. Interestingly, phosphorylation of NTRC appears to control its function as a transcriptional activator primarily by regulating its ATPase activity rather than its DNA binding.

Enzymatic activity of auxiliary transcription factors like NTRC and the activator of T4 late transcription is rare. The maltoseT (MALT) protein of *E. coli* is capable of ATP hydrolysis, but ATP binding appears to be sufficient for its function as a transcriptional activator of σ^{70} holoenzyme (Richet and Raibaud 1989). In eukaryotes, ATP hydrolysis is required for initiation of transcription by mitochondrial RNA polymerase (Narasimhan and Attardi 1987). ATP hydrolysis is also required prior to or concomitant with synthesis of the first phosphodiester bond by RNA polymerase II and factors needed for initiation of transcription by this polymerase appear to have ATPase activity (Bunick et al. 1982; Sawadogo and Roeder 1984; Luse and Jacob 1987; Luse et al. 1987; Buratowski et al. 1989; Conaway and Conaway 1989; Sopta et al. 1989).

Unlike activators of σ^{54} holoenzyme and the activator of T4 late transcription, a number of eukaryotic enhancer-binding proteins that activate transcription by RNA polymerase II may do so by increasing the initial binding of other transcription factors to promoter regions (for review, see Mitchell and Tjian 1989; Ptashne and Gann 1990). Lack of constraint on the amino acid sequence of the activating domains of some eukaryotic enhancer-binding proteins implies that their ability to activate transcription does not depend on a precise interaction with their targets. Whether eukaryotes also contain activators like NTRC—that is to say, activators whose function depends on precise interactions with their targets and whose amino acid sequence is highly constrained—remains to be determined.

ACKNOWLEDGMENTS

We thank Laura Attardi, Peter Geiduschek, Dan Herendeen, and Eva Huala for critical reading of the manuscript and Steve McKnight for excellent editorial comments.

REFERENCES

Austin, S., N. Henderson, and R. Dixon. 1990. Characterisation of the *Klebsiella pneumoniae* nitrogen-fixation regulatory proteins NIFA and NIFL *in vitro. Eur. J. Biochem.* **187:** 353–360.

Beynon, J.L., M.K. Williams, and F.C. Cannon. 1988. Expression and functional analysis of the *Rhizobium meliloti nifA* gene. *EMBO J.* **7:** 7–14.

Beynon, J., M. Cannon, V. Buchanan-Wollaston, and F. Cannon. 1983. The *nif* promoters of *Klebsiella pneumoniae* have a characteristic primary structure. *Cell* **34:** 665–671.

Boles, T.C., J.H. White, and N.R. Cozzarelli. 1990. Structure of plectonemically super-coiled DNA. *J. Mol. Biol.* **213:** 931–951.

Bolle, A., R.H. Epstein, W. Salser, and E.P. Geiduschek. 1968. Transcription during bac-teriophage T4 development: Requirements for late messenger synthesis. *J. Mol. Biol.* **33:** 339–362.

Brent, R. and M. Ptashne. 1985. A eukaryotic transcriptional activator bearing the DNA specificity of a prokaryotic repressor. *Cell* **43:** 729–736.

Buchanan-Wollaston, V., M.C. Cannon, J.L. Beynon, and F.C. Cannon. 1981. Role of the *nifA* gene product in the regulation of *nif* expression in *Klebsiella pneumoniae*. *Nature* **294:** 776–778.

Buck, M. and W. Cannon. 1989. Mutations in the RNA polymerase recognition sequence of the *Klebsiella pneumoniae nifH* promoter permitting transcriptional activation in the absence of NifA binding to upstream activator sequences. *Nucleic Acids Res.* **17:** 2597–2612.

Buck, M., W. Cannon, and J. Woodcock. 1987a. Transcriptional activation of the *Kleb-siella pneumoniae* nitrogenase promoter may involve DNA loop formation. *Mol. Mi-crobiol.* **1:** 243–249.

Buck, M., S. Miller, M. Drummond, and R. Dixon. 1986. Upstream activator sequences are present in the promoters of nitrogen fixation genes. *Nature* **320:** 374–378.

Buck, M., J. Woodcock, W. Cannon, L. Mitchenall, and M. Drummond. 1987b. Posi-tional requirements for the function of *nif*-specific upstream activator sequences. *Mol. Gen. Genet.* **210:** 140–144.

Bunick, D., R. Zandomeni, S. Ackerman, and R. Weinmann. 1982. Mechanism of RNA polymerase II-specific initiation of transcription in vitro: ATP requirement and un-capped runoff transcripts. *Cell* **29:** 877–886.

Buratowski, S., S. Hahn, L. Guarente, and P.A. Sharp. 1989. Five intermediate com-plexes in transcription initiation by RNA polymerase II. *Cell* **56:** 549–561.

Conaway, R.C. and J.W. Conaway. 1989. An RNA polymerase II transcription factor has an associated DNA-dependent ATPase (dATPase) activity strongly stimulated by the TATA region of promoters. *Proc. Natl. Acad. Sci.* **86:** 7356–7360.

Craig, N.L. and H.A. Nash. 1984. *E. coli* integration host factor binds to specific sites in DNA. *Cell* **39:** 707–716.

Drummond, M.H., A. Contreras, and L.A. Mitchenall. 1990. The function of isolated domains and chimaeric proteins constructed from the transcriptional activators NifA and NtrC of *Klebsiella pneumoniae*. *Mol. Microbiol.* **4:** 29–37.

Drummond, M., P. Whitty, and J. Wooton. 1986. Sequence and domain relationships of *ntrC* and *nifA* from *Klebsiella pneumoniae*: Homologies to other regulatory proteins. *EMBO J.* **5:** 441–447.

Dunaway, M. and P. Droge. 1989. Transactivation of the *Xenopus* rRNA gene promoter by its enhancer. *Nature* **341:** 657–659.

Epstein, R.H., A. Bolle, C.M. Steinberg, E. Kellenberg, E.B. De la Tour, R. Chevally, R.S. Edgar, M. Susman, G.H. Denhardt, and A. Lielausis. 1964. Physiological studies of conditional lethal mutants of bacteriophage T4D. *Cold Spring Harbor Symp. Quant. Biol.* **28:** 375–392.

Fischer, H.-M., T. Bruderer, and H. Hennecke. 1988. Essential and non-essential domains in the *Bradyrhizobium japonicum* NifA protein: Identification of indispensable cysteine residues potentially involved in redox reactivity and/or metal binding. *Nucleic Acids Res.* **16:** 2207–2224.

Friedman, D.I. 1988. Integration host factor: A protein for all reasons. *Cell* **55:** 545–554.

Gehring, W.J. 1987. Homeoboxes in the study of development. *Science* **236:** 1245–1252.

Gill, G. and M. Ptashne. 1987. Mutants of GAL4 protein altered in an activation function. *Cell* **51:** 121–126.

Gober, J.W. and L. Shapiro. 1990. Integration host factor is required for the activation of developmentally regulated genes in *Caulobacter*. *Genes Dev.* **4:** 1494–1504.

Goodman, S.D. and H.A. Nash. 1989. Functional replacement of a protein-induced bend in a DNA recombination site. *Nature* **341:** 251–254.

Grimm, C. and N.J. Panopoulos. 1989. The predicted protein product of a pathogenicity locus from *Pseudomonas syringae* pv. *phaseolicola* is homologous to a highly conserved domain of several procaryotic regulatory proteins. *J. Bacteriol.* **171:** 5031–5038.

Guarente, L. 1987. Regulatory proteins in yeast. *Annu. Rev. Genet.* **21:** 425–452.

———. 1988. UASs and enhancers: Common mechanism of transcriptional activation in yeast and mammals. *Cell* **52:** 303–305.

Gussin, G.N., C.W. Ronson, and F.M. Ausubel. 1986. Regulation of nitrogen fixation genes. *Annu. Rev. Genet.* **20:** 567–591.

Herendeen, D.R., K.P. Williams, G.A. Kassavetis, and E.P. Geiduschek. 1990. An RNA polymerase-binding protein that is required for communication between an enhancer and a promoter. *Science* **248:** 573–578.

Herendeen, D.R., G.A. Kassavetis, J. Barry, B.M. Alberts, and E.P. Geiduschek. 1989. Enhancement of bacteriophage T4 late transcription by components of the T4 DNA replication apparatus. *Science* **245:** 952–958.

Hill, S., C. Kennedy, E. Kavanagh, R. Goldberg, and R. Hanau. 1981. Nitrogen fixation gene (*nifL*) involved in oxygen regulation of nitrogenase synthesis in *Klebsiella pneumoniae*. *Nature* **290:** 424–426.

Hoover, T.R., E. Santero, S. Porter, and S. Kustu. 1990. The integration host factor stimulates interaction of RNA polymerase with NIFA, the transcriptional activator for nitrogen fixation operons. *Cell* **63:** 11–22.

Huala, E. and F.M. Ausubel. 1989. The central domain of *Rhizobium meliloti* NifA is sufficient to activate transcription from the *R. meliloti nifH* promoter. *J. Bacteriol.* **171:** 3354–3365.

Inouye, S., A. Nakazawa, and T. Nakazawa. 1988. Nucleotide sequence of the regulatory gene *xylR* of the TOL plasmid from *Pseudomonas putida*. *Gene* **66:** 301–306.

Jarvis, T.C., J.W. Newport, and P.H. von Hippel. 1991. Stimulation of the processivity of the DNA polymerase of bacteriophage T4 by the polymerase accessory proteins. *J. Biol. Chem.* **266:** 1830–1840.

Jarvis, T.C., L.S. Paul, J.W. Hockensmith, and P.H. von Hippel. 1989. Structural and enzymatic studies of the T4 DNA replication system. II. ATPase properties of the polymerase accessory protein complex. *J. Biol. Chem.* **264:** 12717–12729.

Johnston, M. and J. Dover. 1987. Mutations that inactivate a yeast transcriptional regulatory protein cluster in an evolutionarily conserved DNA binding domain. *Proc. Natl. Acad. Sci.* **84:** 2401–2405.

Kassavetis, G.A., T. Elliot, D.P. Rabussay, and E.P. Geiduschek. 1983. Initiation of transcription at phage T4 late promoters with purified RNA polymerase. *Cell* **33:** 887–897.

Keener, J. and S. Kustu. 1988. Protein kinase and phosphoprotein phosphatase activities of nitrogen regulatory proteins NTRB and NTRC of enteric bacteria: Roles of the conserved amino-terminal domain of NTRC. *Proc. Natl. Acad. Sci.* **85:** 4976–4980.

Keener, J., P. Wong, D. Popham, J. Wallis, and S. Kustu. 1987. A sigma factor and auxiliary proteins required for nitrogen-regulated transcription in enteric bacteria. In *RNA polymerase and the regulation of transcription* (ed. W.R. Reznikoff et al.), pp. 159–175. Elsevier, New York.

Kofoid, E.C. and J.S. Parkinson. 1988. Transmitter and receiver modules in bacterial signaling proteins. *Proc. Natl. Acad. Sci.* **85:** 4981–4985.

Kustu, S., E. Santero, J. Keener, D. Popham, and D. Weiss. 1989. Expression of σ54 (*ntrA*)-dependent genes is probably united by a common mechanism. *Microbiol. Rev.* **53:** 367–376.

Leong, J.M., S. Nunes-Duby, C.F. Lesser, P. Youderian, M.M. Susskind, and A. Landy. 1985. The φ80 and P22 attachment sites: Primary structure and interaction with *Escherichia coli* integration host factor. *J. Biol. Chem.* **260:** 4468–4477.

Levine, M. and T. Hoey. 1988. Homeobox proteins as sequence-specific transcription factors. *Cell* **55:** 537–540.

Luse, D.S. and G.A. Jacob. 1987. Abortive initiation by RNA polymerase II in vitro at the adenovirus 2 major late promoter. *J. Biol. Chem.* **262:** 14990–14997.

Luse, D.S., T. Kochel, E.D. Kuempel, J.A. Coppola, and H. Cai. 1987. Transcription initiation by RNA polymerase II in vitro. At least two nucleotides must be added to form a stable ternary complex. *J. Biol. Chem.* **262:** 289–297.

Magasanik, B. 1988. Reversible phosphorylation of an enhancer binding protein regulates the transcription of bacterial nitrogen utilization genes. *Trends Biochem. Sci.* **13:** 475–479.

Maniatis, T., S. Goodbourn, and J.A. Fischer. 1987. Regulation of inducible and tissue-specific gene expression. *Science* **236:** 1237–1244.

Minchin, S.D., S. Austin, and R.A. Dixon. 1989. Transcriptional activation of the *Klebsiella pneumoniae niflA* promoter by NTRC is face-of-the-helix dependent and the activator stabilizes the interaction of sigma 54-RNA polymerase with the promoter. *EMBO J.* **8:** 3491–3499.

Mitchell, P.J. and R. Tjian. 1989. Transcriptional regulation in mammalian cells by sequence-specific DNA binding proteins. *Science* **245:** 371–378.

Morett, E. and M. Buck. 1988. NifA-dependent in vivo protection demonstrates that the upstream activator sequence of *nif* promoters is a protein binding site. *Proc. Natl. Acad. Sci.* **85:** 9401–9405.

———. 1989. In vivo studies on the interaction of RNA polymerase-σ54 with the *Klebsiella pneumoniae* and *Rhizobium meliloti nifH* promoters: The role of NIFA in the formation of an open promoter complex. *J. Mol. Biol.* **210:** 65–77.

Morett, E., W. Cannon, and M. Buck. 1988. The DNA-binding of the transcriptional activator protein NifA resides in its carboxy terminus, recognizes the upstream activator sequences of *nif* promoters and can be separated from the positive control function of NifA. *Nucleic Acids Res.* **16:** 11469–11488.

Mossing, M.C. and M.T. Record, Jr. 1986. Upstream operators enhance repression of the *lac* promoter. *Science* **233:** 889–892.

Mueller-Storm, H., J.M. Sogo, and W. Schaffner. 1989. An enhancer stimulates transcription in *trans* when attached to the promoter via a protein bridge. *Cell* **58:** 767–777. (Published erratum appears in *Cell* [1989] **59:** 405.)

Muller, M.M., T. Gerster, and W. Schaffner. 1988. Enhancer sequences and the regulation of gene transcription. *Eur. J. Biochem.* **176:** 485–495.

Narasimhan, N. and G. Attardi. 1987. Specific requirement for ATP at an early step of in vitro transcription of human mitochondrial DNA. *Proc. Natl. Acad. Sci.* **84:** 4078–4082.

Ninfa, A.J. and B. Magasanik. 1986. Covalent modification of the *glnG* product NRI, by the *glnL* product, NRII, regulates the transcription of the *glnALG* operon in *Escherichia coli. Proc. Natl. Acad. Sci.* **83:** 5909–5913.

Ninfa, A.J., L.J. Reitzer, and B. Magasanik. 1987. Initiation of transcription at the bacterial *glnA*p2 promoter by purified *E. coli* components is facilitated by enhancers. *Cell* **50:** 1039–1046.

Nixon, B.T., C.W. Ronson, and F.M. Ausubel. 1986. Two-component regulatory systems responsive to environmental stimuli share strongly conserved domains with the nitrogen assimilation regulatory genes *ntrB* and *ntrC. Proc. Natl. Acad. Sci.* **83:** 7850–7854.

Ow, D., Y. Xiong, Q. Gu, and S. Shen. 1985. Mutational analysis of the *Klebsiella pneumoniae* nitrogenase promoter: Sequences essential for positive control by *nifA* and *ntrC (glnG)* products. *J. Bacteriol.* **161:** 868–874.

Piperno, J.R., R.G. Kallen, and B.M. Alberts. 1978. Analysis of a T4 DNA replication protein complex. *J. Biol. Chem.* **253:** 5180–5185.

Plon, S.E. and J.C. Wang. 1986. Transcription of the human beta-globin gene is stimulated by an SV40 enhancer to which it is physically linked but topologically uncoupled. *Cell* **45:** 575–580.

Popham, D.L. 1989. "Biochemical studies on the activation of nitrogen-regulated transcription in enteric bacteria." Ph.D. thesis, University of California, Davis.

Popham, D.L., D. Szeto, J. Keener, and S. Kustu. 1989. Function of a bacterial activator protein that binds to transcriptional enhancers. *Science* **243:** 629–635.

Ptashne, M. 1986. Gene regulation by proteins acting nearby and at a distance. *Nature* **322:** 697–701.

———. 1988. How eukaryotic transcriptional activators work. *Nature* **335:** 683–689.

Ptashne, M. and A.A.F. Gann. 1990. Activators and targets. *Nature* **346:** 329–331.

Ramakrishnan, G. and A. Newton. 1990. FlbD of *Caulobacter crescentus* is a homologue of the NTRC (NRI) protein and activates σ54-dependent flagellar gene promoters. *Proc. Natl. Acad. Sci.* **87:** 2369–2373.

Reitzer, L. and B. Magasanik. 1983. Isolation of the nitrogen assimilation regulator NRI, the product of the *glnG* gene of *Escherichia coli. Proc. Natl. Acad. Sci.* **80:** 5554–5558.

———. 1986. Transcription of *glnA* in *E. coli* is stimulated by activator bound to sites far from the promoter. *Cell* **45:** 785–792.

Reitzer, L.J., B. Movsas, and B. Magasanik. 1989. Activation of *glnA* transcription by nitrogen regulator I (NRI)-phosphate in *Escherichia coli*: Evidence for a long range physical interaction between NRI-phosphate and RNA polymerase. *J. Bacteriol.* **171:** 5512–5522.

Richet, E. and O. Raibaud. 1989. MalT, the regulatory protein of the *Escherichia coli* maltose system, is an ATP-dependent transcriptional activator. *EMBO J.* **8:** 981–987.

Roberts, G.P. and W.J. Brill. 1980. Gene-product relationships of the *nif* regulon of *Klebsiella pneumoniae. J. Bacteriol.* **144:** 210–216.

Ronson, C.W., P.M. Astwood, B.T. Nixon, and F.M. Ausubel. 1987. Deduced products of C4-dicarboxylate transport regulatory genes of *Rhizobium leguminosarum* are homologous to nitrogen regulatory gene products. *Nucleic Acids Res.* **15:** 7921–7934.

Santero, E., T. Hoover, J. Keener, and S. Kustu. 1989. In vitro activity of the nitrogen fixation regulatory protein NIFA. *Proc. Natl. Acad. Sci.* **86:** 7346–7350.

Sasse-Dwight, S. and J.D. Gralla. 1988. Probing the *Escherichia coli glnALG* upstream activation mechanism in vivo. *Proc. Natl. Acad. Sci.* **85:** 8934–8938.

———. 1990. Role of eukaryotic-type functional domains found in the prokaryotic enhancer receptor factor σ54. *Cell* **62:** 945–954.

Sawadogo, M. and R.G. Roeder. 1984. Energy requirement for specific transcription initiation by the human RNA polymerase II system. *J. Biol. Chem.* **259:** 5321–5326.

Simms, S.A., M.G. Keane, and J. Stock. 1985. Multiple forms of the CheB methylesterase in bacterial chemosensing. *J. Biol. Chem.* **260:** 10161–10168.

Sopta, M., Z.F. Burton, and J. Greenblatt. 1989. Structure and associated DNA-helicase activity of a general transcription initiation factor that binds to RNA polymerase II. *Nature* **341:** 410–414.

Stock, J.B., A.J. Ninfa, and A.M. Stock. 1989. Protein phosphorylation and regulation of adaptive responses in bacteria. *Microbiol. Rev.* **53:** 450–490.

Struhl, K. 1989. Molecular mechanisms of transcriptional regulation in yeast. *Annu. Rev. Biochem.* **58:** 1051–1077.

Su, W., S. Porter, S. Kustu, and H. Echols. 1990. DNA-looping and enhancer activity: Association between DNA-bound NTRC activator and RNA polymerase at the bacterial *glnA* promoter. *Proc. Natl. Acad. Sci.* **87:** 5504–5508.

Thony, B. and H. Hennecke. 1989. The -24/-12 promoter comes of age. *FEMS Microbiol. Rev.* **63:** 341–358.

Vignais, M.L. and A. Sentenac. 1989. Asymmetric DNA bending induced by the yeast multifunctional factor TUF. *J. Biol. Chem.* **264:** 8463–8466.

Webster, N., J.R. Jin, S. Green, M. Hollis, and P. Chambon. 1988. The yeast UAS$_G$ is a transcriptional enhancer in human HeLa cells in the presence of the GAL4 *trans*-activator. *Cell* **52:** 169–178.

Wedel, A., D.S. Weiss, D. Popham, P. Droge, and S. Kustu. 1990. A bacterial enhancer functions to tether a transcriptional activator near a promoter. *Science* **248:** 486–490.

Wei, G. and S. Kustu. 1981. Glutamine auxotrophs with mutations in a nitrogen regulatory gene, *ntrC*, that is near *glnA*. *Mol. Gen. Genet.* **183:** 392–399.

Weiss, D. S., J. Batut, K.E. Klose, J. Keener, and S. Kustu. 1991. The phosphorylated form of the enhancer-binding protein NTRC has an ATPase activity that is essential for activation of transcription. *Cell* **67:** 155–167.

Weiss, V. and B. Magasanik. 1988. Phosphorylation of nitrogen regulator I (NRI) of *Escherichia coli*. *Proc. Natl. Acad. Sci.* **85:** 8919–8923.

26
Transcriptional Activation by Viral Immediate-Early Proteins: Variations on a Common Theme

Katherine J. Martin and Michael R. Green
Program in Molecular Medicine
University of Massachusetts Medical Center
Worcester, Massachusetts 01605

OVERVIEW

Viral immediate-early proteins are the first viral proteins to be synthesized following infection (or upon reactivation from latency) and are required for the transcription, or the enhancement of transcription, of many viral genes. More than 20 viral immediate-early proteins have been identified. Until recently, it has been generally assumed that these viral proteins function in a manner fundamentally different from that of typical cellular transcriptional activators. In this review, we summarize current evidence indicating that many viral transcriptional activators function through mechanisms that are analogous to those of cellular transcriptional activators: The viral proteins directly participate in the transcription complex to stimulate transcription. Variations on the theme of the typical sequence-specific cellular activators can account for the idiosyncratic features of viral activators, which have been difficult to reconcile with notions of cellular activators. Such characteristics of some viral activators include the lack of specific DNA-binding activity, promiscuous activation, and requirements for RNA elements.

INTRODUCTION

Typical Cellular Activators

Transcriptional initiation by RNA polymerase II is usually regulated by cellular factors that bind to the DNA located upstream of the gene, termed a promoter. Promoters consist of a variety of DNA sequence elements, or regions of about 8–20 bp that conform to one of a number of consensus motifs, which are specifically recognized and bound by DNA-binding proteins. On the basis of the functional characteristics of the proteins that bind to these sequence elements, the promoter can be divided into two distinct regions. The first region, located in the vicinity of the transcription start site and termed a core promoter, conforms to the TATA consensus motif. This region of DNA is bound by the general (or basic) transcription factors that are critical for both basal and activated levels of transcription of all RNA polymerase II transcribed genes (for review, see Saltzman and Weinman 1989). The general transcription factors identified to date include TFIIA, TFIIB, TFIID (which binds directly to the TATA box), TFIIE, TFIIF (RAP30/74), and TFIIG (Reinberg and Roeder 1987; Reinberg et al. 1987; Van Dyke et al. 1988; Buratowski et al. 1989; Sumimoto et al. 1990). Since these factors (with the exceptions of IID and IIF) are currently identified as partially purified cellular fractions, additional general factors will likely be identified.

The second region of the promoter includes DNA elements typically located upstream of the core promoter that are responsible for gene-specific stimulation of the level of transcription. These sequence elements are termed either promoter-proximal elements or enhancers on the basis of their proximity to the transcriptional start site and conform to a variety of consensus sequences that bind to a number of different cellular sequence-specific transcription activators.

Cellular activators have been shown to encode two essential functions that are typically located within separable domains of the protein (Brent and Ptashne 1985; Struhl 1987; for review, see Ptashne 1988). First, a DNA-binding region binds directly to a specific DNA sequence and is responsible for directing the protein to the promoters it activates. Second, an activation region, anchored to the promoter by the DNA-binding domain, somehow increases the level of transcription—most likely by establishing contact with a general transcription factor (for review, see Ptashne 1988; Lillie and Green 1990). This contact may be direct or indirect.

The DNA-binding and activation regions of cellular transcriptional activators can be categorized on the basis of their amino acid sequences. DNA-binding regions include the homeodomain (for review, see Gehring 1987; Scott et al. 1989; Scott and Hayashi 1990), which contains the helix-turn-helix motif (Anderson et al. 1981; Steitz et al. 1982; Otting et al. 1988; for review, see Pabo and Sauer 1984), the POU homeodomain (Herr et al. 1988), the helix-loop-helix homology region (Murre et al. 1989), the zinc finger (Brown et al. 1985; Miller et al. 1985), and the basic region plus leucine zipper domain (Landschulz et al. 1988; Vinson et al. 1989). Activation regions include the acidic (Gill and Ptashne

1987; Hope et al. 1988; Cress and Triezenberg 1991), glutamine-rich (Courey and Tjian 1988), and proline-rich (Mermod et al. 1989) activators.

Viral activators appear superficially different from cellular activators. In particular, three features of viral activators have been difficult to reconcile with the cellular activator paradigm.

1. *Lack of sequence-specific DNA-binding activity.* Some viral activators, including the adenovirus E1A protein and the herpes simplex virus protein VP16, do not bind with high affinity to specific DNA sequences (Ferguson et al. 1985; Marsden et al. 1987).
2. *Promiscuity.* Viral activators can act promiscuously. The herpes simplex virus ICP4 protein and the pseudorabies virus immediate-early protein, for example, can activate transcription from a wide variety of both RNA polymerase II and III promoters that share no apparent common sequence elements (for review, see Berk 1986; Flint and Shenk 1989).
3. *RNA activation sites.* The transcriptional activator of the human immunodeficiency virus, HIV-1 Tat, acts through a specific RNA sequence present in the 5′-untranslated region of genes it activates (for review, see Sharp and Marciniak 1989).

In light of these unusual features, viral activators have been proposed to activate transcription indirectly—perhaps by activating, modifying, or increasing the nuclear concentrations of one or several, general or specific, cellular transcription factors. Although such mechanisms may indeed be employed, recent evidence has begun to indicate that the viral activators function in a manner that may mimic that of typical cellular activators.

We briefly review 12 well-studied viral transcription activators. Aspects of the mechanisms used by these activators that are consistent with the cellular activator paradigm are emphasized. We argue that most of these viral activators conform to the theme of cellular activators.

Viral Transcription Activators

Adenovirus E1A Proteins

The adenoviruses represent a related class of large DNA tumor viruses. Following the infection of permissive host cells, adenovirus genes are expressed in a sequential temporal cascade. The first two classes of proteins expressed, early region 1A (E1A) and early region 1B (E1B), are products of early region 1 of the viral genome. Because of differential splicing of their mRNAs, the E1A and E1B proteins comprise multiple polypeptides. The largest E1A protein produced, which is translated from a 13S RNA message, is a 289-amino-acid nuclear phosphoprotein that is required for transcriptional activation of its own gene as well as other early viral genes (Berk et al. 1979; Jones and Shenk 1979; for review, see Flint and Shenk 1989).

The 289-amino-acid E1A appears to activate transcription through several different mechanisms (for review, see Green 1991). One of the best understood of these is activation by a polypeptide domain within E1A termed region 3. E1A region 3 strongly activates a variety of viral and cellular genes in a manner analogous to cellular transcriptional activators (Lillie and Green 1989; Liu and Green 1990; Martin et al. 1990a). Other mechanisms of transcriptional activation by E1A appear to be exceptions to the paradigm of cellular activators. These include the activation of DNA-binding activity of transcription factor E2F (see Neill et al. 1990 and references therein), region-3-independent transcriptional activation (see, e.g., Zerler et al. 1987; Kaddurah-Daouk et al. 1990), repression of enhancer-mediated transcription (see Rochette-Egly et al. 1990 and references therein), and activation of polymerase III transcribed genes (see Yoshinaga et al. 1986 and references therein). The former two E1A activities are discussed below, as is activation by region 3 of E1A.

E1A Region-3-dependent Transcriptional Activation. Comparisons of E1A sequences of the six adenovirus serotypes have identified three highly conserved regions (Moran and Mathews 1987). One of these, conserved region 3, encodes the 49-amino-acid transcriptional activation domain. Deletion studies have shown that this region is responsible for activation of the early viral genes, E1A, E1B, E2A, E3, and E4 (for review, see Moran and Mathews 1987). This region appears to be structured by a metal-binding site (Culp et al. 1988) and contains the two critical features of typical cellular activators: a promoter-directing region and a transcriptional activation region (Lillie and Green 1989).

The 289-amino-acid E1A protein does not bind to DNA specifically, but apparently uses a different method to associate with promoter regions: The promoter-directing region of E1A can bind to the cellular sequence-specific DNA-binding protein, activating transcription factor-2 (ATF-2) (Liu and Green 1990). ATF-2 is a member of the ATF family of proteins, which comprise at least eight similar members that bind to the consensus sequence 5$'$-GTGACGT$^{AA}_{CG}$-3$'$ (Hai et al. 1989). Evidence for the interaction between ATF-2 and E1A is based on the results of in vivo transient expression assays (Liu and Green 1990) . A fusion protein, consisting of the DNA-binding domain of the yeast GAL4 protein and ATF-2, activated transcription from a GAL4 site-containing promoter only in the presence of E1A. Other members of the ATF family did not support activation in this system. The model derived from these results explains how E1A is targeted to the adenovirus early genes, since ATF sites are present in the vicinity of each of these promoters.

In addition to its promoter-targeting region, conserved region 3 of E1A also encodes a transcriptional activation region (Lillie and Green 1989). Extensive mutagenesis of this region has shown that it has discrete boundaries and requires the core metal-binding site (Martin et al. 1990a). In addition, the E1A activation region does not contain any of the characteristics of cellular activation regions, such as large numbers of acidic or glutamine residues. Consistent with its unique features, it has been suggested that the activation region of E1A interacts with an auxiliary cellular factor, termed an adapter, not required for transcriptional activation by the acidic class of activators (Martin et al. 1990a). Evidence presented in support of this view is that high levels of the E1A activation region were unable to competitively inhibit (squelch) the functioning of acidic activation regions, whereas high levels of acidic activators were able to competitively inhibit activation by E1A.

Other Mechanisms. An extensively analyzed, indirect mechanism through which E1A can activate transcription occurs during the expression of the adenovirus early region 2 (E2) promoter. The E2 promoter contains two binding sites for the cellular E2-specific factor E2F. Upon viral infection, there is an increase in E2F DNA-binding activity (Reichel et al. 1988). This increase is in part the result of a conversion of E2F from a noncooperative to a cooperative DNA-binding form (Hardy and Shenk 1989), which is dependent on a viral early region 4 (E4) gene product (Hardy et al. 1989; Reichel et al. 1989). One of the E4 products, a 19-kD protein from the 6/7 open reading frame, interacts with E2F (Huang and Hearing 1989; Neill et al. 1990). Presumably, the E4 19-kD protein bridges two E2F monomers converting E2F to a cooperative DNA-binding protein. E1A is, of course, required to transcriptionally activate the E4 gene. Thus, E1A indirectly facilitates E2 transcription by activating the expression of another viral gene.

An indication that E1A can act through other mechanisms is that transcriptional activation of some genes by E1A does not require conserved region 3. These types of studies are based on in vivo transient expression assays in which transcriptional activation by the product of the 13S E1A mRNA, which includes region 3, is compared to activation by the product of the 12S E1A mRNA, which is deleted of region 3. E1A activated genes that do not require region 3 include the cellular genes for proliferating cell nuclear antigen (Zerler et al. 1987), creatine kinase B (Kaddurah-Daouk et al. 1990), and perhaps hsp70 (Zerler et al. 1987; Simon et al. 1987). The mechanism(s) involving region-3-independent activation is not clear. One possibility is that the presence of E1A leads to changes in the activity of cellular transcription factors. In this regard, several reports have suggested that adenovirus infection is accompanied by changes in the phosphorylation of cellular transcription factors (Hoeffler et al. 1988; Bagchi et al. 1989; Raychaudhuri et al. 1989). Whether these phosphorylation events require viral proteins in addition to E1A, and whether the phosphorylation is causally related to transcriptional activation, remain to be determined. Another possibility is that E1A regions 1 and/or 2 may activate transcription by perturbing the cell cycle through interactions established between E1A and host-cell proteins important for growth regulation. For example, in a mechanism completely independent of region 3, E1A tightly associates with the product of the retinoblastoma gene (Whyte et al. 1988), a protein involved in preventing oncogenic transformation of cells (for review, see Horowitz et al. 1988; Green 1989). E1A may thus indirectly cause global changes in cellular transcription levels.

Bovine Papillomavirus E2 Protein

Bovine papillomavirus (BPV) is a small DNA tumor virus with a genome of 8 kb. It specifies the synthesis of at least eight viral proteins, including the transcriptional regulatory proteins of the early region (E2) open reading frame. Three E2 proteins are produced: E2, a 48-kD promiscuous transcriptional activator encoded by the entire E2 open reading frame (Sphalholz et al. 1985; Yang et al. 1985; Haugen et al. 1987; Hubbert et al. 1988), and E2-TR and E8/E2, which both act as transcriptional repressors and are encoded by the carboxyl terminus of the E2 open reading frame (Lambert et al. 1987; Yang et al. 1987; Choe et al. 1990).

The E2 protein has been shown to contain the two essential features of cellular sequence-specific DNA-binding proteins: a DNA-binding domain and a transcriptional activation region. Amino acids 286–410, located at the carboxyl terminus of the protein, are responsible for sequence-specific binding to DNA, whereas amino acids 1–210 form an activation region (Androphy et al. 1987; Giri and Yaniv 1988; Haugen et al. 1988; McBride et al. 1988; Moskaluk and Bostia 1988). These two regions are conserved among the different papillomaviruses, whereas a variable-length linker region, located between the two regions, is not.

DNase I footprinting and gel mobility shift assays have shown that the E2 protein binds as a dimer (Dostatni et al. 1988; Mcbride et al. 1989) directly to the DNA sequence $5'$-$ACCN_6GGT$-$3'$ (Androphy et al. 1987; Giri and Yaniv 1988; Moskaluk and Bostia 1988). This sequence functions as an E2 response element by conferring E2 inducibility onto heterologous promoters (Hawley-Nelson et al. 1988).

The E2 protein is also able to promiscuously activate transcription. E2 can induce a number of promoters that do not contain E2-binding sites, albeit to lower levels than promoters that do contain E2-binding sites (Haugen et al. 1987). In addition, the E2 activation region can stimulate transcriptionally active promoters in the absence of its DNA-binding domain (Haugen et al. 1988). This activity likely involves the interaction of E2 with some cellular DNA-binding transcription factors. It has been shown that E2 can interact directly with the cellular transcription factor Sp1, and that this interaction allows Sp1 and E2 to activate transcription synergistically (Li et al. 1991). The interaction between Sp1 and E2 enables E2 to stimulate transcription in the absence of an E2-binding site on the DNA.

An indication that the activation region of the E2 protein may belong to the acidic class of activators is the fact that E2 can activate transcription in yeast (Lambert et al. 1989; Morrissey et al. 1989). Acidic activators are "universal" in that they, apparently unlike any other activation regions, activate transcription in higher and lower eukaryotes (Ptashne and Gann 1990). Two subregions of the E2 *trans*-activation region have been shown by deletion studies to be necessary, although not sufficient, for E2 activation activity (Lambert et al. 1989). The first region comprises the 28 amino acids at the immediate amino terminus of the protein. This region includes the only unusually acidic section of the E2 activation region (six acidic residues) and has a potentially amphipathic character. The second region, amino acids 65–81, is also potentially amphipathic.

The two BPV transcriptional repressors, E2-TR and E8/E2, are encoded by the carboxy-terminal half of the E2 activator protein. Both consist of the E2 DNA-binding and dimerization regions without a transcriptional activation region (Lambert et al. 1987). All three E2 proteins, E2, E2-TR, and E8/E2, are capable of dimerizing with one another and binding to the E2-responsive elements (Dostatni et al. 1988; McBride et al. 1989, 1988). It has been hypothesized that the repressors function by either (or both) of two mechanisms. The repressors may compete with the E2 activator for specific promoter-binding sites and/or they may dimerize with the form of the protein encoded by the intact E2 open reading frame to form activator-repressor heterodimers that are incapable of transcriptional activation.

Epstein-Barr Virus

Epstein-Barr virus (EBV) is a human herpesvirus that infects mainly B cells and epithelial cells. In B cells, EBV is primarily latent, existing as a multicopy unintegrated circular genome. EBV directs the expression of two immediate-early transcriptional activator proteins that are responsible for establishing the lytic phase of the virus, the Z *trans*-activator (Zta) (also termed the *Bam*HI Z left fragment 1 [BZLF1] gene product, factor Epstein-Barr 1 [EB1], and ZEBRA) and R *trans*-activator (Rta) (also termed the *Bam*HI R left fragment 1 [BRLF1] gene product). Zta functions predominantly to interrupt latency, and it has been shown that overexpression of Zta will disrupt latency; however, other viral proteins, e.g., Rta, are likely also involved. Rta is required predominantly for maintenance of the lytic cycle of the virus. Evidence indicates that Zta functions, at least in part, in a manner analogous to that of typical cellular activators, whereas the mechanism(s) of Rta is not clear. These two immediate-early activators are discussed below.

In addition to its immediate-early transcriptional activators, EBV also encodes another transcriptional activator, the Epstein-Barr nuclear antigen-1 (EBNA-1). EBNA-1 is involved in replication of the EBV genome as well as transcriptional regulation of the genes required for latency. Like typical cellular activators, EBNA-1 binds directly to DNA at specific sequences located in the promoters of the genes it activates (Ambinder et al. 1990).

Zta Protein. The 35-kD EBV Zta protein binds as a dimer (Chang et al. 1990; Lieberman and Berk 1990) to specific DNA sites (Zta response elements or ZREs) present in the promoters of Zta responsive genes. The ZREs can confer Zta-dependent inducibility on heterologous promoters (Urier et al. 1989; Lieberman et al. 1990). Although no simple consensus sequence can be found for all ZREs (Lieberman and Berk 1990), many fit the relatively degenerate consensus: 5′-TG(A/T)G(C/T)(A/C)A-3′ (Chang et al. 1990). This consensus sequence includes the DNA-binding sequence for the cellular AP-1 family of activator proteins: 5′-TGAGTCA-3′ (Angel et al. 1987). On the basis of limited amino acid similarities in its carboxy-terminal half, Zta is proposed to be a highly divergent member of the AP-1 family (Farrell et al. 1989), which also includes c-Jun/c-Fos/GCN4. Zta contains a short basic region similar to those of the AP-1 proteins, although it does not contain the canonical leucine zipper region (Landschulz et al. 1988). In place of the leucine zipper, which is responsible for dimerization of AP-1 proteins, Zta has a region of repeated hydrophobic residues that can support dimerization by forming a potentially coiled-coil helical domain (Flemington and Speck

1990). This domain can substitute for the zipper region of c-Fos (Chang et al. 1990).

It has been proposed that Zta may have originated from a cellular AP-1 family DNA-binding protein (Lieberman et al. 1990). The virus may have captured such a protein during its divergence from other herpesviruses.

Based on its ability to bind to DNA, Zta might be anticipated to contain an activation region and to activate transcription by becoming an integral part of the transcription complex. However, the activation region of Zta has not been identified, nor has it been shown that Zta must bind to DNA to activate transcription.

In lymphoid cells, Zta appears to activate transcription by a different mechanism. Zta can activate an early EBV gene (termed BMRF1) only in cooperation with the EBV Rta transcriptional activator protein (Kenney et al. 1989; Urier et al. 1989; Cox et al. 1990). The ZREs are not required for this combined effect (Holley-Guthrie et al. 1990).

Rta Protein. Rta is a 95-kD protein that is present in both the nucleus and cytoplasm of EBV-infected cells (Cox et al. 1990). Like Zta, Rta appears to be capable of two types of transcriptional activation. (1) In epithelial cells, Rta can, on its own, transcriptionally activate certain EBV immediate-early and early genes (including BMRF1). Two Rta response elements have been found in the promoters of these genes. DNase I protection experiments have shown that Rta binds directly and specifically to these sites (Gruffat et al. 1990). (2) In lymphoid cells, transcriptional activation of EBV promoters requires the presence of both Rta and Zta (Holley-Guthrie et al. 1990). The mechanism of Rta/Zta cooperative activation is not clear.

Hepatitis B Virus X Protein

Hepatitis B virus (HBV) is a small DNA hepadnavirus, phylogenetically related to the retroviruses, that produces persistent infections of liver cells (for review, see Ganem and Varmus 1987). The X protein (pX) is a 16.6-kD transcriptional activator protein that augments the transcription of a variety of RNA polymerase II and III transcribed hepatitis and non-viral promoters (Twu and Schloemer 1987; Seto et al. 1988; Spandau and Lee 1988; Colgrove et al. 1989; Levrero et al. 1990; Rufiero and Schneider 1990). Not a classic immediate-early protein, X protein is produced throughout the viral life cycle and apparently plays an important role in augmenting the expression of the HBV mRNAs required for viral replication.

pX activation of class II promoters can occur through AP-1 or AP-2 sites (Seto et al. 1990). When the promoter contains an AP-2 site, pX activation requires the presence of the cellular sequence-specific DNA-binding protein, AP-2. In addition, pX contains an activation region that stimulates transcription when it is tethered in the vicinity of a promoter (Seto et al. 1990). On the basis of these data, it has been proposed that the activation region of pX is brought to the vicinity of the transcription initiation complex by the ability of pX to bind to multiple cellular sequence-specific DNA-binding proteins, including AP-1 and AP-2. The activation region of pX has not been delineated, nor is it known whether this region interacts directly or indirectly with the basic transcription proteins.

It has also been proposed that the HBV protein may activate transcription by catalyzing the phosphorylation of cellular factors involved in transcription. In this regard, it has been shown that the X protein has an intrinsic serine/threonine protein kinase activity, although it has little homology with the known protein kinases (Wu et al. 1990). It is currently not clear if or how this protein kinase activity is related to the ability of the X protein to activate transcription by becoming a part of the transcription complex.

Herpes Simplex Virus

Herpes simplex virus (HSV) contains a large DNA genome encoding at least 70 proteins (for review, see Wagner 1985). These proteins are coordinately expressed in a sequential temporal cascade (Honess and Roizman 1974) and have been grouped into three classes. These include the products of the immediate-early (IE; also termed α) genes, which represent viral transcriptional regulatory proteins. IE gene expression is stimulated by the HSV tegument protein, termed viral protein 16 (VP16), yet is otherwise independent of viral or cellular protein synthesis (Clements et al. 1977; Batterson and Roizman 1983; Campbell et al. 1984). The mechanism of activation by VP16 is described below. Delayed early (DE or β) gene products are involved in DNA synthesis, and their expression requires the activity of the IE proteins (Honess and Roizman 1974; Preston 1979a; Dixon and Schaffer 1980). Late (L or γ) genes of HSV encode the components of the mature virion. L gene expression requires the products of both the IE and DE genes (Holland et al. 1980; O'Hare and Hayward 1985a).

The IE gene products include five infected-cell polypeptides (ICPs): ICP0, ICP4, ICP22, ICP27, and ICP47. All except ICP47 are nuclear phosphoproteins (Wilcox et al. 1980). Three, ICP0, ICP4, and ICP27, have been shown to activate gene transcription. Genetic studies have shown that ICP4 and ICP27 are absolutely required for viral replication (Preston 1979a; Sacks et al. 1985) and that expression of native ICP0 greatly increases the process of lytic viral growth (Stow and Stow 1986). The activities of these three IE proteins (ICP0, ICP4, and ICP27), as well as VP16, are described below.

VP16. The virion protein 16 (VP16) of HSV (also termed Vmw65, αTIF, ICP25) is probably the best-understood transcriptional regulatory protein. It is a component of the packaged viral particle (Batterson and Roizman 1983; Campbell et al. 1984) and thus is presented to the newly infected cell as a functional regulatory molecule immediately upon viral infection. VP16 contains two essential regions: a transcriptional activation region and a promoter-directing region (Triezenberg et al. 1988).

The transcriptional activation region of VP16 is an unusually potent member of the extensively characterized group of acidic activators. The minimal activation region of VP16 contains ten acidic residues that contribute to the activation function of the protein (Triezenberg et al. 1988; Cress and Triezenberg 1991). Certain hydrophobic amino acids of this region also appear to be important for activation, suggesting that the protein must adopt a specific structural state (Cousens et al. 1989; Cress and Triezenberg 1991).

To activate transcription, the activation region of VP16 must be brought to the vicinity of a promoter. VP16 participates in the ordered formation of a multiprotein-DNA complex that includes the cellular Oct-1 protein and at least two other cellular proteins, C1 and C2 (McKnight et al. 1987; Gerster and Roeder 1988; Kristie and Roizman 1988; Kristie et al. 1989; Stern et al. 1989; Kristie and Sharp 1990). This complex forms at specific enhancer elements located within the regulatory regions of the five HSV immediate-early genes. The *cis*-regulatory element that ultimately directs VP16 to the enhancers of the IE genes contains the highly conserved core element 5′-TAATGARAT-3′ (where R is a purine) (Preston et al. 1988). In this complex, specific protein:DNA contacts are made by VP16 and the cellular Oct-1 protein (Kristie et al. 1989; Kristie and Sharp 1990).

ICP4. Infected cell protein 4 (ICP4) (also termed Vmw175, IE175, or VP175), the product of the HSV IE gene 3, is the predominant IE transcriptional regulatory protein of HSV-1. This 175-kD phosphoprotein (Courtney and Benyesh-Melnick 1974) is produced at high levels immediately following the infection of a permissive cell and induces expression of the delayed early and late HSV genes. ICP4 also serves to down-regulate its own expression as well as that of the other HSV IE genes (Preston 1979a,b; Dixon and Schaffer 1980). In vitro, ICP4 is a promiscuous activator that can activate the expression of a variety of non-HSV genes that share no obvious sequence elements (Tremblay et al. 1985; Latchman et al. 1987). ICP4 shows significant amino acid sequence similarity to the IE activator proteins of the pseudorabies, equine herpesvirus type 1, and varicellar zoster viruses (Cheung 1979; McGeoch et al. 1986; Grundy et al. 1989; Vlcek et al. 1989).

By binding directly as a dimer to its high-affinity sites present in the promoters of the HSV IE genes, ICP4 is able to repress transcription (Michael et al. 1988; Kattar-Cooley and Wilcox 1989; Shepard et al. 1989). Transcriptional activation by ICP4, on the other hand, involves binding by the protein as a complex with other infected cells and/or cell proteins to its low-affinity sites (see Papavassiliou et al. 1991 and references therein). The DNA-binding domain of ICP4 has been identified within amino acids 262 and 490 (Wu and Wilcox 1990). This region is sufficient for binding to the high-affinity sites and is predicted to contain the helix-turn-amphipathic helix motif. A second region of the protein contributes to sequence specificity (Shepard et al. 1989; Imbalzano et al. 1990). The sequence requirements of ICP4-binding sites are not clear: Some sites fit the consensus of the high-affinity sites, 5'-ATCGTC-3', but this sequence is not sufficient for binding (Roberts et al. 1988), and other unrelated sequences can also serve as ICP4-binding sites (Kristie and Roizman 1986; Michael et al. 1988; Michael and Roizman 1989). The ability of ICP4 to bind to a variety of DNA sequences may explain its ability to activate a variety of viral and cellular genes.

ICP4 represses transcription of its own and other HSV IE genes apparently by binding to the high-affinity consensus sites located near the transcriptional start sites. Repression and DNA binding to these high-affinity sites are not affected by the phosphorylation state of ICP4 (Papavassiliou et al. 1991). Two models have been proposed to explain this repression. ICP4 bound near the start site may interfere with the formation or passage of the transcription complex (Shepard et al. 1989). Alternatively, the high affinity of ICP4 for this site could allow it to somehow immobilize the transcriptional machinery (Paterson and Everett 1988).

Current evidence regarding the mechanism of transcriptional activation by ICP4 favors a model in which the protein binds to its low-affinity sites by forming a complex with other infected cells and/or cell proteins (see Papavassiliou et al. 1991 and references therein). The state of phosphorylation of ICP4 regulates its ability to form these complexes. Once tethered near the promoter, the activation regions of ICP4 apparently directly or indirectly stimulate the general transcription complex.

ICP4 contains two activation regions, one of which is also involved in transcriptional repression (DeLuca and Schaffer 1988). This activation/repression region, located close to the carboxyl terminus of the protein, does not exhibit sequence similarity to any other known activation region. The second activation region of ICP4 includes 19 serine residues that are sites for phosphorylation (Shepard et al. 1989). Evidence has been presented indicating that the activation potential of ICP4 correlates with its level of phosphorylation (DeLuca and Schaffer 1988). It is possible that the phosphate groups provide negative charges within this region to allow it to function as an acidic activator.

Consistent with descriptions of ICP4 as a bifunctional (DNA-targeting and transcription-activating) protein that forms dimers, it has been noted that mutants in which one function is destroyed can inhibit the function of wild-type ICP4 through the formation of inactive heterodimers. That is, mutations that destroy the activation regions of ICP4 function as inhibitors of activation by wild-type ICP4 as a result of heterodimer formation (Shepard et al. 1990).

ICP27.   ICP27 (also termed Vmw63) modulates transcriptional regulation by ICP4 and/or ICP0 by a mechanism that is still unclear. ICP27 causes the repression of certain early genes and increases the activation of late viral genes (Everett 1986; Rice and Knipe 1988; Sekulovich et al. 1988; Su and Knipe 1989). Experiments involving viral strains bearing an ICP27 temperature-sensitive mutant indicate that ICP27 may be directly or indirectly involved in the phosphorylation of ICP4 (McMahan and Schaffer 1990). However, there is no evidence that ICP27 is itself a kinase or phosphatase, nor has it been unambiguously proven that phosphorylation of ICP4 alters its ability to activate transcription. ICP27 has also been reported to bind DNA (Hay and Hay 1980), although it is not known if this interaction is either direct or specific.

ICP0.   ICP0 (also termed Vmw110) is the product of the HSV IE gene 1. It is able, on its own, to activate transcription of HSV genes (Gelman and Silverstein 1985; O'Hare and Hayward 1985a,b; Quinlan and Knipe 1985); it also can cooperate with ICP4 to activate viral transcription (Everett 1984, 1986). ICP0 binds to DNA in crude cell extracts and is associated with chromatin in infected cell nuclei (Pereira et al. 1977; Hay and Hay 1980; Ackermann et al. 1984).

Detailed mutational studies of ICP0 have shown that multiple regions of the protein are important for both independent activation and synergy with ICP4; some regions are also solely required for one function or the other. In particular, synergy with ICP4 depends on a carboxy-terminal region of ICP0, although this region has only a small effect on the ability of ICP0 to activate gene expression on its own (Everett 1987). A region located close to the amino terminus of the protein, which includes a *trans*-activation domain and a cysteine-rich region, is required for both the independent activation role of ICP0 and synergy with ICP4 (Chen et al. 1991). The cysteine-rich region, like that in the adenovirus E1A protein, has been proposed to form a metal-binding domain. It consists of three partially overlapping cysteine-rich "finger" consensus sequences. The mechanisms ICP0 uses to activate transcription are not clear.

Human Immunodeficiency Virus Tat Protein

The HIV-1 Tat protein is a potent activator of viral gene expression (Arya et al. 1985; Sodroski et al. 1985) and is essential for efficient viral replication (Dayton et al. 1986; Fisher et al. 1986). Tat is a nuclear protein that acts in large part by increasing the rate of transcription from the HIV-1 long terminal repeat (LTR) (Hauber et al. 1987; Kao et al. 1987; Jakobovits et al. 1988; Jeang et al. 1988a; Rice and Mathews 1988; Sadaie et al. 1988; Laspia et al. 1989). The major *cis*-acting element required for Tat-responsiveness, referred to as the *trans*-activation response (TAR) site, is a region of about 40 bp located 3′ to the transcription initiation site (Rosen et al. 1985; Hauber and Cullen 1988; Jakobovits et al. 1988). A variety of experiments suggest that TAR is recognized as RNA rather than DNA (Muesing et al. 1987; Feng and Holland 1988; Berkhout et al. 1989; Dingwall et al. 1989; Garcia et al. 1989; Gatignol et al. 1989; Gaynor et al. 1989; for review, see Sharp and Marciniak 1989). In vitro RNA-binding experiments directly show that Tat binds with specificity to TAR RNA (Dingwall et al. 1989; Weeks et al. 1990).

Recent protein-fusion experiments have shown that binding to nascent RNA is an important component of the Tat response in vivo. In these experiments, Tat was fused to an unrelated RNA-binding protein, either the HIV-1 Rev (Southgate et al. 1990) or R17 (Selby and Peterlin 1990). The Tat-fusion protein was then shown to support Tat responsiveness on a reporter that contained the appropriate heterologous RNA-binding site downstream from the transcription start site. Thus, the specificity of Tat was redirected through an RNA-binding protein, indicating that Tat can indeed function by binding to nascent RNA downstream from the transcription start site. In a related set of experiments, it was shown that Tat could also function when fused to the DNA-binding domain of AP-1/c-Jun (Berkhout et al. 1990) to activate a promoter that contained AP-1-binding sites.

The conclusion of these protein-fusion experiments is that Tat, like a typical cellular activator, contains a promoter-targeting function that directs the protein to the vicinity of its natural promoter, the HIV LTR. In this case, the targeting is at the level of nascent RNA rather than DNA. Nuclear "run-on" experiments have shown that Tat increases the rate of transcriptional initiation (for review, see Sharp and Marciniak 1989). Tat can increase RNA polymerase II density within the first 24 nucleotides of the transcription start site and thus prior to formation of an intact TAR site (Laspia et al. 1989). Since Tat functions following binding to TAR RNA, the first round of transcription, which is required to produce the nascent TAR RNA, must occur in a Tat-independent fashion. Tat would then stimulate subsequent rounds of transcription and thus acts on reinitiation rather than initiation.

An alternative (or additional) proposed mechanism by which Tat augments transcription is by increasing the processivity of RNA polymerase II elongation (for review, see Cullen 1990). Both in vivo (Laspia et al. 1989) and in vitro (Marciniak et al. 1990) studies have provided evidence for this Tat activity. According to this idea, Tat may be acting in a fashion analogous to bacteriophage antiterminators, such as the N protein (for review, see Roberts 1988).

The region of Tat required for binding to RNA is relatively small (Weeks et al. 1990). There are a number of mutations outside this region that interfere with Tat function. These additional mutations are presumably within the "effector" domain of Tat. It seems likely that such a domain would interact with a component of the cellular transcription machinery.

Human T-cell Lymphotrophic Virus Tax Protein

The Tax protein of human T-cell lymphotrophic virus type 1 (HTLV-I) is a potent transcriptional activator that functions on its own promoter/enhancer, the HTLV-I LTR (Felber et al. 1985; Sodroski et al. 1985; Seiki et al. 1986). Tax can activate transcription in the absence of de novo protein synthesis (Jeang et al. 1988b; Giam and Xu 1989). The HTLV-I LTR contains three copies of a 21-bp repeat, which can function as a Tax-dependent transcriptional enhancer to confer Tax-inducibility onto a heterologous promoter in a position- and orientation-independent manner (Fujisawa et al. 1986; Paslakis et al. 1986; Shimotohno et al. 1986; Brady et al. 1987; Rosen et al. 1987). Like other viral enhancers, the HTLV-I LTR contains binding sites for a variety of cellular proteins.

In particular, each 21-bp repeat contains a consensus binding site for the ATF/CREB family of cellular transcription factors (Hai et al. 1989). Saturation mutagenesis of an HTLV-I 21-bp repeat indicates that the ATF site is essential for Tax responsivenesss (Giam and Xu 1989). Binding of these cellular proteins to the HTLV-I LTR is, however, not affected by Tax (Nyborg et al. 1988).

Tax itself does not appear to be a DNA-binding protein (Giam and Xu 1989). Rather, Tax can interact with cellular proteins that bind to the HTLV-I LTR, including a protein that binds at positions 117 and 163 bp upstream of the transcripton start site (Marriott et al. 1989), and perhaps one or more ATF proteins. These properties of Tax are reminiscent of those of the adenovirus E1A protein and suggest a model in which Tax is recruited to the promoter by interacting with a promoter-bound cellular protein.

Like adenovirus E1A, Tax is also a promiscuous activator of transcription. In addition to the HTLV-I LTR, Tax can activate transcription of other viral and cellular genes, including those encoding interleukin-2 and the interleukin-2 receptor (for review, see Greene et al. 1989), c-Fos (Fujii et al. 1988; Nagata et al. 1989), the HIV LTR (Bohnlein et al. 1988), and the SV40 enhancer (Nakamura et al. 1989). Mutational studies show that the region of Tax required for activation of these cellular genes is separable from that required for activation of the HTLV-I LTR (Smith and Greene 1990). The promiscuous activation of cellular genes appears to proceed through a pathway involving the cellular transcription factor, NF-κB (for review, see Greene et al. 1989).

Pseudorabies Virus Immediate-Early Protein

Pseudorabies virus, a member of the herpesvirus family, expresses an IE protein that is required to activate early viral gene transcription (Ihara et al. 1983). The pseudorabies IE protein and the related IE protein of herpes simplex virus, ICP4, can also activate many additional genes (for review, see Tevethia and Spector 1989). For example, pseudorabies virus IE activates transcription of the early genes of adenovirus (Feldman et al. 1982; Tremblay et al. 1985), the cellular β-globin gene (Green et al. 1983), the HIV-1 LTR (Yuan et al. 1989), and genes transcribed by RNA polymerase III (Gaynor and Berk 1983; Ahlers and Feldman 1987). Since these different genes have no common promoter element, it would appear that activation by IE protein is highly promiscuous. On this basis, it has been suggested that IE functions in a manner fundamentally different from that of cellular transcriptional activators (for review, see Berk 1986).

However, it has recently been shown that the pseudorabies virus IE protein has the two prototypical functions of typical cellular activators. IE has a transcriptional activation region, which is likely of the acidic class, and a separable region required for promoter targeting (Cromlish et al. 1989; Martin et al. 1990b). Both these activities are critical for the function of the intact IE protein.

Amino acids 1–34 of the PrV IE protein comprise a relatively small and unusually potent transcriptional activation region (Martin et al. 1990b). This region is relatively acidic, bearing a net charge (–8) comparable to that of activators for which acidity has been shown to be the critical determinant of activation potential (for review, see Mitchell and Tjian 1989). In addition, the results of in vivo competition experiments suggest that IE interacts with the same target used by an acidic activator (Martin et al. 1990b).

A variety of studies indicate that acidic activators directly interact with a basic transcription factor(s) (for review, see Lewin 1990; Ptashne and Gann 1990; Stringer et al. 1990; Lin and Green 1991). Since pseudorabies virus IE protein appears to contain an acidic transcriptional activation region, it also is likely to interact with a basic transcription component. This prediction is supported by the results of Abmayr et al. (1985, 1988), which show that IE increases the rate of formation of a complex containing TFIID and promoter DNA.

The ability of PrV IE to activate transcription promiscuously appears to be conferred by its promoter-targeting region. In this regard, the recent studies by Cromlish et al. (1989) are particularly relevant. These investigators used DNase I footprinting experiments to show that partially purified IE protein can bind directly to multiple, apparently unrelated DNA sequences (Cromlish et al. 1989). Moreover, the addition of oligonucleotides containing these binding sites prevented IE from activating transcription in vitro. This DNA-binding region may be the region of IE that was shown to be capable of directing a heterologous activation region to a promoter in vivo (Martin et al. 1990b). This promoter-targeting function depends on residues located in the carboxy-terminal half of the IE protein. It has been proposed that this region of IE functions by binding directly to diverse DNA sequences and thereby positioning the potent IE transcriptional activation region within the vicinity of a wide variety of promoters (Martin et al. 1990b). Alternatively, it is reasonable to expect that IE may function in a manner analogous to the homologous herpes simplex activator ICP4. Binding of ICP4 to the promoter involves assistance, via protein-protein interactions, with other viral and/or cellular factors. Thus, since IE functions at the promoter apparently by interacting with the general transcription machinery, its ability to promiscuously activate transcription can be explained in a manner consistent with established paradigms of typical eukaryotic activators.

CONCLUSION: FOUR CLASSES OF VIRAL ACTIVATORS

Several viral transcriptional activators do not bind directly to DNA, including adenovirus E1A, herpes simplex VP16, HIV-1 Tat, and apparently hepatitis B X and HTLV-I Tax. This observation initially led to the suggestion that these proteins function in a fundamentally different manner from that of cellular sequence-specific activators. However, it is now apparent that many, if not all, of these viral activators, like cellular activators, do indeed function at the promoter, and do so via interactions with sequence-specific DNA-binding proteins. Similarly, the adenovirus transcriptional activator E1A does not contain an activation region that fits the motifs characterized by cellular activators. Rather than acting on completely different targets, however, this viral activator may bind to an auxiliary cellular transcription factor, an "adapter," which interfaces the E1A activation region to the basic transcriptional machinery.

Viral transcriptional activators that act through mechanisms involving various combinations of the strategies described above allow the delineation of the following four different classes of activators.

1. Activators that bind directly to DNA and that interact directly with a basic transcription factor. Evidence suggests that this may be the motif used by bovine papillomavirus E2, herpes simplex ICP4, and pseudorabies virus IE. Promiscuity is accomplished by several members of this class of activators apparently through an ability to bind to a number of different DNA sequences. In some cases, binding of the viral activator to DNA can be assisted, or even substituted, by interaction with other viral or cellular factors (as in the cases of E2, ICP4, and perhaps IE).
2. Activators that are directed to the vicinity of a promoter by binding to a cellular sequence-specific DNA-binding protein. This class interacts directly with a basic transcription factor. Thus, a complex of two (or more) proteins forms the complete transcriptional activator. The herpes simplex virus VP16 protein uses this mechanism.
3. Viral activators that bind DNA directly, but require an auxiliary cellular factor to interact with the general transcription factors. This class of activators thus requires a complex of at least two proteins to form the complete activator. As yet, no examples for this class are apparent.
4. Viral activators that require at least two additional proteins: a

sequence-specific DNA-binding protein that directs the viral activator to the vicinity of the promoter, and an auxiliary transcription factor that interfaces the viral activator and the general transcription factors. These activators require a complex of at least three proteins to form the complete activator and are represented by the adenovirus E1A protein.

This description of viral activators and the complexes they form reveals a "building-block" strategy. Multiple proteins are complexed, one to the other, to present an appropriate activating surface to the general transcription machinery. Why is such an elaborate protein network necessary? Perhaps it is because only a few (or maybe only one) types of protein surface can directly interact with the general transcripton machinery to activate transcription (for review, see Ptashne and Gann 1990). The apparent diversity of cellular activation regions, and viral activators, may thus be explained by protein-protein interactions with cellular and viral adapters.

ACKNOWLEDGMENTS

We thank Drs. C. Ace and J. Lillie for comments on the manuscript. Work in the laboratory is supported by grants from the National Institutes of Health and by a grant from the Jane Coffin Childs Fund for Medical Research to K.J.M.

REFERENCES

Abmayr, S.M., L.D. Feldman, and R.G. Roeder. 1985. In vitro stimulation of specific RNA polymerase II-mediated transcription by the psuedorabies virus immediate early protein. *Cell* **43:** 821–829.

Abmayr, S.M., J.L. Workman, and R.G. Roeder. 1988. The pseudorabies immediate early protein stimulates in vitro transcription by facilitating TFIID:promoter interactions. *Genes Dev.* **2:** 542–553.

Ackermann, M., D.K. Braun, L. Pereira, and B. Roizman. 1984. Characterization of herpes simplex virus 1 α proteins 0, 4, and 27 with monoclonal antibodies. *J. Virol.* **52:** 108–118.

Ahlers, S.E. and L.T. Feldman. 1987. Effects of a temperature-sensitive mutation in the immediate-early gene of a pseudorabies virus on class II and class III gene transcription. *J. Virol.* **61:** 1103–1107.

Ambinder, R.F., W.A. Shah, D.R. Rawlins, G.S. Hayward, and S.D. Hayward. 1990. Definition of the sequence requirements for binding of the EBNA-1 protein to its palindromic target sites in Epstein-Barr virus DNA. *J. Virol.* **64:** 2369–2379.

Anderson, W.F., D.H. Ohlendorf, Y. Takeda, and B.W. Matthews. 1981. Structure of the cro repressor from bacteriophage λ and its interaction with DNA. *Nature* **290:** 754–758.

Androphy, E.J., D.R. Lowy, and J. Schiller. 1987. Bovine papillomavirus E2 *trans*-activating gene product binds to specific sites in papillomavirus DNA. *Nature* **324**: 70–73.

Angel, P., M. Imagawa, R. Chiu, B. Stein, R.J. Imbra, H.J. Rahmsdorf, C. Jonat, P. Herrlich, and M. Karin. 1987. Phorbol ester-inducible genes contain a common *cis* element recognized by a TPA-modulated *trans*-acting factor. *Cell* **49**: 729–739.

Arya, S.K., C. Guo, S.J. Josephs, and F. Wong-Staal. 1985. *Trans*-activator gene of human T-lymphotropic virus type III (HTLV-III). *Science* **229**: 69–73.

Bagchi, S., P. Raychaudhuri, and J.R. Nevins. 1989. Phosphorylation-dependent activation of the adenovirus-inducible E2F transcription factor in a cell-free system. *Proc. Natl. Acad. Sci.* **86**: 4352–4356.

Batterson, W. and B. Roizman. 1983. Characterization of the herpes simplex virion-associated factor responsible for the induction of α genes. *J. Virol.* **46**: 371–377.

Berk, A.J. 1986. Adenovirus promoters and E1a transactivation. *Annu. Rev. Genet.* **20**: 45–79.

Berk, A.J., F. Lee, T. Harrison, J. Williams, and P.A. Sharp. 1979. Pre-early adenovirus 5 gene product regulates synthesis of early viral messenger RNAs. *Cell* **17**: 935–944.

Berkhout, B., R.H. Silverman, and K.-T. Jeang. 1989. Tat *trans*-activates the human immunodeficiency virus through a nascent RNA target. *Cell* **59**: 273–282.

Berkhout, B., A. Gatignol, A.B. Rabson, and K.-T. Jeang. 1990. TAR-independent activation of the HIV-1 LTR: Evidence that Tat requires specific regions of the promoter. *Cell* **62**: 757–767.

Bohnlein, E., J.W. Lowenthal, M. Siekevitz, D.W. Ballard, B.R. Franza, and W.C. Greene. 1988. The same inducible nuclear proteins regulate mitogen activation of both the interleukin-2 receptor-alpha gene and type 1 HIV. *Cell* **53**: 827–836.

Brady, J., K.-T. Jeang, J. Duvall, and G. Khoury. 1987. Identification of p40ˣ-responsive regulatory sequences within the HTLV-I LTR. *J. Virol.* **61**: 2175–2181.

Brent, R. and M. Ptashne. 1985. A eukaryotic transcriptional activator bearing the DNA specificity of a procaryotic repressor. *Cell* **43**: 729–736.

Brown, R.S., C. Sander, and P. Argos. 1985. The primary structure of transcription factor TFIIIA has 12 consecutive repeats. *FEBS Lett.* **186**: 271–274.

Buratowski, S., S. Hahn, L. Guarente, and P.A. Sharp. 1989. Five intermediate complexes in transcription initiation by RNA polymerase II. *Cell* **56**: 549–561.

Campbell, M.E.M., J.W. Palfreyman, and C.M. Preston. 1984. Identification of herpes simplex virus DNA sequences which encode a *trans*-acting polypeptide responsible for stimulation of immediate early transcription. *J. Mol. Biol.* **180**: 1–19.

Chang, Y.-N., D.L.-Y. Dong, G.S. Hayward, and S.D. Hayward. 1990. The Epstein-Barr virus Zta transactivator: A member of the bZIP family with unique DNA-binding specificity and a dimerization domain that lacks the characteristic heptad leucine zipper motif. *J. Virol.* **64**: 3358–3369.

Chen, J.X., X.X. Zu, and S. Silverstein. 1991. Mutational analysis of the sequence encoding ICP0 from herpes simplex virus type 1. *Virology* **180**: 207–220.

Cheung, A.K. 1979. DNA nucleotide sequence analysis of the immediate-early gene of pseudorabies virus. *Nucleic Acids Res.* **17**: 4637–4646.

Choe, J., P. Vaillancourt, A. Stenlund, and M. Botchan. 1990. Bovine papilloma virus type I encodes two forms of a transcriptional repressor: Structural and functional analysis of new viral cDNA. *J. Virol.* **63**: 1743–1755.

Clements, J.B., R.J. Watson, and N.M. Wilkie. 1977. Temporal regulation of herpes simplex virus type 1 transcription: Location of transcripts on the viral genome. *Cell* **12**: 275–285.

Colgrove, R., G. Simon, and D. Ganem. 1989. Transcriptional activation of homologous and heterologous genes by the hepatitis B virus X gene product in cells permissive for viral replication. *J. Virol.* **63:** 4019–4026.

Courey, A.J. and R. Tjian. 1988. Analysis of Sp1 *in vivo* reveals multiple transcriptional domains, including a novel glutamine-rich activation motif. *Cell* **55:** 887–898.

Courtney, R.J. and M. Benyesh-Melnick. 1974. Isolation and characterisation of a large molecular weight polypeptide of herpes simplex virus type 1. *Virology* **62:** 531–539.

Cousens, D.J., R. Greaves, C.R. Goding, and P. O'Hare. 1989. The C-terminal 79 amino acids of the herpes simplex virus regulatory protein, Vmw65, efficiently activate transcription in yeast and mammalian cells in chimeric DNA-binding proteins. *EMBO J.* **8:** 2337–2342.

Cox, M., J. Leahy, and J.M. Hardwick. 1990. An enhancer within the divergent promoter of Epstein-Barr virus responds synergistically to the transactivators Rta and Zta. *J. Virol.* **64:** 313–321.

Cress, W.D. and S.J. Treizenberg. 1991. Critical structural elements of the VP16 transcriptional activation domain. *Science* **251:** 87–90.

Cromlish, W.A., S.M. Abmayr, J.L. Workman, M. Horikoshi, and R.G. Roeder. 1989. Transcriptionally active immediate-early protein of pseudorabies virus binds to specific sites on class II gene promoters. *J. Virol.* **63:** 1869–1876.

Cullen, B.R. 1990. The HIV-1 Tat protein: An RNA sequence specific processivity factor? *Cell* **63:** 655–657.

Culp, J.S., L.C. Webster, D.J. Friedman, C.L. Smith, W.J. Huang, F.Y.-H. Wu, M. Rosenberg, and R.P. Ricciardi. 1988. The 289-amino acid E1a protein of adenovirus binds zinc in a region that is important for *trans*-activation. *Proc. Natl. Acad. Sci.* **85:** 6450–6454.

Dayton, A.I., J.G. Sodroski, C.A. Rosen, W.C. Goh, and W.A. Haseltine. 1986. The *trans*-activator gene of the human T cell lymphotropic virus type III is required for replication. *Cell* **44:** 941–947.

DeLuca, N.A. and P.A. Schaffer. 1988. Physical and functional domains of the herpes simplex virus transcriptional regulatory protein ICP4. *J. Virol.* **62:** 732–743.

Dingwall, C., I. Ernberg, M.J. Gait, S.M. Green, S. Heaphy, J. Karn, A.D. Lowe, M. Singhy, M.A. Skinner, and R. Valerio. 1989. Human immunodeficiency virus 1 tat protein binds trans-activation responsive region (TAR) RNA in vitro. *Proc. Natl. Acad. Sci.* **86:** 6925–6929.

Dixon, R.A.F. and P.A. Schaffer. 1980. Fine structure mapping and functional analysis of temperature-sensitive mutants in the protein VP175. *J. Virol.* **36:** 189–203.

Dostatni, N., T. Francoise, and M. Yaniv. 1988. A dimer of BPV-1 E2 containing a protease resistant core interacts with its DNA target. *EMBO J.* **7:** 3807–3816.

Everett, R.D. 1984. Transactivation of transcription by herpes virus products: Requirements for two HSV-1 immediate early polypeptides for maximum activity. *EMBO J.* **3:** 3135–3141.

———. 1986. The products of herpes simplex virus type 1 (HSV-1) immediate-early genes 1, 2, and 3 can activate HSV-1 gene expression in *trans*. *J. Gen. Virol.* **67:** 2507–2513.

———. 1987. A detailed mutational analysis of Vmw110, a *trans*-acting transcriptional activator encoded by herpes simplex virus type 1. *EMBO J.* **6:** 2069–2076.

Farrell, P.J., D.T. Rowe, C.M. Rooney, and T. Kouzarides. 1989. Epstein-Barr virus BZLF *trans*-activator specifically binds to a consensus AP-1 site and is related to c-*fos*. *EMBO J.* **8:** 127–132.

Felber, B.K., H. Paskalis, C. Kleinman-Ewing, F. Wong-Staal, and G.N. Pavlakis. 1985.

The pX protein of HTLV-I is a transcriptional activator of its long terminal repeats. *Science* **229:** 675–679.

Feldman, L.T., M.J. Imperiale, and J.R. Nevins. 1982. Activation of early adenovirus transcription by the herpes virus. *Proc. Natl. Acad. Sci.* **79:** 4952–4956.

Feng, S. and E.C. Holland. 1988. HIV-1 tat *trans*-activation requires the loop sequences within TAR. *Nature* **334:** 165–167.

Ferguson, B., B. Krippl, O. Andrisani, N. Jones, H. Westphal, and M. Rosenberg. 1985. E1A 13S and 12S mRNA products made in *Escherichia coli* both function as nucleus-localized transcription activators but do not directly bind DNA. *Mol. Cell. Biol.* **5:** 2653–2661.

Fisher, A.G., S.F. Feinberg, S.F. Josephs, M.E. Harper, L.M. Marselle, G. Reyes, M.A. Gonda, A. Aldovini, C. Debouk, R.C. Gallo, and F. Wong-Staal. 1986. The *trans*-activator gene of HTLV-III is essential for virus replication. *Nature* **320:** 367–371.

Flemington, E. and S.H. Speck. 1990. Evidence for coiled-coil dimer formation by an Epstein-Barr virus transactivator that lacks a heptad repeat of leucine residues. *Proc. Natl. Acad. Sci.* **87:** 9459–9463.

Flint, J. and T. Shenk. 1989. Adenovirus E1a protein paradigm viral transactivator. *Annu. Rev. Genet.* **23:** 141–161.

Fujii, M., P. Sassone-Corsi, and I.M. Verma. 1988. c-*fos* promoter *trans*-activation by the tax$_1$ protein of human T-cell leukemia virus type I. *Proc. Natl. Acad. Sci.* **85:** 8526–8530.

Fujisawa, J.-I., M. Seiki, M. Sato, and M. Yoshida. 1986. Transcriptional enhancer sequence of HTLV-I is responsible for transactivation mediated by p40^x of HLTV-I. *EMBO J.* **5:** 713–718.

Ganem, D.E. and H.E. Varmus. 1987. The molecular biology of the hepatitis B viruses. *Annu. Rev. Biochem.* **56:** 651–693.

Garcia, J., D. Harrich, E. Soultanakis, F.K. Wu, R. Mitsuyasu, and R.B. Gaynor. 1989. Human immunodeficiency virus type 1 LTR TATA and TAR region sequences required for transcriptional regulation. *EMBO J.* **8:** 765–778.

Gatignol, A., A. Kumar, A. Rabson, and K.-T. Jeang. 1989. Identification of cellular proteins that bind to the human immunodeficiency virus type 1 *trans*-activation-responsive TAR element RNA. *Proc. Natl. Acad. Sci.* **86:** 7828–7832.

Gaynor, R.B. and A.J. Berk. 1983. *cis*-acting induction of adenovirus transcription. *Cell* **33:** 683–693.

Gaynor, R., E. Soultanakis, M. Kuwabara, J. Garcia, and D.S. Sigman. 1989. Specific binding of HeLa cell nuclear protein to RNA sequences in the human immunodeficiency virus transactivating region. *Proc. Natl. Acad. Sci.* **86:** 4858–4862.

Gehring, W.J. 1987. Homeo boxes in the study of development. *Science* **236:** 1245–1252.

Gelman, I.H. and S. Silverstein. 1985. Identification of immediate early genes from herpes simplex virus that transactivate the virus thymidine kinase gene. *Proc. Natl. Acad. Sci.* **82:** 5265–5269.

Gerster, T. and R.G. Roeder. 1988. A herpesvirus *trans*-activating protein interacts with transcription factor OTF-1 and other cellular proteins. *Proc. Natl. Acad. Sci.* **85:** 6347–6351.

Giam, C.-Z. and Y.-L. Xu. 1989. HTLV-I tax gene product activates transcription via pre-existing cellular factors and cAMP response element. *J. Biol. Chem.* **264:** 15236–15241.

Gill, G. and M. Ptashne. 1987. Mutants of GAL4 protein altered in an activation formation. *Cell* **51:** 121–126.

Giri, I. and M. Yaniv. 1988. Structural and mutational analysis of E2 *trans*-activating proteins of papillomaviruses reveals three distinct functional domains. *EMBO J.* **7:** 2823-2829.

Green, M.R. 1989. When the products of oncogenes and anti-oncogenes meet. *Cell* **56:** 1-3.

————. 1991. Activities of adenovirus E1A proteins. In *Origins of human cancer: A comprehensive review* (ed. J. Brugge et al.), p. 383-392. Cold Spring Harbor Laboratory Press, Cold Spring Harbor, New York.

Green, M.R., R. Treisman, and T. Maniatis. 1983. Transcriptional activation of cloned human β-globin by viral immediate-early gene products. *Cell* **35:** 137-148.

Greene, W.C., E. Bohnlein, and D.W. Ballard. 1989. HIV-1, HTLV-1 and normal T-cell growth: Transcriptional strategies and surprises. *Immunol. Today* **10:** 272-277.

Gruffat, H., E. Manet, A. Rigolet, and A. Sergeant. 1990. The enhancer binding factor R of Epstein-Barr virus (EBV) is a sequence-specific DNA binding protein. *Nucleic Acids Res.* **18:** 6835-6843.

Grundy, F.J., R.P. Bauman, and D.J. O'Callaghan. 1989. DNA sequence and comparative analysis of the equine type 1 immediate early gene. *Virology* **172:** 223-236.

Hai, T., F. Liu, W. Coukos, and M.R. Green. 1989. Transcription factor ATF cDNA clones: An extensive family of leucine zipper proteins able to selectively form DNA-binding heterodimers. *Genes Dev.* **3:** 2083-2090.

Hardy, S. and T. Shenk. 1989. E2F from adenovirus-infected cells binds to DNA containing two properly oriented and spaced recognition sites. *Mol. Cell. Biol.* **9:** 4495-4506.

Hardy, S., D.A. Engel, and T. Shenk. 1989. An adenovirus early region 4 gene product is required for induction of the infection-specific form of cellular E2F activity. *Genes Dev.* **3:** 1062-1074.

Hauber, J. and B.R. Cullen. 1988. Mutational analysis of the *trans*-activation-responsive region of the human immunodeficiency virus type 1 long terminal repeat. *J. Virol.* **62:** 673-679.

Hauber, J., A. Perkin, E.P. Heimer, and B.R. Cullen. 1987. *Trans*-activation of human immunodeficiency virus gene expression is mediated by nuclear events. *Proc. Natl. Acad. Sci.* **84:** 6364-6368.

Haugen, T.H., T.P. Cripe, G.D. Ginder, M. Karin, and L.P. Turek. 1987. *Trans*-activation of an upstream early gene promoter of bovine papilloma virus-1 by a product of the viral E2 gene. *EMBO J.* **6:** 145-152.

Haugen, T.H., L.P. Turek, F.M. Mercurio, T.P. Cripe, B.J. Olson, R.D. Anderson, D. Seidl, M. Karin, and J. Schiller. 1988. Sequence-specific and general activation by the bovine papillomavirus-1 E2 *trans*-activator require an N-terminal amphipathic helix-containing E2 domain. *EMBO J.* **7:** 4245-4253.

Hawley-Nelson, P., E.J. Androphy, D.R. Lowy, and J.T. Schiller. 1988. A specific DNA recognition sequence of the bovine papillomavirus E2 protein is an E2-dependent enhancer. *EMBO J.* **7:** 525-531.

Hay, R.T. and J. Hay. 1980. Properties of the herpesvirus-induced "immediate-early" polypeptides. *Virology* **104:** 230-234.

Herr, W., R.A. Sturm, R.G. Clerc, L.M. Corcoran, D. Baltimore, P.A. Sharp, H.A. Ingraham, M.G. Rosenfeld, M. Finney, G. Ruvkun, and H.R. Horvitz. 1988. The POU domain: A large conserved region in the mammalian *pit-1*, *oct-1*, *oct-2* and *Caenorhabditis elegans unc-86* gene products. *Genes Dev.* **2:** 1513-1516.

Hoeffler, W.K., R. Kovelman, and R.G. Roeder. 1988. Activation of transcription factor IIIC by the adenovirus E1a protein. *Cell* **53:** 907-920.

Holland, L.E., K.P. Anderson, C. Shipman, Jr., and E.K. Wagner. 1980. Viral DNA synthesis is required for the efficient expression of specific herpes simplex virus type 1 mRNA species. *Virology* **101:** 10–24.

Holley-Guthrie, E.A., E.B. Quinlivan, E.-C. Mar, and S. Kenney. 1990. The Epstein-Barr Virus (EBV) BMRF1 promoter for early antigen (EA-D) is regulated by the EBV trans-activators, BRLF1 and BZLF1, in a cell-specific manner. *J. Virol.* **64:** 3753–3759.

Honess, R.W. and B. Roizman. 1974. Regulation of herpesvirus macromolecular synthesis. I. Cascade regulation of the synthesis of three groups of viral proteins. *J. Virol.* **14:** 8–19.

Hope, I.A., S. Mahadevan, and K. Struhl. 1988. Structural and functional characterization of the short acidic transcriptional activation region of yeast GCN4 protein. *Nature* **333:** 635–640.

Horowitz, J.M., S.H. Friend, R.A. Weinberg, P. Whyte, K. Buchkovitz, and E. Harlow. 1988. Anti-oncogenes and the negative regulation of cell growth. *Cold Spring Harbor Symp. Quant. Biol.* **53:** 843–847.

Huang, M.-M. and P. Hearing. 1989. The adenovirus early region 4 open reading frame 6/7 protein regulates the DNA binding activity of the cellular transcription factor, E2F, through a direct complex. *Genes. Dev.* **3:** 1699–1710.

Hubbert, N.L., J.T. Schiller, D.R. Lowy, and E.J. Androphy. 1988. Bovine papilloma virus-transformed cells contain multiple E2 proteins. *Proc. Natl. Acad. Sci.* **85:** 5864–5868.

Ihara, S., L. Feldman, S. Watanabe, and T. Ben-Porat. 1983. Characterization of the immediate-early function of pseudorabies virus. *Virology* **131:** 437–454.

Imbalzano, A.N., A.A. Shepard, and N.A. DeLuca. 1990. Functional relevance of specific interactions between herpes simplex virus type 1 ICP4 and sequences from the promoter-regulatory domain of the viral thymidine kinase gene. *J. Virol.* **64:** 2620–2631.

Jakobovits, A., D.H. Smith, E.B. Jakobovits, and D.J. Capon. 1988. A discrete element 3′ of human immunodeficiency virus (HIV-1) and HIV-2 mRNA initiation sites mediates transcriptional activation by an HIV *trans*-activator. *Mol. Cell. Biol.* **8:** 2555–2561.

Jeang, K.-T., P.R. Shank, and A. Kumar. 1988a. Transcriptional activation of homologous viral long terminal repeats by the human immunodeficiency virus type 1 or the human T-cell leukemia virus type 1 tat proteins occurs in the absence of de novo protein synthesis. *Proc. Natl. Acad. Sci.* **85:** 8291–8295.

Jeang, K.-T., I. Boros, J. Brady, M. Radonovich, and G. Khoury. 1988b. Characterization of cellular factors that interact with the human T-cell leukemia virus type I p40^x-responsive 21-base-pair sequence. *J. Virol.* **62:** 4499–4509.

Jones, N. and T. Shenk. 1979. An adenovirus type 5 early gene function regulates expression of other early viral genes. *Proc. Natl. Acad. Sci.* **76:** 3665–3669.

Kaddurah-Daouk, R., J.W. Lillie, G.H. Daouk, M.R. Green, R. Kingston, and P. Schimmel. 1990. Induction of a cellular enzyme for energy metabolism by transforming domains of adenovirus E1a. *Mol. Cell. Biol.* **10:** 1476–1483.

Kao, S.-Y., A.F. Calman, P.A. Luciw, and B.M. Peterlin. 1987. Anti-termination of transcription within the long terminal repeat of HIV-1 by tat gene product. *Nature* **330:** 489–493.

Kattar-Cooley, P. and K.W. Wilcox. 1989. Characterization of the DNA-binding properties of herpes simplex virus regulatory protein ICP4. *J. Virol.* **63:** 393–704.

Kenney, S., J. Kamine, E. Holley-Guthrie, J.-C. Lin, E.-C. Mar, and J. Pagano. 1989. The Epstein-Barr virus (EBV) BZLF1 immediate-early gene product differentially affects latent versus productive EBV promoters. *J. Virol.* **63:** 1729–1736.

Kristie, T.M. and B. Roizman. 1986. ICP4, the major regulatory protein of herpes simplex virus type 1, is stably and specifically associated with promoter-regulatory domains of HSV genes and of selected other viral genes. *Proc. Natl. Acad. Sci.* **83:** 3218–3222.

———. 1988. Differentiation of DNA contact points of host proteins binding at the *cis* site for virion-mediated induction of a gene of herpes simplex virus 1. *J. Virol.* **62:** 1145–1157.

Kristie, T.M. and P.A. Sharp. 1990. Interactions of the Oct-1 POU subdomains with specific DNA sequences and with the HSV α-transactivator protein. *Genes Dev.* **4:** 2383–2396.

Kristie, T.M., J.H. LeBowitz, and P.A. Sharp. 1989. The octamer-binding proteins form multi-protein-DNA complexes with the HSV αTIF regulatory protein. *EMBO J.* **8:** 4229–4238.

Lambert, P.F., B.A. Spalholz, and P.M. Howley. 1987. A transcriptional repressor encoded by BPV-1 shares a common carboxyl-terminal domain with the E2 transactivator. *Cell* **50:** 69–78.

Lambert, P.F., N. Dostatni, A.A. McBride, M. Yaniv, P.M. Howley, and B. Arcangioli. 1989. Functional analysis of the papilloma virus E2 *trans*-activator in *Saccharomyces cerevisiae. Genes Dev.* **3:** 38–48.

Landschulz, W.H., P.F. Johnson, and S.L. McKnight. 1988. The leucine zipper: A hypothetical structure common to a new class of DNA binding proteins. *Science* **240:** 1759–1764.

Laspia, M.F., A.P. Rice, and M.B. Mathews. 1989. HIV-1 tat protein increases transcriptional initiation and stabilizes elongation. *Cell* **59:** 283–292.

Latchman, D.S., J.K. Estridge, and L.M. Kemp. 1987. Transcriptional induction of the ubiquitin gene during herpes simplex virus infection is dependent upon the viral immediate-early protein ICP4. *Nucleic Acids Res.* **15:** 7283–7293.

Levrero, M., C. Balsano, G. Natoli, M.L. Avantaggiati, and E. Elfassi. 1990. Hepatitis B virus X protein transactivates the long terminal repeats of human immunodeficiency virus types 1 and 2. *J. Virol.* **64:** 3082–3086.

Lewin, B. 1990. Commitment and activation at Pol II promoters: A tail of protein-protein interaction. *Cell* **61:** 1161–1164.

Li, R., J.D. Knight, S.P. Jackson, R. Tjian, and M.R. Botchan. 1991. Direct interaction between Sp1 and the BPV enhancer E2 protein mediates synergistic activation of transcription. *Cell* **65:** 493–505.

Lieberman, P.M. and A.J. Berk. 1990. *In vitro* transcriptional activation, dimerization and DNA-binding specificity of the Epstein-Barr virus Zta protein. *J. Virol.* **64:** 2560–2568.

Lieberman, P.M., J.M. Hardwick, J. Sample, G.S. Hayward, and S.D. Hayward. 1990. The Zta transactivator involved in induction of lytic cycle gene expression in Epstein-Barr virus-infected lymphocytes binds to both AP-1 and ZRE sites in target promoter and enhancer regions. *J. Virol.* **64:** 1143–1155.

Lillie, J.W. and M.R. Green. 1989. Transcription activation by the adenovirus E1a protein. *Nature* **338:** 39–44.

———. 1990. Activator's target in sight. *Nature* **341:** 279–280.

Lin, Y.-S. and M.R. Green. 1991. Mechanism of action of an acidic transcriptional activator in vitro. *Cell* **64:** 971–981.

Liu, F. and M.R. Green. 1990. A specific member of the ATF transcription factor family can mediate transcription activation by the adenovirus E1a protein. *Cell* **61:** 1217–1224.

Marciniak, R.A., B.J. Cainan, A.D. Frankel, and P.A. Sharp. 1990. HIV-1 Tat protein *trans*-activates transcription in vitro. *Cell* **63:** 791–802.

Marriott, S.J., I. Boros, J.F. Duvall, and J.N. Brady. 1989. Indirect binding of the human T-cell leukemia virus type I tax$_1$ to a responsive element in the viral long terminal repeat. *Mol. Cell. Biol.* **9:** 1452–4160.

Marsden, H.S., M.E.M. Campbell, L. Haarr, M.C. Frame, D.S. Parris, M. Murphy, R.G. Hope, M.T. Muller, and C.M. Preston. 1987. The 65,000-M_r DNA-binding and virion *trans*-inducing proteins of herpes simplex virus type 1. *J. Virol.* **61:** 2428–2437.

Martin, K.J., J.W. Lillie, and M.R. Green. 1990a. Evidence for interaction of different eukaryotic transcriptional activators with distinct cellular targets. *Nature* **346:** 147–152.

————. 1990b. Transcriptional activation by the pseudorabies virus immediate-early protein. *Genes. Dev.* **4:** 2376–2382.

McBride, A.A., J.C. Byrne, and P.M. Howley. 1989. E2 polypeptides encoded by bovine papillomavirus I form dimers through the carboxyl-terminal DNA binding domain: Transactivation is mediated through the conserved amino-terminal domain. *Proc. Natl. Acad. Sci.* **86:** 510–514.

McBride, A.A., R. Schlegel, and P.M. Howley. 1988. The carboxy-terminal domain shared by the bovine papillomavirus E2 transactivator and repressor proteins contains a specific DNA binding activity. *EMBO J.* **7:** 533–539.

McGeoch, D.J., A. Dolan, S. Donald, and D.H.K. Brauer. 1986. Complete DNA sequence of the short repeat region in the genome of herpes simplex virus type 1. *Nucleic Acids Res.* **14:** 1727–1745.

McKnight, J.L.C., T.M. Kristie, and B. Roizman. 1987. The binding of virion protein mediating α gene induction in herpes simplex virus 1 infected cells to its *cis* site requires cellular proteins. *Proc. Natl. Acad. Sci.* **84:** 7061–7065.

McMahan, L. and P.A. Schaffer. 1990. The repressing and enhancing functions of the herpes simplex virus regulatory protein ICP27 map to c-terminal regions and are required to modulate viral gene expression very early in infection. *J. Virol.* **64:** 3471–3485.

Mermod, N., E.A. O'Neill, T.J. Kelly, and R. Tjian. 1989. The proline-rich transcriptional activator of CTF/NF-1 is distinct from the replication and DNA binding domain. *Cell* **58:** 741–753.

Michael, N. and B. Roizman. 1989. Binding of the herpes simplex virus major regulatory protein to viral DNA. *Proc. Natl. Acad. Sci.* **86:** 9808–9812.

Michael, N., D. Spector, P. Mavromara-Nazos, T.M. Kristie, and B. Roizman. 1988. The DNA-binding properties of the major regulatory protein 4 of herpes simplex virus. *Science* **239:** 1531–1534.

Miller, J., A.D. McLachlan, and A. Klug. 1985. Repetitive zinc-binding domains in the protein transcription factor IIIA from *Xenopus* oocytes. *EMBO J.* **4:** 1609–1614.

Mitchell, P.J. and R. Tjian. 1989. Transcriptional regulation in mammalian cells by sequence-specific DNA binding proteins. *Science* **245:** 371–378.

Moran, E. and M.B. Mathews. 1987. Multiple functional domains in the adenovirus E1a gene. *Cell* **48:** 177–178.

Morrissey, L.C., J. Barsoum, and E.J. Androphy. 1989. *trans* activation by the bovine papillomavirus E2 protein in *Saccharomyces cerevisiae. J. Virol.* **63:** 4422–4425.

Moskaluk, C.A. and D. Bostia. 1988. Interaction of the bovine papillomavirus type 1 E1 transcriptional control protein with the viral enhancer: Purification of the DNA-binding domain and analysis of its contact points with DNA. *J. Virol.* **62:** 1925–1931.

Muesing, M.A., D.H. Smith, and D.J. Capon. 1987. Regulation of mRNA accumulation by a human immunodeficiency virus *trans*-activator protein. *Cell* **48:** 691–701.

Murre, C., P.S. McCaw, H. Vaessin, M. Caudy, L.Y. Jan, Y.N. Jan, C.V. Cabrera, J.N. Buskin, S.D. Hauschka, A.B. Lassar, H. Weintraub, and D. Baltimore. 1989. Interactions between heterologous helix-loop-helix proteins generate complexes that bind specifically to a common DNA sequence. *Cell* **58:** 537–544.

Nagata, K., K. Ohtani, M. Nakamura, and K. Sugamura. 1989. Activation of endogenous c-*fos* proto-oncogene expression by human T-cell leukemia virus type I-encoded p40^{tax} protein in the human T-cell line, Jurkat. *J. Virol.* **63:** 3220–3226.

Nakamura, M., M. Niki, K. Nagata, K. Ohtani, S. Saito, Y. Hinuma, and K. Sugamura. 1989. Cell line-dependent response of the enhancer element of simian virus 40 tp transactivator p40^{tax} encoded by human T-cell leukemia virus type I. *J. Biol. Chem.* **264:** 20189–20192.

Neill, S.D., C. Hemstrom, and A. Virtanen. 1990. An adenovirus E1 gene product *trans*-activates E2 transcription and stimulates stable E2F binding through a direct association with E2F. *Proc. Natl. Acad. Sci.* **87:** 2008–2012.

Nyborg, J.K., W.S. Dynan, I.S.Y. Chen, and W. Wachsman. 1988. Binding of host factors to DNA sequences in the long terminal of human T cell leukemia virus type I: Implications for viral gene expression. *Proc. Natl. Acad. Sci.* **85:** 1457–1461.

O'Hare, P. and G.S. Hayward. 1985a. Evidence for a direct role for both the 175,000- and 110,000-molecular-weight immediate-early proteins of herpes simplex virus in the *trans*-activation of delayed-early promoters. *J. Virol.* **53:** 751–760.

———. 1985b. Three *trans*-acting regulatory proteins of herpes simplex virus modulate immediate-early gene expression in a pathway involving positive and negative feedback regulation. *J. Virol.* **56:** 723–733.

Otting, G., Y.-Q. Qian, M. Muller, M. Affolter, W. Gehring, and K. Wuthrich. 1988. Secondary structure determination for the *Antennapedia* homeodomain by nuclear magnetic resonance and evidence for a helix-turn-helix motif. *EMBO J.* **7:** 4305–4309.

Pabo, C.O. and R.T. Sauer. 1984. Protein-DNA recognition. *Annu. Rev. Biochem.* **53:** 293–321.

Papavassiliou, A.G., K.W. Wilcox, and S.J. Silverstein. 1991. The interaction of ICP4 with cell/infected cell factors and its state of phosphorylation modulate differential recognition of leader sequences in herpes simplex virus DNA. *EMBO J.* **10:** 397–402.

Paslakis, H., B.K. Felber, and G.N. Pavlakis. 1986. *cis*-acting sequences responsible for the transcriptional activation of human T-cell leukemia virus type I constitute a conditional enhancer. *Proc. Natl. Acad. Sci.* **83:** 6558–6562.

Paterson, T. and R.D. Everett. 1988. Mutational dissection of the HSV-1 immediate-early protein Vmw175 involved in transcriptional transactivation and repression. *Virology* **166:** 186–196.

Pereira, L., M.H. Wolff, M. Fenwick, and B. Roizman. 1977. Regulation of herpesvirus macromolecular synthesis. V. Properties of polypeptides made in HSV-1 and HSV-2 infected cells. *Virology* **77:** 733–749.

Preston, C.M. 1979a. Control of herpes simplex virus type 1 mRNA synthesis in cells infected with wild-type virus or the temperature-sensitive mutant *ts*K. *J. Virol.* **29:** 275–284.

———. 1979b. Abnormal properties of an immediate early polypeptide in cells infected with the herpes simplex virus type 1 mutant *ts*K. *J. Virol.* **32:** 357–369.

Preston, C.M., M.C. Frame, and M.E.M. Campbell. 1988. A complex formed between cell components and an HSV structural polypeptide binds to a viral immediate early gene regulatory DNA sequence. *Cell* **52:** 425–434.

Ptashne, M. 1988. How transcriptional activators work. *Nature* **335:** 683–689.

Ptashne, M. and A.A.F. Gann. 1990. Activators and targets. *Nature* **346:** 329–331.

Quinlan, M.P. and D.M. Knipe. 1985. Stimulation of expression of a herpes simplex virus DNA-binding protein by two viral functions. *Mol. Cell. Biol.* **5:** 957–963.

Raychaudhuri, P., S. Bagchi, and J.R. Nevins. 1989. DNA-binding activity of the adenovirus-induced E4F transcription factor is regulated by phosphorylation. *Genes Dev.* **3:** 620–627.

Reichel, R., I. Kovesdi, and J.R. Nevins. 1988. Activation of a pre-existing cellular factor as the basis for adenovirus E1a-mediated transcriptional control. *Proc. Natl. Acad. Sci.* **85:** 387–390.

Reichel, R., S. Neill, I. Kovesdi, M.C. Simon, P. Raychaudhuri, and J.R. Nevins. 1989. The adenovirus E4 gene, in addition to the E1a gene, is important for *trans*-activation of E2 transcription and E2F activation. *J. Virol.* **63:** 3643–3650.

Reinberg, D. and R.G. Roeder. 1987. Factors involved in specific transcription by mammalian RNA polymerase II. Purification and functional analysis of initiation factors IIB and IIE. *J. Biol. Chem.* **262:** 3310–3321.

Reinberg, D., M. Horikoshi, and R.G. Roeder. 1987. Factors involved in specific transcription by mammalian RNA polymerase II. Functional analysis of initiation factors IIA and IID and identification of a new factor operating downstream of the initiation site. *J. Biol. Chem.* **262:** 3322–3330.

Rice, A.P. and M.B. Mathews. 1988. Transcriptional but not translational regulation of HIV-1 by the tat gene product. *Nature* **332:** 551–553.

Rice, S.A. and D.M. Knipe. 1988. Gene-specific transactivation by herpes simplex virus type 1 alpha protein ICP27. *J. Virol.* **62:** 3814–3823.

Roberts, J.W. 1988. Phage lambda and the regulation of transcription termination. *Cell* **52:** 5–6.

Roberts, M.S., A. Boundy, P. O'Hare, M.C. Pizzorno, D.M. Ciufo, and G.S. Hayward. 1988. Direct correlation between a negative autoregulatory response element at the cap site of the herpes simplex virus type 1 IE175 (4) promoter and a specific binding site for the IE175 (ICP4) protein. *J. Virol.* **62:** 4307–4320.

Rochette-Egly, C., C. Fromental, and P. Chambon. 1990. General repression of enhanson activity by the adenovirus-2 E1a proteins. *Genes Dev.* **4:** 137–150.

Rosen, C.A., J.G. Sodroski, and W.A. Haseltine. 1985. The location of *cis*-acting regulatory sequences in the human T cell lymphotropic virus type III (HTLV-III/LAV) long terminal repeat. *Cell* **41:** 813–823.

Rosen, C.A., R. Park, J.G. Sodroski, and W.A. Haseltine. 1987. Multiple sequence elements are required for regulation of human T-cell leukemia virus gene expression. *Proc. Natl. Acad. Sci.* **84:** 4919–4923.

Rufiero, B. and R.J. Schneider. 1990. The hepatitis B virus X-gene product transactivates both RNA polymerase II and III promoters. *EMBO J.* **9:** 497–504.

Sacks, W.R., C.C. Greene, D.P. Aschman, and P.A. Schaffer. 1985. Herpes simplex virus type I ICP27 is an essential regulatory protein. *J. Virol.* **55:** 796–805.

Sadaie, M.R., J. Rappaport, T. Benter, S.F. Josephs, R. Willis, and F. Wong-Staal. 1988. Missense mutations in an infectious human immunodeficiency viral genome: Functional mapping of tat and identification of the rev splice acceptor. *Proc. Natl. Acad. Sci.* **85:** 9224–9228.

Saltzman, A.G. and R. Weinman. 1989. Promoter specificity and modulation of RNA polymerase II transcription. *FASEB J.* **3:** 1723–1733.

Scott, M.P. and S. Hayashi. 1990. What determines the specificity of action of *Drosophila* homeodomain proteins? *Cell* **63:** 883–894.

Scott, M.P., J.W. Tamkun, and G.W. Hartzell, III. 1989. The structure and function of the homeodomain. *B.B.A. Rev. Cancer* **989:** 25–48.

Seiki, M., J. Inoue, T. Takeda, and M. Yoshida. 1986. Direct evidence that p40^x of human T-cell leukemia virus type I is a *trans*-acting transcriptional activator. *EMBO J.* **5:** 561–565.

Sekulovich, R.E., K. Leary, and R.M. Sandri-Goldin. 1988. The herpes simplex virus type 1 α protein ICP27 can act as a *trans*-repressor in combination with ICP4 and ICP0. *J. Virol.* **62:** 4510–4522.

Selby, M.J. and B.M. Peterlin. 1990. *trans*-activation by HIV-1 tat via a heterologous RNA binding protein. *Cell* **62:** 769–776.

Seto, E., P.J. Mitchell, and T.S.B. Yen. 1990. Transactivation by the hepatitis B virus X protein depends on AP-2 and other transcription factors. *Nature* **344:** 72–74.

Seto, E., T. Yen, B.M. Peterlin, and J. Ou. 1988. Transactivation of the human immunodeficiency virus long terminal repeat by the hepatitis B virus X protein. *Proc. Natl. Acad. Sci.* **85:** 8286–8290.

Sharp, P.A. and R.A. Marciniak. 1989. HIV TAR: An RNA enhancer? *Cell* **59:** 229–230.

Shepard, A.A., A.N. Imbalzano, and N.A. DeLuca. 1989. Separation of primary structural components conferring autoregulation, transactivation, and DNA-binding properties to the herpes simplex virus transcriptional regulatory protein ICP4. *J. Virol.* **63:** 1203–1211.

Shepard, A.A., P. Tolentino, and N. DeLuca. 1990. *trans*-dominant inhibition of herpes simplex virus transcriptional regulatory protein ICP4 by heterodimer formation. *J. Virol.* **64:** 3916–3926.

Shimotohno, K., M. Takanao, T. Teruuchi, and M. Miwa. 1986. Requirements of multiple copies of a 21-nucleotide sequence in the U3 region of human T-cell leukemia virus type I and type II long terminal repeats for *trans*-acting activation of transcription. *Proc. Natl. Acad. Sci.* **83:** 8112–8116.

Simon, M.C., K. Kitchener, H. Kao, E. Hickey, L. Weber, R. Voellmy, N. Heintz, and J.R. Nevins. 1987. Selective induction of human heat shock gene transcription by the adenovirus E1a gene products, including the 12S E1a product. *Mol. Cell. Biol.* **7:** 2884–2890.

Smith, M.R. and W.C. Greene. 1990. Identification of HTLV-I tax *trans*-activator mutants with novel transcriptional phenotypes. *Genes Dev.* **4:** 1875–1885..

Sodroski, J., C. Rosen, F. Wong-Staal, S.Z. Salahuddin, M. Popovic, S. Arya, R.C. Gallo, and W.A. Haseltine. 1985. *trans*-acting transcriptional regulation of human T-cell leukemia virus type III long terminal repeat. *Science* **227:** 171–173.

Southgate, C., M.L. Zapp, and M.R. Green. 1990. Activation of transcription by HIV-1 Tat protein tethered to nascent RNA through another protein. *Nature* **345:** 640–642.

Spandau, D.F. and C.H. Lee. 1988. *trans*-activation of viral enhancers by the hepatitis B virus X protein. *J. Virol.* **62:** 427–434.

Sphalholz, B.A., Y.-C. Yang, and P.M. Howley. 1985. Transactivation of a bovine papillomavirus transcriptional regulatory element by the E2 gene product. *Cell* **42:** 183–191.

Steitz, T.A., D.H. Ohlendorf, D.B. McKay, W.F. Anderson, and B.W. Matthews. 1982. Structural similarities in DNA-binding domains of catabolite gene activator and cro repressor proteins. *Proc. Natl. Acad. Sci.* **79:** 3097–3100.

Stern, S., M. Tanaka, and W. Herr. 1989. The Oct-1 homeodomain directs formation of a multiprotein-DNA complex with the HSV transactivator VP16. *Nature* **341:** 624–630.

Stow, N.D. and E.C. Stow. 1986. Isolation and characterization of a herpes simplex virus type 1 mutant containing a deletion within the gene encoding the immediate early polypeptide Vmw110. *J. Gen. Virol.* **67:** 2571–2585.

Stringer, K.F., C.J. Ingles, and J. Greenblatt. 1990. Direct and selective binding of an acidic transcriptional activator domain to the TATA-box factor TFIID. *Nature* **345:** 783–786.

724 K.J. Martin and M.R. Green

Struhl, K. 1987. Promoters, activator proteins and the mechanism of transcription initiation in yeast. *Cell* **49**: 295–297.

Su, L. and D.M. Knipe. 1989. Herpes simplex virus α protein ICP27 can inhibit and augment viral gene transactivation. *Virology* **170**: 496–504.

Sumimoto, H., Y. Ohkuma, T. Yamamoto, M. Horikoshi, and R.G. Roeder. 1990. Factors involved in specific transcription by mammalian RNA polymerase II: Identification of general transcription factor TFIIG. *Proc. Natl. Acad. Sci.* **87**: 9158–9162.

Tevethia, M.J. and D.J. Spector. 1989. Heterologous transactivation among viruses. *Prog. Med. Virol.* **36**: 120–190.

Tremblay, M.L., S.-P. Yee, R.H. Persson, S. Bacchetti, J.R. Smiley, and P.E. Branton. 1985. Activation and inhibition of the 72,000-Da early protein of adenovirus type 5 in mouse cells constitutively expressing an immediate-early protein of herpes simplex virus type 1. *Virology* **144**: 35–45.

Triezenberg, S.J., R.C. Kingsbury, and S.L. McKnight. 1988. Functional dissection of VP16, the *trans*-activator of herpes simplex virus immediate early gene expression. *Genes Dev.* **2**: 718–729.

Twu, J.S. and R.H. Schloemer. 1987. Transcriptional *trans*-activating function of hepatitis B virus. *J. Virol.* **61**: 3448–3453.

Urier, G., M. Buisson, P. Chambard, and A. Sergeant. 1989. The Epstein-Barr virus early protein EB1 activates transcription from different responsive elements including AP-1 sites. *EMBO J.* **8**: 1447–1453.

Van Dyke, M.W., R.G. Roeder, and M. Sawadogo. 1988. Physical analysis of transcription initiation complex assembly on a class II gene promoter. *Science* **241**: 1335–1338.

Vinson, C.R., P.B. Sigler, and S.L. McKnight. 1989. Scissors-grip model for DNA recognition by a family of leucine zipper proteins. *Science* **246**: 911–916.

Vlcek, C., V. Paces, and M. Schwyzer. 1989. Nucleotide sequence of the pseudorabies virus immediate early gene, encoding a strong *trans*-activator protein. *Virus Genes* **2**: 335–346.

Wagner, E.K. 1985. Individual HSV transcripts: Characterization of specific genes. In *The herpesviruses* (ed. B. Roizman), vol. 3, pp. 45–104. Plenum Press, New York.

Weeks, K.M., C. Ampe, S.C. Schultz, T.A. Steitz, and D.M. Crothers. 1990. Fragments of the HIV-1 tat protein specifically bind TAR RNA. *Science* **249**: 1281–1285.

Whyte, P., J.J. Buchkovich, J.M. Horowitz, S.H. Friend, M. Raybuck, R. Weinberg, and E. Harlow. 1988. Association between an oncogene and an anti-oncogene: The adenovirus E1a proteins bind to the retinoblastoma gene product. *Nature* **334**: 124–129.

Wilcox, K.W., A. Kohn, E. Sklyanskay, and B. Roizman. 1980. Herpes simplex virus phosphoproteins I. Phosphate cycles on and off some viral polypeptides and can alter their affinity for DNA. *J. Virol.* **33**: 167–182.

Wu, C.L. and K.W. Wilcox. 1990. Codons 262 to 490 from the herpes simplex virus ICP4 gene are sufficient to encode a sequence-specific DNA binding protein. *Nucleic Acids Res.* **18**: 531–538.

Wu, J.Y., Z.Y. Zhou, A. Judd, C.A. Cartwright, and W.S. Robinson. 1990. The hepatitis B virus-encoded transcriptional *trans*-activator hbx appears to be a novel protein serine/threonine kinase. *Cell* **63**: 687–695.

Yang, Y.-C., H. Okayama, and P.M. Howley. 1985. Bovine papilloma virus contains multiple transforming genes. *Proc. Natl. Acad. Sci.* **82**: 1030–1034.

Yang, Y.-C., B.A. Spalholz, M.S. Rabson, and P.M. Howley. 1987. Dissociation of transforming and *trans*-activating functions for bovine papillomavirus type-1. *Nature* **318**: 575–577.

Yoshinaga, S., N. Dean, M. Han, and A.J. Berk. 1986. Adenovirus stimulation of transcription by RNA polymerase III: Evidence for an E1a-dependent increase in transcription factor IIIC concentration. *EMBO J.* **5:** 343–354.

Yuan, R., C. Bohan, F.C.H. Shiao, R. Robinson, H.J. Kaplan, and A. Srinvason. 1989. Activation of HIV LTR-directed expression: Analysis with pseudorabies virus immediate early gene. *Virology* **172:** 92–99.

Zerler, B., R. Roberts, M.B. Mathews, and E. Moran. 1987. Different functional domains of the adenovirus E1a gene are involved in the regulation of host cell cycle products. *Mol. Cell. Biol.* **7:** 821–829.

27

Adenovirus E1A *trans*-Activation: Understanding It Will Require Learning How the General Transcription Factors Function

Arnold J. Berk
Department of Microbiology and Molecular
Genetics, and Molecular Biology Institute
University of California
Los Angeles, California 90024-1570

OVERVIEW

Adenovirus E1A protein stimulates transcription from a variety of promoters composed of binding sites for several different cellular transcription factors (TFs). This could be accomplished if E1A increased the activity of a general transcription factor. TFIID binds to TATA boxes and initiates the ordered assembly of other general transcription factors and RNA polymerase II. TFIID is also required for transcription from some TATA-less promoters. TFIID activity is increased in extracts of adenovirus-infected cells and may be the general factor targeted by E1A. Recent results show that E1A binds specifically to TFIID. Consequently, E1A may activate transcription from multiple promoters by binding to TFIID and modifying its function. E1A may also perform other functions that increase the activity of promoter-specific factors.

INTRODUCTION

The adenovirus 2 large E1A protein is a powerful activator of viral transcription (Jones and Shenk 1979). Unlike most transcription factors that have been studied in detail, it stimulates transcription from a very broad set of promoters. The E1A region maps near the left end of the 36-kb linear double-stranded DNA viral genome. During the early phase of infection, the RNA transcribed from this region is spliced into two predominant alternative mRNAs of 13S and 12S (Perricaudet et al. 1979). The 13S mRNA encodes an acidic nuclear phosphorylated protein of 289 residues. The 12S mRNA encodes a related nuclear phosphoprotein of 243 residues, identical in sequence to the larger protein except for 46 residues deleted from near the middle of the protein as a consequence of the altered splicing of the 12S mRNA. The large E1A protein has far more transcription-stimulating activity than the 243-residue protein or smaller E1A proteins expressed from other alternatively spliced E1A mRNAs that are produced during the late phase of infection (Montell et al. 1982, 1984; Winberg and Shenk 1984).

The E1A region is the first to be expressed after viral infection because it is under the control of a strong enhancer region (for review, see Jones et al. 1988). Once expressed, the large E1A protein stimulates transcription from six viral promoters: the E1A promoter itself and promoters E1B, MLP, E2 early, E3, and E4, which are distributed along the entire length of the viral genome and promote transcription on both strands of the viral DNA (Berk et al. 1979; Jones and Shenk 1979; Nevins 1981). These six promoter regions (for review, see Jones et al. 1988) have little DNA sequence relatedness, and no simple consensus control element can be found that might uniquely mediate the response to E1A protein. In accord with this lack of a specific sequence element in the responsive promoters, the large E1A protein itself has very low affinity for DNA (Ferguson et al. 1985). Moreover, the low affinity of E1A for DNA that can be measured is not sequence specific (Chatterjee et al. 1988).

The ability to respond to the transcription-stimulating activity of the E1A protein, referred to as E1A *trans*-activation, is not limited to adenovirus promoters. Most promoters that have been tested are subject to E1A *trans*-activation. These include globin gene promoters (Green et al. 1983; Allan et al. 1984; Svensson and Akusjarvi 1984), the rat preproinsulin I promoter (Gaynor et al. 1984), the HTLV-I and -II promoters (Chen et al. 1985), and the herpes simplex virus type I glycoprotein D (Everett and Dunlop 1984) and thymidine kinase promoters (Weeks and Jones 1985). Recently, we substituted the initiator region from the human terminal transferase promoter, which normally functions only in developing lymphocytes, for the E1B promoter in adenovirus 2. Such experiments have shown that even this promoter element, which does not contain a TATA box (Smale and Baltimore 1989), is *trans*-activated by the large E1A protein (R. Pei and A.J. Berk, unpubl.).

Clearly, E1A acts differently from the more conventional transcription factors that function by binding to specific promoter elements. It also acts differently from the herpes simplex virus transcription factor VP16 which, although not a high-affinity DNA-binding protein, associates with host-cell sequence-specific binding proteins (McKnight et al. 1987; Gerster and Roeder 1988; O'Hare and Goding 1988; Kristie et al. 1989) and consequently also acts on a highly restricted set of promoters through a specific *cis*-regulatory DNA sequence.

How does E1A *trans*-activate so many different types of promoters? At present there is no clear answer. In this paper, I present my point of view, although I alert readers that there are different opinions on this fascinating and controversial question which can be found in other recent reviews and papers (Flint and Shenk 1989; Lillie and Green 1989; Nevins 1989; Martin et al. 1990).

PROMOTER SEQUENCES THAT MEDIATE E1A *TRANS*-ACTIVATION

To analyze the mechanism of E1A *trans*-activation, we first asked what DNA sequences in the E1B promoter are required to respond to E1A *trans*-activation. We chose the E1B promoter for two reasons. First, there are only 68 bp between the E1A and E1B transcription units. Consequently, we thought the E1B promoter might not be very complex. Second, it is possible to construct and propagate viral mutants that are defective in the expression of essential E1B-encoded proteins. This is because of the development of the 293 cell line (Graham et al. 1977). This cell line was derived from a human embryonic kidney cell by transformation with sheared adenovirus DNA. It contains an integrated copy of the E1A and E1B transcription units and expresses the encoded proteins constitutively. Consequently, 293 cells can complement viral mutants defective in essential E1A or E1B functions.

Initial experiments using a deletion mutant missing sequences between the E1B start site (designated +1) and a point 68 bp into the E1B transcription unit (Wu et al. 1987), as well as a fusion of the E1B upstream region to a nonviral reporter gene (Dery et al. 1987), showed that the region from −365 to +5 is sufficient to mediate full response to E1A. An extensive set of viral mutants with deletions and linker-scanning mutations from −365 to +5 was constructed (Wu et al. 1987; Wu and Berk 1988). Each E1B promoter mutant was constructed in an E1A-deficient viral background that prevented the expression of the large E1A protein. This allowed us to compare the "basal" level of transcription of the various E1B promoter mutants to the "activated" level resulting from the effects of the E1A protein. Basal conditions were achieved by infecting HeLa cells with virus isolates containing each E1B promoter mutant, whereas activated conditions resulted from coinfection of HeLa cells with an E1B-deleted adenovirus mutant that expresses normal levels of E1A protein (Wu et al. 1987; Wu and Berk 1988).

The results of these experiments demonstrated that the E1B promoter is unusually simple. The only mutations that significantly affected E1B expression were those that altered the TATA box and a nearby binding site for transcription factor Sp1 (Dynan and Tjian 1983; Kadanoga et al. 1987; see Courey and Tjian, this volume). Moreover, only mutations in the TATA box interfered with E1A *trans*-activation. These results indicated that for the E1B promoter, E1A *trans*-activation must be mediated through the TATA box, presumably via the general transcription factors that interact with this common promoter element. These general factors include TFIIA, B, D, E, F (for review, see Saltzman and Weinmann 1989), and BTF-3 (Zheng et al. 1990).

Although mutagenesis of the E1B promoter region provided a simple picture of the sequences required for E1A *trans*-activation, similar studies from other laboratories of other early adenovirus promoters revealed a more complex picture. Specifically, E1A *trans*-activation was not necessarily mediated only through a TATA box. The E3 promoter was found to contain at least three promoter elements in addition to a TATA box (for review, see Jones et al. 1988), and mutation of the TATA box did not eliminate E1A *trans*-activation (Leff et al. 1985; Garcia et al. 1987). The transcription control region of the E1A gene itself is complex and makes use of a powerful enhancer region (for review, see Jones et al. 1988). Deletion of the E1A TATA box reduces E1A *trans*-activation but does not eliminate it (Hearing and Shenk 1985). The E2 early promoter consists of binding sites for several cellular transcription factors (for review, see Jones et al. 1988) upstream of a nonconsensus TATA box (TTAAGA), which nonetheless fixes the transcription start site (Murthy et al. 1985; Zajchowski et al. 1985; Manohar et al. 1990). Again, mutations in the TATA box do not greatly affect E1A *trans*-activation. The E4 transcription control region also consists of binding sites for several cellular transcription factors upstream of a TATA box (for review, see Jones et al. 1988). In contrast to the E1B promoter, deletion of sequences upstream of the E4 TATA box eliminates its response to E1A (Gilardi and Perricaudet 1984, 1986; Lee and Green 1987).

These results suggested that many different promoter elements are capable of mediating the response to E1A. In complex promoters, such as E1A, E3, E2 early, and E4, mutation of one E1A-responsive promoter element might leave other E1A-responsive elements intact and able to continue to mediate E1A *trans*-activation. To test this idea, we constructed simple synthetic promoters consisting of binding sites for one or two transcription factors and tested their response to E1A after substituting them for the E1B promoter in adenovirus (Pei and Berk 1989).

The first results that emerged from these experiments showed that a single binding site for transcription factor E2F, which interacts with the E2 early promoter (Kovesdi et al. 1986), behaved similarly to a single Sp1 site. A single E2F site resulted in a weak promoter generating several start sites that did not respond to E1A.

Results with a single cAMP response element (CRE) (Roesler et al. 1988) differed from those with Sp1 and E2F. CRE sites have also been referred to as ATF sites in the context of adenovirus early promoters (Lee et al. 1987). CRE/ATF sites occur in the E1A, E2 early, E3, and E4 transcriptional control regions and interact with multiple sequence-specific binding proteins in mammalian cells (Hai et al. 1989). In contrast to the situation for single Sp1 and E2F sites, a single CRE/ATF site resulted in a fairly strong promoter generating transcripts from multiple start sites that all responded to E1A. Thus, both the E1B TATA box and a CRE/ATF site can individually yield a promoter that responds to E1A. To test whether the mechanism of E1A *trans*-activation through the CRE/ATF site was similar to or distinct from the mechanism of activation through the E1B TATA box, we constructed a promoter consisting of a CRE/ATF site plus an E1B TATA box. We observed a similar level of E1A activation from the combined promoter elements as from the individual promoter elements, which favors a model with similar mechanisms of E1A activation for each promoter element.

In contrast to the results for single Sp1 and E2F sites, we found that two E2F sites (Pei and Berk 1989) resulted in a promoter that did respond to E1A. As in the experiment with a CRE/ATF site plus E1B TATA box promoter, we found that the level of activation for a promoter composed of two E2F sites plus the E1B TATA box was similar to that observed for two E2F sites alone and for the E1B TATA box alone (R. Pei and A.J. Berk, unpubl.).

The most important conclusion of these studies is that many different transcription factor binding sites can generate promoters that are *trans*-activated by the large E1A protein. The question remains, however, as to how E1A functions in a mechanistic sense.

BIOCHEMICAL STUDIES ON ADENOVIRUS-INFECTED CELL EXTRACTS

During infection of HeLa cells by adenovirus 2, E1A protein reaches peak concentrations at 20 hours postinfection (Spindler and Berk 1984). Extracts prepared from HeLa cells infected with wild-type adenovirus 2 at 20 hours postinfection have five- to tenfold higher in vitro transcriptional activity compared to extracts of mock-infected cells (Leong and Berk 1986). This higher in vitro activity requires expression of the large E1A protein and not the smaller E1A proteins, just as *trans*-activation in vivo requires the large E1A protein (Montell et al. 1982, 1984; Winberg and Shenk 1984). The higher activity of the adenovirus-2-infected cell extracts results from an increase in the fraction of template molecules that are transcribed rather than from an increase in the frequency of reinitiation (Leong and Berk 1986).

Chromatographic fractionation of cell extracts indicates that at least five protein fractions in addition to RNA polymerase II are required for transcription initiation (for review, see Saltzman and Weinmann 1989). In the terminology established by the Roeder laboratory, these are referred to as TFIIA, B, D, E, and F. TFIID is a sequence-specific DNA-binding protein that binds to the TATA box (Davison et al. 1983; Fire et al. 1984; Parker and Topol 1984; Sawadogo and Roeder 1985). The binding of TFIID initiates a cascade of assembly in which TFIIA binds to the TFIID-DNA complex, followed by TFIIB, then RNA polymerase II plus TFIIF, and finally TFIIE (Van Dyke et al. 1988; Buratowski et al. 1989). Since E1A activates transcription from the E1B TATA box, it could bind to or somehow modify the activity of any one of these general transcription factors. The E1A protein could also conceivably increase the activity of RNA polymerase II.

The adenovirus 2 major late promoter was used as the template in the biochemical studies of general transcription factors mentioned above. Consequently, we used this promoter to characterize the general transcription factors extracted from adenovirus-infected cells. Chromatographic fractionation of the infected cell extract revealed that the component responsible for its higher activity eluted in the high-salt fraction ("D fraction") from a phosphocellulose column (Leong et al. 1988). This is the protein fraction in which TFIID elutes from phosphocellulose (Matsui et al. 1980). TFIIA, B, E, and F, and RNA polymerase II activities were similar whether prepared from HeLa cells infected with wild-type adenovirus or an E1A mutant. The D fraction from infected cell extracts had high activity on a major late promoter construct containing only the TATA box and cap site region, as well as on the human β-globin promoter (Leong et al. 1988). These observations led us to suggest that during the course of adenovirus infection, the large E1A protein increases the activity of TFIID. I return to this issue in a subsequent section of this chapter.

Most of the large E1A protein in the infected cell extract elutes from phosphocellulose between 0.1 and 0.35 M KCl ("B fraction"). However, the B fraction from wild-type adenovirus-infected cell extracts exhibits equivalent transcriptional activity to the B fraction from E1A mutant infected cells. This behavior is consistent with our earlier results that E1A protein partially purified from adenovirus-infected cell extracts (assayed with anti-E1A antibody) fails to stimulate transcription when added to an extract from uninfected HeLa cells (A. Tsukamoto and A.J. Berk, unpubl.). There are reports that large E1A protein expressed in and purified from *Escherichia coli* stimulates transcription in vitro from several adenovirus promoters (Spangler et al. 1987; Bruner et al. 1988). The reason for the discrepancy in our results is not clear. Although most of the large E1A protein is found in the B fraction, lower levels can be detected in the D fraction (Leong et al. 1988). The latter observation raises the possibility that E1A protein present in the D fraction may be functionally different from that found in the B fraction. It follows that the elution properties of E1A may be influenced either by covalent modification or association with cellular proteins.

If E1A *trans*-activation is mediated through TFIID, how does it induce transcription from promoters that do not have a TATA box? As stated above, TFIID plays a central role in transcription from promoters containing a TATA box. No other general transcription factors, nor RNA polymerase, can interact with the adenovirus major late promoter until TFIID binds to the TATA box (Van Dyke et al. 1988; Buratowski et al. 1989). It has not been possible to study directly the factor requirements for most promoters that lack a TATA box because they are extremely weak promoters in vitro, but the promoter of the terminal transferase gene is an exception (Smale and Baltimore 1989). Transcription from the terminal transferase promoter is influenced markedly by an "initiator element" (Smale and Baltimore 1989), which is subject to E1A *trans*-activation (R. Pei and A.J. Berk, unpubl.). When we explored the transcription factor requirements for in vitro transcription from a promoter containing this initiator element, we found that it required a factor that cochromatographs with TFIID (Smale et al. 1990). Moreover, both activities exhibited similar heat lability. Apparently, TFIID is required for transcription from the terminal transferase initiator. TFIID may associate with the terminal transferase promoter via promoter interactions with another factor, perhaps one that binds directly to the initiator DNA sequence. Regardless of how TFIID interacts with the terminal transferase promoter, it is a good candidate for mediating the action of E1A protein on the initiator element, even though the promoter does not contain a TATA box.

TFIID

The observation that the E1B TATA box can be *trans*-activated by E1A, coupled with the fact that the phosphocellulose D fraction from adenovirus-infected cells has higher activity than the D fraction from cells infected with E1A mutants, points to TFIID as a possible target for E1A action. Any rigorous test of this model requires a direct analysis of TFIID protein derived from uninfected and adenovirus-infected cells. Purification of mammalian TFIID, however, has proven to be extremely difficult. A breakthrough came when it was reported that an activity in extracts of the yeast *Saccharomyces cerevisiae* could replace the TFIID fraction in cell-free transcription reactions wherein all other components were of mammalian origin (Buratowski et al. 1988; Cavallini et al. 1988). This demonstrated the remarkable evolutionary conservation of the complex protein-protein interactions involved in transcription initiation by RNA polymerase II. Fortuitously, yeast TFIID, unlike its mammalian counterpart, fractionated as a discrete protein species on ion exchange and gel filtration columns (Buratowski et al. 1988).

Using in vitro complementation of the mammalian transcription system as an assay, yeast TFIID protein was purified. Microsequencing allowed derivation of partial amino acid sequence, which in turn led to isolation of the yeast gene encoding TFIID (Cavallini et al. 1989; Eisenmann et al. 1989; Hahn et al. 1989; Horikoshi et al. 1989; Schmidt et al. 1989). Using sequence information provided by the yeast TFIID gene, we were able to clone a cDNA encoding the human TFIID (Kao et al. 1990). Other investigators have also succeeded in cloning the human TFIID cDNA (Hoffmann et al. 1990; Peterson et al. 1990). Having isolated the human TFIID cDNA, we were able to express the protein in *E. coli*, purify it, and raise specific antisera to it. Such antibody reagents have been crucial to our study of the putative link between E1A and TFIID.

We have considered three general mechanisms by which E1A protein might influence TFIID activity. First, it could cause an increase in the concentration of TFIID protein. Second, the specific activity of TFIID might be regulated in the uninfected cell by posttranslational modification, such as phosphorylation, and E1A might influence such modification. Third, E1A protein might alter TFIID function by binding it directly.

Using the TFIID gene as a probe on Northern blots, and specific anti-TFIID rabbit sera on Western blots, we found that adenovirus infection of HeLa cells does not increase the concentration of either TFIID mRNA (R. Pei and A.J. Berk, unpubl.) or TFIID protein (Q. Zhou and A.J. Berk, unpubl.). These results argue against the first proposed mechanism of E1A activation. By immunoprecipitating TFIID protein from extracts of cells labeled in vivo with [^{32}P]phosphate, we have observed a low level of ^{32}P incorporation. However, adenovirus infection failed to alter the labeling of TFIID with ^{32}P (Q. Zhou and A.J. Berk, unpubl.), thus providing evidence counter to the second hypothetical mechanism.

To examine direct binding of E1A to TFIID, we constructed a vaccinia virus vector (Elroy-Stein et al. 1989) that expresses high levels of the large E1A protein and a second vaccinia virus vector that expresses high levels of TFIID (C.C. Kao and A.J. Berk, unpubl.). HeLa cells co-infected with these vaccinia virus vectors were labeled with [^{35}S]methionine at 20 hours postinfection. Under these conditions, a large fraction of the labeled methionine is incorporated into E1A and TFIID. Immunoprecipitation with an anti-E1A rabbit antiserum or an anti-E1A monoclonal antibody resulted in the precipitation of E1A protein plus a significant fraction of the labeled TFIID. Neither protein was immunoprecipitated with control antiserum or a control monoclonal antibody. Similarly, immunoprecipitation with the anti-TFIID antiserum resulted in coprecipitation of labeled TFIID and E1A protein.

A coprecipitating complex that included both E1A and TFIID could also be formed by mixing extracts of cells singly infected with the vaccinia E1A and TFIID vectors. Incubation of either of the extracts at 68°C for 10 minutes prior to mixing prevented the formation of the coprecipitating complex. The coprecipitating complexes were stable to washing with buffers containing 0.8 M LiCl or 0.05% SDS but were disrupted by concentrations of SDS of 0.1% or higher (C.C. Kao and A.J. Berk, unpubl.). These results suggest that E1A protein indeed can form a specific complex with TFIID. Further work will be required to determine the biochemical properties of the complex formed between E1A and TFIID and whether or not other cellular proteins are present in the complex.

These results are consistent with the third hypothetical model for E1A *trans*-activation. That is, E1A forms an intimate association with TFIID and in some manner stimulates transcription initiation. It is not clear at this point whether the E1A TFIID interaction is direct or whether it is mediated by intervening cellular proteins. Additional work will be required to determine the functional significance of the E1A-TFIID interaction we have observed. However, it is worth noting that the herpes simplex virus transcriptional activator VP16 has also been shown to bind specifically to TFIID (Stringer et al. 1990).

CONCLUSIONS AND PERSPECTIVES

Because of their rapid generation time, viruses experience ample opportunity for natural selection to optimize their replication strategy. The E1A proteins of adenovirus play crucial roles in priming host cells for the lytic infection. To maximize viral DNA replication, E1A proteins bind to, and presumably inactivate, the RB protein (Whyte et al. 1988). E1A also binds to a 107-kD protein related to the RB protein, and yet another 300-kD cellular protein (Egan et al. 1988; Whyte et al. 1989; Stein et al. 1990). These critical host-cell proteins interact with two regions in the amino-terminal half of the large E1A protein that are highly conserved between the several different human and simian adenoviruses (for review, see Flint and Shenk 1989).

The strong transcriptional *trans*-activation function of the large E1A protein depends principally on a third highly conserved region that is unique to the large E1A protein. As described above, this function is able to stimulate transcription from a wide variety of promoter sequences that are binding sites for different cellular transcription factors. These results imply that the large E1A protein affects the function of one or more general transcription factors required for transcription from most promoters transcribed by RNA polymerase II. The very recent experiments described in the latter part of this paper, using vaccinia vectors that overexpress TFIID and large E1A protein, indicate that these proteins associate with one another. It thus appears that in its *trans*-activating function, E1A protein also binds to a critical host-cell protein and modifies its function. This model is consistent with the results of Lillie and Green (1989), which show that in transfection experiments, fusion of the E1A protein to the DNA-binding domain of GAL4 greatly stimulates *trans*-activation from a promoter with GAL4-binding sites. Lillie and Green concluded that E1A functions in a direct manner at the promoter.

The challenge for the future remains to determine precisely how E1A stimulates transcription. Liu and Green (1990) have provided indirect evidence from transfection experiments with E1A fusion proteins that the large E1A protein can bind to a transcription factor called ATF-2. A simple model would be that E1A protein acts as an "adapter" or "coactivator," connecting ATF-2 and other DNA-binding transcription factors to TFIID. Several groups have recently postulated the existence of such "bridging" factors (Berger et al. 1990; Kelleher et al. 1990; Peterson et al. 1990; Pugh and Tjian 1990). However, this model is probably oversimplified. E1A protein might function by increasing the ability of TFIID to compete with nucleosomes for TATA-box binding, as has been suggested for another promiscuous viral *trans*-activator, the pseudorabies virus immediate-early protein (Workman et al. 1988). There is also evidence that expression of the large E1A protein can lead to increased phosphorylation of E2F and E4F, transcription factors interacting with elements of the E2 early and E4 promoters, respectively, and that this phosphorylation increases the DNA-binding activities of these factors

(Raychaudhuri et al. 1989, 1990). E1A-induced phosphorylation of TFIIIC (Hoeffler et al. 1988) has also been proposed as a mechanism to explain the increased activity of this RNA polymerase III transcription factor following adenovirus infection (Hoeffler and Roeder 1985; Yoshinaga et al. 1986). E1A expression also greatly augments the cAMP-induced increase in c-*fos* and *junB* mRNA levels in the lymphocytic cell line S49, suggesting that E1A can activate the expression of specific genes encoding transcription factors (Muller et al. 1989). Apparently, E1A protein stimulates transcription by several independent or interdependent mechanisms.

It seems likely that a thorough understanding of E1A *trans*-activation will require a better understanding of how the general transcription factors TFIIA, B, E, F, D, and BTF3, as well as the aforementioned "bridging" factors, function. Our pursuit of the mechanism of E1A *trans*-activation has led directly to the study of the general transcription factors. Cloning of the genes encoding these general factors is a major goal, as it will provide large quantities of purified protein, specific immunological reagents, and opportunities for site-directed mutagenesis. It can be said in closing that we are only at the beginning of a long journey that may lead to a clear understanding of how transcription is regulated in mammalian cells.

ACKNOWLEDGMENTS

This work was supported by grant CA-25235 from the National Cancer Institute, Department of Health and Human Services. I am grateful to members of my laboratory and colleagues at UCLA for many stimulating discussions and valuable criticisms.

REFERENCES

Allan, M., J. Zhu, P. Montague, and J. Paul. 1984. Differential response of multiple ε-globin cap sites to *cis*- and *trans*-acting controls. *Cell* **38:** 399–407.

Berger, S.L., W.D. Cress, A. Cress, S.J. Triezenberg, and L. Guarente. 1990. Selective inhibition of activated but not basal transcription by the acidic activation domain of VP16: Evidence for transcriptional adaptors. *Cell* **61:** 1199–1208.

Berk, A.J., F. Lee, T. Harrison, J. Williams, and P.A. Sharp. 1979. A pre-early adenovirus 5 gene product regulates synthesis of early viral messenger RNAs. *Cell* **17:** 935–944.

Bruner, M., B. Dalie, R. Spangler, and M.L. Harter. 1988. Purification and biological characterization of an adenovirus type 2 E1A protein expressed in *E. coli. J. Biol. Chem.* **263:** 3984–3989.

Buratowski, S.P., S. Hahn, L. Guarente, and P.A. Sharp. 1989. Five intermediate complexes in transcription initiation by RNA polymerase II. *Cell* **56:** 549–561.

Buratowski, S.P., S. Hahn, P.A. Sharp, and L. Guarente. 1988. Function of a yeast TATA-element binding protein in a mammalian transcription system. *Nature* **334:** 37–42.

Cavallini, B., J. Huet, J. Plassat, A. Sentenac, J. Egly, and P. Chambon. 1988. A yeast activity can substitute for HeLa cell TATA box factor. *Nature* **334:** 77–80.

Cavallini, B., I. Faus, H. Matthes, J.M. Chipoulet, B. Winsor, J.-M. Egly, and P. Chambon. 1989. Cloning of the gene encoding the yeast protein BTF1Y, which can substitute for the human TATA box-binding factor. *Proc. Natl. Acad. Sci.* **86:** 9803–9807.

Chatterjee, P.K., M. Bruner, S.J. Flint, and M.L. Harter. 1988. DNA-binding properties of an adenovirus 286R E1A protein. *EMBO J.* **7:** 835–841.

Chen, I.S.Y., A.J. Cann, N. Shah, and R.B. Gaynor. 1985. Functional relationship between HTLV-II *x* and adenovirus E1A proteins in transcriptional activation. *Science* **230:** 570–573.

Davison, B.L., J.M. Egly, E.R. Mulvihill, and P. Chambon. 1983. Formation of stable preinitiation complexes between eukaryotic class B transcription factors and promoter sequences. *Nature* **301:** 680–686.

Dery, C.V., C.H. Herrmann, and M.B. Mathews. 1987. Response of individual adenovirus promoters to the products of the E1A gene. *Oncogene* **2:** 15–23.

Dynan, W.S. and R. Tjian. 1983. Isolation of transcription factors that discriminate between different promoters recognized by RNA polymerase II. *Cell* **32:** 79–87.

Egan, C., T.N. Jelsma, J.A. Howe, S.T. Bayley, B. Ferguson, and P.A. Branton. 1988. Mapping of cellular protein-binding sites on the products of early-region 1A of human adenovirus type 5. *Mol. Cell. Biol.* **8:** 3955–3959.

Eisenmann, D.M., C. Dollard, and F. Winston. 1989. *SPT15*, the gene encoding the yeast TATA factor TFIID, is required for normal transcription initiation in vivo. *Cell* **58:** 1183–1191.

Elroy-Stein, O., T.R. Fuerst, and B. Moss. 1989. Cap-independent translation of mRNA conferred by encephalomyocarditis virus 5′ sequence improves the performance of the vaccinia virus/bacteriophage T7 hybrid expression system. *Proc. Natl. Acad. Sci.* **86:** 6126–6130.

Everett, R.D. and M. Dunlop. 1984. *Trans*-activation of plasmid borne promoters by adenovirus and several herpes group viruses. *Nucleic Acids Res.* **12:** 5969–5978.

Ferguson, B., B. Krippl, O. Andrisani, N. Jones, H. Wesphal, and M. Rosenberg. 1985. E1A 13S and 12S mRNA products made in *Escherichia coli* both function as nucleus-localized transcription activators but do not directly bind DNA. *Mol. Cell. Biol.* **5:** 2653–2661.

Fire, A., M. Samuels, and P.A. Sharp. 1984. Interactions between RNA polymerase II, factors, and template leading to accurate initiation of transcription. *J. Biol. Chem.* **259:** 2509–2516.

Flint, J. and T. Shenk. 1989. Adenovirus E1A protein: Paradigm viral transactivator. *Annu. Rev. Genet.* **23:** 141–161.

Garcia, J., F. Wu, and R. Gaynor. 1987. Upstream regulatory regions required to stabilize binding to the TATA sequence in an adenovirus early promoter. *Nucleic Acids Res.* **15:** 8367–8385.

Gaynor, R.B., D. Hillman, and A.J. Berk. 1984. Adenovirus early region 1A protein activates transcription of a nonviral gene introduced in to mammalian cells by infection or transfection. *Proc. Natl. Acad. Sci.* **81:** 1193–1197.

Gerster, T. and R.G. Roeder. 1988. A herpes virus *trans*-activating protein interacts with transcription factor OTF-1 and other cellular proteins. *Proc. Natl. Acad. Sci.* **85:** 6347–6351.

Gilardi, P. and M. Perricaudet. 1984. The E4 transcription unit of Ad2: Far upstream sequences are required for its transactivation by E1A. *Nucleic Acids Res.* **12:** 7877–7888.

————. 1986. The E4 promoter of adenovirus type 2 contains an E1A-dependent *cis* acting element. *Nucleic Acids Res.* **14:** 9035–9049.

Graham, F.G., J. Smiley, W. Russel, and R. Nairn. 1977. Characteristics of a human cell line transformed by DNA from adenovirus type 5. *J. Gen. Virol.* **36:** 59–72.

Green, M.R., R. Treisman, and T. Maniatis. 1983. Transcriptional activation of cloned human β-globin genes by viral immediate-early gene products. *Cell* **35:** 137–145.

Hahn, S., S. Buratowski, P.A. Sharp, and L. Guarente. 1989. Isolation of the gene encoding the yeast TATA binding protein TFIID: A gene identical to the *SPT15* suppressor of Ty element insertions. *Cell* **58:** 1173–1181.

Hai, T., F. Liu, W.J. Coukos, and M.R. Green. 1989. Transcription factor ATF cDNA clones: An extensive family of leucine zipper proteins able to selectively form DNA-binding heterodimers. *Genes Dev.* **3:** 2083–2090.

Hearing, P. and T. Shenk. 1985. Sequence-independent autoregulation of the adenovirus type 5 transcription unit. *Mol. Cell. Biol.* **5:** 3214–3221.

Hoeffler, W.K. and R.G. Roeder. 1985. Enhancement of RNA polymerase III transcription by the E1A gene product of adenovirus. *Cell* **41:** 955–963.

Hoeffler, W.K., R. Kovelman, and R.G. Roeder. 1988. Activation of transcription factor IIIC by the adenovirus E1A protein. *Cell* **53:** 907–920.

Hoffmann, A., E. Sinn, T. Yamamoto, J. Wang, A. Roy, M. Horikoshi, and R.G. Roeder. 1990. Highly conserved core domain and unique N terminus with presumptive regulatory motifs in a human TATA factor (TFIID). *Nature* **346:** 387–390.

Horikoshi, M., C.K. Wang, H. Fujii, J.A. Cromlish, P.A. Weil, and R.G. Roeder. 1989. Cloning and structure of a yeast gene encoding a general transcription factor TFIID that binds to the TATA box. *Nature* **341:** 299–303.

Jones, N.C. and T. Shenk. 1979. An adenovirus type 5 early gene function regulates expression of other early viral genes. *Proc. Natl. Acad. Sci.* **76:** 3665–3669.

Jones, N.C., P.W.J. Rigby, and E.B. Ziff. 1988. *Trans*-acting protein factors and the regulation of eukaryotic transcription: Lessons from studies on DNA tumor viruses. *Genes Dev.* **2:** 267–281.

Kadonaga, J.T., K.R. Carner, F.R. Masiarz, and R. Tjian. 1987. Isolation of a cDNA encoding transcription factor Sp1 and functional analysis of the DNA binding domain. *Cell* **51:** 1079–1090.

Kao, C.C., P.M. Lieberman, M.C. Schmidt, Q. Zhou, R. Pei, and A.J. Berk. 1990. Cloning a transcriptionally active human TATA binding factor. *Science* **248:** 1646–1650.

Kelleher, R.J., III, P.M. Flanagan, and R.D. Kornberg. 1990. A novel mediator between activator proteins and the RNA polymerase II transcription apparatus. *Cell* **61:** 1209–1215.

Kovesdi, I., R. Reichel, and J.R. Nevins. 1986. Identification of a cellular factor involved in E1A-mediated coordinate gene control. *Cell* **45:** 219–228.

Kristie, T.M., J.H. LeBowitz, and P.A. Sharp. 1989. The octamer-binding proteins form multi-protein-DNA complexes with the HSV αTIF regulatory protein. *EMBO J.* **8:** 4229–4238.

Lee, K.A.W. and M.R. Green. 1987. A cellular transcription factor E4F1 interacts with an E1a-inducible enhancer and mediates constitutive enhancer function *in vitro*. *EMBO J.* **6:** 1345–1353.

Lee, K.A.W., T.Y. Hai, L. SivaRaman, B. Thimmappaya, H.C. Hurst, N.C. Jones, and M.R. Green. 1987. A cellular transcription factor ATF activates transcription of multiple E1A-inducible adenovirus early promoters. *Proc. Natl. Acad. Sci.* **84:** 8355–8359.

Leff, T., J. Corden, R. Elkaim, and P. Sassone-Corsi. 1985. Transcriptional analysis of the adenovirus-5 EIII promoter: Absence of sequence specificity for stimulation by E1A gene products. *Nucleic Acids Res.* **13**: 1209–1221.

Leong, K. and A.J. Berk. 1986. Adenovirus early region 1A protein increases the number of template molecules transcribed in cell-free extracts. *Proc. Natl. Acad. Sci.* **83**: 5844–5848.

Leong, K., L. Brunet, and A.J. Berk. 1988. Factors responsible for the higher transcriptional activity of extracts of adenovirus-infected HeLa cells fractionate with the TATA box transcription factor. *Mol. Cell. Biol.* **8**: 1765–1774.

Lillie, J.W. and M.R. Green. 1989. Transcription activation by the adenovirus E1a protein. *Nature* **338**: 39–44.

Liu, F. and M.R. Green. 1990. A specific member of the ATF transcription factor family can mediate transcription activation by the adenovirus E1a protein. *Cell* **61**: 1217–1224.

Manohar, C.F., J. Kratochvil, and B. Thimmappaya. 1990. The adenovirus EII early promoter has multiple EIA-sensitive elements, two of which function cooperatively in basal and virus-induced transcription. *J. Virol.* **64**: 2457–2466.

Martin, K.J., J.W. Lillie, and M.R. Green. 1990. Evidence for interaction of different eukaryotic transcriptional activators with distinct cellular targets. *Nature* **346**: 147–152.

Matsui, T., J. Segall, P.A. Weill, and R.G. Roeder. 1980. Multiple factors required for accurate initiation of transcription by purified RNA polymerase II. *J. Biol. Chem.* **255**: 11992–11996.

McKnight, J.L.C., T.M. Kristie, and B. Roizman. 1987. Binding of the virion protein mediating α gene induction in herpes simplex virus 1-infected cells to its *cis* site requires cellular proteins. *Proc. Natl. Acad. Sci.* **84**: 7061–7065.

Montell, C., G. Courtois, C. Eng, and A.J. Berk. 1984. Complete transformation by adenovirus 2 requires both E1A proteins. *Cell* **36**: 951–961.

Montell, C., E. Fisher, M. Caruthers, and A.J. Berk. 1982. Resolving the function of overlapping genes by site-specific mutagenesis at a mRNA splice site. *Nature* **295**: 380–384.

Muller, U., M.P. Roberts, D.A. Engel, W. Doerfler, and T. Shenk. 1989. Induction of transcription factor Ap-1 by adenovirus E1A and cAMP. *Genes Dev.* **3**: 1991–2002.

Murthy, S.C.S., G.P. Bhat, and B. Thimmappaya. 1985. Adenovirus EIIa early promoter: Transcription control elements and induction by the viral pre-early E1A gene, which appears to be sequence independent. *Proc. Natl. Acad. Sci.* **82**: 2230–2234.

Nevins, J.R. 1981. Mechanism of activation of early viral transcription by the adenovirus E1A gene product. *Cell* **26**: 213–220.

———. 1989. Mechanisms of viral-mediated *trans*-activation of transcription. *Adv. Virus Res.* **37**: 35–83.

O'Hare, P. and C.R. Goding. 1988. Herpes simplex virus regulatory elements and the immunoglobulin octamer domain bind a common factor and are both targets for virion transactivation. *Cell* **52**: 435–445.

Parker, C.S. and J. Topol. 1984. A *Drosophila* RNA polymerase II transcription factor contains a promoter region specific DNA binding activity. *Cell* **36**: 357–369.

Pei, R. and A.J. Berk. 1989. Multiple transcription factor binding sites mediate adenovirus E1A transactivation. *J. Virol.* **63**: 3499–3506.

Perricaudet, M., G. Akusjarvi, A. Virtanen, and U. Pettersson. 1979. Structure of two spliced mRNAs from the transforming region of human group C adenoviruses. *Nature* **281**: 694–697.

Peterson, M.G., N. Tanese, B.F. Pugh, and R. Tjian. 1990. Functional domains and upstream activation properties of cloned human TATA binding protein. *Science* **248:** 1625–1630.

Pugh, B.F. and R. Tjian. 1990. Mechanism of transcriptional activation by Sp1: Evidence for coactivators. *Cell* **61:** 1187–1197.

Raychaudhuri, P., S. Bagchi, and J.R. Nevins. 1989. DNA-binding activity of the adenovirus-induced E4F transcription factor is regulated by phosphorylation. *Genes Dev.* **3:** 620–627.

Raychaudhuri, P., S. Bagchi, S.D. Neill, and J.R. Nevins. 1990. Activation of the E2F transcription factor in adenovirus-infected cells involves E1A-dependent stimulation of DNA-binding activity and induction of cooperative binding mediated by an E4 gene product. *J. Virol.* **64:** 2702–2710.

Roesler, W.J., G.R. Vandenbark, and R.W. Hanson. 1988. Cyclic AMP and the induction of eukaryotic gene transcription. *J. Biol. Chem.* **236:** 9063–9066.

Saltzman, A.G. and R. Weinmann. 1989. Promoter specificity and modulation of RNA polymerase II transcription. *FASEB J.* **3:** 1723–1733.

Sawadogo, M. and R.G. Roeder. 1985. Interaction of a gene-specific transcription factor with the adenovirus major late promoter upstream of the TATA box region. *Cell* **43:** 165–175.

Schmidt, M.C., C.C. Kao, R. Pei, and A.J. Berk. 1989. Yeast TATA-box transcription factor gene. *Proc. Natl. Acad. Sci.* **86:** 7785–7789.

Smale, S.T. and D. Baltimore. 1989. The "initiator" as a transcription control element. *Cell* **57:** 103–111.

Smale, S.T., M.C. Schmidt, A.J. Berk, and D. Baltimore. 1990. Transcriptional activation by Sp1 as directed through TATA or initiator: Specific requirement for mammalian transcription factor IID. *Proc. Natl. Acad. Sci.* **87:** 4509–4513.

Spangler, R., M. Bruner, B. Dalie, and M.L. Harter. 1987. Activation of adenovirus promoters by the adenovirus E1A protein in cell-free extracts. *Science* **237:** 1044–1046.

Spindler, K.R. and A.J. Berk. 1984. Rapid intracellular turnover of adenovirus 5 early region 1A proteins. *J. Virol.* **52:** 706–710.

Stein, R.W., M. Corrigan, P. Yaciuk, J. Whelan, and E. Moran. 1990. Analysis of E1A-mediated growth regulation functions: Binding of a 300-kilodalton cellular product correlates with E1A enhancer repression function and DNA synthesis-inducing activity. *J. Virol.* **64:** 4421–4427.

Stringer, K.F., C.J. Ingles, and J. Greenblatt. 1990. Direct and selective binding of an acidic transcriptional activation domain to the TATA-box factor TFIID. *Nature* **345:** 783–786.

Svensson, C. and G. Akusjarvi. 1984. Adenovirus 2 early region 1A stimulates expression of both viral and cellular genes. *EMBO J.* **3:** 789–794.

Van Dyke, M.W., R.G. Roeder, and M. Sawadogo. 1988. Physical analysis of transcription preinitiation complex assembly on a class II gene promoter. *Science* **241:** 1335–1338.

Weeks, D.L. and N.C. Jones. 1985. Adenovirus E3 promoter: Sequences required for activation by E1A. *Nucleic Acids Res.* **13:** 5389–5402.

Whyte, P., N.M. Williamson, and E. Harlow. 1989. Cellular targets for transformation by the adenovirus E1A proteins. *Cell* **56:** 67–75.

Whyte, P., J.J. Buchkovich, J.M. Horowitz, S.H. Friend, M. Raybuck, R.A. Weinberg, and E. Harlow. 1988. Association between an oncogene and an anti-oncogene: The adenovirus E1A proteins bind to the retinoblastoma gene product. *Nature* **334:** 124–129.

Winberg, C. and T. Shenk. 1984. Dissection of overlapping functions within the adenovirus type 5 E1A gene. *EMBO J.* **3:** 1907–1912.

Workman, J.L., S.M. Abmayr, W.A. Cromlish, and R.G. Roeder. 1988. Transcriptional regulation by the immediate early protein of pseudorabies virus during in vitro nucleosome assembly. *Cell* **55:** 211–219.

Wu, L. and A.J. Berk. 1988. Transcriptional activation by the pseudorabies virus immediate early protein requires the TATA box element in the adenovirus 2 E1B promoter. *Virology* **167:** 318–322.

Wu, L., D.S.E. Rosser, M.C. Schmidt, and A.J. Berk. 1987. A TATA box implicated in E1A transcriptional activation of a simple adenovirus 2 promoter. *Nature* **326:** 512–515.

Yoshinaga, S., N. Dean, M. Han, and A.J. Berk. 1986. Adenovirus stimulation of transcription by RNA polymerase III: Evidence for an E1A-dependent increase in transcription factor IIIC concentration. *EMBO J.* **5:** 343–354.

Zajchowski, E.A., H. Boeuf, and C. Kedinger. 1985. The adenovirus-2 early EIIa transcription unit possesses two overlapping promoters with different sequence requirements for E1a-dependent stimulation. *EMBO J.* **4:** 1293–1300.

Zheng, X.M., D. Black, P. Chambon, and J.M. Egly. 1990. Sequencing an expression of complementary DNA for the general transcription factor BTF3. *Nature* **344:** 556–559.

28

Mechanisms of Transcriptional Control as Revealed by Studies of Human Transcription Factor Sp1

Albert J. Courey
Department of Chemistry and Biochemistry
University of California
Los Angeles, California 90024-1569

Robert Tjian
Howard Hughes Medical Institute
Department of Molecular and Cellular Biology
University of California
Berkeley, California 94720

OVERVIEW

Specificity protein 1 (Sp1) is a promoter-selective transcription factor that binds DNA (GC boxes) and activates a wide range of vertebrate genes. Studies of Sp1 have revealed that combinations of regulatory proteins interact with promoter/enhancers and with each other to generate transcriptional specificity. The analysis of Sp1 function also provided evidence for the notion that distantly bound factors can mediate activation by direct protein:protein interactions with factors bound close to the initiation site. Studies of Sp1 have helped establish the concept that transcription factors are remarkably modular proteins with multiple structurally distinct functional domains responsible for DNA recognition (Zn fingers) and transcriptional activation (glutamine-rich domains). Recently, in vitro reconstitution experiments with Sp1 led to the discovery of coactivators, a novel class of transcription factors that are thought to mediate communication between site-specific regulatory factors and the general transcriptional machinery.

INTRODUCTION

By the late 1970s, many of the principles underlying the regulation of bacterial gene expression were firmly established. In particular, it was clear that much of this regulation occurred at the level of transcriptional initiation and involved the action of sigma factors and sequence-specific DNA-binding proteins (Miller and Reznikoff 1978; Rodriguez and Chamberlin 1982; for review, see McClure 1985). These proteins were found to interact with promoter elements close to the transcriptional start site and to modulate the activity of RNA polymerase. Furthermore, biochemical and genetic analyses were beginning to illuminate the mechanisms whereby these proteins could alter the rate of transcriptional initiation.

At the same time, our understanding of eukaryotic gene regulation was at a far more rudimentary stage of development (for review, see Breathnach and Chambon 1981). The biochemical analysis of eukaryotic transcriptional promoters had suggested that, in general, only relatively small promoter regions were required for accurate initiation in vitro. Comparison of these sequences revealed little in common other than a small moiety called a TATA box that was found directly upstream of most, but not all, transcriptional start sites. At this stage, it was not clear that the selective regulation of gene expression in eukaryotes would involve interactions between sequence-specific DNA-binding proteins and promoters, as was the case in prokaryotes, since no such promoter-specific interactions had been identified. Many suspected that promoters would serve only to define the transcriptional start site and that the crucial events controlling gene expression occurred at levels other than that of transcriptional initiation. This notion was reinforced by the finding that correctly regulated gene expression in vivo was frequently found to require much larger chromosomal regions than did accurate transcriptional initiation in vitro. Studies exploring the question of transcriptional regulation tended to focus on more global mechanisms whereby entire chromosomal domains were thought to be activated or deactivated. This global type of regulation was thought to be driven by dramatic changes in chromatin structure, which would alter the accessibility of the template to the transcriptional apparatus (see, e.g., Weintraub and Groudine 1976; Saragosti et al. 1980; Stadler et al. 1980; Wu 1980).

In this context, the discovery of eukaryotic promoter-specific transcription factors (Engelke et al. 1980; Dynan and Tjian 1983a,b; Parker and Topol 1984), which can selectively activate promoters in fractionated cell-free extracts, provided a critical conceptual framework for investigations into the mechanisms underlying eukaryotic gene regulation. The subsequent finding that these factors must bind promoter-proximal *cis*-regulatory DNA elements to exert their effects suggested that the control of eukaryotic transcription might occur by an elaborated form of the combinatorial control mechanism regulating prokaryotic gene expression. Furthermore, the fact that these factors were active in vitro, in the absence of assembled chromatin, indicated that gene activation and repression could occur independently of global changes in chromatin structure, although such changes are clearly of significance (see, e.g., Workman et al. 1988).

In this chapter, we focus on the discovery and analysis of Sp1, one of the earliest RNA polymerase II (pol II) transcription factors isolated. These studies revealed a number of general principles governing the action of eukaryotic regulatory proteins. They also led to both technical and conceptual advances that contributed to the recent explosion of information in the field of eukaryotic gene regulation.

IDENTIFICATION OF A SEQUENCE-SPECIFIC TRANSCRIPTION FACTOR

Unlike bacterial RNA polymerase, eukaryotic polymerases are not, by themselves, capable of recognizing promoters and accurately initiating transcription. Purified RNA pol II (the RNA polymerase responsible for transcribing nuclear protein coding genes) initiates transcription more or less randomly (for review, see Lewis and Burgess 1982). However, in the presence of crude whole-cell or nuclear extracts, RNA pol II is capable of accurately initiating transcription from a wide variety of viral and cellular promoters. Efficient promoter utilization appears to involve a number of protein factors (for review, see Saltzman and Weinmann 1989). To determine if the same factors are required for the transcription of all promoters, chromatographically fractionated extracts were assayed for transcriptional activity on a variety of promoters. In this way, Sp1 was identified as a fraction required for the efficient transcription of the simian virus 40 (SV40) early promoter, but not for the β-globin promoter, the adenovirus 2 major late promoter, or the avian sarcoma virus long terminal repeat (LTR) promoter (Fig. 1A) (Dynan and Tjian 1983a).

It was next asked whether or not the Sp1-dependence of the SV40 early promoter could be ascribed to any specific *cis*-regulatory sequences. If so, did Sp1 bind directly to these sequences in much the same manner as a prokaryotic activator protein? In answer to these questions, it was shown that the ability of the SV40 early promoter to respond to Sp1 was completely dependent on six tandem repeats of a 10-bp element that, because of its high GC content, was termed a GC box (Dynan and Tjian 1983b). Together, these tandem repeats comprise the three 21-bp repeat elements of the SV40 intergenic control region (Fig. 1B) that had previously been shown to be essential for early promoter activity (Fromm and Berg 1982; Everett et al. 1983). These 21-bp repeats were

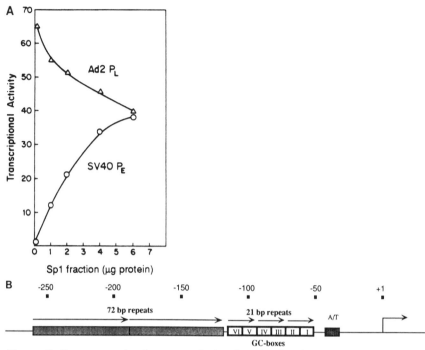

Figure 1   Promoter-selective transcriptional activation by Sp1. (*A*) Transcriptional activity of the SV40 early and adenovirus major late promoters. In this experiment (Dynan and Tjian 1983a), the in vitro activities of the two promoters have been plotted as a function of the concentration of Sp1 added to the partially fractionated cell-free transcription system. Sp1 strongly activates the SV40 early promoter, whereas the adenovirus major late promoter is slightly inhibited by the addition of the factor. Although the experiment shown here utilized a relatively crude Sp1-containing fraction, identical results are obtained with homogeneous Sp1 preparations (Briggs et al. 1986). (*B*) Structure of the Sp1-responsive SV40 early promoter. This promoter contains a number of repeated structural features. The three 21-bp repeats actually contain six tandem repeats of a 10-bp element called a GC box. Deletion of the GC boxes eliminates the ability of the promoter to respond to Sp1.

viewed as proximal promoter elements, since, unlike the 72-bp repeat enhancer elements, their activity quickly dissipated as they were moved away from the transcriptional start site (Moreau et al. 1981). DNase I footprinting assays demonstrated that Sp1 bound directly to these GC-rich sequence elements (Fig. 2A) (Dynan and Tjian 1983b). Thus, Sp1 appeared to represent a eukaryotic counterpart of prokaryotic activators such as the cAMP receptor protein (CRP) or the cI protein of bacteriophage λ, since it was able to bind sequences close to the start site

A

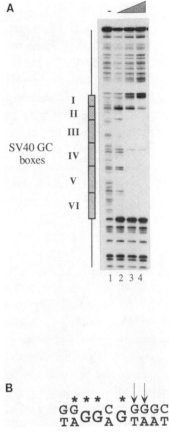

SV40 GC
boxes

I
II
III
IV
V
VI

1 2 3 4

B

★ ★ ★   ★ ↓ ↓
GG   C   GGGC
  GG   G
TA   A   TAAT

Figure 2 Sp1 binds GC boxes. (*A*) DNase I footprint assay. Purified Sp1 specifically protects the GC boxes in the 21-bp repeat region from DNase I digestion.
(*B*) The consensus Sp1-binding site. This consensus sequence is derived from a
wide variety of Sp1-binding sites (Kadonaga et al. 1988a). Most good Sp1-
binding sites do not differ from this consensus at more than one position. A
recent analysis of GC boxes from several hundred RNA pol II promoters
(Bucher 1990) confirms the consensus shown here. However, the consensus sequence derived from that analysis contains a few additional degeneracies, and
the conservation was observed to extend two additional base pairs in each direction. The binding of Sp1 to this site alters the rate at which purine residues are
methylated by DMS (Gidoni et al. 1984). Stars indicate the positions of protection from methylation and arrows indicate the positions of enhanced methylation. Interestingly, only the strand shown exhibits a DMS footprint. Neither en-
hancements nor protections are observed on the other strand.

and activate transcriptional initiation by RNA polymerase.
   At about the same time that Sp1 was first biochemically characterized, another eukaryotic sequence-specific transcription factor was iden-

tified in the form of the glucocorticoid receptor (GR). This protein was shown to bind and activate the LTR promoter of the mouse mammary tumor virus in a ligand-dependent manner (Payvar et al. 1983). Thus, two of the earliest identified RNA pol II sequence-specific factors were initially shown to bind viral promoters. Although both Sp1 and GR are cellular proteins, the possibility remained that sequence-specific transcriptional activators were normally utilized only by viral promoters in an effort to coopt the cellular transcriptional machinery. However, this notion was rapidly dispelled by the discovery that both of these factors can modulate the activity of a variety of cellular promoters. These include a bidirectional mouse promoter that was identified by virtue of its homology with the SV40 control region (Dynan et al. 1985) and the mouse dihydrofolate reductase (DHFR) promoter (Dynan et al. 1986) in the case of Sp1, and the lysozyme and uteroglobin promoters in the case of GR (for review, see Yamamoto 1985).

A comparison of a large variety of binding sites for Sp1 (Kadonaga et al. 1988a) led to the consensus 10-bp recognition sequence shown in Figure 2B. Most specific Sp1-binding sites do not differ from this consensus in more than one position, with the central residues tending to be the most highly conserved. Whereas the affinity of any given site is somewhat context-dependent, the consensus does have good predictive value (Bucher 1990). Dimethyl sulfate (DMS) protection and methylation interference studies demonstrate that Sp1 contacts DNA largely through interactions in the major groove (Gidoni et al. 1984, 1985; Holler et al. 1988). A combination of DMS and methidium propyl-EDTA (MPE) footprinting experiments suggests that the most important protein/DNA contacts are within the 10-bp recognition sequence (Fig. 2B) (Gidoni et al. 1984, 1985; Briggs et al. 1986; Holler et al. 1988). Sp1 is unable to bind simultaneously to adjacent sites if the center-to-center distance of these sites is less than 10 bp. Thus, Sp1 bound to the high-affinity GC box V in the SV40 control region sterically excludes Sp1 from binding to GC box IV, a site with an intrinsically lower affinity, since the center-to-center distance between these sites is only 9 bp (Gidoni et al. 1985).

The multiple adjacent binding sites for Sp1 within the SV40 control region are reminiscent of the operators of bacteriophage λ, which contain multiple adjacent binding sites for both the cro and cI repressors (Ptashne 1986). Binding of the cI protein to these adjacent operator sites is cooperative due to favorable protein:protein contacts between adjacently bound repressor molecules. Consequently, it was of interest to determine if Sp1 bound cooperatively to adjacent sites within the SV40 early promoter. However, mutagenesis of each of the GC boxes in SV40 had no discernible effect on the affinity of adjacent sites for Sp1 (Gidoni et al. 1985). Thus, Sp1 molecules bound to adjacent sites are apparently unable to make favorable protein:protein contacts.

There does not appear to be any common theme to the promoters that interact with Sp1. For example, Sp1 does not seem to regulate the differentiation of a single tissue type or the expression of a unified set of genes involved in a specific biological process. Some of the promoters to which Sp1 binds would be expected to be active in a wide variety of tissues at most times throughout the life of a vertebrate organism (so-called housekeeping genes). This does not imply, however, that Sp1 expression and activity are unregulated. Evidence for a role of Sp1 in developmentally regulated gene expression is presented in a subsequent section of this chapter.

PURIFICATION AND CLONING OF SP1

All the aforementioned studies, which examined the DNA binding and transcriptional properties of Sp1, utilized a relatively crude Sp1-containing protein fraction that was only about 1% pure. To determine the subunit composition of this factor and, in particular, to determine if the DNA binding and transcriptional functions of the Sp1 fraction were conferred by the same or different polypeptides, it was necessary to purify the protein to homogeneity. The availability of pure Sp1 would also facilitate studies of protein modifications. Finally, with pure Sp1 in hand, it would be relatively straightforward to isolate Sp1 cDNA and genomic clones, thereby facilitating a reverse genetic analysis of the function of this factor.

Before Sp1 could be purified further, formidable technical challenges needed to be overcome. In the years following the identification of Sp1, a number of DNA-binding activities that interacted with a variety of *cis*-regulatory elements had been identified. Attempts to purify these factors, any one of which might represent less than 0.01% of total cell protein, by conventional means were generally unsuccessful. These failures led many researchers to consider the possibility of using DNA affinity chromatography. Sequence-specific factors bind their target sites with high affinity and specificity. Thus, it would seem relatively straightforward to purify these factors on the basis of this sequence specificity. However, initial attempts to develop procedures for sequence-specific DNA affinity chromatography yielded disappointingly low degrees of purification. In retrospect, it is clear that this was because the nuclei of higher cells contain a host of nonspecific DNA-binding proteins that copurify, up to the stage of affinity chromatography, with the sequence-specific factors of interest. The solution to this problem turned out to be quite straightforward. Crude protein fractions were preincubated with nonspecific competitor DNAs (e.g., calf-thymus DNA or poly dI-dC) before being applied to columns in which the sequence-specific target site had been immobilized on a solid support. Under these conditions, nonspecific DNA-binding proteins associated with the soluble competitor DNA rather than with the immobilized recognition site, and thereby flowed through the column. The sequence-specific factor of interest bound to the column and could be subsequently eluted (usually with salt) in a significantly purified form (Kadonaga and Tjian 1986; for an alternative strategy, see Rosenfeld and Kelly 1986). Although this procedure was originally developed to purify Sp1, it has been successfully applied to a wide variety of sequence-specific DNA-binding proteins (see, e.g., Lee et al. 1987; Mitchell et al. 1987; Wu et al. 1987; Biggin et al. 1988; Santoro et al. 1988). A single round of sequence-specific affinity chromatography generally gives a few hundredfold purification, and two such cycles are usually sufficient to generate a homogeneous preparation of a sequence-specific transcription factor. The overall extent of purification achieved is often 10,000- to 20,000-fold.

When analyzed by denaturing gel electrophoresis, affinity-purified preparations of human Sp1 appeared as a heterogeneous array of bands centered around an apparent molecular mass of 100 kD with the two most prominent bands at 95 kD and 105 kD (Briggs et al. 1986; Jackson et al. 1990). Subsequent analysis showed that this heterogeneity was due to multiple posttranslational modifications of a single polypeptide (Jackson et al. 1990; S. Jackson and R. Tjian, unpubl.). Furthermore, homogeneous Sp1 preparations were found to be just as active in stimulating the in vitro transcription of GC-box-containing promoters as were the crude fractions used in earlier experiments (Briggs et al. 1986). Thus, it was apparent that the DNA binding and transcriptional functions of this factor were conferred by a single polypeptide.

Once purified Sp1 was in hand, it was possible to identify cDNA clones encoding this transcription factor. This was accomplished by determining a partial protein sequence and then designing oligonucleotide probes based on this sequence to screen a cDNA library. The resulting cDNA isolates (Kadonaga et al. 1987, 1988b) were found to encode a polypeptide of 778 amino acids that exhibited a number of interesting features. Near its carboxy-terminal end, Sp1 contains three tandemly repeated units bearing sequence similarity to the Cys-2His-2 zinc finger motif (Fig. 3A) first identified in the pol III transcription factor TFIIIA (Brown et al. 1985; Miller et al. 1985). Zinc fingers had previously been implicated in the DNA-binding activity of TFIIIA, and thus the zinc finger region in Sp1 represented an obvious candidate for the

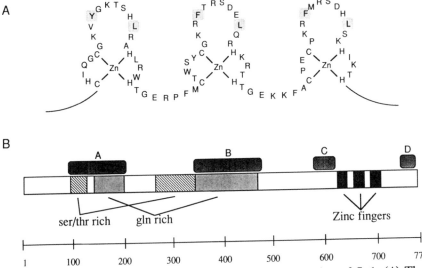

Figure 3 Relationship between the structure and the function of Sp1. (*A*) The Sp1 zinc fingers. Each finger is stabilized by a zinc cation that coordinates a pair of cysteine and a pair of histidine residues. Each finger is believed to fold into a globular structure consisting of both a two-stranded antiparallel β-sheet and an α-helix (Berg 1988; Parraga et al. 1988; Lee et al. 1989; Pavletich and Pabo 1991). The folding of this structure brings the shaded hydrophobic residues together at the center where they form an oily core. (*B*) The structural and functional features of Sp1. The positions of the glutamine-rich (~30% glutamine) and the serine/threonine rich (~50% serine and threonine residues) regions as well as the position of the DNA-binding zinc finger motifs are indicated. Above the sequence the approximate positions of the Sp1 activation domains are indicated. Domains A and B, which coincide with the glutamine-rich regions, are the two most potent activation domains. Domain D does not have an independent activation function but appears to interact with the glutamine-rich domains to somehow enhance their function. Domain D also plays an important role in transcriptional synergism. Domain C is a weak activator with a high density of basic amino acids.

DNA-binding domain of the protein. Strong support for this notion came from the finding that the DNA-binding activity of Sp1 has an absolute requirement for zinc cations (Kadonaga et al. 1987). Aside from the zinc fingers, the most noteworthy features of the Sp1 amino acid sequence are alternating serine/threonine-rich and glutamine-rich regions that constitute much of the amino-terminal two-thirds of the protein (Fig. 3B). In the following section, we outline experiments designed to investigate the relationship between structural and functional properties of Sp1.

STRUCTURE/FUNCTION RELATIONSHIPS

DNA Binding

The three tandemly arranged zinc finger motifs of Sp1 have been strongly implicated in the DNA-binding activity of the protein. Deleted forms of Sp1 lacking all the sequences either amino-terminal or carboxy-terminal to the zinc fingers were found to exhibit wild-type DNA-binding activity as judged by DNase I footprinting (Kadonaga et al. 1987, 1988b; Courey and Tjian 1988). In addition, point mutations that inactivate any one of the three zinc fingers (by replacing one of the crucial zinc-coordinating cysteine residues with another amino acid) have been shown to reduce the binding affinity of Sp1 by at least an order of magnitude (A.J. Courey and J. Ladika, unpubl.). Thus, the three zinc fingers are both necessary and sufficient for the DNA-binding activity of the protein.

Interestingly, the presence of zinc fingers in Sp1 was predicted in advance of the determination of the Sp1 sequence (Rhodes and Klug 1986). This prediction was based on a model for the structure of the zinc finger/DNA complex in which it was assumed that each finger would interact with about 5 bp of DNA. The finding that Sp1 contains three fingers, and that all three are required for the efficient recognition of a 10-bp target sequence, is more consistent with the DNA:protein interaction model initially proposed by Berg (1986, 1988, 1990) in which each turn of the helix was postulated to interact with three Cys-2His-2 zinc fingers. Experiments examining the relative binding specificities of wild-type and mutant forms of Sp1 and Krox-20 (an Sp1-related zinc finger protein) also strongly suggested that each zinc finger interacted with 3 bp of DNA (Nardelli et al. 1991). Finally, a recently published X-ray structure of the zif268 zinc finger domain bound to DNA (Pavletich and Pabo 1991) provides conclusive evidence in favor of the Berg model.

Transcriptional Activation

A Rapid and Sensitive Assay for Sp1 Transcriptional Activity

To study the transcriptional function of Sp1, a rapid in vivo assay for Sp1 mutants was needed in which wild-type and mutant Sp1 genes could be tested for their ability to complement an Sp1 deficiency. Such an assay required a host cell line that lacked endogenous Sp1 activity. Since Sp1-deficient mammalian cell lines were not available, we decided to test *Drosophila* tissue culture cells. Extracts of these cells contained no detectable Sp1-like DNA binding or transcriptional activity, yet they could respond to the inducing effect of Sp1. That is, exogenously added

Sp1 was capable of stimulating the transcription of Sp1-responsive promoters in soluble transcription extracts derived from *Drosophila* cells (Croston et al. 1991; U. Heberlein and A.J. Courey, unpubl.). With these findings in mind, a cotransfection assay for Sp1 activity was developed. In this assay, wild-type or mutant Sp1 genes were introduced into cultured *Drosophila* cells along with an Sp1-responsive reporter promoter fused to the gene encoding bacterial chloramphenicol acetyltransferase (CAT). The cells were subsequently lysed, and the CAT activity of the resulting extracts was taken as a measure of the transcriptional activity of the input Sp1 mutant. Using such an assay, it was possible to show that the rate of transcriptional initiation is exquisitely sensitive to the presence or absence of functional forms of Sp1. Depending on the reporter promoter, induction levels of up to 500-fold were routinely obtained (Courey and Tjian 1988).

The Transcriptional Activation and DNA-binding Functions of Sp1 Can Be Uncoupled

The finding that Sp1 can activate transcription in reconstituted cell-free systems argues against models for transcriptional activation involving changes in chromatin structure or targeting to subnuclear locales such as the nuclear matrix. However, two other models for Sp1-mediated transcriptional activation remained tenable. In the first, Sp1 was postulated to induce a change in the DNA structure upon binding to the promoter. This altered DNA structure would then serve as a preferred template for the general transcriptional machinery. According to this model, DNA binding should be intimately coupled to a critical structural change in the template. It should therefore be difficult or impossible to uncouple DNA binding from transcriptional activation. Mutations that eliminate or severely alter the DNA-binding activity of Sp1 should also eliminate the activation function. Conversely, structural alterations that do not affect DNA binding should not affect the ability of the factor to activate transcription. In the alternative model, DNA binding would serve only to tether Sp1 to the template where it could then interact with the general transcriptional machinery, either directly or indirectly, to stimulate initiation. In this case, it might be possible to uncouple the DNA binding and transcriptional activation functions of Sp1 by mutagenesis.

A number of experiments have demonstrated that the aforementioned uncoupling is, in fact, possible. First, an amino-terminal deletion of Sp1 that extends to the amino-terminal border of the zinc finger region was found to inactivate this protein in the *Drosophila* cell culture assay without significantly affecting the DNA-binding properties of the factor or its ability to accumulate in the nucleus (Courey and Tjian 1988). Second, when the amino-terminal two-thirds of Sp1 (lacking the zinc finger domain) was attached to the transcriptionally inactive GAL4 DNA-binding domain, the fusion protein efficiently activated transcription of promoters containing GAL4-binding sites (G. Gill, unpubl.). Finally, in a phenomenon known as superactivation, DNA-binding-deficient forms of Sp1 were able to interact with DNA-binding-competent forms of the factor to stimulate transcription synergistically (Courey et al. 1989). Superactivation is discussed more fully later in this chapter. These findings strongly support a model whereby Sp1 binds to the template and then activates the basic transcriptional apparatus through protein:protein interactions. Experiments designed to explore the factors involved in this interaction (coactivators) are discussed at the end of this chapter.

The Discovery of a Class of Activation Domains Rich in Glutamine Residues

What amino acid sequences, in addition to the zinc fingers of Sp1, are required for the activation of Sp1-responsive promoters? In other words, what is the nature of the transcriptional activation domain(s) of Sp1? The answer to this question was something of a surprise (Fig. 3B). First, with the use of both the *Drosophila* cell cotransfection assay and in vitro transcription assays, Sp1 was found to contain multiple independent activation domains (Courey and Tjian 1988; Kadonaga et al. 1988b). Second, the two most potent of these domains were found to correspond to the two glutamine-rich regions in the amino-terminal portion of the protein. These domains are characterized by the presence of about 30% glutamine residues and by an almost total lack of charged amino acid residues. Their primary structure is distinct from the acidic domains characterized by the groups of Ptashne and Struhl in studies of GAL4 (see Gann et al., this volume) and GCN4 (see Struhl et al., this volume). The activation domains of Sp1 also differ from the proline-rich activation domains exemplified by the CAAT-box binding transcription factor (CTF) (Mermod et al. 1989).

We suspect that the glutamine-rich activation domains of Sp1 are actually prototypes for a large class of functionally related activation regions. This is because a number of eukaryotic transcriptional regulators, including many DNA-binding proteins involved in the control of *Drosophila* embryogenesis, contain glutamine-rich regions (Courey and Tjian 1988). Indeed, we have shown that a glutamine-rich region from the *Drosophila Antp* protein can functionally replace the glutamine-rich regions normally present in Sp1 (Courey et al. 1989). In addition, embryo injection assays using mutant forms of the *Drosophila bicoid* gene have shown that a glutamine-rich region in the transcription factor encoded by that gene is required for its ability to activate the *hunchback* promoter (Driever et al. 1989). Furthermore, glutamine-rich sequences in the Oct-2 (Tanaka and Herr 1990) transcription factor and in the CREB transcription factor (Gonzalez et al. 1991) have been implicated in the activation function of those proteins. Although at present obscure, the molecular mechanisms by which glutamine-rich domains activate transcription represent an active topic of investigation.

SP1 CAN ACT FROM BOTH PROXIMAL AND DISTAL SITES

The SV40 early promoter was one of the first eukaryotic transcriptional control regions to be characterized in detail (Benoist and Chambon 1981; Fromm and Berg 1982). These early studies established a dichotomy between proximal promoter elements and enhancer elements. Proximal promoter elements, which include the 21-bp repeats, were thought to function only when located within 100–200 bp of the transcriptional start site (Moreau et al. 1981), whereas enhancer elements, of which the SV40 72-bp repeats were the first known example, remain functional even when placed several thousand base pairs upstream or downstream from the transcriptional start site (Banerji et al. 1981). Consequently, Sp1, which binds the GC boxes of the 21-bp repeats, has usually been considered a proximal promoter factor that could only activate transcription when bound close to the transcriptional start site. However, we decided to reassess the distance dependence of Sp1 transcriptional activity using the *Drosophila* cell cotransfection assay (Courey et al. 1989). Such experiments involved the use of reporter templates containing a single proximal GC box located 50 bp upstream of the transcriptional start site of the CAT reporter, multiple distal GC boxes located 1.7 kb downstream from the start site, or a combination of proximal and distal GC boxes (Fig. 4A). When assayed independently, the single proximal box or the multiple distal boxes were found to mediate only a weak or moderate Sp1 response. However, when combined, the distal and proximal GC boxes acted synergistically to give a strong Sp1 response that was far greater than the additive effects of the proximal and distal sites. Given these results, why had previous attempts to demonstrate enhancer-like activity of GC boxes failed? The answer comes from the finding that, in the absence of proximal GC boxes, distal GC boxes are only functional in the presence of high concentrations of Sp1. Since past transfection assays had relied on the low levels of endogenous Sp1 normally present in mammalian cell lines, the activity of distant binding sites was not detected. Using the cotransfection assay, we were able to supply the tenfold higher concentration of Sp1 required to observe the activity of distal GC boxes. These results raise the possibility that there may, in fact, be no fundamental distinction between proximal promoter factors and enhancer factors.

Sp1:Sp1 Interactions and DNA Looping

The finding that proximal and distal GC boxes can activate transcription synergistically suggests that distantly tethered molecules of Sp1 are able to interact with one another in a functionally productive manner. We were interested to determine if this synergistic interaction required that

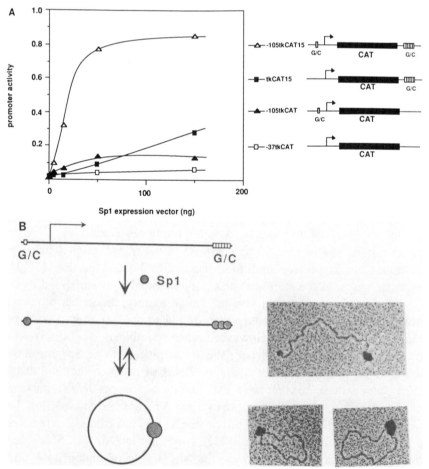

Figure 4 (See facing page for legend.)

to glutamine residues (Lees-Miller and Anderson 1989; S. Lees-Miller, unpubl.). Although it is not clear how this modification activates Sp1, we favor the idea that phosphorylation induces a conformational change that activates the glutamine-rich domains. This type of regulation could serve to prevent the formation of nonproductive complexes between Sp1 and the general transcriptional apparatus in the absence of DNA. If so, this might explain why abnormally high intracellular concentrations of the glutamine-rich domains do not repress transcription as is the case with acidic activation domains (Gill and Ptashne 1988).

The phosphorylation of Sp1 in vivo is dependent on the DNA-binding activity of the protein even though the sites of modification (which are similar or identical to the sites of in vitro modification) are outside the DNA-binding domain (Jackson et al. 1990). This strongly suggests that the same DNA-dependent protein kinase that was found to modify Sp1 in cell extracts also modifies the protein in vivo. Infection of cells with SV40 was shown to result in a significant increase in the extent of Sp1 phosphorylation (Jackson et al. 1990). This may simply reflect an increase in the intracellular concentration of Sp1-binding sites as the viral DNA replicates. Alternatively, viral infection may directly stimulate kinase activity, or inhibit the opposing phosphatase enzyme, thereby stimulating the expression of the early viral transcription unit. The possibility that the virus could inhibit an opposing phosphatase is attractive, since the SV40 small T antigen specifically interacts with protein phosphatase IIA (Pallas et al. 1990).

COMMUNICATION BETWEEN SP1 AND THE GENERAL TRANSCRIPTIONAL APPARATUS REQUIRES COACTIVATOR PROTEINS

The finding that the DNA binding and transcriptional activation functions of Sp1 can be uncoupled by mutagenesis suggests that the activation domains interact directly with some other protein factor to stimulate transcriptional initiation. The direct substrate for Sp1 action could be RNA pol II itself (which consists of at least 10 distinct polypeptides, Lewis and Burgess 1982; Sentenac et al., this volume), one of the general transcription factors (Saltzman and Weinmann 1989; Buratowski and Sharp, this volume), or a previously uncharacterized factor. Attempts to demonstrate a direct interaction between RNA pol II and Sp1 have been unsuccessful. In particular, the speculation that Sp1 might interact with the carboxy-terminal heptapeptide repeat tail of the pol II large subunit appears to be unfounded, since deletion of this tail does not adversely affect Sp1-mediated transcriptional activation (Zehring and Greenleaf 1990).

Does Sp1 interact with one of the general transcriptional factors?

Thus far, investigations aimed at addressing this question have focused on the TATA-box-binding factor TFIID. This particular factor was chosen for two reasons. First, binding of TFIID to the template appears to be a rate-limiting step in assembly of an active transcription complex (Fire et al. 1984; Hawley and Roeder 1985). Consequently, this step would seem to be a likely target for regulatory factors. Second, a number of other sequence-specific factors such as USF (Sawadogo and Roeder 1985) and ATF (Horikoshi et al. 1988) have been shown to interact with TFIID on the DNA.

As expected, Sp1 is able to stimulate the transcription of GC-box-containing promoters in a reconstituted system containing RNA pol II, TFIID, and the other previously defined general transcription factor fractions (TFIIA, TFIIB, TFIIE, and TFIIF) (Pugh and Tjian 1990). Surprisingly, however, when the relatively crude TFIID fractions were replaced with highly purified yeast TFIID, Sp1 was unable to stimulate transcriptional initiation, despite the fact that basal level promoter activity was unaffected. Likewise, transcription systems reconstituted with the expressed products of either the human (Peterson et al. 1990) or *Drosophila* (Hoey et al. 1990) TFIID genes, in place of the crude TFIID fraction, were also unresponsive to Sp1. Thus, the crude human TFIID fraction seems to contain one or more uncharacterized factors required for Sp1-mediated transcriptional activation. We have referred to these factors as coactivators. It has been postulated that these factors act as a bridge between Sp1 and TFIID (Fig. 6), since truncation of the amino-terminal portion of TFIID blocks the action of the coactivator. However, numerous alternative models might also explain the data (Ptashne and Gann 1990). For example, Sp1 may interact directly with TFIID, and this interaction may then induce a conformational change in TFIID, allowing it to interact productively with the coactivator.

These newly discovered coactivator proteins may represent a novel class of transcription factors. Different classes of activation domains may interact with different coactivators to stimulate transcriptional initiation. Indeed, the evidence for multiple coactivators is steadily mounting (Triezenberg et al. 1988; Berger et al. 1990; Kelleher et al. 1990; Pugh and Tjian 1990). By providing another level of specificity in the pathway to transcriptional initiation, coactivators could increase the potential for diverse cell-type-specific patterns of gene expression. For example, a developing organism could contain overlapping but noncoincident domains of expression of Sp1 and its cognate coactivator. Only where these domains overlap would Sp1-responsive genes be switched on. An additional level of diversity could be available if factors such as Sp1 utilize different sets of coactivators in conjunction with different types of basal

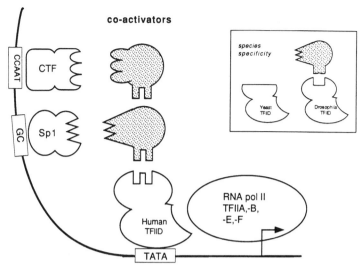

Figure 6   Possible mechanism for the action of coactivators. In this model (Pugh and Tjian 1990), the coactivators are postulated to act as bridges between TFIID and promoter-selective factors. Sp1 and CTF, which contain different types of activation domains, are predicted to activate transcription via different coactivators. The model accounts for the inability of yeast TFIID to mediate Sp1-responsive transcription by postulating that yeast TFIID is unable to interface with the appropriate coactivator. Furthermore, the available data suggest that, whereas the Sp1/coactivator interface has been conserved between *Drosophila* and vertebrates, the coactivator/TFIID interface has diverged such that *Drosophila* TFIID cannot interact with the human coactivator.

level promoter elements. Evidence that this might be the case is provided by the finding that an additional coactivator (the "tethering factor") is required for Sp1-mediated activation of promoters lacking TATA boxes. Only where the domains of expression of Sp1 and both its coactivators overlap would one expect to observe expression of the subset of Sp1-responsive genes that lack TATA boxes. Thus, coactivators add a new dimension to the combinatorial array of transcription factors regulating the temporal and spatial patterns of gene expression.

Interestingly, a number of viral *trans*-activators have many of the properties associated with coactivators. For example, both VP16 and E1A, which do not bind DNA with high specificity on their own, have been shown to stimulate transcription by forming complexes with cellular sequence-specific transcription factors (Stern et al. 1989; Liu and Green 1990). Thus, these *trans*-activator proteins may co-opt the cellular transcriptional machinery by functioning as viral analogs of cellular coactivator proteins.

Currently, biochemical approaches are being used to isolate and characterize coactivators. For example, it has been shown that TFIID, as purified from eukaryotic cell extracts, is actually a complex of the TATA-binding protein (TBP) and several tightly bound polypeptides called TBP-associated factors (TAFS; Dynlacht et al. 1991). With the use of denaturants, it has been possible to separate the TAFs from TBP and to show that one or more of the TAF polypeptides confer coactivator function.

It may also be possible to use genetic approaches to identify coactivators. For example, genetic studies of yeast transcription (see, e.g., Winston, this volume) have identified many genes that are required for transcriptional initiation. Some of these genes encode proteins of known function (e.g., TFIID), whereas some encode proteins that have not been functionally characterized. Perhaps some of the members of the latter class will be found to encode coactivator proteins. In addition, since yeast appear to lack some of the coactivators present in other organisms (Pugh and Tjian 1990), it may be possible to clone higher eukaryotic coactivators by genetic complementation in yeast.

CONCLUSIONS AND PERSPECTIVE

In summary, the studies of Sp1 described in this chapter have provided insight into the mechanisms of eukaryotic transcriptional control. The discovery of Sp1 helped establish the idea that eukaryotic gene regulation utilizes promoter-specific transcription factors and that these factors can bind directly to *cis*-regulatory DNA elements. Methods developed to purify Sp1 have proven applicable to a wide variety of sequence-specific DNA-binding proteins. The finding that Sp1 is active in *Drosophila* cells not only provided a convenient assay system for this and other factors, but also helped to demonstrate that the mechanisms of eukaryotic transcriptional control are highly conserved. Studies with this heterologous system provide support for the idea that the activity of distally bound factors may be mediated by direct protein:protein interactions with proximally bound factors. The reverse genetic analysis of Sp1 has also revealed a novel class of glutamine-rich activation domains. These studies reinforce the idea that transcription factors can be remarkably modular proteins comprising multiple structurally distinct functional domains. Studies of the posttranslation modification of Sp1 have revealed two types of modification, O-linked glycosylation and DNA-dependent phosphorylation, both of which may play important regulatory roles. Finally, in vitro studies in which the activity of Sp1 has been examined in cell-free systems from diverse organisms have helped to reveal

polymerase II transcription. *FASEB J.* **3:** 1723–1733.

Santoro, C., N. Mermod, P.C. Andrews, and R. Tjian. 1988. Cloning of cDNAs encoding human CCAAT-box binding proteins: A family of transcription and replication factors. *Nature* **334:** 218–224.

Saragosti, S., G. Moyne, and M. Yaniv. 1980. Absence of nucleosomes in a fraction of SV40 chromatin between the origin of replication and the region coding for the late leader RNA. *Cell* **20:** 65–73.

Sawadogo, M. and R.G. Roeder. 1985. Interaction of a gene-specific transcription factor with the adenovirus major late promoter upstream of the TATA box region. *Cell* **43:** 165–175.

Stadler, J., A. Larsen, J.D. Engel, M. Dolan, M. Groudine, and H. Weintraub. 1980. Tissue-specific DNA cleavages in the globin chromatin domain introduced by DNAse I. *Cell* **20:** 451–460.

Stern, S., M. Tanaka, and W. Herr. 1989. The Oct-1 homoeodomain directs formation of a multiprotein-DNA complex with the HSV transactivator VP16. *Nature* **341:** 624–630.

Su, W., S.P. Jackson, R. Tjian, and H. Echols. 1991. DNA Looping between sites for transcriptional activation—Self-association of DNA-bound SP1. *Genes Dev.* **5:** 820–826.

Tanaka, M. and W. Herr. 1990. Differential transcriptional activation by Oct-1 and Oct-2: Interdependent activation domains induce Oct-2 phosphorylation. *Cell* **60:** 375–386.

Triezenberg, S.J., S.L. LaMarco, and S.L. McKnight. 1988. Evidence of DNA: Protein interactions that mediate HSV-1 immediate early gene activation by VP16. *Genes Dev.* **2:** 730–742.

Weintraub, H. and M. Groudine. 1976. Chromosomal subunits in active genes have an altered conformation. *Science* **193:** 848–856.

Workman, J.L., S.M. Abmayr, W.A. Cromlish, and R.G. Roeder. 1988. Transcriptional regulation by the immediate early protein of pseudorabies virus during in vitro nucleosome assembly. *Cell* **55:** 211–219.

Wu, C. 1980. The 5′ ends of *Drosophila* heat shock genes in chromatin are hypersensitive to DNase I. *Nature* **286:** 854–860.

Wu, C., S. Wilson, B. Walker, I. Dawid, T. Paisley, V. Zimarino, and H. Ueda. 1987. Purification and properties of *Drosophila* heat shock activator protein. *Science* **238:** 1247–1253.

Yamamoto, K.R. 1985. Steroid receptor regulated transcription of specific genes and gene networks. *Annu. Rev. Genet.* **19:** 209–252.

Zehring, W.A. and A.L. Greenleaf. 1990. The carboxyl-terminal repeat domain of RNA polymerase II is not required for transcription factor Sp1 to function in vitro. *J. Biol. Chem.* **265:** 8351–8353.

29
CCAAT/Enhancer Binding Protein

Steven L. McKnight
Howard Hughes Research Laboratories
Department of Embryology
Carnegie Institution of Washington
Baltimore, Maryland 21210

OVERVIEW

In this chapter, I review the biochemical and regulatory properties of CCAAT/enhancer binding protein (C/EBP). The active form of C/EBP is composed of two polypeptide chains held together by short amphipathic α helices. The dimer interface, termed the "leucine zipper," mimics the intertwining of α helices in coiled-coil proteins such as keratins and lamins. A polypeptide segment immediately amino-terminal to the leucine zipper is rich in basic amino acids. Dimerization brings two such "basic regions" into close apposition, forming a bivalent DNA contact surface. The basic regions are structurally disordered in the absence of DNA but become α helical once bound. At least five distinct C/EBP-related proteins have been described; all bind DNA in a manner similar to C/EBP and can form mixed dimers in vitro. The amino acid sequences of the C/EBP-related proteins are strikingly similar in the basic and leucine zipper regions, yet differ markedly outside the DNA-binding domain. Various lines of evidence have indicated that the originally defined form of C/EBP, now termed C/EBPα, may play a key role in terminal cell differentiation. Its temporal pattern of expression is tightly correlated to the conversion of 3T3-L1 fibroblasts into nondividing, fat-laden adipocytes. Antisense inhibition of C/EBPα expression blocks adipocyte conversion. Moreover, premature expression of C/EBPα stimulates the terminal differentiation of adipocytes and causes arrest of mitotic growth in a variety of cultured cell types.

INTRODUCTION

Studies on C/EBP began in 1984, when Peter Johnson and Barbara Graves were searching independently for proteins in rat liver nuclear ex-

Present address: Tularik, Inc., 270 East Grand Avenue, South San Francisco, California 94080.

tracts that might bind to promoter elements of the herpes simplex virus (HSV) thymidine kinase (TK) gene and the long terminal repeat (LTR) of Moloney murine sarcoma virus (MoMSV). A heat-stable activity capable of binding selectively to the CCAAT elements of the TK promoter and MoMSV LTR was initially identified and partially purified (Graves et al. 1986). In addition, the same extracts contained a factor that bound selectively to the enhancer "core homology" of several tumor viruses including MoMSV, simian virus 40 (SV40), and polyomavirus. The activities responsible for both CCAAT and enhancer core binding copurified as a single polypeptide denoted C/EBP (Johnson et al. 1987).

Partial amino acid sequence of purified C/EBP facilitated cloning of a cDNA capable of encoding a 42-kD polypeptide (Landschulz et al. 1988b). The initially purified, 20-kD polypeptide proved to be a proteolytic fragment of C/EBP; indeed, fragments as small as 14 kD retained DNA-binding activity and could be purified from rat liver nuclear extracts (Landschulz et al. 1988b). The localization of proteolytic digestion sites provided evidence that the C/EBP DNA-binding domain was near the carboxyl terminus of the intact protein.

The availability of a cDNA clone encoding C/EBP allowed production of large amounts of easily purified protein in bacterial cells. Such protein, in turn, expedited functional studies. In addition, the deduced amino acid sequence of C/EBP revealed similarities with the products of several proto-oncogenes, leading to speculations regarding a newly defined group of DNA-binding proteins (Landschulz et al. 1988a). Finally, the cloned gene facilitated studies of the tissue and cell-type distribution of C/EBP (Birkenmeier et al. 1989) and provided a means of isolating a family of closely related genes that encode C/EBP-like proteins (Cao et al. 1991; Williams et al. 1991).

This chapter reviews information that has been gained from studies of C/EBP. The first half of the chapter focuses on the biochemical properties of C/EBP and related proteins that bind to DNA via the basic region-leucine zipper (bZIP) motif. The second half of the chapter outlines attempts to define other functional activities associated with C/EBP and presents information derived from studies of C/EBP-related proteins. I hereby summarize the known properties of C/EBP and provide a framework for future studies of its more paradoxical properties.

Identification and Purification of C/EBP

Early work on transcriptional control elements associated with the promoter of the HSV TK gene and LTR of MoMSV led to the definition of several distinct *cis*-regulatory motifs (McKnight and Kingsbury 1982;

Graves et al. 1985). DNA fragments bearing these regulatory DNA sequences were used in DNase I footprinting assays to detect sequence-specific DNA-binding proteins in soluble extracts prepared from rat liver nuclei. Such assays revealed a proteinaceous activity that bound selectively to regions encompassing the CCAAT motifs of the two viral DNAs (Graves et al. 1986). This activity was designated CCAAT-binding protein (CBP).

Barbara Graves's initial studies on CBP revealed four unusual properties. First, its sequence-specific DNA-binding activity was heat-stable. Second, its DNase I footprint was asymmetric relative to the CCAAT sequence, extending substantially upstream of the first cytosine residue but only minimally downstream from the terminal thymine residue. Third, point mutational studies revealed extensive degeneracy in DNA sequence specificity. Whereas relatively dramatic reductions in CBP binding were observed when adenosine to cytosine transversions were introduced at the third and fourth positions of the consensus, cytosine to guanine and thymine to guanine transversions at the second and fifth positions reduced binding affinity only modestly. Finally, a cytosine to guanine transversion at the first position of the consensus, whether tested in the context of the TK promoter or the MoMSV LTR, created a more avid CBP substrate (Graves et al. 1986).

It was initially assumed that mammalian cells, including hepatocytes, might rely on a single DNA-binding protein to act at all CCAAT homologies. Concurrent work provided evidence for multiple CCAAT-binding proteins including NF1/CTF (Jones and Tjian 1985), CPC/HAP2 (Chodosh et al. 1988), and NFY (Dorn et al. 1988). Indeed, in retrospect, our own observation that cytosine to guanine transversions in the CCAAT motifs of the TK promoter and MoMSV LTR impeded transcription initiation while creating higher-affinity substrates for CBP (Graves et al. 1986) was inconsistent with an activating role for CBP in the transcription of these two genes. The question arose, therefore, as to whether CBP represented a bona fide transcription factor. Moreover, if it did, what were its functionally relevant target genes?

Because the CBP footprint was asymmetric with respect to the CCAAT homologies in the TK promoter and MoMSV LTR, the underlying sequences were inspected for clues regarding the nature of its optimal binding site. Such analyses led to the speculation that the true CBP substrate was dyad-symmetric, consisting of directly abutted half-sites bearing the pentanucleotide sequence 5'-GCAAT-3' (Graves et al. 1986). Comparisons of a large number of CBP-binding sites supported this interpretation, assigning particular emphasis to the juxtaposition of two consecutive thymine residues separated by three or four base pairs from a consecutive pair of adenine residues (Ryden and Beemon 1989). The definition of an optimal binding site implied that CBP might act as a dimer but did not indicate how the protein might interact with divergent DNA substrates.

The purification of a single polypeptide corresponding to CBP did little to clarify the issue of DNA-binding specificity. Peter Johnson, working with the same rat liver nuclear extracts that had been used for the identification and initial characterization of CBP, used DNase I footprinting to track purification of an enhancer core binding activity. The enhancer core motif had been identified in the intergenic control regions of SV40 (Zenke et al. 1986) and polyomavirus (Herbomel et al. 1984), and in the LTR of MoMSV (Graves et al. 1985). Footprinting and methylation protection assays indicated that Johnson's activity bound in a similar manner to the enhancer core motifs of each of these viruses, and, like CBP, was heat-stable. Surprisingly, the CCAAT and enhancer core binding activities copurified as a single, 20-kD polypeptide (Johnson et al. 1987).

Two divergent assessments of our work emerged at this point. I, on the one hand, felt that a protein capable of binding to CCAAT and enhancer core motifs simply had to be interesting and important. Graves and Johnson were more circumspect, considering the possibility that their efforts had been misdirected and favoring renaming the protein either McBind-all or McScription factor.

Cloning of the C/EBP Gene

Bill Landschulz, working with Graves and Johnson, succeeded in deriving partial amino acid sequence from a proteolytic fragment of the binding factor. A 14-amino-acid peptide was synthesized and used to generate antiserum in rabbits. The antiserum led, in turn, to the cloning of an encoding cDNA (Landschulz et al. 1988b). The bacterially expressed translation product was shown to footprint both the CCAAT motif and the enhancer core homology. Subsequent to Landschulz's study, the polypeptide was ignominiously denoted CCAAT/enhancer binding protein (C/EBP).

Sequence Relatedness to Myc and Fos and Conception of the Leucine Zipper

A search of the National Biomedical Research Fund (NBRF) protein data base revealed a region of amino acid sequence similarity between a carboxy-terminal segment of C/EBP and the products of the *myc* and *fos* proto-oncogenes. Because a proteolytic fragment consisting of the carboxy-terminal 14 kD of C/EBP retained sequence-specific affinity for DNA (Landschulz et al. 1988b), it was assumed that the Myc- and Fos-related regions might help pinpoint aspects of C/EBP important for its role in DNA binding. The Myc-related region of C/EBP, located between amino acid residues 313 and 336, contained 14 identities. The Fos-related region, located between residues 286 and 400, was marked by 9 identities and was centered within a polypeptide segment rich in arginine and lysine residues.

Further inspection of the C/EBP sequence revealed a lack of proline and glycine residues within the 50 amino acids that spanned the Myc- and Fos-related regions, and led to speculation that the DNA-binding domain of C/EBP might be largely α helical. Moreover, the analogous regions of Fos and Myc, nuclear proteins whose functions were otherwise not understood at the time, were also free of prolines and glycines. We imagined that the related, helix-permissive regions of C/EBP, Myc, and Fos might represent a common protein structural motif tailored for specific interaction with DNA, and that Myc and Fos, like C/EBP, might turn out to be site-specific DNA-binding proteins.

In an inspired and independent move, Landschulz plotted the helix-permissive sequence of C/EBP on a "helical wheel." Such a display revealed a heptad repeat of leucine residues covering 35 amino acids. Similarly spaced leucine repeats were also apparent in the Myc and Fos sequences. Given the hydrophobic nature of the leucine side chain and the amphipathic distribution of leucines in the putative α helices of the three proteins, we hypothesized that this motif might represent a dimerization interface (Landschulz et al. 1988a). Because each of the proteins exhibited a strict heptad repeat of leucines, the hypothetical structure was termed the leucine zipper (Fig. 1). The zipper was imagined as a simple molecular nexus, bringing the adjacent, arginine- and lysine-rich polypeptide regions into close apposition. This paired set of basic regions, rather than the zipper, was predicted to represent the protein surface that would mediate direct contact with DNA.

We suggested that leucine side chains of one polypeptide might interdigitate along the longitudinal helical axis with those of its partner, creating either a parallel or antiparallel dimer interface (Landschulz et al. 1988a). Using an innovative strategy, O'Shea, Kim, and colleagues provided clear evidence for the parallel association of the GCN4 leucine zipper (O'Shea et al. 1989). More importantly, they proposed that the interacting surfaces corresponded to the traditional coiled-coil intertwining of α helices. Thus, instead of interdigitating along the longitudinal helical axis, analogous to the teeth of a zipper, leucine residues of one helix

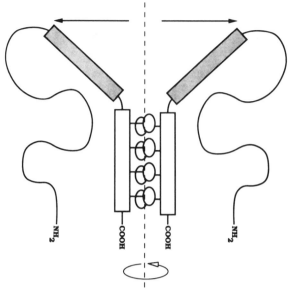

Figure 1 Schematic model of C/EBP DNA-binding domain. Two C/EBP polypeptide chains are joined by their respective leucine zippers. Dashed line reflects an axis of twofold rotational symmetry. Shaded rectangles represent basic regions that are presumed to make direct contact with dyad half-sites represented by abutted arrows. (Reprinted, with permission, from Landschulz et al. 1989 [Copyright held by the AAAS].)

were predicted to be disposed in a lateral orientation with respect to the leucines of its helical partner. Thus, although the original leucine zipper idea (Landschulz et al. 1988a) was based on Francis Crick's "knobs and holes" model for α-helical intertwining (Crick 1952), we did not appreciate that the zipper would fit that model perfectly. Recent X-ray crystallographic studies of the leucine zipper of GCN4 confirmed the predictions of O'Shea and colleagues (1991) and provided the first high-resolution structure for a coiled-coil pair of α helices.

Two C/EBP relatives, the yeast transcription factor GCN4 and the product of the *jun* proto-oncogene, added information important for development of the leucine zipper idea. In the case of GCN4, Hope and Struhl (1986) provided strong evidence for dimerization and showed that the dimer-forming region of GCN4 was close to or coincident with the DNA-binding domain. Like C/EBP, GCN4 bound to a symmetric site on DNA consisting of directly abutted half-sites (Hill et al. 1986). In addition, both Jun and GCN4 contained within their DNA-binding domain heptad repeats of leucine residues just carboxy-terminal to segments rich in basic amino acids. However, unlike C/EBP and GCN4, which were understood to function as homodimers, Jun could be detected in a heteromeric complex with Fos, forming a sequence-specific DNA-binding activity termed AP1 (Franza et al. 1988; Rauscher et al. 1988a,b; Turner and Tjian 1989). Thus, Fos and Jun were predicted to heterodimerize through their respective zippers (Landschulz et al. 1988a). Extensive evidence supporting the role of leucine zippers in the dimerization of GCN4 and Fos:Jun has subsequently appeared (see Struhl; Curran and Vogt; both this volume).

To assess the role of the leucine zipper in dimerization of C/EBP, amino acid substitutions were systematically introduced into the hypothetical dimer interface. Mutant proteins were synthesized in bacteria and tested for dimerization by glutaraldehyde-mediated cross-linking. Such studies provided clear evidence for C/EBP dimerization and showed that dimerization could be inhibited by subtle mutations in the leucine repeat motif (Landschulz et al. 1989). Moreover, a strict concordance was observed between dimer-forming ability and DNA binding.

Although an intact leucine zipper was inferred to be critical for C/EBP and related proteins to bind DNA, direct substrate contact was assumed to occur through the adjacent basic region. Consistent with this hypothesis, mutations in the basic region of C/EBP resulted in proteins that retained dimer-forming activity yet failed to bind DNA (Landschulz et al. 1989). Indeed, such proteins displayed dominant inhibitory effects on DNA binding by native C/EBP. It thus appeared that the active conformation of C/EBP required the zipper-mediated joining of two intact basic regions.

A second experiment undertaken to examine the role of the basic region entailed the construction and assay of chimeric proteins composed in part of C/EBP and GCN4 (Agre et al. 1989). These studies revealed that a chimera containing the basic region of C/EBP and the leucine zipper of GCN4 bound to the C/EBP-specific DNA-binding site, whereas a chimera containing the basic region of GCN4 and the leucine zipper of C/EBP bound selectively to the GCN4 recognition site.

Perhaps the most convincing evidence that DNA contact is mediated through the basic regions of this class of proteins came from studies of synthetic GCN4 peptides. A synthetic peptide 33 residues in length and corresponding to the basic region of GCN4 was covalently cross-linked through its carboxyl terminus by a disulfide bond. This fused peptide displayed specific affinity for DNA; upon reduction of the disulfide bond, DNA-binding activity was abrogated (Talanian et al. 1990). This imaginative experiment showed that a paired set of basic regions could make specific contact with DNA in the absence of the leucine zipper. Thus, in the context of the intact proteins, the leucine zippers are necessary but not sufficient for DNA binding. The class of proteins (C/EBP, GCN4, Fos, and Jun) requiring both basic region and zipper have been termed bZIP proteins. This distinction may be useful, because certain DNA-binding proteins rely on leucine zippers that are not immediately adjacent to a basic region (Gregor et al. 1990; Fisher et al. 1991; Ruezinsky et al. 1991), and others contain a basic region without an associated zipper (Bowerman et al. 1992).

Scissors-grip Model for DNA-bound C/EBP

An understanding of six properties of C/EBP and other bZIP proteins led to a speculative model for the structure of the DNA-bound bZIP segment (Vinson et al. 1989). First, the dimerization interface corresponds to the leucine zipper (Landschulz et al. 1988a). Second, the paired zippers associate in parallel (O'Shea et al. 1989). Third, the basic region located just amino-terminal to the zipper represents the DNA contact surface (Agre et al. 1989; Landschulz et al. 1989; Talanian et al. 1990). Fourth, the optimal binding sites for bZIP proteins consist of directly abutted, dyad-symmetric half-sites (Graves et al. 1986; Hill et al. 1986). Fifth, the basic region in all bZIP proteins resides at a fixed and invariant position relative to the leucine zipper (Landschulz et al. 1988b; Agre et al. 1989; Vinson et al. 1989). Sixth, the entire bZIP region is free of helix-destabilizing proline and glycine residues (Vinson et al. 1989).

On the basis of this information, it was proposed that the DNA contact surfaces of bZIP proteins might emerge from the dimer interface in a manner analogous to the arms of a Y emerging from its stem. According to this concept, each basic region was hypothesized to individually recognize each half-site of the dyad-symmetric recognition sequence (Fig. 1). The model further envisioned continuous α helices extending from the paired zippers through the unpaired basic regions. As rationalized by Vinson et al. (1989), such a scheme accounted for the invariant positioning of the basic region relative to the leucine zipper. Moreover, since α helices had long been recognized to be of suitable dimensions for penetration of the major groove of DNA and were known to be used in DNA recognition by other, well-studied regulatory proteins (Pabo and Sauer 1984), it was postulated that the basic regions of bZIP proteins would enter the major groove from a common location (the cleft of the Y) and track divergently.

The importance of proper spatial alignment of the basic region and zipper domains was documented by Agre et al. (1989), who showed that functional GCN4-C/EBP and C/EBP-GCN4 chimeras could only be obtained if proper alignment was maintained. Chimeric proteins that either deleted or inserted five amino acids between basic region and leucine zipper, although capable of dimerization, were incapable of binding DNA. More systematic experiments conducted by Struhl and colleagues on GCN4 (see Struhl, this volume) established that insertions of between one and six residues yield nonfunctional proteins, but that many different heptapeptide inserts between basic region and zipper yield variants capable of selective binding to DNA.

The resulting model for C/EBP binding to DNA implied an apparent disparity between the length of the basic region (if configured as a continuous α helix) and the path length of the DNA recognition site. Inspection of conserved residues within the basic regions of eleven bZIP proteins revealed that each basic region consists of a minimum of 16 amino acids (Vinson et al. 1989), which should produce continuous α helices 24 Å in length (16 residues x 1.6 Å axial rise per residue). In contrast, the dyad half-sites recognized by bZIP proteins contain no more than five base pairs (Graves et al. 1986; Hill et al. 1986), indicating a major groove "tracking distance" along the recognition sequence of about 16 Å. It was therefore speculated that the α helix encompassing the basic region might curve or kink at some point, allowing it to track the major groove over a longer distance (Vinson et al. 1989). If the basic regions of a bZIP protein were not so angulated, their more distal aspects would protrude out the back side of the DNA substrate (relative to the side of initial approach). Alternatively, the DNA-binding site might be substantially distorted to facilitate continuous protein:DNA interaction. Evidence favoring the latter interpretation has been reported by Curran and colleagues (Kerppola and Curran 1991).

A potential helix angulation point within the basic region was suggested on the basis of two observations (Vinson et al. 1989). First, all bZIP proteins contain an asparagine residue located at an invariant position within the basic region. Asparagine commonly "caps" the amino termini of α helices by forming a hydrogen bond between its side chain and the peptide bond two or three residues internal to the α helix (Richardson and Richardson 1988). Second, the peptide bond that links this invariant asparagine to the preceding arginine is, relative to all others in the C/EBP DNA-binding domain, exceptionally sensitive to cleavage by trypsin (Shuman et al. 1990). This localized protease sensitivity might imply that the asparagine resides in a structurally disordered, bent, or kinked region.

According to the "scissors-grip" model (Vinson et al. 1989), the basic regions begin DNA contact close to the center of the dyad-symmetric binding site, then track continuously in the major groove around the back side of the DNA (Fig. 2). If bound to DNA in this clamp-like conforma-

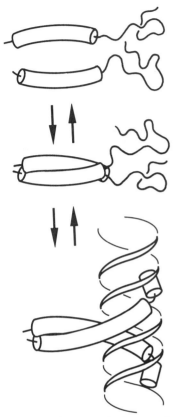

Figure 2 Hypothetical steps during the binding of C/EBP to DNA. In the absence of DNA the subunits of C/EBP are in equilibrium between the monomeric (*top*) and dimeric (*middle*) states. DNA binding (*bottom*) leads to a conformational change in the basic region, involving a transition from random coil to α helix. (Reprinted, with permission, from Shuman et al. 1990 [copyright held by the AAAS].)

tion, how might bZIP proteins reversibly associate and dissociate from their substrates? To accommodate this dilemma, Vinson et al. (1989) hypothesized that the basic region might exchange between structurally ordered and disordered states as the protein binds and releases DNA.

Substrate-induced Conformation of the Basic Region

Several experimental observations have provided support for the scissors-grip model and the substrate-induced conformation of the basic region. Hydroxyl radicals cleave DNA via reactions initiated predominantly within the minor groove of DNA (Tullius et al. 1987) and hydrolyze the DNA to which C/EBP binds in a manner unimpeded by bound protein (Vinson et al. 1989). It thus appears that protein:DNA contacts between C/EBP and its substrate are mediated almost exclusively through the major groove. This interpretation has been strongly supported by ethylnitrosourea interference assays, which revealed blockage of C/EBP binding by modification of backbone phosphates farther in the 5' direction than 3' direction relative to the dyad center (Nye and Graves 1990). Such a pattern of "5' stagger" is a hallmark of major groove interaction (Pabo and Sauer 1984).

Two studies of DNA binding by GCN4 are also consistent with the scissors-grip model. Using a sensitive exonucleolytic assay, Crothers and colleagues found that the outermost limits of GCN4 interaction occur eight base pairs from the dyad center (Gartenberg et al. 1990). Dervan and colleagues obtained similar results (Oakley and Dervan 1990) using derivatives of GCN4 containing an iron:EDTA complex conjugated to specific amino acid residues in the basic region. When bound to DNA, such derivatives facilitate the local release of hydroxyl radical ions with resultant hydrolysis of the DNA. These experiments revealed that protein fragments derivatized in the distal-most segment of the basic region led to cleavage events on the side of DNA opposite the dyad center.

Evidence has also been reported favoring substrate-induced changes in protein conformation that occur when bZIP proteins interact with their specific sites on DNA. The basic region of C/EBP is, for example, far more sensitive to proteolytic digestion by trypsin in the absence of DNA than when bound to its specific substrate (Shuman et al. 1990). The classic experiments of Anfinson and colleagues showed that structural order correlates with protease insensitivity (Taniuchi and Anfinson 1968; Taniuchi et al. 1969). In addition, the circular dichroism spectra of C/EBP and GCN4 change markedly when the proteins associate with DNA (O'Neil et al. 1990; Weiss et al. 1990; K.T. O'Neil and J.D. Shuman, unpubl.).

Polypeptide fragments corresponding to the DNA-binding domains of the two proteins appear to be roughly 50% α helical in the absence of DNA; when bound to a specific DNA substrate, however, the measured α-helical content approaches 100%. The observation that synthetic peptides corresponding to the leucine zipper alone exist in an α-helical conformation in the absence of DNA (O'Shea et al. 1989) allows tentative assignment of the aforementioned, substrate-induced change in helical content to the basic region. Figure 2 summarizes our interpretations as to how bZIP proteins bind and release their specific recognition sites on DNA.

Localization of Two Transcriptional Activation Domains within C/EBP

A presumptive role for C/EBP in gene activation was inferred from transient transfection assays in which a C/EBP expression vector and a "target gene" were introduced into cultured human hepatoma cells (HepG2 cells), which otherwise contain low amounts of endogenous C/EBP. The target gene consisted of the promoter of the rat serum albumin gene, which harbors an avid binding site for C/EBP, fused to the mRNA-coding segment of the HSV TK gene (Zaret et al. 1988). Such assays, legitimized by several experimental controls, revealed a significant activation function.

It is important to note that such experiments do not rigorously test the role of C/EBP in controlling albumin gene expression in the intact liver. For example, transfected HepG2 cells produce abnormally high levels of C/EBP. Likewise, the target for C/EBP activation in this assay was an episomal copy of the albumin promoter driving expression of a viral reporter gene. Moreover, liver cells contain at least two C/EBP-related proteins that might regulate albumin transcription (see Crabtree et al., this volume). Despite these uncertainties, transient transfection of HepG2 cells provided an assay for localizing functional domains of C/EBP. Studies of nine deletion mutants that systematically removed 20–30 amino acid segments of the amino-terminal region of the protein identified two putative transcriptional activation domains, one close to the amino terminus, the other in the central region of the protein (Friedman et al. 1989).

Little is known of the mechanisms by which the activation domains of C/EBP function. Neither shows an abundance of particular amino acid residues (e.g., aspartic acid, glutamic acid, proline, or glutamine) that have been correlated with the activation regions of other transcription factors (Mitchell and Tjian 1989). C/EBP's capacity to activate gene expression in vitro (Cheneval et al. 1991; P. Lamb and S. McKnight, unpubl.) should facilitate biochemical studies of its mechanism of activation. Given the tissue- and cell-type selectivity of C/EBP expression (Birkenmeier et al. 1989), it will be interesting to determine whether its activation domains interact directly with components of the general transcription apparatus or, rather, with specialized cofactors that might themselves display restricted cell-type distribution.

C/EBP Expression in Terminally Differentiated Cells

In developing mice, C/EBP mRNA is first detected in liver, lung, and intestine shortly before birth. Peak accumulation in these tissues occurs at birth, and lower levels of C/EBP transcripts are found in suckling pups and adults. Indirect immunofluorescence studies using various C/EBP-specific antisera revealed mature hepatocytes and adipocytes as the major sites of C/EBP protein accumulation in adult liver and adipose tissue, respectively (Birkenmeier et al. 1989). More recent assays indicate that C/EBP is also expressed in mature enterocytes that populate the epithelial lining of the gut, keratinocytes in the skin, and bronchial epithelial cells in the lung (Z. Cao and S. McKnight, unpubl.). Such studies imply that C/EBP may be selectively expressed in terminally differentiated cells.

The correlation between C/EBP expression and terminal cell differentiation was strengthened by studies using cultured 3T3-L1 cells. Confluent monolayers of these adipoblastic cells can be induced with a hormone cocktail to differentiate, over a period of roughly a week, into fat-laden adipocytes (Green and Kehinde 1975). Northern and Western blot assays carried out using C/EBP-specific probes revealed a tight correlation between C/EBP expression and terminal cell differentiation (Birkenmeier et al. 1989). C/EBP is not expressed in growing 3T3-L1 adipoblasts yet begins to appear 3–4 days after exposure of the cells to the hormone cocktail. Indirect immunofluorescence detection techniques have shown that the earliest cells to show signs of lipid droplet accumulation correlate precisely with those that are first to express C/EBP (Fig. 3).

Differentiation of 3T3-L1 cells entails induction of a battery of "fat-specific" genes. The products of such genes, including a fatty acid binding protein termed 422, the enzyme stearoyl (CoA) desaturase, and the insulin-responsive glucose transporter, facilitate the prolific synthesis and storage of triglycerides. Lane and colleagues have provided evidence that C/EBP *trans*-activates each of these genes during the course of adipocyte differentiation (Christy et al. 1989; Kaestner et al. 1990). Further support for a role of C/EBP in the terminal differentiation of adipocytes has come from two types of studies. First, antisense inhibition of C/EBP expression has been shown to block acquisition of the "fatty" phenotype (Samuelsson et al. 1991; Lin and Lane 1992). Second, premature expression of C/EBP markedly accelerates the adipogenic differentiation program (Umek et al. 1991).

The latter study required the production of a conditional form of the protein, which was required to circumvent the propensity of ectopically expressed C/EBP to inhibit cell growth. Yamamoto and colleagues had shown that proteins otherwise unaffected by steroid hormones, such as the E1A protein of adenovirus, become hormone-dependent when fused to the hormone-binding domain of a receptor (Picard et al. 1988; Eilers et

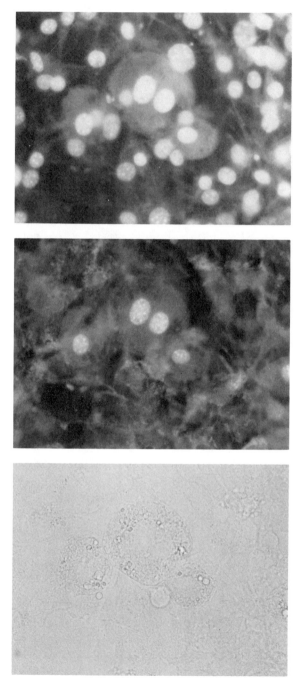

Figure 3 (*See facing page for legend.*)

al. 1989). Thus, intact C/EBP was fused to the hormone-binding domain of the estrogen receptor (ER), producing a chimera (C/EBP-ER) that displays C/EBP activity only in the presence of estrogen (Umek et al. 1991).

Cultured 3T3-L1 cells were stably transformed with an expression vector encoding C/EBP-ER fusion protein and propagated in culture medium stripped of endogenous estrogen. Hormone treatment of these cells led to abrupt mitotic arrest, whereas control 3T3-L1 cells were unaffected following estrogen presentation. These findings explained our prior inability to recover stably transformed cell lines expressing C/EBP and led to the speculation that C/EBP might play a bona fide role in growth control (Umek et al. 1991).

Interestingly, the mitotic arrest induced by activated C/EBP-ER was not accompanied by any phenotypic signs of differentiation. The growth-arrested 3T3-L1 cells did not accumulate fat droplets typical of fully differentiated adipocytes and failed to induce the expression of gene products diagnostic of terminal differentiation. However, estrogen-mediated activation of C/EBP-ER did accelerate markedly the rate of differentiation induced by the cocktail of hormones that stimulate adipogenesis (insulin, methylisobutylxanthine, and dexamethasone). These results support the interpretation that C/EBP is involved in terminal adipocyte differentiation, yet they infer additional regulatory events early in the differentiation process that require the hormone regimen. As discussed in the final section of this chapter, it is apparent that two C/EBP-related proteins are expressed early during adipocyte conversion in direct response to two of the three "adipogenic" hormones (Cao et al. 1991).

C/EBP-related Proteins

The first evidence for C/EBP-related proteins came from studies of interleukin-6 (IL-6) gene regulation by Kishimoto and colleagues (Akira et al. 1990). IL-6 synthesis can be induced in certain cultured cells by other cytokines, including interleukin-1 (IL-1) and tumor necrosis factor

Figure 3 Immunofluorescence localization of C/EBPα in differentiating adipocytes. 3T3-L1 cells were grown to confluence and induced to differentiate following exposure to insulin, dexamethasone, and methylisobutylxanthine. After 4 days, the cells were stained with DAPI to reveal nuclei (*top*) and antiserum specific to C/EBPα (*middle*). The same field was also photographed by phase-contrast microscopy to visualize cytoplasmic fat droplets (*bottom*). Note correlation between cells containing nuclear C/EBPα and cytoplasmic fat droplets. Figure prepared from observations made by Z. Cao and S. McKnight (unpubl.).

(TNF). IL-1-mediated induction of IL-6 gene expression has been shown to act through a palindromic *cis*-regulatory element 150 nucleotides upstream of the IL-6 transcription start site (Isshiki et al. 1990). A radioactively labeled derivative of this sequence (5′-ATTGCACAAT-3′), which forms a 9 out of 10 match to the consensus C/EBP binding site (5′-ATTGCGCAAT-3′), was used to probe an expression library of recombinant bacteriophage containing cDNA inserts from stimulated human monocytes. A single recombinant phage was recovered and shown to encode a C/EBP-related protein, denoted NF-IL6, that bound specifically to the relevant sequence (Akira et al. 1990).

Subsequent studies implicated NF-IL6 in the regulation of additional genes. For example, activation of "acute-phase" genes in rodent hepatocytes involves proteins variously termed IL-6DBP (Poli et al. 1990) or AGP/EBP (Chang et al. 1990), which are virtually identical to human NF-IL6. Likewise, Schibler and colleagues identified a factor termed liver activator protein (LAP) that binds specifically to the same site in the serum albumin promoter as does C/EBP and shares amino acid sequence identity with NF-IL6 (Descombes et al. 1990). Low-stringency probing with DNA sequences encoding the bZIP region of C/EBP yielded two additional isolates of the mouse equivalent of NF-IL6, termed CRP-2 (Williams et al. 1991) and C/EBPβ (Cao et al. 1991). For simplicity, the original member of the C/EBP family has been renamed C/EBPα, and the protein variously termed NF-IL6, AGP/EBP, LAP, and CRP-2 has been denoted C/EBPβ. Additional C/EBP family members (see below) have been designated C/EBPγ, C/EBPδ, and C/EBPε in chronological order of their discovery (Cao et al. 1991).

It is intriguing that C/EBPβ has been implicated in the regulation of both IL-6 and acute-phase gene expression. IL-6 is a potent mediator of the acute-phase response (Andus et al. 1987; Gauldie et al. 1987). Thus, the same transcription factor (C/EBPβ) appears to regulate the expression of the gene encoding the mediator of the acute-phase response (IL-6) as well as various of its target genes, including haptoglobin (Oliviero and Cortese 1989), hemopexin (Poli and Cortese 1989), C-reactive protein (Majello et al. 1990), and α_1-antitrypsin (Chang et al. 1990).

In a remarkable series of experiments, Kishimoto and colleagues (Isshiki et al. 1990) have demonstrated the reciprocal expression of C/EBPα and C/EBPβ. Under normal circumstances, tissues such as liver, fat, and gut appear to employ C/EBPα in the expression of certain cell-specific genes (Birkenmeier et al. 1989; Christy et al. 1989; Umek et al. 1991). During the acute-phase response, presumably in response to IL-6 and/or other cytokines, C/EBPα mRNA is replaced by C/EBPβ. As a direct consequence, acute-phase genes are activated, and expression of

C/EBPα-responsive genes is diminished (Isshiki et al. 1990). It is unclear how the respective levels of C/EBPα and C/EBPβ mRNA are reciprocally regulated. The transcriptional promoters of both genes do contain avid C/EBP-binding sites, raising the possibility of auto- or cross-regulation by the various C/EBP isoforms.

Another vivid demonstration of the consequences of reciprocally regulated expression of C/EBPα and C/EBPβ has come from studies of cultured adipocytes. Treatment of fully differentiated 3T3-L1 cells with various cytokines, such as TNF, induces expression of C/EBPβ, eliminates expression of C/EBPα, and causes the fat-laden adipocytes to discontinue expression of fat-specific genes and lose all overt signs of the differentiated phenotype (Ron et al. 1992). These and related studies on hepatic expression of C/EBPα and C/EBPβ indicate that the two proteins, despite sharing highly related DNA-binding properties, may control very distinctive sets of target genes.

Three additional C/EBP-related proteins have recently been described. C/EBPγ, also termed Ig/EBP-1, was isolated as a factor that binds to a *cis*-regulatory element of the immunoglobulin gene enhancer (Roman et al. 1990). A fourth family member, variously termed CRP-3 (Williams et al. 1991) or C/EBPδ (Cao et al. 1991), was identified by low-stringency probing using C/EBPα gene sequences, as was a fifth family member, designated CRP-1 or C/EBPε (Williams et al. 1991). Relatively little is known of the biological functions of the γ, δ, and ε family members.

The five C/EBP family members display highly related DNA-binding domains, with exceptional amino acid sequence relatedness localized within the basic region (see Fig. 4B). Indeed, four of the five family members bear identical sequences spanning the central 16 residues of the basic region, and the fifth family member exhibits only 4 conservative changes. Substantial amino acid sequence similarity is also apparent in the respective dimerization domains (see Fig. 4C). Not surprisingly, extensive cross-dimerization among family members has been observed in vitro (Roman et al. 1990; Cao et al. 1991) and in extracts prepared from various tissues of adult mice (Williams et al. 1991). Although the functional consequences of heterodimer formation have not been established, coincident expression of more than one "isoform" in a single cell type has been clearly established (Cao et al. 1991; Z. Cao and S. McKnight, unpubl.).

The amino-terminal segments of the various C/EBP-related proteins are generally dissimilar except for a region encompassing about 30 amino acids that is related in the α, β, δ, and ε isoforms (Williams et al. 1991). This region (Fig. 4A) resides within one of the two experimentally defined activation domains of C/EBPα (Friedman et al. 1989). Conceivably, these related segments represent a common activation domain shared by four of the five C/EBP family members.

The biological roles of the various C/EBP-related proteins are only

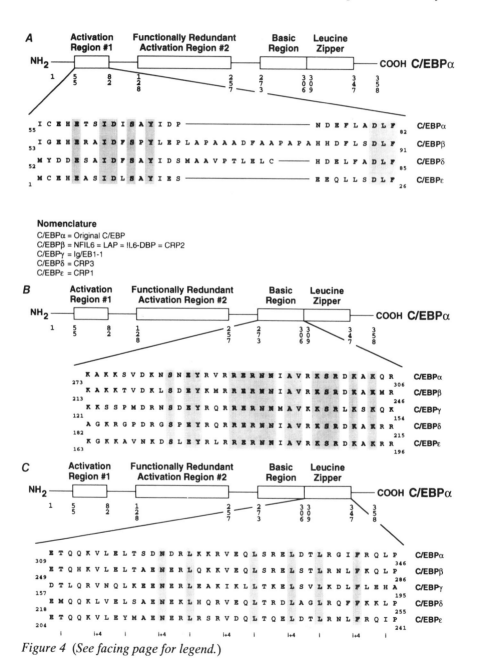

Figure 4 (See facing page for legend.)

beginning to be understood. As mentioned previously, C/EBPα appears to function in terminal cell differentiation and C/EBPβ in the activation of certain cytokines and acute-phase genes. C/EBPδ has been tentatively implicated in the response of cultured 3T3-L1 adipoblasts to hormonal stimulants of terminal cell differentiation (Cao et al. 1991). Undifferentiated 3T3-L1 cells do not express any of the five C/EBP isoforms. When exposed to the hormone mixture that triggers differentiation, the β and δ C/EBP isoforms are rapidly produced (Fig. 5). By treating confluent, undifferentiated adipoblasts with individual hormones in the presence of cycloheximide, Cao et al. (1991) demonstrated direct transcriptional induction of the C/EBPβ gene by methylisobutylxanthine (a phosphodiesterase inhibitor that increases intracellular levels of cAMP) and of the C/EBPδ gene by the synthetic glucocorticoid, dexamethasone.

Conceivably, the β and γ C/EBP isoforms may constitute relay points along the adipocyte differentiation pathway. Recall, for example, that premature expression of C/EBPα in 3T3-L1 cells failed to evoke overt differentiation (Umek et al. 1991). The stimulatory role of C/EBPα was observed only in cells that had also been exposed to a hormone cocktail that included the direct inducers of C/EBPβ and C/EBPδ. It is especially interesting to note that the optimal, empirically defined hormone regimen for 3T3-L1 cell differentiation entails the sequential administration (for 2 days) and withdrawal of the hormonal inducers of the synthesis of C/EBPβ and C/EBPδ. This hormonal regimen causes the transient synthesis of C/EBPβ and C/EBPδ during the early period of differentiation. As outlined in Figure 5, perhaps these "early" C/EBP isoforms execute "preparatory" steps essential for the subsequent action of C/EBPα (Cao et al. 1991).

Figure 4 Anatomy of C/EBPα and comparisons of amino acid sequences of five C/EBP isoforms. Top of each figure shows linear representation of C/EBPα identifying locations of four functional domains (activation regions 1 and 2, basic region, and leucine zipper). Bottom segments of each figure provide alignment of amino acid sequences in regions of known function. Numbers before and after each amino acid sequence designate the location of the sequence relative to the intact polypeptide. Invariant residues are shaded gray. Lowercase letters (i) and (i+4) below sequences of leucine zippers (*C*) identify hydrophobic residues located on the same helical face. Amino acid sequences were obtained from Landschulz et al. (1988b), Akira et al. (1990), Roman et al. (1990), Cao et al. (1991), and Williams et al. (1991). Regions of amino acid sequence similarity between activating region 1 of C/EBPα and similarly located regions of C/EBPβ, C/EBPδ, and C/EBPε (*A*) were first discovered by Johnson and colleagues (Williams et al. 1991).

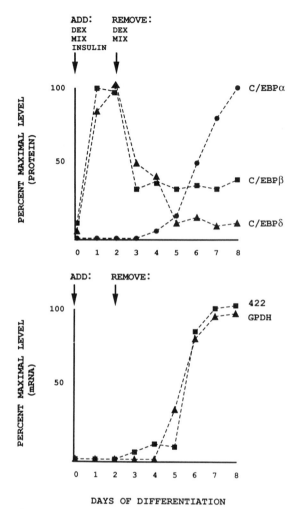

Figure 5 Temporal expression profiles of C/EBP isoforms (*top*) and fat-specific genes (*bottom*) during differentiation of 3T3-L1 cells. Accumulation of C/EBP isoforms was determined by Western blotting using isoform-specific antisera. Accumulation of mRNAs encoded by two fat-specific genes (GPDH and 422) was determined by Northern blotting. Note correlations between presentation/withdrawal of methylisobutylxanthine (MIX)/dexamethasone (DEX) and respective induction and decline of the C/EBPβ and C/EBPγ isoforms. Note also temporal correlation between appearance of C/EBPα isoform and accumulation of mRNAs encoded by fat-specific genes. (Reprinted, with permission, from Cao et al. 1991.)

Immunohistochemical analysis of lung, intestine, and liver has revealed generally concordant expression patterns for the various C/EBP-related proteins. Their regulatory activities may, on the one hand, be redundant. Alternatively, despite sharing substantively similar DNA-binding activity, the various C/EBP isoforms may mediate distinctive regulatory functions. Distinguishing between these two extremes will be a challenging and important task.

CONCLUSIONS AND PERSPECTIVES

Studies of C/EBP, an obscure protein that oozed its way out of the murky goop of homogenized rat liver, have provided insight into two important problems. An examination of its capacity to bind DNA helped define a broad family of factors that bind DNA via a novel structural motif. These bZIP proteins bind to DNA as either homo- or heterodimers offering the potential (yet to be fully understood or appreciated) for a wide diversity of regulatory specificities.

A second avenue of research opened by studies of C/EBP concerns its role in terminal cell differentiation. The recurrent correlation between C/EBPα expression and terminal cell differentiation raises the possibility that this protein may play a selective role in growth arrest and cell specialization. Again, although potentially exciting observations have been made regarding the capacity of C/EBPα to directly regulate growth and differentiation of adipocytes, our present understanding of the problem is relatively obscure. How, for example, can the same protein stimulate cell differentiation in diverse tissue types? Why does the C/EBPα isoform, to the exclusion of its close relatives, cause growth arrest? If the various C/EBPs are indeed functionally distinct, what molecular properties distinguish one family member from the next? Given that these studies have provided more questions than answers, it is apparent that the most exciting research on C/EBP remains to be conducted.

ACKNOWLEDGMENTS

I am deeply indebted to Barbara Graves, Peter Johnson, and Bill Landschulz for their courage in pursuing the purification of C/EBP throughout a 3-year period of uncertainty. I also thank the many colleagues and students who have worked with me on C/EBP during the past 7 years. Substantive contributions were made by Chris Hug, Jimmy Montoya, Eli Adashi, Ed Birkenmeier, Peter Agre, Chuck Vinson, Bob Umek, Alan Friedman, Jon Shuman, Paul Sigler, Zhaodan Cao, Wen-chen Yeh, Mary Anderson, Marie Classon, and Fabienne Charles de la Brousse. I acknowledge the valuable assistance of my longtime technician, Bob Kingsbury; my secretary, Christine Norman; Carnegie's computer specialist, Bill Kupiec, for help in preparation of Figures 3 and

4; and Betty Addison for cleaning the mountains of glassware that invariably result from rat liver preparations. Finally, I thank Kelly LaMarco for helping edit this and many other manuscripts that have been published by the McKnight laboratory during the past 5 years.

REFERENCES

Agre, P., P.F. Johnson, and S.L. McKnight. 1989. Cognate DNA binding specificity retained after leucine zipper exchange between GCN4 and C/EBP. *Science* **246:** 922–926.

Akira, S., H. Isshiki, T. Sugita, O. Tanabe, S. Kinoshita, Y. Hishio, T. Nakajima, T. Hirano, and T. Kishimoto. 1990. A nuclear factor of IL-6 expression (NF-IL6) is a member of a C/EBP family. *EMBO J.* **9:** 1897–1906.

Andus, T., T. Geiger, T. Hirano, H. Northoff, U. Ganter, J. Bauer, T. Kishimoto, and P.C. Heinrich. 1987. Recombinant human B cell stimulatory factor 2 (BSF-2/IFN-beta2) regulates beta-fibrinogen and albumin mRNA levels in Fao-9 cells. *FEBS Lett.* **221:** 18–22.

Birkenmeier, E.H., B. Gwynn, S. Howard, J. Jerry, J.I. Gordon, W.H. Landschulz, and S.L. McKnight. 1989. Tissue-specific expression, developmental regulation and genetic mapping of the gene encoding C/EBP. *Genes Dev.* **3:** 1146–1156.

Bowerman, B., B.A. Eaton, and J.R. Priess. 1992. skn-1, a maternally expressed gene required to specify the fate of ventral blastomeres in the early *C. elegans* embryo. *Cell* **68:** 1061–1076.

Cao, Z., R.M. Umek, and S.L. McKnight. 1991. Regulated expression of three C/EBP isoforms during adipose conversion of 3T3-L1 cells. *Genes Dev.* **5:** 1538–1552.

Chang, C.-J., T.-T. Chen, H.-Y. Lei, D.-S. Chen, and S.-C. Lee. 1990. Molecular cloning of a trnascription factor, AGP/EBP, that belongs to members of the C/EBP family. *Mol. Cell. Biol.* **10:** 6642–6653.

Cheneval, D., R.J. Christy, D. Geiman, P. Cornelius, and M.D. Lane. 1991. Cell-free transcription directed by the 422 adipose P2 gene promoter: Activation by the CCAAT/enhancer binding protein. *Proc. Natl. Acad. Sci.* **88:** 8465–8469.

Chodosh, L.A., J. Olesen, S. Hahn, A.S. Baldwin, L. Guarente, and P.A. Sharp. 1988. A yeast and a human CCAAT-binding protein have heterologous subunits that are functionally interchangeable. *Cell* **53:** 25–35.

Christy, R.J., V.W. Yang, J.M. Ntambi, D.E. Geiman, W.H. Landschulz, A.D. Friedman, Y. Nakabeppu, T.J. Kelly, and M.D. Lane. 1989. Differentiation-induced gene expression in 3T3-L1 preadipocytes: CCAAT/enhancer binding protein interacts with and activates the promoters of two adipocyte-specific genes. *Genes Dev.* **3:** 1323–1335.

Crick, F.H.C. 1952. Is alpha-keratin a coiled coil? *Nature* **170:** 882.

Descombes, P., M. Chojkier, S. Lichtsteiner, E. Falvey, and U. Schibler. 1990. LAP, a novel member of the C/EBP gene family, encodes a liver-enriched transcriptional activator protein. *Genes Dev.* **4:** 1541–1551.

Dorn, A., J. Bollekens, A. Staub, C. Benoist, and D. Mathis. 1988. A multiplicity of CCAAT box-binding proteins. *Cell* **50:** 863–872.

Eilers, M., D. Picard, K.R. Yamamoto, and J.M. Bishop. 1989. Chimaeras of Myc oncoprotein and steroid receptors cause hormone-dependent transformation of cells. *Nature* **340:** 66–68.

Fisher, D.E., C.S. Carr, L.A. Parent, and P.A. Sharp. 1991. TFEB has DNA-binding and oligomerization properties of a unique helix-loop-helix/leucine-zipper family. *Genes Dev.* **5:** 2342–2352.

Franza, B.R., Jr., F.J. Rauscher III, S.F. Josephs, and T. Curran. 1988. The Fos complex and Fos-related antigens recognize sequence elements that contain AP-1 binding sites. *Science* **239:** 1150–1153.

Friedman, A.D., W.H. Landschulz, and S.L. McKnight. 1989. CCAAT/enhancer binding protein activates the promoter of the serum albumin gene in cultured hepatoma cells. *Genes Dev.* **3:** 1314–1322.

Gartenberg, M.R., C. Ampe, T.A. Steitz, and D.M. Crothers. 1990. Molecular characterization of the GCN4-DNA complex. *Proc. Natl. Acad. Sci.* **87:** 6034–6038.

Gauldie, J., C. Richards, D. Haarnish, P. Landsdorp, and H. Baumann. 1987. Interferon b2/B cell stimulating factor type 2 shares identity with monocyte-derived hepatocyte stimulating factor and regulates the major acute phase protein response in liver cells. *Proc. Natl. Acad. Sci.* **84:** 7251–7255.

Graves, B.J., R.N. Eisenman, and S.L. McKnight. 1985. Delineation of transcriptional control signals within the Moloney murine sarcoma virus long terminal repeat. *Mol. Cell. Biol.* **5:** 1948–1958.

Graves, B., P.F. Johnson, and S.L. McKnight. 1986. Homologous recognition of a promoter domain common to the MSV LTR and the HSV *tk* gene. *Cell* **44:** 565–576.

Gregor, P.D., M. Sawadogo, and R.G. Roeder. 1990. The adenovirus major late transcription factor USF is a member of the helix-loop-helix group of regulatory proteins and binds DNA as a dimer. *Genes Dev.* **4:** 1730–1740.

Green, H. and O. Kehinde. 1975. An established preadipose cell line and its differentiation in culture. II. Factors affecting the adipose conversion. *Cell* **5:** 19–27.

Herbomel, P., B. Bourachot, and M. Yaniv. 1984. Two distinct enhancers with different cell specificities coexist in the regulatory region of polyoma. *Cell* **39:** 653–662.

Hill, D.E., I.A. Hope, J.P. Macke, and K. Struhl. 1986. Saturation mutagenesis of the yeast his3 regulatory site: Requirements for transcriptional induction and for binding by GCN4 activator protein. *Science* **234:** 451–457.

Hope, I.A. and K. Struhl. 1986. Functional dissection of a eukaryotic transcriptional actvator protein, GCN 4 of yeast. *Cell* **46:** 885–894.

Isshiki, H., S. Akira, O. Tanabe, T. Nakajima, T. Shimamoto, T. Hirano, and T. Kishimoto. 1990. Constitutive and IL-1 inducible factors interact with the IL-1 responsive element in the IL-6 gene. *Mol. Cell. Biol.* **10:** 2757–2764.

Johnson, P.F., W.H. Landschulz, B.J. Graves, and S.L. McKnight. 1987. Identification of a rat liver nuclear protein that binds to the enhancer core element of three animal viruses. *Genes Dev.* **1:** 133–146.

Jones, K.A. and R. Tjian. 1985. Sp1 binds to promoter sequences and activates herpes simplex virus "immediate-early" gene transcription *in vitro*. *Cell* **42:** 559–572.

Kaestner, K.H., R.J. Christy, and M.D. Lane. 1990. Mouse insulin-responsive glucose transporter gene: Characterization of the gene and *trans*-activation by the CCAAT/enhancer binding protein. *Proc. Natl. Acad. Sci.* **87:** 251–255.

Kerppola, T.K. and T. Curran. 1991. DNA bending by Fos and Jun: The flexible hinge model. *Science* **254:** 1210–1214.

Landschulz, W.H., P.F. Johnson, and S.L. McKnight. 1988a. The leucine zipper: A hypothetical structure common to a new class of NDA binding proteins. *Science* **240:** 1759–1764.

———. 1989. The DNA binding domain of the rat liver nuclear protein C/EBP is bipartite. *Science* **243:** 1681–1688.

Landschulz, W.H., P.F. Johnson, E.Y. Adashi, B.J. Graves, and S.L. McKnight. 1988b. Isolation of a recombinant copy of the gene encoding C/EBP. *Genes Dev.* **2:** 786–800.

Lin, F.-T. and M.D. Lane. 1992. Antisense CCAAT/enhancer-binding protein RNA suppresses coordinate gene expression and triglyceride accumulation during differentiation of 3T3-L1 preadipocytes. *Genes Dev.* **6:** 533–544.

Majello, B., R. Arcone, C. Toniatti, and G. Ciliberto. 1990. Constitutive and IL5-induced nuclear factors that interact with the human c-reactive protein promoter. *EMBO J.* **9:** 457–465.

McKnight, S.L. and R. Kingsbury. 1982. Transcriptional control signals of a eukaryotic protein-coding gene. *Science* **217:** 316–324.

Mitchell, P.J. and R. Tjian. 1989. Transcriptional regulation in mammalian cells by sequence-specific DNA binding proteins. *Science* **245:** 371–378.

Nye, J.A. and B.J. Graves. 1990. Alkylation interference identifies essential DNA contacts for sequence-specific binding of the eukaryotic transcription factor C/EBP. *Proc. Natl. Acad. Sci.* **87:** 3992–3996.

Oakley, M.G. and P.B. Dervan. 1990. Structural motif of the GCN4 DNA binding domain characterized by affinity cleaving. *Science* **249:** 847–850.

Oliviero, S. and R. Cortese. 1989. The human haptoglobin gene promoter: Interleukin-6-responsive element interacts with a DNA-binding protein induced by interleukin-6. *EMBO J.* **8:** 1145–1151.

O'Neil, K.T., R.H. Hoess, and W.F. DeGrado. 1990. Design of DNA-binding peptides based on the leucine zipper motif. *Science* **249:** 774–778.

O'Shea, E.K., R. Rutkowski, and P.S. Kim. 1989. Evidence that the leucine zipper is a coiled coil. *Science* **243:** 538–542.

O'Shea, E.K., J.D. Klemm, P.S. Kim, and T. Alber. 1991. X-ray structure of the GCN4 leucine zipper, a two-stranded, parallel coiled coil. *Science* **254:** 539–544.

Pabo, C.O. and R.T. Sauer. 1984. Protein-DNA recognition. *Annu. Rev. Biochem.* **53:** 293–321.

Picard, D., S.J. Salser, and K.R. Yamamoto. 1988. A movable and regulable inactivation function within the steroid binding domain of the glucocorticoid receptor. *Cell* **54:** 1073–1080.

Poli, V. and R. Cortese. 1989. Interleukin 6 induces a liver-specific nuclear protein that binds to the promoter of acute-phase genes. *Proc. Natl. Acad. Sci.* **86:** 7547–7551.

Poli, V., F.P. Mancini, and R. Cortese. 1990. IL-6DBP, a nuclear protein involved in interleukin-6 signal transduction, defines a new family of leucine zipper proteins related to C/EBP. *Cell* **63:** 643–653.

Rauscher, F.J., III, P.J. Voulalas, B.R. Franza, Jr., and T. Curran. 1988a. Fos and Jun bind cooperatively to the AP-1 site: Reconstitution *in vitro*. *Genes Dev.* **2:** 1687–1699.

Rauscher, F.J., III, D.R. Cohen, T. Curran, T.J. Bos, P.K. Vogt, D. Bohmann, R. Tjian, and B.R. Franza, Jr. 1988b. Fos-associated protein p39 is the product of the *jun* proto-oncogene. *Science* **240:** 1010–1016.

Richardson, J.S. and D.C. Richardson. 1988. Amino acid preferences for specific locations at the ends of α helices. *Science* **240:** 1648–1652.

Roman, C., J.S. Platero, J.D. Shuman, and K. Calame. 1990. Ig/EBP-1: A ubiquitously expressed immunoglobulin enhancer binding protein that is similar to C/EBP and heterodimerizes with C/EBP. *Genes Dev.* **4:** 1404–1415.

Ron, D., R.E. Brasier, R.E. McGehee, Jr. and J.F. Habener. 1992. Tumor necrosis factor-induced reversal of adipocytic phenotype of 3T3-L1 cells is preceded by a loss of nuclear CCAAT/enhancer binding protein. *J. Clin. Invest.* **89:** 223–233.

Ruezinsky, D., H. Beckmann, and T. Kadesch. 1991. Modulation of the IgH enhancer's cell type specificity through a genetic switch. *Genes Dev.* **5:** 29–37.

Ryden, T.A. and K. Beemon. 1989. Avian retroviral long terminal repeats bind CCAAT/enhancer-binding protein. *Mol. Cell. Biol.* **9:** 1155–1164.

Samuelsson, L., K. Stromberg, K. Vikman, G. Bjursell, and S. Enerback. 1991. The CCAAT/enhancer binding protein and its role in adipocyte differentiation: Evidence for direct involvement in terminal adipocyte development. *EMBO J.* **10:** 3787–3793.

Shuman, J.D., C.R. Vinson, and S.L. McKnight. 1990. Evidence of changes in protease sensitivity and subunit exchange rate on DNA binding by C/EBP. *Science* **249:** 771–774.

Talanian, R.V., C.J. McKnight, and P.S. Kim. 1990. Sequence-specific DNA binding by a short peptide dimer. *Science* **249:** 769–771.

Taniuchi, H. and C.B. Anfinsen. 1968. Steps in the formation of active derivatives of staphylococcal nuclease during trypsin digestion. *J. Biol. Chem.* **243:** 4778–4786.

Taniuchi, H., L. Moravek, and C.B. Anfinsen. 1969. Ligand-induced resistance of staphylococcal nuclease and nuclease-T to proteolysis by subtilisin, alpha-chymotrypsin, and thermolysin. *J. Biol. Chem.* **244:** 4600–4606.

Tullius, T.D., B.A. Dombroski, M.E. Churchill, and L. Kam. 1987. Hydroxyl radical footprinting: A high-resolution method for mapping protein-DNA contacts. *Methods Enzymol.* **155:** 537–558.

Turner, R. and R. Tjian. 1989. Leucine repeats and an adjacent DNA binding domain mediate the formation of functional cFos-cJun heterodimers. *Science* **243:** 1689–1694.

Umek, R.M., A.D. Friedman, and S.L. McKnight. 1991. CCAAT/enhancer binding protein: A component of a differentiation switch. *Science* **251:** 288–292.

Vinson, C.R., P.B. Sigler, and S.L. McKnight. 1989. Scissors-grip model for DNA recognition by a family of leucine zipper proteins. *Science* **246:** 911–916.

Weiss, M.A., T. Ellenberger, C.R. Wobbe, J.P. Lee, S.C. Harrison, and K. Struhl. 1990. Folding transition in the DNA-binding domain of GCN4 on specific binding to DNA. *Nature* **347:** 575–578.

Williams, S.C., C.A. Cantwell, and P.F. Johnson. 1991. A family of C/EBP-related proteins capable of forming covalently linked leucine zipper dimers *in vitro*. *Genes Dev.* **5:** 1553–1567.

Zaret, K.S., C.M. Dipersio, D.A. Jackson, W.J. Montigny, and D.L. Weinstat. 1988. Conditional enhancement of liver-specific gene transcription. *Proc. Natl. Acad. Sci.* **85:** 9076–9080.

Zenke, M., T. Grundstrom, H. Matthes, M. Wintzerith, C. Schatz, A. Wildeman, and P. Chambon. 1986. Multiple sequence motifs are involved in SV40 enhancer function. *EMBO J.* **5:** 387–397.

30

Dangerous Liaisons: Fos and Jun, Oncogenic Transcription Factors

Tom Curran
Department of Molecular Oncology and Virology
Roche Institute of Molecular Biology
Roche Research Center
Nutley, New Jersey 07110

Peter K. Vogt
Department of Microbiology
University of Southern California School of Medicine
and Norris Cancer Center
Los Angeles, California 90033-1054

OVERVIEW

The oncogenes *fos* and *jun* encode proteins that belong to a class of transcription factors characterized by a leucine zipper dimerization domain
and an amino-terminally adjacent DNA-binding domain, rich in basic
amino acids. Together with the Jun-related proteins, JunB and JunD, and
Fos family proteins, Fra1 and FosB, Jun and Fos are major components
of the transcriptional regulator AP-1. Jun proteins can form homodimers
but more avidly dimerize with Fos and its relatives to bind to the consensus sequence TGACTCA. Fos and Jun can also dimerize with members of the cAMP responsive element binding (CREB) protein family;
these heterodimers have a preferential affinity for the CRE consensus sequence TGACGTCA. Jun also interacts with the glucocorticoid receptor,
affecting hormone-dependent transcriptional regulation.

Besides the well-defined dimerization and DNA contact surfaces,
both Jun and Fos proteins contain less well delineated transcriptional activator domains. For Fos, two such domains have been identified, an
acidic region and a proline-rich region. Jun contains a major amino-
terminal *trans*-activation domain, encompassing strongly acidic regions.
A second glutamine/proline-rich region adjacent to the DNA-binding
domain may affect transcriptional activation indirectly.

jun and *fos* have strong oncogenic potential that is particularly evident
when these genes are transduced by retroviruses. The *fos* oncogene

shows a pronounced tropism for osteogenic target cells in vivo. *jun* transforms primarily fibroblasts. For *fos*, the minimal oncogenic domain includes only the DNA-binding and dimerization regions. For *jun*, it also
encompasses the major *trans*-activator domain. Cellular *fos* or *jun* can
transform cells in culture, but the viral versions of these genes are more
potent carcinogens as a result of mutations in coding and noncoding
domains. In viral *jun*, these mutations include the deletion of negative
regulatory sites. Both *jun* and *fos* also interfere with myogenic differentiation in culture. Similar to other proteins that function as dimers, the activities of Fos and Jun can be suppressed by transdominant negative
mutants. As an example, a Fos protein with an inactive DNA-binding
domain will suppress oncogenicity by Jun.

ORIGIN OF THE *FOS* AND *JUN* ONCOGENES

The study of oncogenes has yielded insights into several different fields
of research. As a class, oncogenes can be viewed as genes that provide
critical regulatory functions in the signal transduction processes that govern cell growth and differentiation. The usurpation of these functions by
mutation or inappropriate expression of oncogenes following recombination with retroviruses leads to deregulation of normal growth, ultimately
resulting in tumorigenesis. Thus, oncogenesis has provided a genetic approach for investigating the regulation of cell growth. The identification
and characterization of oncogenes has elucidated several sequential
molecular events initiated by the interaction of polypeptide growth factors with their cognate receptors (for review, see Reddy et al. 1988). In
addition to inducing several short-term biochemical responses, growth
factors (and many other stimulatory agents) activate a program of gene
expression that is believed to coordinate the long-term phenotypic
response of a cell to stimulation. The oncogenes c-*fos* and c-*jun*[1] have
provided a paradigm for this cellular "immediate-early" response to environmental cues.

In the majority of cell types, c-*fos* and c-*jun* are expressed at relatively low levels; however, they can be induced rapidly and transiently by an
array of stimuli (Curran 1988). Their protein products, c-Fos and c-Jun,
are transcriptional regulators that are thought to contribute to long-term
adaptive responses by regulating expression of specific target genes.
(Curran and Franza 1988; Vogt and Bos 1990; Morgan and Curran
1991). The role of *cis*-acting elements in the regulation of c-*fos* expres-

---

[1]c-*fos* and c-*jun* designate cellular genes. Altered versions of these genes, transduced by
retroviruses, are referred to as v-*fos* and v-*jun*. The corresponding proteins are c-Fos, c-Jun, v-Fos,
and v-Jun, respectively. *fos* (Fos) or *jun* (Jun) collectively designate viral as well as cellular versions.

as the region essential for inducing transformation (Jenuwein and Müller 1987; Yoshida et al. 1989). The leucine zipper is a dimerization interface that has several properties of the coiled-coil structure. It was described initially as a heptad repeat of leucine residues in C/EBP (Landschulz et al. 1988b). The leucines participate in hydrophobic interactions among parallel α-helices to mediate dimerization (Gentz et al. 1989; Landschulz et al. 1989; O'Shea et al. 1989a,b). Dimerization brings into close juxtaposition regions of Fos and Jun, immediately amino-terminal of the zipper, that are rich in basic amino acids (Gentz et al. 1989). These basic regions were predicted to form the DNA contact surface in leucine zipper proteins (Landschulz et al. 1988a). This was demonstrated to be the case in Fos and Jun by mutagenesis (Kouzarides and Ziff 1988; Gentz et al. 1989; Ransone et al. 1989; Turner and Tjian 1989) and cross-linking studies (Risse et al. 1989; Abate et al. 1990d). Thus, in Fos-Jun heterodimers, the DNA-binding domain is a bimolecular structure that is assembled as a result of leucine zipper dimerization.

Although many transcription factors contain leucine zipper structures, dimerization is highly selective (O'Shea et al. 1989b; for review, see Kerppola and Curran 1991). Fos family proteins form heterodimers with Jun family proteins but do not form stable homodimers (Rauscher et al. 1988a; O'Shea et al. 1989b). The inability of Fos to form stable homodimers has been ascribed to the presence of a large number of acidic residues in positions e and g of the zipper (O'Shea et al. 1992). The close proximity of these negatively charged amino acids likely disrupts the close complementary packing required at the coiled-coil interface. Jun family proteins dimerize more promiscuously; they can form homodimers, heterodimers within the Jun family, and heterodimers with Fos family members (Nakabeppu et al. 1988). The relative affinity of Jun homodimers for DNA is, however, less than that of Fos-Jun heterodimers (Halazonetis et al. 1988; Nakabeppu et al. 1988; Rauscher et al. 1988a). A further complexity has been uncovered by the finding that certain CREB proteins can also form heterodimers with Jun and Fos. The transcription factor known variously as CREBP-1 (Maekawa et al. 1989), ATF-2 (Hai et al. 1989), or mXBP (Kara et al. 1990) forms heterodimers with Jun that bind to CRE sites preferentially over AP-1 sites (Benbrook and Jones 1990; Ivashkiv et al. 1990; Macgregor et al. 1990). ATF-3 will form heterodimers with Jun but not with Fos. Finally, yet another ATF family member, ATF-4, will form heterodimers with both Fos and Jun that bind to CRE sites (Hai and Curran 1991).

These findings call into question the rather strict definitions of AP-1 and CREB transcription factors. Indeed, it has been suggested that members of the *fos* and *jun* gene families, together with certain members of the CREB/ATF family, can be grouped into a superfamily of leucine zipper proteins based on dimerization specificities (Hai and Curran 1991). An additional complication has been uncovered by the recent discovery that FosB (Nakabeppu and Nathans 1991) and a new CREB protein (CREM) (Foulkes et al. 1991) undergo alternative splicing. In the case of FosB, a splice variant, ΔFosB, has been described that lacks an activation domain. The transcription factor CREM has alternative DNA-binding domains in separate exons. Thus, regulation of splicing can contribute, positively or negatively, to the function of AP-1 and CRE transcription factors.

The structural basis of dimerization selectivity is not fully understood, although some clues have emerged from mutagenesis studies and comparisons of the leucine zipper sequences. Zipper interactions clearly involve more than the conserved leucine residues that are present in all proteins of this class. Amino acid substitutions in sequences outside the zipper region can also affect dimerization. In the case of Fos and Jun, the dimer-forming region extends beyond the leucines to a conserved histidine residue that is seven amino acids carboxy-terminal of the last leucine (Cohen and Curran 1990). Mutagenesis studies have also shown that residues between the leucines, and even certain mutations within the arginine/lysine-rich DNA-binding region, affect dimerization (Gentz et al. 1989; Hirai and Yaniv 1989; Ransone et al. 1989; Nicklen and Casari 1990; for review, see Vogt and Morgan 1990). Domain-swapping studies indicate that although the zipper is the primary component responsible for dimerization and the basic region is the primary component responsible for DNA binding (Bos et al. 1989; Kouzarides and Ziff 1989; Nakabeppu and Nathans 1989; Neuberg et al. 1989; Sellers and Struhl 1989), regions outside these structures also contribute (Cohen and Curran 1990; Ransone et al. 1990b).

The leucine zipper is best described as a coiled-coil structure that entails hydrophobic interactions involving amino acids in the *a* and *d* positions of an α-helix (Crick 1953) and electrostatic interactions involving amino acids at other positions. Mutagenesis analysis has shown that many combinations of hydrophobic residues are nonfunctional and suggests that the leucines in the heptad repeat have a special function in the zipper (Kouzarides and Ziff 1988; Gentz et al. 1989; Landschulz et al. 1989; Schuermann et al. 1989; Turner and Tjian 1989; Hu et al. 1990; Ransone et al. 1990a,b; for review, see Vogt and Morgan 1990). The only amino acid that is not tolerated is proline, which introduces a break into an α-helix. The Fos:Jun situation is likely to be even more complex than that of C/EBP or GCN4. Fos and Jun have five leucine heptad repeats, rather than the four present in GCN4. Moreover, Fos and Jun contain a critical histidine residue seven amino acids carboxy-terminal of the last leucine (Cohen and Curran 1990). Thus, the d position is invariant in the Fos and Jun families and is composed of five consecutive leucines and the carboxy-terminal histidine. The a position in coiled-coil proteins is usually occupied by hydrophobic amino acids. However, all the Fos family members contain lysines at the a position of two heptad repeats. Interestingly, ATF-4 also has one of these lysines (Hai et al. 1989). Although lysines are charged amino acids, they can participate in hydrophobic interactions through methylene groups located at the β, γ, and ε positions of their four-carbon side chain. Fos peptides were unable to form homodimers at neutral pH, where repulsive ionic effects may occur, but did form homodimers under low pH conditions (O'Shea et al. 1989b). This specificity can be conferred by eight amino acids from the e and g positions of the Fos zipper (O'Shea et al. 1992). A critical role in dimerization specificity may also be played by the glutamic acid residue located at position 168 in Fos (Nicklen and Casari 1990). Mutation of this residue, which lies in the c position of the second heptad repeat, to an oppositely charged lysine amino acid results in a Fos protein that has some capacity to form homodimers.

The leucine zipper can be regarded as a mechanism for generating regulatory diversity. A large number of dimeric complexes can be assembled from a relatively small number of components. Heterodimeric complexes between Fos, Jun, and ATF proteins often have DNA-binding specificities distinct from the parental homodimers (Hai and Curran 1991), and they also differ in their transcriptional and oncogenic activities (Chiu et al. 1989; Schütte et al. 1989). The molecular basis of selective dimerization awaits a detailed resolution of leucine zipper structures by X-ray crystallography and nuclear magnetic resonance techniques. Given the pace of research in this topical area, it is likely that this information will be available in the near future.

DNA BINDING

One of the surprising features of the Fos, Jun, CREB, and ATF transcription factor families is that although they have similar DNA-binding specificities, the basic amino acid sequences in the DNA-binding region are not highly related between the families (Fig. 1) (for review, see Kerppola and Curran 1991). However, although the AP-1 site is usually listed as TGACTCA and the CRE site as TGACGTCA, it should be kept in mind that these are consensus sites and that many variations of these sequences can be avidly bound by various homo- and heterodimeric pairs

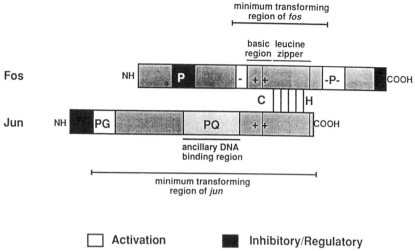

Figure 1 Schematic representation of the functional domains in Fos and Jun. A roughly proportional illustration of the Fos-Jun heterodimer indicates the positions of the leucine zipper and basic regions in each protein. The leucines are represented by bars and the basic region by (+). The locations of the histidine residue (H) that participates in dimerization and the cysteine residue (C) involved in redox regulation of DNA binding are shown. The proline/glutamine-rich ancillary DNA-binding domain and the proline-rich (P), acidic (–), proline/acidic (-P-), and proline/glycine-rich (PG) regions that affect the in vitro transcription properties in Fos and Jun are shown in boxes. The inhibitory/regulatory region of Jun that is deleted in v-*jun* is illustrated by a black box. NH is the amino terminus and COOH is the carboxyl terminus. The activator regions are shown as white boxes and the inhibitory/regulatory regions as black boxes.

of Fos, Jun, ATF, and CREBP (Franza et al. 1988; Rauscher et al. 1988a,b; Risse et al. 1989; Sonnenberg et al. 1989; Ryseck and Bravo 1991). Furthermore, these short dyads are only the core sequences of the recognition element. Evidence has been presented indicating that nucleotides outside the dyad symmetric core elements contribute to the determination of DNA-binding specificity (Ryseck and Bravo 1991). Fos and Jun can bind to both AP-1 and CRE sequences with differing affinities, depending on the partner with which they form dimers (Hai and Curran 1991), although the half-sites of the CRE are spaced by an additional nucleotide and (assuming a standard B form DNA structure) by a rotation of 34°. Thus, it is possible that one function of the leucine zipper is to position the basic regions in an appropriate configuration in three-dimensional space to interact with the similar half-sites in both AP-1 and CRE elements.

Within families of leucine zipper proteins, there is a remarkable degree of conservation of the basic region amino acids (Fig. 1). The conservation is not restricted to the basic residues alone. There is an invariant asparagine located 18 residues amino-terminal of the first leucine of the zipper. This asparagine has been proposed to form an amino cap in the scissors-grip model of DNA binding (Vinson et al. 1989). An alanine residue located between the two halves of the basic region is conserved in all members of ATF, Fos, and Jun families, and a cysteine residue flanked by two basic amino acids is conserved in all members of the Fos and Jun families. This cysteine has been shown to regulate DNA binding in vitro by a novel redox mechanism (Abate et al. 1990b). Oxidized Fos and Jun cannot bind to DNA efficiently. However, DNA-binding activity can be stimulated by adding high levels (5 mM) of dithiothreitol (DTT) or by adding a nuclear factor that reduces the oxidized cysteine. At present, the exact nature of the oxidation product is not known. It is conceivable that redox regulation could be employed in vivo to regulate the activities of the many Fos and Jun family dimers. Substitution of the cysteine with serine results in active proteins that do not require high DTT or a cellular factor for DNA-binding activity (Abate et al. 1990a). Interestingly, v-*jun* and several other leucine zipper proteins contain serine in this position.

Two models of DNA-protein recognition have been proposed for leucine zipper proteins. In the scissors-grip model, an α-helical segment of each basic region contacts each half-site of the dyad symmetric DNA-binding domain by tracking continuously along the major groove (Vinson et al. 1989). To maintain continuous contact with DNA, a bend is envisioned in the basic region at the invariant asparagine residue. In contrast, in the induced helical fork model (O'Neil et al. 1990), no bend in the basic region is proposed. The DNA-binding domain is suggested to be a continuous α-helix extending from the leucine zipper. Both models are supported by data indicating that the DNA-binding domains of Fos, Jun, and GCN4 adopt an α-helical conformation when in contact with DNA (Patel et al. 1990; Talanian et al. 1990; Weiss et al. 1990). However, both models have the limitation that they assume that the proteins interact with standard B form DNA. Recent studies that utilize circular permutation and phasing analysis suggest that Fos-Jun heterodimers and Jun homodimers induce bending of the DNA substrate (Kerppola and Curran 1991). Interestingly, the orientation of the bend induced by Fos-Jun heterodimers is opposite to that induced by Jun homodimers. This may be consistent with UV cross-linking studies which suggest that the Fos-Jun complex makes asymmetric contacts with DNA (Risse et al. 1989). Thus, the DNA-protein interaction is a dynamic process that may involve structural alterations in protein and DNA. An alteration in Fos-

Jun structure in the presence of DNA has been implicated by studies using fluorescein-tagged proteins (Patel et al. 1990). This raises the interesting possibility that DNA-bound and non-DNA-bound protein complexes can be distinguished by conformational differences. At present, the exact nature of the structural transition and the specific DNA-protein contacts is not clear.

The leucine zipper and basic regions of Fos and Jun comprise the primary DNA-binding structure. However, amino acids outside this region have been shown to play a role in DNA binding (Cohen and Curran 1990; Ransone et al. 1990a). Recently, Jun has been shown to contain an ancillary DNA-binding domain (Abate et al. 1991). This region lies on the immediate amino-terminal side of the basic region and exhibits a high content of proline and glutamine residues. Early studies identified this region as being important for transcriptional activation (Bohmann and Tjian 1989). However, several other studies carried out in yeast (Struhl 1988), in mammalian cells (Angel et al. 1989; Hirai et al. 1990), and in soluble extracts derived from HeLa cells (Abate et al. 1991) did not reveal any transcription-enhancing activity in this region. The effect of the proline/glutamine-rich region on the DNA-binding activity of Jun homodimers was detected in gel shift assays but not in DNase I footprinting analysis (Abate et al. 1991). This may reflect the more sensitive nature of the gel shift assay to subtle alterations in the stability of DNA-protein interactions. Thus, the proline/glutamine-rich region of Jun may act to stabilize the protein-DNA interaction and thereby indirectly have an impact on transcriptional activation.

TRANSCRIPTIONAL REGULATION BY FOS AND JUN

Numerous studies have been published on the regulation of transcription by Fos and Jun in vivo and in vitro. It is clear that the regulatory functions of these proteins are complex and that they are affected by a multitude of independent parameters, including physiologically relevant variables as well as potentially trivial variations in conditions of assay. Thus, not all the published work is in agreement, and the results obtained from in vitro and in vivo experiments are sometimes contradictory. It is likely that the conclusions of some of these studies will be revised in the light of future discoveries, and to some extent this has already occurred. Rather than concentrating on the discrepancies among various reports, we attempt to relate the general findings. However, it should be kept in mind that Fos and Jun are only two of the proteins that contribute to a complex system that regulates gene transcription in response to environmental signals. In the studies that have been performed to date, many of the other components (transcription factors, enzymes, etc.) have not yet been defined.

TRANSCRIPTIONAL REGULATION IN VIVO

When tested individually in transient transfection assays, both *fos* and *jun* are capable of activating, to some degree, genes that contain an AP-1-binding site (see, e.g., Setoyama et al. 1986; Angel et al. 1988b). Evidence has also been presented that isolated segments of each protein can function as transcriptional "activation domains" when expressed as fusion proteins in yeast (Lech et al. 1988; Struhl 1988). Studies on the collagenase promoter have indicated that the activating effects of intact Fos protein are mediated by an AP-1 site (Lucibello et al. 1988; Schönthal et al. 1988). Since Fos does not bind to DNA efficiently as a homodimer, it is likely that these effects are dependent on interactions with members of the Jun or ATF/CREB families. When assayed in concert, *fos* and *jun* produce a dramatic synergistic activation of AP-1-dependent transcription (Chiu et al. 1988; Sassone-Corsi et al. 1988b; Muegge et al. 1989; Sonnenberg et al. 1989). A substantial degree of experimental variability has been encountered in these studies, particularly when the assays are performed in different cell types. Most of the published studies have been carried out using F9 teratocarcinoma cells. Although it was originally suggested that F9 cells contain no AP-1 activity (Angel et al. 1987), it is now clear that they do express several members of the Fos and Jun family and that cell extracts do exhibit AP-1 DNA-binding activity (Yang-Yen et al. 1990a). It is likely that the activities of Fos and Jun are influenced by other proteins that may be expressed in a cell-type-specific manner (Baichwal and Tjian 1990).

A competitive interaction between Fos-Jun heterodimers and the receptors for vitamins A and D has been observed using the 5′ regulatory region of the osteocalcin gene (Owen et al. 1990; Schüle et al. 1990a,b). In this case, Fos and Jun functioned as inhibitors of vitamin D_3-induced gene expression. Recent experiments have revealed a complex interaction between Fos, Jun, and the glucocorticoid receptor in the transcription of several genes (Diamond et al. 1990; Jonat et al. 1990; Lucibello et al. 1990; Schüle et al. 1990a,b; Yang-Yen et al. 1990b). In one study, the ratio of Fos to Jun was found to determine whether the glucocorticoid receptor functioned as a positive or negative regulator of the proliferin gene (Diamond et al. 1990). Fos and Jun can also stimulate transcription synergistically in association with the product of the *ets* oncogene (B. Wasylyk et al. 1990).

Taken together, these results indicate that the functions of Fos and

Jun are determined by the intracellular environment in which they are expressed. In each cell type, the presence of resident or inducible transcription factors may influence both the selection of gene targets and the transcriptional effect of Fos-Jun family heterodimers. Furthermore, as discussed previously, Fos and Jun can form heterodimeric complexes with members of the CREB/ATF families (Benbrook and Jones 1990; Ivashkiv et al. 1990; Macgregor et al. 1990; Hai and Curran 1991). These proteins may be expressed in a cell-type- and stimulus-specific manner. Moreover, in cotransfection assays, JunB has been reported to function as a repressor of transcription mediated by the canonical AP-1-binding site (Chiu et al. 1989). Thus, the formation of specific heterodimers in different cell types will also determine the function of Fos and Jun.

An additional level of complexity is provided by posttranslational modification. Both Fos and Jun are phosphorylated (Curran et al. 1984, 1987; Barber and Verma 1987; Müller et al. 1987), and the degree of phosphorylation of Fos can be affected by certain extracellular stimuli (Curran and Morgan 1986; Barber and Verma 1987; Morgan and Curran 1989; Boyle et al. 1991). Not surprisingly, Fos and Jun function in diverse signal transduction pathways (Morgan and Curran 1991). Thus, a great variety of parameters must be involved in determining their functional specificity. A cautionary note regarding the interpretation of cotransfection experiments arises from indications that both Fos (see below) and Jun (Angel et al. 1988a) exhibit autoregulatory properties. Moreover, they are known to affect expression of several immediate-early transcription factors (Gius et al. 1990). Therefore, it is difficult to distinguish specific activation functions of Fos and Jun from indirect effects resulting from alterations in the endogenous levels of other transcriptional regulatory proteins.

TRANSCRIPTIONAL REGULATION IN VITRO

The transcriptional functions of Fos and Jun have also been studied directly using in vitro transcription systems. For these studies, basal polymerase II promoter elements are linked to reiterated AP-1-binding sites. Such constructs have been tested using nuclear extracts depleted of endogenous AP-1 activity (by affinity chromatography or competition with oligonucleotides containing AP-1-binding sites) and supplemented with Fos and Jun polypeptides. Although these conditions may be considerably different from the typical environments in which Fos and Jun function (AP-1 sites are not usually reiterated and located adjacent to promoters), they have allowed the delineation of transcriptional regulatory domains in Fos and Jun. A summary of the functional domains in the Fos-Jun complex is illustrated in Figure 2.

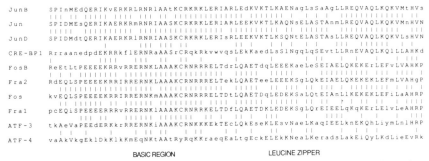

Figure 2 Sequence similarities among Fos, Jun, and ATF family members that form heterodimers. The sequences are listed so that the most closely related are adjacent to each other. Single-letter amino acid code is used: Uppercase and vertical bars indicate identity. The primary sequences obtained from a data base search are: JunB(mouse) (Ryder et al. 1988); Jun(human) (Hattori et al. 1988); JunD(mouse) (Ryder et al. 1989); CRE-BP1(human) (Maekawa et al. 1989); FosB(mouse) (Zerial et al. 1989); Fra-2(human) (Matsui et al. 1990); Fos(human) (van Straaten et al. 1983); Fra-1(rat) (Cohen and Curran 1988); ATF-3 and ATF-4 (human) (Hai et al. 1989). (Corrections have been made in the ATF-3 and ATF-4 sequences based on D. Cohen and T. Curran, unpubl.) The positions of the basic region and the leucine zipper are indicated. The alignment was prepared using the genalign program developed by Intelligenetics Inc. This figure is based on a more extensive alignment presented by Kerppola and Curran (1991).

Jun contains a single major transcriptional activation region located between amino acids 90 and 186 (Baichwal and Tjian 1990; Abate et al. 1991). This region can function as an activating domain when linked onto the GCN4 DNA-binding domain and assayed in *Saccharomyces cerevisiae* (Struhl 1988). This 96-amino-acid segment is rich in prolines and glycines and is the major activating domain of the Fos-Jun complex (Abate et al. 1990c). Two activating domains have been identified in Fos: an acidic region (amino acids 116–139) and a proline-acidic region (amino acids 211–270) (Abate et al. 1991). The proline-acidic region was also identified as an activating domain in cotransfection assays (Hirai et al. 1990). As expected, Fos does not function as a transcriptional activator on its own in vitro. Its in vitro function requires the Jun polypeptide, which must contain an intact leucine zipper and basic region. The two activating domains in Fos appear to function additively, whereas the Jun activating domain functions synergistically in association with those of Fos (Abate et al. 1990c, 1991). Analysis of the activating domains in Fos and Jun has been complicated by the presence of several domains that appear to exert a negative effect on transcription in vitro and in vivo. (Bohmann and Tjian 1989; Baichwal and Tjian 1990; Abate et al. 1991). A negative domain of Jun, termed the δ region, is located between amino acids 40 and 66. Intriguingly, this region is deleted in v-*jun*. The δ region of Jun has been proposed to interact with a cell-type-specific inhibitory protein (Baichwal and Tjian 1990). There are two negative domains in Fos, a proline-rich region between amino acids 58 and 116 and a carboxy-terminal region located between amino acids 321 and 380. In the context of the Fos-Jun heterodimer, the inhibitory regions of Fos are more potent than that of Jun (Abate et al. 1991).

An alternative hypothesis to the inhibitory protein concept is that these regions of Fos and Jun are regulatory sites that are affected by post-translational modification in vivo. The carboxy-terminal serine-rich region of Fos is also the domain that represses SRE-mediated transcriptional activation (see below). Thus, the transcriptional properties of the Fos-Jun heterodimer result from the integration of several positive and negative domains. These regions are only partially conserved among members of the *fos* and *jun* gene families. It is possible that each of the regions interacts with a specific protein involved in transcriptional regulation. The selection of target genes by various leucine zipper heterodimers could therefore be determined by a key-in-lock mechanism specified by multiple protein-protein contacts in addition to DNA binding.

REPRESSION OF SRE

As outlined in the preceding section, Fos can function as a positive or negative modulator of AP-1-dependent transcription. Fos can also act as a repressor of serum responsive element (SRE)-mediated transcription (see Treisman, this volume). This property was initially encountered as an autorepression effect of Fos. In cotransfection assays, Fos was observed to reduce both basal and inducible levels of transcription mediated by the c-*fos* promoter (Sassone-Corsi et al. 1988a; Wilson and Treisman 1988; Lucibello et al. 1989). Both the SRE (Konig et al. 1989; Subramanian et al. 1989; Gius et al. 1990; Rivera et al. 1990) and an AP-1 site (Sassone-Corsi et al. 1988a; Wilson and Treisman 1988) in the c-*fos* promoter have been implicated as targets of Fos-mediated repression. Very strong evidence has been presented that Fos-mediated repression can act through the SRE. This inhibitory effect is not restricted to the c-*fos* promoter. Fos can repress several SREs, including those located in the promoter of the immediate-early gene *egr-1* (Gius et al. 1990). There is some controversy concerning the region of Fos responsible for repression. Initially, a comparison of v-Fos and c-Fos implicated the carboxyl terminus of c-Fos in repression (Wilson and Treisman 1988). A detailed mutagenesis analysis confirmed this suggestion and mapped the negative regulatory region to a serine-rich domain in the carboxy-terminal 27 amino acids (Gius et al. 1990). Furthermore, c-Jun was found to be incapable of repressing SRE-mediated transcription and did not affect Fos-mediated repression. Consistent with these observations, fusion of the c-Fos carboxyl terminus to c-Jun conferred the repression function. In contrast, others suggested that Jun enhanced the repression function of Fos (Konig et al. 1989; Lucibello et al. 1989). Furthermore, in one of these studies, mutagenesis analysis implicated the leucine zipper in repression (Lucibello et al. 1989). However, in this case, most of the mutations were made and analyzed in a Fos protein that lacked the carboxyl terminus. The molecular mechanism of repression is not yet clear, although phosphorylation of the carboxyl terminus has been implicated (Ofir et al. 1990). The serine-rich carboxy-terminal region is conserved among Fos family members, and at least one of the *fos*-related genes, *fra-1* (Cohen and Curran 1988), is capable of repression. Thus, SRE repression by Fos-related proteins may provide a critical inhibitory component of the cellular immediate-early response to stimulation.

ONCOGENIC TRANSFORMATION BY FOS AND JUN

When considering the biochemical and molecular properties of transcription factors discussed in the previous section, it should be kept in mind that *fos* and *jun* are oncogenes. Under certain conditions, they are capable of causing dramatic alterations in cell growth. The molecular basis of cellular transformation is not yet known. However, it is presumed that the Fos and Jun proteins regulate expression, negatively or positively, of target genes whose products contribute to the neoplastic phenotype.

The isolation of *fos* and *jun* was part of a broad research effort on the induction of tumors by retroviruses (for review, see Weiss et al. 1982, 1985). Although the study of retrovirus-induced tumors dates back to the discovery of Rous sarcoma virus (RSV) (Rous 1910), modern retrovirology was shaped by the introduction of oncogenic transformation assays in cell culture (Temin and Rubin 1958) and the discovery of reverse transcriptase as the key enzyme in the retroviral life cycle (Baltimore 1970; Temin and Mizutani 1970; for review, see Varmus 1988). Retroviruses are comparatively simple viruses whose genome consists of two allelic positive-strand RNA molecules that replicate through a DNA intermediate. Because of their relatively small size, it was felt that retroviral genomes could only contain one gene, or a small number of genes, that conferred the oncogenic phenotype on the infected cell. The belief that such oncogenes existed was borne out by studies on RSV that led to the identification of *src*, the first gene whose expression was found to be sufficient for the induction of oncogenesis. Today more than 30 retroviral oncogenes are known (for review, see Bishop 1983, 1985). Their universal relevance for cancer and the control of cell growth in general became evident when it was discovered that they were derived from normal cellular genes that regulate cellular proliferation and differentiation (Stehelin et al. 1976; for review, see Bishop 1983; Varmus 1984).

The isolation of the *fos* and *jun* oncogenes illustrates several features of the field of oncogene research. In some animal species, notably the chicken and the cat, retrovirus-induced tumors are common and may constitute the majority of malignancies occurring in these animals. A significant proportion of these tumors contain retroviruses that have incorporated an oncogene into their genome and are able to transduce this cell-derived oncogenic information into other cells. Retroviruses isolated from spontaneous avian or feline tumors therefore constitute an important resource for the isolation of oncogenes. Although in several instances the same oncogene has been isolated from different retroviruses, it is likely that more oncogenes await discovery.

v-*jun* was identified in an oncogenic retrovirus that had been isolated from a spontaneous chicken sarcoma (Cavalieri et al. 1985). This virus, ASV-17, was part of a collection of similar pathogens obtained from the same chicken processing plant. The term *jun* alludes to the Japanese word for 17, *ju-nana* (Maki et al. 1987). v-*fos* was first found in murine retroviruses (Finkel et al. 1966, 1973). As part of a program to investigate health risks in the nuclear energy and defense industries, Dr. Miriam Finkel studied the role of viruses in spontaneous and radiation-induced bone tumors in mice. This effort culminated in the isolation of FBJ-MSV from a spontaneous bone tumor and FBR-MSV from a ^{90}Sr-induced tumor. The oncogene name *fos* was derived from the *F*BJ *o*steogenic *s*arcoma virus (Curran and Teich 1982a).

THE *JUN* TRANSFORMING GENE

Many oncogenes are significantly more oncogenic when they are transduced in mutated form by a retrovirus. Comparisons between the cellular and viral versions of the gene have in many instances identified the structural and functional changes that can turn the cellular gene into an efficient oncogene. Knowledge of these critical changes has greatly contributed to our understanding of oncogenic mechanisms.

ASV-17 induces fibrosarcomas and transforms avian embryo fibroblasts and primitive muscle cells in culture (Cavalieri et al. 1985;

Maki et al. 1987; Ball et al. 1988). In contrast to the in vivo and in vitro oncogenicity of the viral Jun protein (v-Jun), the cellular Jun protein (c-Jun) encoded by the chicken genome is significantly less efficient in deregulating cell growth (Bos et al. 1990). The retroviral vector RCAS (a construct based on the genome of nondefective RSV) has been used to express the v-*jun* insert of ASV-17 and the chicken c-*jun* derived from the cDNA of the cellular message. In chicken embryo fibroblast cultures, the two Jun proteins, expressed at comparable levels, show a striking difference in transforming efficiency. The construct carrying the viral gene induces about 20 times more transformed cell foci per milligram of DNA than does the construct containing the cellular gene.

In addition to this quantitative difference in oncogenic activity, there appears to be a qualitative difference as well: Although all the v-*jun*-induced foci release virus that is tumorigenic in the chicken, only a few of the c-*jun* foci do. The increase of oncogenic activity in v-*jun* must be caused by specific structural differences between the cellular and viral versions of the gene. Identification of these oncogenic changes pinpoints domains of the Jun protein that are important in transformation.

STRUCTURAL AND FUNCTIONAL REQUIREMENTS
FOR TRANSFORMATION BY JUN

A comparison of the nucleotide sequence of viral and cellular *jun* identifies four differences (Nishimura and Vogt 1988): (1) v-*jun* encodes a fusion protein with 220 amino-terminal amino acids derived from the retroviral *gag* gene. c-*jun* has no *gag* sequences. (2) v-*jun* has suffered an 81-nucleotide, in-frame deletion in the 5′ third of the *jun* coding domain. (3) There are three amino acid substitutions in the viral protein. (4) The v-*jun* message lacks the extensive 3′-nontranslated region of c-*jun*, including the presumed mRNA instability signal AUUUA. Deletion mutations and reciprocal recombinants between c-*jun* and v-*jun* indicate that two of these differences between the viral and cellular genes are necessary for efficient oncogenic transformation: removal of the 3′-untranslated region that contributes to message destabilization and introduction of the 27-amino-acid deletion in the *jun* coding domain (Bos et al. 1990). Either one of the changes alone is insufficient for high-level oncogenicity. The other two differences between viral and cellular *jun*, the presence of *gag* sequences and the amino acid substitutions in the carboxy-terminal half, may contribute to oncogenic transformation but do not appear to play a major role in determining transforming potential. In an interesting contrast to the chicken cellular gene, the mouse and human c-*jun* genes expressed in RSV-based vectors show greater transforming efficiency (Castellazzi et al. 1990; Suzuki et al. 1991; J.I. Morgan et al., unpubl.). The structural basis for this enhanced oncogenicity remains to be identified.

The 27-amino-acid deletion in v-Jun inactivates the δ region that functions as a negative control domain of trans-activation (Baichwal and Tjian 1990). Consequently, in the presence of the negative regulator interacting with the δ region, v-Jun is a more effective transcriptional activator than c-Jun, suggesting that transcriptional activation may be instrumental in bringing about oncogenic transformation by Jun (Bohmann and Tjian 1989). This suggestion is also supported by deletion analyses of Jun that correlate oncogenic transformation with transcriptional activation. In v-Jun, an amino-terminal deletion of 33 amino acids, leaving much of the main trans-activator domain intact, has a small but significant positive effect on transforming activity. A larger amino-terminal deletion of 109 amino acids removes a portion of the major activator domain and virtually abolishes oncogenicity in chicken cells.

A more extensive deletion analysis relating oncogenic transformation to transcriptional activation has been carried out with human c-Jun (Alani et al. 1991). Human c-Jun transforms the established rat fibroblast line R-1 acting as a single oncogene; it can also transform primary rat embryo fibroblasts, but in this cell it needs the cooperation of an activated ras oncogene. This ability of the human c-Jun to cotransform primary rat embryo fibroblasts shows a perfect correlation with trans-activation. All deletions affecting the function of the major trans-activator domain abolish oncogenic activity. There are two prerequisites for transcriptional activation by Jun: dimerization of the Jun protein with another molecule of Jun, with a molecule of Fos, or with another related leucine zipper protein; and sequence-specific binding to DNA. Mutations that interfere with either dimerization or DNA binding also abolish transforming activity.

Chicken cells transformed by ASV-17 or by RCAS vectors carrying an oncogenic variant of v-jun do not overexpress c-fos (T.J. Bos and P.K. Vogt, unpubl.). Sarcomas in v-jun transgenic mice also do not show an overexpression of c-fos, although they do overexpress v-jun (Schuh et al. 1990). Furthermore, transformation of chicken embryo fibroblasts by human c-jun is not correlated with increased fos expression (Suzuki et al. 1991). It is therefore likely that Jun-induced transformation is mediated primarily by Jun homodimers.

Recently, a potentially new function of Jun has been identified: By binding to an AP-1 site in the polyomavirus enhancer Jun can stimulate polyomavirus DNA synthesis (Murakami et al. 1990, 1991; C. Wasylyk et al. 1990). This observation raises the possibility that the oncogenic effect of Jun may be mediated by deregulating DNA synthesis rather than transcription. Preliminary tests using several Jun deletion mutants have indeed established a correlation between stimulation of polyomavirus DNA synthesis and oncogenic transformation. The amino-terminal deletion of *gag* sequences that causes enhanced transformation by Jun also stimulates DNA synthesis. The larger 109-amino-acid amino-terminal deletion that blocks transformation does not stimulate DNA synthesis. The short 33-amino-acid amino-terminal deletion of the *jun* coding domain shows somewhat reduced transforming and stimulatory activity for DNA synthesis (J.I. Morgan et al., unpubl.). The data suggest that the major *trans*-activator domain that is virtually removed by the more extensive deletion also plays a role in stimulating DNA synthesis. The possibility of a relationship between stimulation of DNA synthesis and oncogenic activity needs further study, however. Mutants that discriminate between *trans*-activation and stimulation of DNA synthesis could provide decisive information, but there are also indications from work on papillomaviruses that *trans*-activation and stimulation of DNA synthesis may be intimately related (Mohr et al. 1990). At present, both proposals, namely, that Jun transforms by deregulating transcription or by stimulating DNA synthesis, are compatible with available data.

EFFECTS OF JUN ON CELL GROWTH AND DIFFERENTIATION

Myoblasts obtained from skeletal muscle of chicken or quail embryos fuse into postmitotic myotubes during a few days of primary cell culture. They then go on to differentiate into striated muscle that can contract spontaneously in the culture dish. In the course of cell fusion and differentiation, muscle-specific genes are activated at the level of transcription. These include desmin, muscle-specific myosin, and creatine phosphokinase. The process of myoblast fusion and differentiation is inhibited by several oncogenes including *src*, *myc*, *ras*, and *fos* (for review, see Alemà and Tatò 1987; Boettiger 1989). Viral *jun* also prevents myoblast fusion and keeps the mononuclear cells in active, proliferative growth (M. Grossi and F. Tatò; H. Su et al.; both in prep.). The *jun*-transformed myoblasts also fail to turn on muscle-specific genes.

The expression of Jun prevents the initiation of a complex myogenic differentiation program, most likely by specifying a genetic program that is somehow incompatible with terminal cell differentiation. However, a few myotubes arise in clones of quail myoblasts infected with ASV-17 or with a v-*jun* expression vector. Interestingly, these myotubes expressing muscle-specific proteins do not express *jun* in their nuclei. Apparently, the transforming *jun* oncogene is either down-regulated or lost from the fusing myoblasts. A partially temperature-sensitive mutant of ASV-17, unable to produce foci at the restrictive temperature but still able to induce colony formation in soft agar, is also temperature-sensitive with respect to its interference with myogenesis (H. Su et al.; in prep.). This mutant allows the formation of large myotubes under nonpermissive conditions, and mutated *jun* product is expressed in these myotubes. Not surprisingly, the differentiation inhibitory activity of Jun is correlated with oncogenic potential. Jun deletion mutants that fail to transform avian fibroblasts do not interfere with myogenesis; chicken c-Jun, which is only weakly oncogenic, is also inefficient in blocking differentiation.

Myogenic differentiation in culture offers challenging opportunities to study gene regulation. The key muscle-specific proteins are well characterized, and their genes have been cloned (see, e.g., Buckingham 1985; for review, see Rosenthal 1989). Several genes controlling the differentiation of skeletal muscle have been isolated and sequenced. The prototype is MyoD, a transcriptional regulator characterized by a basic DNA-binding domain and an adjacent helix-loop-helix dimerization region (Davis et al. 1987; Tapscott et al. 1988; Weintraub et al. 1989; also, see Lassar and Weintraub, this volume). Related genes belonging to the MyoD family include *myogenin*, *Myf5*, *MRF4*, and in avian species, *CMD-1* and *qmf-1* (for review, see Olson 1990). The products of these genes bind to *cis*-acting sequences of muscle-specific genes, thereby controlling transcription. Inhibitors of myogenesis are now being studied for their interaction with these muscle-specific regulators. Growth factors, as well as certain activated oncogenes that prevent muscle differentiation (e.g., *fos* and *ras*) have already been shown to interfere with the expression of MyoD (Konieczny et al. 1989; Lassar et al. 1989). For oncogenic *jun*, this also appears to be a reasonable, albeit untested, assumption. The stage thus seems to be set for a molecular analysis of the interaction between *jun* and *fos* and the myogenic differentiation program.

An interesting effect is seen if human c-Jun is ectopically expressed in P19 mouse embryonal carcinoma cells (de Groot et al. 1990). The cells lose their oncogenic phenotype and differentiate into endoderm and mesoderm-like colonies. A possible mechanism for this differentiation-promoting effect of c-Jun is a transient activation of the promoter of the retinoic acid receptor (RAR)β gene. c-Jun, by acting synergistically with RARα, may activate transcription from the RARβ gene. Up-regulated RARβ is known to induce the differentiation of embryonal carcinoma cells. The observations on the role of Jun in retinoic-acid-dependent differentiation call to mind recent reports on a direct interaction between Jun and steroid hormone receptors (Diamond et al. 1990; Schüle et al. 1990a,b). As mentioned earlier in this chapter, there may be widespread

al. 1988a), the nonfunctional heterodimer will predominate in equimolar mixtures of Fos and Jun. Thus, mutated derivatives of Fos lacking a functional basic region can suppress the DNA-binding activity of Jun *in trans*. This was first revealed in mutagenesis studies that examined the effects of DNA-binding activity in vitro (Gentz et al. 1989), and it was later shown that mutated *fos* genes could suppress the transcriptional activity of *jun* in cotransfection assays (Ransone et al. 1990a). This procedure has now been applied to the study of cellular transformation. A suppressor *fos* gene (sup*fos*) with a nonfunctional DNA-binding domain reverses cellular transformation by *jun* (H. Okuno et al., in prep.). Furthermore, cells expressing sup*fos* can no longer be transformed by viruses that carry c-*jun*. Such observations support the view that cellular transformation by *jun* is mediated by transcriptionally active homodimers. Leucine zipper suppressor genes could be used to investigate the functional consequences of *fos* and *jun* expression in numerous environments. At present, no naturally occurring proteins have been identified that could function as suppressor molecules to regulate the function of Fos or Jun in the same way that the Id protein has been suggested to regulate MyoD (Benezra et al. 1990).

The fact that two independently isolated oncogenes function as a dimeric transcription factor complex implies that a limited number of signaling pathways are involved in cell transformation. Indeed, several other oncogenes, including *ras*, *sis*, *erb^B*, *ets*, and *src*, to name but a few, impinge on different aspects of this pathway (for review, see Reddy et al. 1988). Thus, the study of retroviral genetics has revealed a complex signal transduction cascade that conveys information from the outside of the cell, through a series of proto-oncogenes, to the nucleus. In the nucleus, complex interactions among transcription factors, second messengers, and the genome interpret these signals into the selective regulation of gene expression. In this fashion, the normal cell responds appropriately and the cancer cell responds inappropriately to environmental cues.

ACKNOWLEDGMENTS

P.K.V. is supported by U.S. Public Health Service research grant CA-42564 and by grant 1951 from the Council for Tobacco Research. We thank Sarah Olivo, Esther Olivo, and Arianne Helenkamp for their help in producing the manuscript.

REFERENCES

Abate, C., D. Luk, and T. Curran. 1990a. A ubiquitous nuclear protein stimulates the DNA-binding activity of Fos and Jun indirectly. *Cell Growth Differ.* **1:** 455–462.

————. 1991. Transcriptional regulation by Fos and Jun *in vitro:* Interaction among multiple activator and regulatory domains. *Mol. Cell. Biol.* **11:** 3624–3632.

Abate, C., L. Patel, F.J. Rauscher III, and T. Curran. 1990b. Redox regulation of Fos and Jun DNA-binding activity in vitro. *Science* **249:** 1157–1161.

Abate, C., D. Luk, E. Gagne, R.G. Roeder, and T. Curran. 1990c. Fos and Jun cooperate in transcriptional regulation via heterologous activation domains. *Mol. Cell. Biol.* **10:** 5532–5535.

Abate, C., D. Luk, R. Gentz, F.J. Rauscher III, and T. Curran. 1990d. Expression and purification of the leucine zipper and the DNA-binding domains of Fos and Jun: Both Fos and Jun directly contact DNA. *Proc. Natl. Acad. Sci.* **87:** 1032–1036.

Alani, R., P. Brown, B. Binetruy, H. Dosaka, R. Rosenberg, P. Angel, M. Karin, and M.J. Birrer. 1991. The transactivating domain of the c-Jun proto-oncoprotein is required for cotransformation of rat embryo cells. *Mol. Cell. Biol.* **11:** 6286–6295.

Alemà, S. and F. Tatò. 1987. Interaction of retroviral oncogenes with the differentiation program of myogenic cells. *Adv. Cancer Res.* **49:** 1–28.

Angel, P., K. Hattori, T. Smeal, and M. Karin. 1988a. The *jun* proto-oncogene is positively autoregulated by its product, Jun/AP-1. *Cell* **55:** 875–885.

Angel, P., T. Smeal, J. Meek, and M. Karin. 1989. *jun* and v-*jun* contain multiple regions that participate in transcriptional activation in an interdependent manner. *New Biol.* **1:** 35–43.

Angel, P., E.A. Allegretto, S.T. Okino, K. Hattori, W.J. Boyle, T. Hunter, and M. Karin. 1988b. Oncogene *jun* encodes a sequence-specific *trans*-activator similar to AP-1. *Nature* **332:** 166–171.

Angel, P., M. Imagawa, R. Chiu, B. Stein, R.J. Imbra, H.J. Rahmsdorf, C. Jonat, P. Herrlich, and M. Karin. 1987. Phorbol ester-inducible genes contain a common *cis* element recognized by a TPA-modulated *trans*-acting factor. *Cell* **49:** 729–739.

Baichwal, V.R. and R. Tjian. 1990. Control of c-Jun activity by interaction of a cell-specific inhibitor with regulatory domain δ: Differences between v and c-Jun. *Cell* **63:** 815–825.

Ball, A.R., Jr., T.J. Bos, C. Löliger, L.P. Nagata, T. Nishimura, H. Su, H. Tsuchie, and P.K. Vogt. 1988. *jun*: Oncogene and transcriptional regulator. *Cold Spring Harbor Symp. Quant. Biol.* **53:** 687–693.

Baltimore, D. 1970. RNA dependent DNA polymerase in virions of RNA tumour viruses. *Nature* **226:** 1209–1211.

Barber, J.R. and I.M. Verma. 1987. Modification of *fos* proteins: Phosphorylation of c-*fos*, but not v-*fos*, is stimulated by 12-tetradecanoyl-phorbol-13-acetate and serum. *Mol. Cell. Biol.* **7:** 2201–2211.

Benbrook, D.M. and N.C. Jones. 1990. Heterodimer formation between CREB and JUN proteins. *Oncogene* **5:** 295–302.

Benezra, R.R., L. Davis, D. Lockshon, D. Turner, and H. Weintraub. 1990. The protein Id: A negative regulator of helix-loop-helix DNA binding proteins. *Cell* **61:** 49–59.

Bishop, J.M. 1983. Cellular oncogenes and retroviruses. *Annu. Rev. Biochem.* **52:** 301–354.

————. 1985. Viral oncogenes. *Cell* **42:** 23–38.

Boettiger, D. 1989. Interaction of oncogenes with differentiation programs. *Curr. Top. Microbiol. Immunol.* **147:** 31–78.

Bohmann, D. and R. Tjian. 1989. Biochemical analysis of transcriptional activation by Jun: Differential activity of c- and v-Jun. *Cell* **59:** 709–717.

Bohmann, D., T.J. Bos, A. Admon, T. Nishimura, P.K. Vogt, and R. Tjian. 1987. Human proto-oncogene c-*jun* encodes a DNA binding protein with structural and functional properties of transcription factor AP-1. *Science* **238**: 1386–1392.

Bos, T.J., F.J. Rauscher III, T. Curran, and P.K. Vogt. 1989. The carboxy terminus of the viral-Jun oncoprotein is required for complex formation with the cellular Fos protein. *Oncogene* **4**: 123–126.

Bos, T.J., D. Bohmann, H. Tsuchie, R. Tjian, and P.K. Vogt. 1988. v-*jun* encodes a nuclear protein with enhancer binding properties of AP-1. *Cell* **52**: 705–712.

Bos, T.J., F.S. Monteclaro, F. Mitsunobu, A.R. Ball, Jr., C.H.W. Chang, T. Nishimura, and P.K. Vogt. 1990. Efficient transformation of chicken embryo fibroblasts by c-Jun requires structural modification in coding and noncoding sequences. *Genes Dev.* **4**: 1677–1687.

Boyle, W.J., T. Smeal, L.H.K. Defize, P. Angel, J.R. Woodgett, M. Karin, and T. Hunter. 1991. Activation of protein kinase C decreases phosphorylation of c-Jun at sites that negatively regulate its DNA-binding activity. *Cell* **64**: 573–584.

Buckingham, M.E. 1985. Actin and myosin multigene families: Their expression during the formation of skeletal muscle. *Essays Biochem.* **20**: 79–109.

Castellazzi, M., J.-P. Dangy, F. Mechta, S.-I. Hirai, M. Yaniv, J. Samarut, A. Lassailly, and G. Brun. 1990. Overexpression of avian or mouse c-*jun* in primary chick embryo fibroblasts confers a partially transformed phenotype. *Oncogene* **5**: 1541–1547.

Cavalieri, F., T. Ruscio, R. Tinoco, S. Benedict, C. Davis, and P.K. Vogt. 1985. Isolation of three new avian sarcoma viruses: ASV 9, ASV 17, and ASV 25. *Virology* **143**: 680–683.

Chiu, R., P. Angel, and M. Karin. 1989. Jun-B differs in its biological properties from, and is a negative regulator of, c-Jun. *Cell* **59**: 979–986.

Chiu, R., W.J. Boyle, J. Meek, T. Smeal, T. Hunter, and M. Karin. 1988. The c-Fos protein interacts with c-Jun/AP-1 to stimulate transcription of AP-1 responsive genes. *Cell* **54**: 541–552.

Cohen, D.R. and T. Curran. 1988. *fra*-1: A serum-inducible, cellular immediate-early gene that encodes a Fos-related antigen. *Mol. Cell. Biol.* **8**: 2063–2069.

———. 1990. Analysis of dimerization and DNA binding functions in Fos and Jun by domain-swapping: Involvement of residues outside of the leucine zipper/basic region. *Oncogene* **5**: 929–939.

Cohen, D.R., P.C.P. Ferreira, R. Gentz, B.R. Franza, Jr., and T. Curran. 1989. The product of a *fos*-related gene, *fra*-1, binds cooperatively to the AP-1 site with Jun: Transcription factor AP-1 is comprised of multiple protein complexes. *Genes Dev.* **3**: 173–184.

Crick, F.H.C. 1953. The packing of α helices: Simple coiled coils. *Acta Crystallogr.* **6**: 689–697.

Curran, T. 1988. The *fos* oncogene. In *The oncogene handbook* (ed. E.P. Reddy et al.), pp. 307–325. Elsevier, Amsterdam.

———. 1991. Fos and Jun: Intermediary transcription factors. In *Molecular aspects of cellular regulation* (ed. P. Cohen and J.G. Foulkes), vol. 6, pp. 295–308. Elsevier, Amsterdam.

Curran, T. and B.R. Franza, Jr. 1988. Fos and Jun: The AP-1 connection. *Cell* **55**: 395–397.

Curran, T. and J.I. Morgan. 1986. Barium modulates c-*fos* expression and post-translational modification. *Proc. Natl. Acad. Sci.* **83**: 8521–8524.

Curran, T. and N.M. Teich. 1982a. Candidate product of the FBJ murine osteosarcoma virus oncogene: Characterization of a 55,000-dalton phosphoprotein. *J. Virol.* **42**: 114–122.

———. 1982b. Identification of a 39,000-dalton protein in cells transformed by the FBJ murine osteosarcoma virus. *Virology* **116:** 221–235.

Curran, T. and I.M. Verma. 1984. FBR murine osteosarcoma virus. I. Molecular analysis and characterization of a 75,000-dalton *gag-fos* fusion product. *Virology* **135:** 218–228.

Curran, T., M.B. Gordon, K.L. Rubino, and L.C. Sambucetti. 1987. Isolation and characterization of the c-*fos*(rat) cDNA and analysis of post-translational modification *in vitro*. *Oncogene* **2:** 79–84.

Curran, T., A.D. Miller, L. Zokas, and I.M. Verma. 1984. Viral and cellular *fos* proteins: A comparative analysis. *Cell* **36:** 259–268.

Curran, T., C. Van Beveren, N. Ling, and I.M. Verma. 1985. Viral and cellular *fos* proteins are complexed with a 39,000 dalton cellular protein. *Mol. Cell. Biol.* **5:** 167–172.

Curran, T., G. Peters, C. Van Beveren, N.M. Teich, and I.M. Verma. 1982. FBJ murine osteosarcoma virus: Identification and molecular cloning of biologically active proviral DNA. *J. Virol.* **44:** 674–682.

Davis, R.L., W. Weintraub, and A.B. Lassar. 1987. Expression of a single transfected cDNA converts fibroblasts to myoblasts. *Cell* **51:** 987–1000.

de Groot, R.P., F.A.E. Kruyt, P.T. Van Der Saag, and W. Kruijer. 1990. Ectopic expression of c-*jun* leads to differentiation of P19 embryonal carcinoma cells. *EMBO J.* **9:** 1831–1837.

Diamond, M.I., J.N. Miner, S.K. Yoshinaga, and K.R. Yamamoto. 1990. Transcription factor interactions: Selectors of positive or negative regulation from a single DNA element. *Science* **249:** 1266–1272.

Distel, R.J., H.-S. Ro, B.S. Rosen, D.L. Groves, and B.M. Spiegelman. 1987. Nucleoprotein complexes that regulate gene expression in adipocyte differentiation: Direct participation of c-*fos*. *Cell* **49:** 835–844.

Finkel, M.P. and B.O. Biskis. 1968. Experimental induction of osteosarcomas. *Prog. Exp. Tumor Res.* **10:** 72–111.

Finkel, M.P., B.O. Biskis, and P.B. Jinkins. 1966. Virus induction of osteosarcomas in mice. *Science* **151:** 698–701.

Finkel, M.P., C.A. Reilly, Jr., B.O. Biskis, and I.L. Greco. 1973. Bone tumor viruses. (*Colston Papers*) *Colston Res. Soc. Proc. Symp.* **24:** 353–366.

Foulkes, N.S., B.M. Laoide, F. Schlotter, and P. Sassone-Corsi. 1991. Transcriptional antagonist cAMP-responsive element modulator (CREM) down-regulates c-Fos cAMP-induced expression. *Proc. Natl. Acad. Sci.* **88:** 5448–5452.

Franza, B.R., Jr., F.J. Rauscher III, S.F. Josephs, and T. Curran. 1988. The Fos complex and Fos-related antigens recognize sequence elements that contain AP-1 binding sites. *Science* **239:** 1150–1153.

Friedman, A.D., S.J. Trezenberg, and S.L. McKnight. 1988. Expression of a truncated viral *trans*-activator selectively impedes lytic infection by its cognate virus. *Nature* **335:** 452–454.

Gentz, R., F.J. Rauscher III, C. Abate, and T. Curran. 1989. Parallel association of Fos and Jun leucine zippers juxtaposes DNA binding domains. *Science* **243:** 1695–1699.

Gius, D., X. Cao, F.J. Rauscher III, D.R. Cohen, T. Curran, and V.P. Sukhatme. 1990. Transcriptional activation and repression by Fos are independent functions: The C-terminus represses immediate-early gene expression via CArG elements. *Mol. Cell. Biol.* **10:** 4243–4255.

Hai, T. and T. Curran. 1991. Fos/Jun and ATF/CREB cross-family dimerization alters DNA binding specificity. *Proc. Natl. Acad. Sci.* **88:** 3720–3724.

Hai, T., F. Liu, W.J. Coukos, and M.R. Green. 1989. Transcription factor ATF cDNA clones: An extensive family of leucine zipper proteins able to selectively form DNA-binding heterodimers. *Genes Dev.* **3:** 2083–2090.

Halazonetis, T.D., K. Georgopoulous, M.E. Greenberg, and P. Leder. 1988. c-Jun dimerizes with itself and with c-Fos, forming complexes of different DNA binding affinities. *Cell* **55:** 917–924.

Hattori, K., P. Angel, M.M. Le Beau, and M. Karin. 1988. Structure and chromosomal localization of the functional intronless human JUN protooncogene. *Proc. Natl. Acad. Sci.* **85:** 9148–9152.

Hirai, S.-I. and M. Yaniv. 1989. Jun DNA-binding is modulated by mutations between the leucines or by direct interaction of Fos with the TGACTCA sequence. *New Biol.* **1:** 181–191.

Hirai, S.-I., B. Bourachot, and M. Yaniv. 1990. Both Jun and Fos contribute to transcription activation by the heterodimer. *Oncogene* **5:** 39–46.

Holt, J.T., T.V. Gopal, A.D. Moulton, and A.W. Nienhuis. 1986. Inducible production of c-*fos* antisense RNA inhibits 3T3 cell proliferation. *Proc. Natl. Acad. Sci.* **83:** 4794–4798.

Hope, I.A. and K. Struhl. 1987. GCN4, a eukaryotic transcriptional activator protein, binds as a dimer to target DNA. *EMBO J.* **6:** 2781–2784.

Hu, J.C., E.K. O'Shea, P.S. Kim, and R.T. Sauer. 1990. Sequence requirements for coiled-coils: Analysis with λ repressor-GCN4 leucine zipper fusions. *Science* **250:** 1400–1403.

Iba, H., Y. Shindo, H. Nishina, and T. Yoshida. 1988. Transforming potential and growth stimulating activity of the v-*fos* and c-*fos* genes carried by avian retrovirus vectors. *Oncogene Res.* **2:** 121–133.

Imler, J.L., E. Ugarte, C. Wasylyk, and B. Wasylyk. 1988. v-*jun* is a transcriptional activator, but not in all cell lines. *Nucleic Acid Res.* **16:** 3005–3012.

Ito, E., J.L. Sonnenberg, and R. Narayanan. 1989. Nerve growth factor-induced differentiation in PC-12 cells is blocked by *fos* oncogene. *Oncogene* **4:** 1193–1199.

Ivashkiv, L.B., H.-C. Liou, C.J. Kara, W.W. Lamph, I.M. Verma, and L.H. Glimcher. 1990. mXBP/CRE-BP2 and c-Jun form a complex which binds to the cyclic AMP, but not to the 12-*O*-tetradecanoylphorbol-13-acetate, response element. *Mol. Cell. Biol.* **10:** 1609–1621.

Jenuwein, T. and R. Müller. 1987. Structure-function analysis of *fos* protein: A single amino acid change activates the immortalizing potential of v-*fos*. *Cell* **48:** 647–657.

Jenuwein, T., D. Müller, T. Curran, and R. Müller. 1985. Extended life span and tumorigenicity of nonestablished mouse connective tissue cells transformed by the *fos* oncogene of FBR-MSV. *Cell* **41:** 629–637.

Jonat, C., H.J. Rahmsdorf, K.-K. Park, A.C.B. Cato, S. Gebel, H. Ponta, and P. Herrlich. 1990. Antitumor promotion and antiinflammation: Down-modulation of AP-1 (Fos/Jun) activity by glucocorticoid hormone. *Cell* **62:** 1189–1204.

Kara, C.J., H.-C. Liou, L.B. Ivashkiv, and L.H. Glimcher. 1990. A cDNA for a cyclic AMP response element binding protein which is distinct from CREB and expressed preferentially in brain. *Mol. Cell. Biol.* **10:** 1347–1357.

Kerppola, T.K. and T. Curran. 1991. Transcription factor interactions: Basics on zippers. *Curr. Opin. Biol.* **1:** 71–79.

Konieczny, S.F., B.L. Drobes, S.L. Menke, and F.J. Taparowsky. 1989. Inhibition of myogenic differentiation by the H-*ras* oncogene is associated with the down regulation of the MyoD1 gene. *Oncogene* **4:** 473–481.

Konig, H., H. Ponta, U. Rahmsdorf, M. Buscher, A. Schönthal, H. Ramsdorf, and P. Herrlich. 1989. Autoregulation of Fos: The dyad symmetry element as the major target of repression. *EMBO J.* **8:** 2559–2566.

Kouzarides, T. and E. Ziff. 1988. The role of the leucine zipper in the fos-jun interaction. *Nature* **336:** 646–651.

—————. 1989. Leucine zippers of *fos, jun* and GCN4 dictate dimerization specificity and thereby control DNA binding. *Nature* **340:** 568–571.

Landschulz, W.H., P.F. Johnson, and S.L. McKnight. 1988a. The leucine zipper: A hypothetical structure common to a new class of DNA binding proteins. *Science* **240:** 1759–1764.

—————. 1989. The DNA binding domain of the rat liver nuclear protein C/EBP is bipartite. *Science* **243:** 1681–1688.

Landschulz, W.H., P.F. Johnson, E.Y. Adashi, B.J. Graves, and S.L. McKnight. 1988b. Isolation of a recombinant copy of the gene encoding C/EBP. *Genes Dev.* **2:** 786–800.

Lassar, A.B., M.J. Thayer, R.W. Overell, and H. Weintraub. 1989. Transformation by activated Ras or Fos prevent myogenesis by inhibiting expression of MyoD1. *Cell* **5:** 659–667.

Lech, K., K. Anderson, and R. Brent. 1988. DNA-bound Fos proteins activate transcription in yeast. *Cell* **52:** 179–184.

Lee, W., P. Mitchell, and R. Tjian. 1987. Purified transcription factor AP-1 interacts with TPA-inducible enhancer elements. *Cell* **49:** 741–752.

Lucibello, F.C., C. Lowag, M. Neuberg, and R. Müller. 1989. *Trans*-repression of the mouse c-*fos* promoter: A novel mechanism of Fos-mediated *trans*-regulation. *Cell* **59:** 999–1007.

Lucibello, F.C., E.P. Slater, K.U. Jooss, M. Beato, and R. Müller. 1990. Mutual *trans*-repression of Fos and the glucocorticoid receptor: Involvement of a functional domain in Fos which is absent in FosB. *EMBO J.* **9:** 2827–2834.

Lucibello, F.C., M. Neuberg, J.B. Hunter, T. Jenuwein, M. Schuermann, R. Wallich, B. Stein, A. Schönthal, P. Herrlich, and R. Müller. 1988. Transactivation of gene expression by *fos* protein: Involvement of a binding site for the transcription factor AP-1. *Oncogene* **3:** 43–51.

Macgregor, P.F., C. Abate, and T. Curran. 1990. Direct cloning of leucine zipper proteins: Jun binds cooperatively to the CRE with CRE-BP1. *Oncogene* **5:** 451–458.

Maekawa, T., H. Sakura, C. Kanei-Ishii, T. Sudo, T. Yoshimura, J. Fujisawa, M. Yoshida, and S. Ishii. 1989. Leucine zipper structure of the protein CREBP1 binding to the cAMP response element in brain. *EMBO J.* **8:** 2023–2028.

Maki, Y., T.J. Bos, C. Davis, M. Starbuck, and P.K. Vogt. 1987. Avian sarcoma virus 17 carries the jun oncogene. *Proc. Natl. Acad. Sci.* **84:** 2848–2852.

Matsui, M., M. Tokuhara, Y. Konuma, N. Nomura, and R. Ishizaki. 1990. Isolation of human fos-related genes and their expression during monocyte-macrophage differentiation. *Oncogene* **5:** 249–255.

Meijlink, F., T. Curran, A.D. Miller, and I.M. Verma. 1985. Removal of a 67 base pair sequence in the noncoding region of the proto-oncogene *fos* converts it to a transforming gene. *Proc. Natl. Acad. Sci.* **82:** 4987–4991.

Miller, A.D., I.M. Verma, and T. Curran. 1985. Deletion of the *gag* region from FBR murine osteosarcoma virus does not affect its enhanced transforming activity. *J. Virol.* **55:** 521–526.

Mohr, I.J., R. Clark, S. Sun, E.J. Androphy, P. MacPherson, and M.R. Botchan. 1990. Targeting the E1 replication protein to the papillomavirus origin of replication by complex formation with the E2 transactivator. *Science* **250:** 1694–1699.

Morgan, J.I. and T. Curran. 1989. Stimulus-transcription coupling in neurons: Role of cellular immediate-early genes. *Trends Neurosci.* **12:** 459–462.

—————. 1991. Stimulus-transcription coupling in the nervous system: Involvement of the inducible proto-oncogenes *fos* and *jun*. *Annu. Rev. Neurosci.* **14**: 421–451.

Muegge, K., T.M. William, J.A. Kant, M. Karin, R. Chiu, A. Schmidt, U. Siebenlist, H.A. Young, and S.K. Durum. 1989. Interleukin 1 costimulatory activity on the interleukin 2 promoter via AP-1. *Science* **246**: 249–251.

Müller, R. and E. Wagner. 1984. Differentiation of F9 teratocarcinoma stem cells after transfer of c-*fos* proto-oncogenes. *Nature* **311**: 438–442.

Müller, R., R. Bravo, J. Burckhardt, and T. Curran. 1984. Induction of c-*fos* gene and protein by growth factors precedes activation of c-*myc*. *Nature* **312**: 716–720.

Müller, R., R. Bravo, D. Müller, C. Kurz, and R. Rentz. 1987. Different types of modification in c-*fos* and its associated protein p39: Modulation of DNA binding by phosphorylation. *Oncogene Res.* **2**: 19–32.

Murakami, Y., M. Asano, M. Satake, and Y. Ito. 1990. A tumor promoting phorbol ester, TPA, enhances polyomavirus DNA replication by activating the function of the viral enhancer. *Oncogene* **5**: 5–13.

Murakami, Y., M. Satake, Y. Yamaguchi-Iwai, M. Sakai, M. Muaramatsu, and Y. Ito. 1991. The nuclear oncogenes, c-*jun* and c-*fos*, as regulators of DNA replication. *Proc. Natl. Acad. Sci.* **88**: 3947–3951.

Nakabeppu, Y. and D. Nathans. 1989. The basic region of Fos mediates specific DNA binding. *EMBO J.* **8**: 3833–3841.

———. 1991. A naturally occurring truncated form of Fos B that inhibits Fos/Jun transcriptional activity. *Cell* **64**: 751–759.

Nakabeppu, Y., K. Ryder, and D. Nathans. 1988. DNA-binding activities of three murine *jun* proteins: Stimulation by *fos*. *Cell* **55**: 907–915.

Neuberg, M., M. Schuermann, J.B. Hunter, and R. Müller. 1989. Two functionally different regions in Fos are required for the sequence-specific DNA interaction of the Fos/Jun protein complex. *Nature* **338**: 589–590.

Nicklen, M.J.H. and G. Casari. 1990. A single site mutation in a truncated Fos protein allows it to interact with the TRE *in vitro*. *Oncogene* **6**: 173–179..

Nishikura, K. and J.M. Murray. 1987. Antisense RNA of proto-oncogene c-*fos* blocks renewed growth of quiescent 3T3 cells. *Mol. Cell. Biol.* **7**: 639–649.

Nishimura, T. and P.K. Vogt. 1988. The avian cellular homolog of the oncogene *jun*. *Oncogene* **3**: 659–663.

Nishizawa, M., N. Goto, and S. Kawai. 1987. An avian transforming retrovirus isolated from a nephroblastoma that carries the *fos* gene as the oncogene. *J. Virol.* **61**: 3733.

Ofir, R., V.J. Dwarki, D. Rashid, and I.M. Verma. 1990. Phosphorylation of the C terminus of Fos protein is required for transcriptional transrepression of the c-*fos* promoter. *Nature* **348**: 80–83.

Olson, E.N. 1990. MyoD family: A paradigm for development? *Genes Dev.* **4**: 1454–1461.

O'Neil, K.T., R.H. Hoess, and W.F. DeGrado. 1990. Design of DNA-binding peptides based on the leucine zipper motif. *Science* **249**: 774–778.

O'Shea, E.K., R. Rutkowski, and P.S. Kim. 1989a. Evidence that the leucine zipper is a coiled coil. *Science* **243**: 538–542.

———. 1992. Mechanism of specificity in the Fos-Jun oncoprotein heterodimer. *Cell* **68**: 699–708.

O'Shea, E.K., R. Rutkowski, W.F. Stafford III, and P.S. Kim. 1989b. Preferential heterodimer formation by isolated leucine zippers from Fos and Jun. *Science* **245**: 646–648.

Owen, T.A., R. Bortell, S.A. Yocum, S.L. Smock, M. Zhang, C. Abate, V. Shalhoub, N. Aronin, K.L. Wright, A.J. van Wijnen, J.L. Stein, T. Curran, J.B. Lian, and G.S. Stein.

1990. Coordinate occupancy of AP-1 sites in the vitamin D responsive and CCAAT box elements by Fos-Jun in the osteocalcin gene: A model for phenotype suppression of transcription. *Proc. Natl. Acad. Sci.* **87:** 9990–9994.

Patel, L., C. Abate, and T. Curran. 1990. Altered protein conformation on DNA binding by Fos and Jun. *Nature* **347:** 572–575.

Price, C.H.G., M. Moore, and D.B. Jones. 1972. FBJ virus-induced tumors in mice: A histopathological study of FBJ virus tumors and their relevance to murine and human osteosarcoma arising in bone. *Br. J. Cancer* **26:** 15–27.

Ransone, L.J., J. Visvader, P. Sassone-Corsi, and I.M. Verma. 1989. Fos-Jun interaction: Mutational analysis of the leucine zipper domain of both proteins. *Genes Dev.* **3:** 770–781.

Ransone, L.J., J. Visvader, P. Wamsley, and I.M. Verma. 1990a. *Trans*-dominant negative mutants of Fos and Jun. *Proc. Natl. Acad. Sci.* **87:** 3806–3810.

Ransone, L.J., P. Wamsley, K.L. Morley, and I.M. Verma. 1990b. Domain swapping reveals the modular nature of Fos, Jun and CREB proteins. *Mol. Cell. Biol.* **10:** 4565–4573.

Rauscher, F.J., III, P.J. Voulalas, B.R. Franza, Jr., and T. Curran. 1988a. Fos and jun bind cooperatively to the AP-1 site: Reconstitution in vitro. *Genes Dev.* **2:** 1687–1699.

Rauscher, F.J., III, L.C. Sambucetti, T. Curran, R.J. Distel, and B.M. Spiegelman. 1988b. Common DNA binding site for Fos protein complexes and transcription factor AP-1. *Cell* **52:** 471–480.

Rauscher, F.J., III, D.R. Cohen, T. Curran, T.J. Bos, P.K. Vogt, D. Bohmann, R. Tjian, and B.R.Franza, Jr. 1988c. Fos-associated protein p39 is the product of the *jun* proto-oncogene. *Science* **240:** 1010–1016.

Reddy, E.P., A.M. Skalka, and T. Curran, eds. 1988. *The oncogene handbook.* Elsevier, Amsterdam.

Riabowol, K.T., R.J. Bosatka, E.B. Ziff, N.J. Lamb, and J.R. Feramisco. 1988. Micro-injection of Fos specific antibodies blocks DNA synthesis in fibroblast cells. *Mol. Cell. Biol.* **8:** 1670–1677.

Risse, G., K. Jooss, M. Neuberg, H.-J. Brüller, and R. Müller. 1989. Asymmetrical recognition of the palindromic AP1 binding site (TRE) by Fos protein complexes. *EMBO J.* **8:** 3825–3832.

Rivera, V.M. and M.E. Greenberg. 1990. Growth factor-induced gene expression: The ups and downs of c-*fos* regulation. *New Biol.* **2:** 751–758.

Rivera, V.M., M. Sheng, and M.E. Greenberg. 1990. The inner core of the serum response element mediates both the rapid induction and subsequent repression of c-*fos* transcription following serum stimulation. *Genes Dev.* **4:** 255–268.

Rosenthal, N. 1989. Muscle cell differentiation. *Cell Biol.* **1:** 1094–1101.

Rous, P. 1910. A transmissible avian neoplasm: Sarcoma of the common fowl. *J. Exp. Med.* **12:** 696–705.

Roux, P., J.-M. Blanchard, A. Fernandez, N. Lamb, P. Jeanteur, and M. Piechaczyk. 1990. Nuclear localization of c-*fos*, but not v-*fos* proteins, is controlled by extracellular signals. *Cell* **63:** 341–351.

Rüther, U., E.F. Wagner, and R. Müller. 1985. Analysis of the differentiation-promoting potential of inducible c-*fos* genes introduced into embryonal carcinoma cells. *EMBO J.* **4:** 1775–1781.

Rüther, U., D. Komitowski, F.R. Schubert, and E.F. Wagner. 1989. c-*fos* expression induces bone tumors in transgenic mice. *Oncogene* **4:** 861–865.

Rüther, U., C. Garber, D. Komitowski, R. Müller, and E.F. Wagner. 1987. Deregulated c-

fos expression interferes with normal bone development in transgenic mice. *Nature* **325:** 412–416.

Ryder, K., L.F. Lau, and D. Nathans. 1988. A gene activated by growth factors is related to the oncogene v-*jun*. *Proc. Natl. Acad. Sci.* **85:** 1487–1491.

Ryder, K., A. Lanahan, E. Perez-Albuerne, and D. Nathans. 1989. Jun-D: A third member of the Jun gene family. *Proc. Natl. Acad. Sci.* **86:** 1500–1503.

Ryseck, R.P. and R. Bravo. 1991. c-Jun, JunB and JunD differ in their binding affinities to AP-1 and CRE consensus sequences: Effect of Fos proteins. *Oncogene* **6:** 533–542.

Sassone-Corsi, P., J.C. Sisson, and I.M. Verma. 1988a. Transcriptional autoregulation of the proto-oncogene *fos*. *Nature* **334:** 314–319.

Sassone-Corsi, P., W.W. Lamph, M. Kamps, and I.M. Verma. 1988b. *fos*-associated cellular p39 is related to nuclear transcription factor AP-1. *Cell* **54:** 553–560.

Schönthal, A., P. Herrlich, H.J. Rahmsdorf, and H. Ponta. 1988. Requirement for *fos* gene expression in the transcriptional activation of collagenase by other oncogenes and phorbol esters. *Cell* **54:** 325–334.

Schuermann, M., M. Neuberg, J.B. Hunter, T. Jenuwein, R.-P. Ryseck, R. Bravo, and R. Müller. 1989. The leucine repeat motif in fos protein mediates complex formation with Jun/AP-1 and is required for transformation. *Cell* **56:** 507–516.

Schuh, A.C., S.J. Keating, F.S. Monteclaro, P.K. Vogt, and M.L. Breitman. 1990. Obligatory wounding requirement for tumorigenesis in v-*jun* transgenic mice. *Nature* **346:** 756–760.

Schüle, R., K. Umesono, D.J. Mangelsdorf, J. Bolado, J.W. Pike, and R.M. Evans. 1990a. Jun-Fos and receptors for vitamins A and D recognize a common response element in the human osteocalcin gene. *Cell* **61:** 497–504.

Schüle, R., P. Rangarajan, S. Kliewer, L.J. Ransone, J. Bolado, N. Yang, I.M. Verma, and R.M. Evans. 1990b. Functional antagonism between oncoprotein c-Jun and the glucocorticoid receptor. *Cell* **62:** 1217–1226.

Schutte, J., J.D. Minna, and M.J. Birrer. 1988. Deregulated expression of human transcription factor c-*jun* transforms primary rat embryo cells in cooperation with an activated c-Ha-*ras* gene and Rat 1a cells as a single gene. *Proc. Natl. Acad. Sci.* **86:** 2257–2261.

Schütte, J., J. Viallet, M. Nau, S. Segal, J. Fedorko, and J. Minna. 1989. *jun*-B inhibits and c-*fos* stimulates the transforming and *trans*-activating activities of c-*jun*. *Cell* **59:** 987–997.

Sellers, J.W. and K. Struhl. 1989. Changing Fos oncoprotein to a Jun-independent DNA-binding protein with GCN4 dimerization specificity by swapping "leucine zippers." *Nature* **341:** 74–76.

Setoyama, C., R. Frunzio, G. Liau, M. Mudryj, and B. De Crombrugghe. 1986. Transcriptional activation encoded by the v-*fos* gene. *Proc. Natl. Acad. Sci.* **83:** 3213–3217.

Sonnenberg, J.L., J.F. Rauscher III, J.I. Morgan, and T. Curran. 1989. Regulation of proenkephalin by Fos and Jun. *Science* **246:** 1622–1625.

Stacey, D.W., T. Watson, H.-F. Kung, and T. Curran. 1987. Microinjection of transforming *ras* protein induces c-*fos* expression. *Mol. Cell. Biol.* **7:** 523–527.

Stehelin, D., H.E. Varmus, J.M. Bishop, and P.K. Vogt. 1976. DNA related to the transforming gene(s) of avian sarcoma viruses is present in normal avian DNA. *Nature* **260:** 170–173.

Struhl, K. 1987. The DNA-binding domains of the *jun* oncoprotein and the yeast GCN4 transcriptional activator protein are functionally homologous. *Cell* **50:** 841–846.

————. 1988. The JUN oncoprotein, a vertebrate transcription factor, activates transcription in yeast. *Nature* **332:** 649–650.

Subramanian, M., L.J. Schmidt, C.E. Crutchfield III, and M.J. Getz. 1989. Negative regulation of serum-responsive enhancer elements. *Nature* **330:** 64–66.

Suzuki, T., Y. Hashimoto, H. Okuno, H. Sato, H. Nishina, and H. Iba. 1991. High level expression of human c-*jun* gene causes cellular transformation of chicken embryo fibroblasts. *Jpn. J. Cancer Res.* **82:** 58–64.

Talanian, R.V., C.J. McKnight, and P.S. Kim. 1990. Sequence-specific DNA binding by a short peptide dimer. *Science* **249:** 769–771.

Tapscott, S.J., R.L. Davis, M.J. Thayer, P.-F. Cheng, H. Weintraub, and A.B. Lassar. 1988. MyoD1. A nuclear phosphoprotein requiring a *myc* homology region to convert fibroblasts to myoblasts. *Science* **242:** 405–411.

Temin, H.M. and S. Mizutani. 1970. RNA-directed DNA polymerase in virions of Rous sarcoma virus. *Nature* **226:** 1211–1213.

Temin, H.M. and H. Rubin. 1958. Characteristics of an assay for Rous sarcoma virus and Rous sarcoma cells in tissue culture. *Virology* **6:** 669–688.

Treisman, R. 1985. Transient accumulation of c-*fos* RNA following serum stimulation requires a conserved 5′ element and c-*fos* 3′ sequences. *Cell* **42:** 889–902.

————. 1990. The SRE: A growth factor responsive transcriptional regulator. In *Seminar in cancer biology, transcription factors, differentiation and cancer* (ed. N.C. Jones), vol. 1, pp. 47–58. W.B. Saunders, London.

Turner, R. and R. Tjian. 1989. Leucine repeats and an adjacent DNA binding domain mediate the formation of functional cFos-cJun heterodimers. *Science* **243:** 1689–1694.

Van Beveren, C., S. Enami, T. Curran, and I.M. Verma. 1984. FBR murine osteosarcoma virus. II. Nucleotide sequence of the provirus reveals that the genome contains sequences acquired from two cellular genes. *Virology* **135:** 229–243.

van Straaten, F., R. Müller, T. Curran, C. Van Beveren, and I.M. Verma. 1983. Complete nucleotide sequence of a c-*onc* gene: Deduced amino acid sequence of the human c-*fos* protein. *Proc. Natl. Acad. Sci.* **80:** 3183–3187.

Varmus, H.E. 1984. The molecular genetics of cellular oncogenes. *Annu. Rev. Genet.* **18:** 533–612.

————. 1988. Retroviruses. *Science* **240:** 1427–1435.

Vinson, C.R., P.B. Sigler, and S.L. McKnight. 1989. A scissors-grip model for DNA recognition by a family of leucine zipper proteins. *Science* **246:** 911–916.

Vogt, P.K. and T.J. Bos. 1990. Jun: Oncogene and transcription factor. *Adv. Cancer Res.* **55:** 1–35.

Vogt, P.K. and I. Morgan. 1990. The genetics of *jun*. *Semin. Cancer Biol.* **1:** 27–36.

Vogt, P.K., T.J. Bos, and R.F. Doolittle. 1987. Homology between the DNA-binding domain of the GCN4 regulatory protein of yeast and the carboxyl-terminal region of a protein coded for by the oncogene *jun*. *Proc. Natl. Acad. Sci.* **84:** 3316–3319.

Wagner, E.F., R.L. Williams, and U. Rüther. 1989. C-Fos and polyoma middle T oncogenic expression in transgenic mice and embryonal stem cell chimeras. *NATO ASI Ser. H Cell Biol.* **26:** 301–310.

Ward, J.M. and D.M. Young. 1976. Histogenesis and morphology of periosteal sarcomas induced by FBJ virus in NIH Swiss mice. *Cancer Res.* **36:** 3985–3992.

Wasylyk, B., C. Wasylyk, P. Flores, A. Begue, D. Leprince, and D. Stehelin. 1990. The c-*ets* proto-oncogenes encode transcription factors that cooperate with c-Fos and c-Jun for transcriptional activation. *Nature* **346:** 191–193.

Wasylyk, C., J.L. Imler, and B. Wasylyk. 1988. Transforming but not immortalizing oncogenes activate the transcription factor PEA1. *EMBO J.* **7:** 2475–2483.

Wasylyk, C., J. Schneikert, and B. Wasylyk. 1990. Oncogene v-*jun* modulates DNA replication. *Oncogene* **5:** 1055–1058.

Weintraub, H., S.J. Tapscott, R.L. Davis, M.J. Thayer, M.A. Adam, A.B. Lassar, and D. Miller. 1989. Activation of muscle-specific genes in pigment, nerve, fat, liver, and fibroblast cell lines by forced expression of MyoD. *Proc. Natl. Acad. Sci.* **86:** 5434–5438.

Weiss, M.A., T.E. Ellenberger, C.R. Wobbe, J.B. Lee, S.C. Harrison, and K. Struhl. 1990. Folding transition in the DNA-binding domain of GCN4 on specific binding to DNA. *Nature* **347:** 575–578.

Weiss, R., N. Teich, H.E. Varmus, and J. Coffin, eds. 1982. *Molecular biology of tumor viruses*, 2nd edition: *RNA tumor viruses*. Cold Spring Harbor Laboratory, Cold Spring Harbor, New York.

———. 1985. *Molecular biology of tumor viruses,* 2nd edition: *RNA tumor viruses 2/Supplements and appendixes.* Cold Spring Harbor Laboratory, Cold Spring Harbor, New York.

Wilson, T. and R. Treisman. 1988. Fos C-terminal mutations block down-regulation of c-*fos* transcription following serum stimulation. *EMBO J.* **8:** 4193–4202.

Yang-Yen, H.-F., R. Chui, and M. Karin. 1990a. Elevation of AP-1 activity during F9 cell differentiation is due to increased c-*jun* transcription. *New Biol.* **2:** 351–361.

Yang-Yen, H.F., J.-C. Chambard, Y.-L. Sun, T. Smeal, T.J. Schmidt, J. Drouin, and M. Karin. 1990b. Transcriptional interference between c-Jun and the glucocorticoid receptor: Mutual inhibition of DNA binding due to direct protein-protein interaction. *Cell* **62:** 1205–1215.

Yoshida, T., Y. Shindo, K. Ohta, and H. Iba. 1989. Identification of a small region of the v-*fos* gene product that is sufficient for transforming potential and growth stimulating activity. *Oncogene Res.* **5:** 79–89.

Zerial, M., L. Toschi, R.-P. Ryseck, M. Schuermann, R. Müller, and R. Bravo. 1989. The product of a novel growth factor activated gene, *fos* B, interacts with JUN proteins enhancing their DNA binding activity. *EMBO J.* **8:** 805–813.

can accommodate a major structural disruption, the insertion of a single base pair, in the center of its compact binding site. Although many DNA-binding proteins are highly sensitive to spacing changes in the target site, some proteins tolerate or even prefer different spacings between half-sites (Sadler et al. 1983; Falvey and Grindley 1987; Sauer et al. 1988). However, in all these cases of flexibility, the sequence at the center of the binding site is relatively unimportant, and the protein dimerization region resides in a distinct structural domain from the region required for DNA contacts; thus, the DNA interaction surfaces of the two monomers are structurally independent. In contrast, the dimerization and DNA-binding functions of GCN4 are localized to the 60 carboxy-terminal residues (Hope and Struhl 1986, 1987), a region that appears to be a single structural domain as determined by proteolytic mapping (Hope et al. 1988).

The ATGA<u>CG</u>TCAT sequence recognized by GCN4 strongly resembles sites bound by the yeast and mammalian ATF/CREB family of proteins (Hai et al. 1988; Roesler et al. 1988). Like GCN4, these proteins bind as dimers, and they contain leucine zipper motifs and adjacent basic regions (Hoeffler et al. 1988; Gonzalez et al. 1989; Hai et al. 1989). Thus, GCN4 and the ATF/CREB protein family recognize adjacent ATGAC half-sites but have different spacing requirements. In support of this idea, the mammalian AP-1 protein family, which recognizes the same sequences as GCN4 (Bohmann et al. 1987; Struhl 1987a), is immunologically related to the ATF/CREB protein family (Hai et al. 1988). Thus, the GCN4/AP-1 and ATF/CREB classes of proteins likely belong to the same evolutionarily conserved superfamily of proteins that recognize essentially identical half-sites (Fig. 2). This situation resembles that of the estrogen and thyroid hormone receptors, which recognize similar half-sites with distinct spatial constraints (Glass et al. 1988; Umesono and Evans 1989).

Although DNA-binding specificity is defined largely by the ATGAC half-sites, the region of DNA covered by the bound protein is considerably more extensive (Gartenberg et al. 1990). When GCN4 is incubated with a collection of different-sized oligonucleotides containing a given target site, optimal binding is observed only with DNAs containing at least an 18-bp region encompassing the half-sites. Chemical modification experiments reveal that GCN4 contacts essentially all nucleosides and phosphates over a region spanning one and a half turns of the DNA helix. GCN4 interacts primarily, and possibly exclusively, with the major groove of DNA. The protein yields no detectable footprint with hydroxyl radical (a reagent specific for minor groove interactions) (Gartenberg et al. 1990), and affinity cleavage experiments involving an iron-EDTA modified protein indicate that the amino termini of the dimeric DNA-binding domain lie in the major groove 9–10 bp apart (Oakley and Dervan 1990).

NATURE OF THE GCN4 DNA-BINDING DOMAIN

Extensive deletion analysis of the 281-amino-acid GCN4 protein indicates that the 56 carboxy-terminal amino acids are sufficient both for dimerization and for specific DNA binding (Hope and Struhl 1986, 1987; Weiss et al. 1990). The DNA-binding domain can be isolated from the full-length protein as a proteolytically stable fragment, indicating that it folds independently of the remainder of the protein (Hope et al. 1988). Moreover, GCN4 and the Jun oncoprotein bind the same DNA sequences (Struhl 1987a), yet amino acid sequence conservation between these proteins is restricted to the 65 carboxy-terminal residues (Fig. 3) (Vogt et al. 1987).

The GCN4 DNA-binding domain contains the bZIP structural motif found in a class of eukaryotic transcription factors that includes C/EBP and the Jun and Fos oncoproteins (Landschulz et al. 1988). Within the bZIP domain is a leucine zipper that consists of four or five leucines spaced exactly seven amino acids apart, embedded within a region whose sequence is consistent with the formation of an amphipathic α-helix. Adjacent to the leucine zipper is a conserved region that is rich in basic

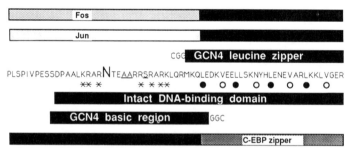

Figure 3 The GCN4 DNA-binding domain. The sequence of the 65 carboxy-terminal residues is shown with conserved features highlighted as follows: leucine residues that define the leucine zipper (closed circles); alternate hydrophobic residues that form the coiled-coil interface (open circles); positively charged residues that define the basic region (asterisks); other conserved residues in the basic region (underlined); the invariant asparagine (large bold N). Shown above the sequence are a leucine zipper peptide and Fos-GCN4 or Jun-GCN4 chimeric proteins that all display GCN4 dimerization specificity. Shown below are the intact bZIP domain, a basic region peptide, and a GCN4-C/EBP chimeric protein, all of which display GCN4 DNA-binding specificity.

residues and contains a quartet of uncharged residues including two alanines, a serine/cysteine, and an invariant asparagine (Fig. 3). The spacing between the leucine zipper and the basic region is precisely maintained in this family of DNA-binding proteins.

Distinct Subdomains for Dimerization and DNA Binding

Chimeric proteins have been used to prove that the GCN4 leucine zipper confers the specific dimerization properties of the intact protein and that the adjacent basic region is sufficient for specific DNA binding (Fig. 3). The basis of such experiments is that the various bZIP proteins have distinct dimerization and DNA-binding properties, despite having common sequence motifs. In the case of the dimerization, GCN4, Jun, and Fos contain the conserved leucines in the zipper and interact with the same DNA sites, yet the only functional species are GCN4 homodimers, Jun homodimers, and Fos-Jun heterodimers. However, precise replacement of the Fos zipper by the GCN4 zipper generates a Fos-GCN4 chimeric protein with GCN4 dimerization specificity; it binds DNA as a homodimer or as a heterodimer with GCN4, but not as a heterodimer with Jun (Kouzarides and Ziff 1989; Sellers and Struhl 1989). Conversely, GCN4 and C/EBP recognize different DNA sequences, and analysis of similar zipper-basic region chimeric proteins indicates that DNA-binding specificity tracks with the basic region (Agre et al. 1989).

The fact that leucine zipper and basic regions can be interchanged between different family members to generate chimeric proteins with predicted dimerization and DNA-binding specificities indicates that these conserved motifs encode distinct structural subdomains. More compellingly, synthetic peptides corresponding to the isolated subdomains are functionally active (Fig. 3). Synthetic leucine zippers form dimers of appropriate specificity (O'Shea et al. 1989a,b), and a synthetic basic region (dimerized via a disulfide bond) can specifically interact with the correct target sequences, although with reduced affinity (Talanian et al. 1990).

The Leucine Zipper

The original structural concept of the leucine zipper invoked an α-helical dimer formed primarily by interdigitation of leucine residues within the hydrophobic interface (Landschulz et al. 1988). In support of this idea, a GCN4 leucine zipper peptide (the 33 carboxy-terminal residues) forms stable α-helical dimers in solution (O'Shea et al. 1989a). The same region exists as a dimeric α-helical structure in the context of a functional DNA-binding domain, although it is considerably less stable than the zipper peptide, probably due to repulsion of the basic regions (O'Neil et al. 1990; Weiss et al. 1990). However, in contrast to the prediction of the initial interdigitation model, the α-helices associate in the parallel rather than antiparallel arrangement (O'Shea et al. 1989a). Moreover, X-ray scattering studies demonstrate that the GCN4 leucine zipper is similar to the coiled-coil structure found in muscle filament proteins (Rasmussen et al. 1991), and DNA binding by GCN4 is maintained when the leucine zipper is replaced by an artificial coiled coil (O'Neil et al. 1990). In the coiled coil, the dimerization interface is not formed by leucine interdigitation, but rather by interaction of the leucines with hydrophobic residues predicted to lie on the same side of the α-helix.

Because the canonical leucine residues are common to all zipper proteins, nonconserved residues in the various zipper regions must have critical roles in generating distinct dimerization specificities and hence zipper association properties. In fact, the GCN4 leucine zipper is surprisingly tolerant of mutations in the leucine residues (Struhl 1989; Hu et al. 1990; vanHeeckeren et al. 1992). A wide variety of single substitutions at any of the four leucines including basic (Arg-267 and Arg-274) and acidic (Glu-260) amino acids behave indistinguishably from wild-type GCN4, and some derivatives containing two leucine substitutions display detectable but reduced function. The observations do not imply that the leucines are functionally unimportant, but rather indicate that numerous other interactions within the coiled coil are crucial for efficient dimerization.

Nuclear magnetic resonance experiments carried out on a 58-residue DNA-binding domain yield an estimated lifetime between 10 and 1000 milliseconds for GCN4 dimers (Weiss et al. 1990). In conjunction with the dissociation constant of GCN4 for DNA, this suggests that unfolding and reassembly of GCN4 occurs easily, thereby facilitating subunit exchange. This property, which is also observed for C/EBP (Shuman et al. 1990) and is probably generally true for bZIP proteins, makes it possible for organisms to rapidly change the spectra of homodimeric and heterodimeric species in response to environmental and developmental signals.

Spacing between the Leucine Zipper and Basic Region

The precisely conserved spacing relationship between the subdomains led to the suggestion that the leucine zipper positions the basic region for specific DNA binding (Landschulz et al. 1988; Vinson et al. 1989). In support of this idea, disruption of this spacing by insertion of two, four, five, or six amino acids between the GCN4 leucine zipper and basic region abolishes GCN4 function (Agre et al. 1989; Pu and Struhl 1991a). More convincingly, insertion of a surprisingly wide variety of seven-amino-acid sequences results in proteins displaying weak to wild-type levels of GCN4 activity (Fig. 4) (Pu and Struhl 1991a). Thus, the correct spatial relationship is retained upon the insertion of an integral number of α-helical turns (7 residues) between the zipper and basic region. Interestingly, heterodimers between GCN4 and several heptapeptide insertion proteins fail to bind DNA; i.e., both proteins contain an acceptable spacing between the leucine zipper and basic region, but the distinct spacings are not mutually compatible (Fig. 4). These results strongly suggest that the leucine zipper symmetrically orients the two basic regions along the adjacent half-sites and that the region between the two subdomains is α-helical. In addition, they suggest that GCN4 homodimers are the primary, and possibly the sole, mediators of GCN4 function in yeast cells (because it is extremely unlikely that GCN4 and the heptapeptide insertions can form DNA-binding heterodimers with a common set of other leucine zipper proteins).

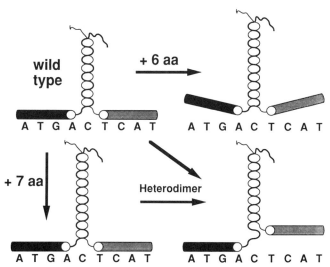

Figure 4 The leucine zipper symmetrically positions the adjacent basic regions for DNA binding. The spacing between the leucine zipper (intertwined wavy lines perpendicular to the DNA) and both adjacent basic regions (cylinders; black representing the left monomer and gray representing the right monomer) must be correct for high-affinity binding (shown by a close, parallel arrangement of both basic regions to the DNA sequence). The region between the zipper and basic region is shown as α-helical because this spacing can be altered by the insertion of an integral number of α-helical turns (Pu and Struhl 1991a).

GCN4 Undergoes a Global Folding Transition upon Specific DNA Binding

DNA-binding domains are generally prefolded structures that specifically interact with the DNA helix by virtue of complementary surfaces. In striking contrast, the GCN4 DNA-binding domain undergoes a global folding transition upon specific interaction with DNA (Fig. 5) (O'Neil et al. 1990; Talanian et al. 1990; Weiss et al. 1990). In the absence of DNA, the dimeric DNA-binding domain (56 carboxy-terminal residues) is approximately 70% α-helical, as determined by circular dichroism spectroscopy. This α-helicity is accounted for by the leucine zipper, thereby implying that the adjoining basic region is largely unstructured in the absence of DNA. However, addition of a GCN4-binding site increases the α-helix content to at least 95%, indicating that the basic region acquires substantial α-helical structure when it specifically binds to DNA. These observations are consistent with, but not specific to, the scissors-grip (Vinson et al. 1989) and induced fork (O'Neil et al. 1990) models, which predict that the leucine zipper symmetrically positions the diverging pair of α-helical basic regions for specific DNA binding to abutting half-sites.

Although the basic region is largely unstructured in the absence of DNA, the α-helical content of the GCN4 DNA-binding domain increases to about 80% at lower temperatures (Weiss et al. 1990). This partial α-helical transition is also observed with a 26-residue peptide correspond-

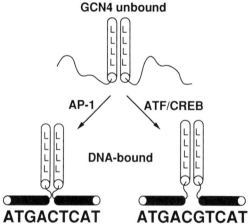

Figure 5 GCN4 undergoes a global folding transition upon specific binding to DNA (Weiss et al. 1990). Unbound GCN4 is shown as dimerized leucine zipper (cylinders with leucine residues indicated) and unstructured basic regions (wavy lines). Upon binding to the AP-1 or ATF/CREB sites, the basic regions become almost completely α-helical (black cylinders). In order to accommodate the different half-site spacing of these binding sites, the region between the leucine zipper and basic region is shown as being flexible.

ing to the basic region, suggesting that these conformational properties are locally determined. These observations suggest that in the absence of DNA, the basic region of GCN4 exists as an ensemble of structures, with the folded state being significantly populated only at low temperature. More importantly, specific target sequences stabilize the α-helical conformation of the basic region, thus inducing the fit between protein and DNA.

In the protein-DNA complex, GCN4 is structurally quite rigid due to its almost completely α-helical nature. However, the protein undergoes the same global folding transition when bound to the ATF/CREB site that contains an additional base pair between the adjacent half-sites, suggesting some degree of flexibility in the protein-DNA complex. Since the DNA structure is not differentially affected by GCN4 binding, the alternative half-site spacings are accommodated by flexibility in the protein (Weiss et al. 1990). Flexibility in protein conformation, not a protein-induced bend in DNA, also appears to account for the anomalous electrophoretic behavior of protein-DNA complexes (Gartenberg et al. 1990). The most likely structural basis for this flexibility is at or near the bifurcation where the helices of the two basic regions split off from the dimeric coiled coil of the leucine zipper (Fig. 5).

DNA Binding

It has been proposed that the quartet of highly conserved, nonpolar residues in the basic region (corresponding to Asn-235, Ala-238, Ala-239, and Ser-242 in GCN4) lie on the face of the α-helix that docks against the DNA (O'Neil et al. 1990). In support of this idea, DNA-binding activity is retained in a derivative in which five nonconserved residues on the putative solvent-exposed surface are changed to alanine or glutamine (O'Neil et al. 1990). Surprisingly, however, these highly conserved residues are not essential for DNA binding by GCN4 (Pu and Struhl 1991b). At positions 238 and 239, a variety of nonpolar residues can functionally substitute for the conserved alanines; in general, increasing the size of the side chain results in decreased GCN4 function (Pu and Struhl 1991b). For the invariant asparagine (Asn-235), most substitutions abolish GCN4 DNA binding, but the Trp-235 protein displays nearly wild-type function, and the Gln-235 and Ala-235 proteins show detectable activity. The ability of an amino acid to functionally substitute for Asn-235 does not correlate with its preference for assuming the N-cap position of an α-helix (Richardson and Richardson 1988). This argues against a specific prediction of the scissors-grip model (Vinson et al. 1989) that the invariant asparagine functions primarily to form an N-cap structure that permits the α-helical basic region to bend sharply so that it can wrap around the DNA. However, the more general feature of this model, that the basic region bends to maximize the protein-DNA interface, remains to be addressed.

Strong clues to the direct protein-DNA contacts involved in high-affinity binding have come from GCN4 derivatives that display altered DNA-binding specificity (Fig. 6). Such altered specificity mutants were identified by genetically selecting for proteins that can activate transcription from promoters containing symmetrically mutated binding sites. For example, wild-type GCN4 binds the optimal ATGACTCAT sequence much more efficiently than TTGACTCAA, whereas the Trp-235 protein binds these sites with similar affinity (Tzamarias et al. 1992). Moreover, the Trp-235, Ala-235, and Gln-235 proteins strongly discriminate against GTGACTCAC, a site efficiently bound by GCN4. These results strongly suggest a direct interaction between Asn-235 and the ±4 position of the target site. At the +3 position, a protein containing Tyr-238 instead of the conserved Ala-238 has the novel property of efficiently recognizing ACGACTCGT (J. Kim et al., unpubl.). Similarly, changing Ala-239 to Val-239 results in a protein that possesses near wild-type affinity

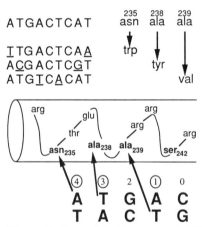

Figure 6 Potential alignment of GCN4 along the DNA as inferred by altered specificity mutants (Tzamarias et al. 1992; J. Kim et al., unpubl.). Shown below the optimal binding site and relevant wild-type GCN4 residues (Asn-235, Ala-238, and Ala-239) are the amino acid substitutions that display GCN4 activity on the indicated binding sites with symmetric mutations (underlined). These results suggest a model in which the crucial α-helix in the basic region (cylinder) specifically binds the target DNA (positions −4 to 0 corresponding to the left half-site indicated) via direct interactions (arrows) between the indicated amino acids (bold and numbered) and base pairs (circled).

for ATG<u>TC</u>A<u>C</u>AT, a site not recognized by GCN4. Taken together, these observations strongly support a model in which the α-helical surface defined by amino acid positions 235, 238, and 239 is aligned along the DNA with direct contacts to ±4, ±3, and ±1, respectively (Fig. 6). Given that hydrophobic interactions between alanine residues and 5-methyl groups of thymines are often found in protein-DNA complexes, it seems likely that Ala-238 and Ala-239 interact respectively with the thymine methyl groups at ±3 and ±1. However, conclusive proof of this hypothesis awaits a high-resolution structure of the protein-DNA complex.

Although highly conserved features of protein families are presumed to be fundamentally important for function, many such features of bZIP proteins are not essential for GCN4 DNA binding. The spacing between the zipper and basic region can be altered by inserting an integral number of helical turns; the invariant asparagine and conserved alanines can be substituted, and in some instances, generate proteins with altered binding specificity; and the canonical leucine residues in the zipper can be varied considerably. Thus, it seems very likely that there are eukaryotic transcriptional regulatory factors that lack some or many of the defining characteristics of bZIP proteins, yet nevertheless are structurally and functionally homologous.

NATURE OF THE GCN4 TRANSCRIPTIONAL ACTIVATION REGION

Extensive deletion analysis has defined the regions of GCN4 required for transcriptional activation in vivo (Fig. 7) (Hope and Struhl 1986; Hope et

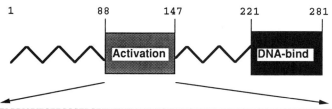

Figure 7   DNA-binding and transcriptional activation functions of GCN4. Shown are locations of the DNA-binding domain (black box), transcriptional activation region (gray box), and nonessential portions (wavy lines) of GCN4 (281 amino acids in length; boundary residues indicated) (Hope and Struhl 1986). Shown below is the sequence of the activation region with acidic residues underlined. Although the acidic region is 60 amino acids in length, a variety of derivatives containing only 40 residues display full activity in vivo (Hope et al. 1988).

al. 1988). Surprisingly, approximately 60% of the GCN4 coding sequence can be deleted without significantly affecting the ability of the protein to activate transcription. However, deleted proteins retaining only the DNA-binding domain cannot activate transcription. In fact, such derivatives bind DNA in vivo and repress transcription from certain promoters, thus inhibiting cell growth in the absence of amino acids (Hope and Struhl 1986). For transcriptional activation in vivo (Hope and Struhl 1986; Hope et al. 1988) or in vitro (Ponticelli and Struhl 1990), a short region of GCN4 located in the center of the protein is required in addition to the DNA-binding domain. This transcriptional activation region is functionally autonomous; it stimulates transcription when fused to a heterologous DNA-binding domain such as the LexA repressor, and its activity is independent of its spacing and orientation with respect to the DNA-binding domain (Hope and Struhl 1986; Hope et al. 1988).

Short Acidic Sequences Are Sufficient for Transcriptional Activation

The transcriptional activation region of GCN4 maps within a central region of the protein that contains 30% acidic residues over a 60-amino-acid stretch (Fig. 7) (Hope and Struhl 1986). Surprisingly, different portions of the GCN4 acidic region are equally capable of activating transcription even though their primary sequences are dissimilar. As few as 35–40 amino acids from this acidic region joined to the GCN4 DNA-binding domain are sufficient for transcriptional activation (Hope et al. 1988). Thus, the yeast GCN4 transcriptional activation function is defined by a short acidic region whose precise sequence is relatively unimportant. In accord with these nonstringent sequence requirements, the GCN4 activation region is much more sensitive to proteolytic cleavage than the DNA-binding domain (Hope et al. 1988). Functional studies on yeast GAL4 (Ma and Ptashne 1987a) and the Jun oncoprotein (Struhl 1988) indicate that transcriptional activation is mediated by acidic regions that are not homologous to each other or to the GCN4 acidic region. Moreover, acidic character is the common feature of activation regions selected from *Escherichia coli* DNA segments (Ma and Ptashne 1987b). Thus, transcriptional activation regions do not have defined tertiary structures such as are found in active sites of enzymes or in conventional structural domains.

Although many different acidic sequences can serve as transcriptional activation regions, and negative charge is clearly important, other structural features influence the level of transcriptional stimulation. Progressive deletion of the GCN4 activation region indicates that transcriptional activity is directly related to the length of the acidic region but not precisely related to the number of acidic residues (Hope et al. 1988). The strong correlation between the length of the GCN4 activation region and level of transcriptional activity is strongly suggestive of a repeating structure consisting of units that act additively. This repeating unit could be an amphipathic α-helix, since the GCN4 acidic region is compatible with such a structure, and stepwise loss in activation potential is correlated with the removal of two α-helical turns (Hope et al. 1988). Similarly, the level of activation mediated by selected *E. coli* segments is only loosely correlated with net negative charge (Ma and Ptashne 1987b), and acidic peptides of identical amino acid composition but distinct sequence and α-helical potential can have very different transcriptional activation properties (Giniger and Ptashne 1987). However, because many other acidic activation regions are unlikely to form amphipathic helices, a simple relationship between this structure and function appears unlikely.

The GCN4 Activation Domain Is Monomeric

Because GCN4 binds DNA as a dimer, it brings two acidic activation regions to the promoter. However, a Fos-Jun heterodimeric DNA-binding domain containing only a single GCN4 acidic region activates transcription (Fig. 8) (Oliviero and Struhl 1991). The clearest example is the combination of Fos containing the GCN4 acidic region and the Jun DNA-binding domain; neither protein can activate transcription alone because the Fos derivative is unable to bind DNA and the Jun derivative lacks an activation region. Nevertheless, this heterodimer activates transcription as efficiently as a Fos-Jun combination in which both moieties contain a GCN4 acidic region. Thus, the activation domain is a monomeric structure, and the number of acidic regions on a DNA-bound protein does not significantly affect the level of transcription.

The monomeric nature of acidic activation domains increases the complexity of regulation that can be mediated by protein families that contain common dimerization motifs such as the leucine zipper and the helix-loop-helix (Murre et al. 1989). For example, proteins lacking an activation region can stimulate transcription if they associate into DNA-binding heteromers with partners that contain an activation domain. Conversely, the ability of a gene product to stimulate transcription does not necessarily indicate that the protein itself contains an activation function. In fact, conventional mapping of the transcriptional activation function on such a protein would instead uncover a motif necessary for oligomerization and/or DNA binding. For these reasons, an individual protein may serve as a transcriptional activator or repressor, depending

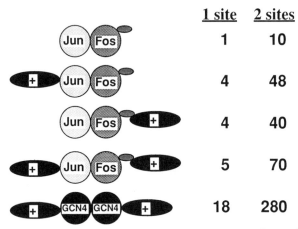

	1 site	2 sites

Jun Fos — 1 — 10

+ Jun Fos — 4 — 48

Jun Fos + — 4 — 40

+ Jun Fos + — 5 — 70

+ GCN4 GCN4 + — 18 — 280

Figure 8 Transcriptional activities of Fos-Jun heterodimers containing GCN4 activation regions. The indicated heterodimers were generated in yeast cells by cointroducing Fos and Jun molecules (bZIP domains indicated by shaded circles; the small oval on the Fos moiety represents nondeleted sequences outside the bZIP region that weakly contribute to transcriptional activation) that either did or did not contain a GCN4 activation region (black oval with plus). For each heterodimer (and for GCN4 homodimers), the relative level of transcription from promoters containing one or two optimal AP-1 target sites upstream of the *his3* TATA region and structural gene is indicated. The indicated levels of transcription are almost exclusively due to Fos-Jun heterodimers; yeast cells containing only the Jun or Fos derivative confer very little, if any, transcriptional activity. For details see Oliviero and Struhl (1991).

on the environmental or developmental situation that affects the presence or activity of other cross-oligomerizing members of the protein family.

TRANSCRIPTIONAL ACTIVATION MECHANISMS

It has been hypothesized that the DNA-binding domains of transcription factors serve merely to bring the protein to the DNA target, whereupon the activation region can interact with a component(s) of the basic transcription machinery (Brent and Ptashne 1985). Given that acidic regions are short and variable in sequence, it is likely that they constitute acidic surfaces necessary for protein-protein interactions (Hope and Struhl 1986). In accord with this idea, the yeast GAL4 activator protein cannot stimulate transcription by a heterologous transcription machinery such as bacteriophage T7 RNA polymerase (Chen et al. 1987). Since acidic regions are necessary for yeast activator proteins to function in mammalian cells (Kakidani and Ptashne 1988; Webster et al. 1988) and for mammalian activator proteins to function in yeast cells (Schena and Yamamoto 1988; Struhl 1988), it is likely that they contact some part of the basic transcription machinery that is conserved functionally throughout the eukaryotic kingdom.

Evidence for a Functional Interaction between GCN4 and TFIID

The yeast *his3* promoter contains two functional TATA-like elements, T_R and T_C, but GCN4 can only activate transcription dependent on the T_R element (Fig. 9) (Struhl 1986). The T_R element is defined primarily by the canonical TATA sequence, TATAAA, that interacts with the general transcription factor IID. Almost all single mutations of this sequence significantly reduce transcription in vitro (Chen and Struhl 1988), with the resulting levels being strongly correlated with the level of TFIID-dependent transcription in vitro (Wobbe and Struhl 1990). In contrast, the T_C element is surprisingly tolerant of single base substitution muta-

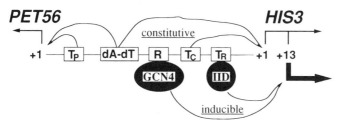

Figure 9 Independent regulation of divergently transcribed genes by selective interaction between GCN4 and TATA elements. *his3* (a histidine biosynthetic gene) and *pet56* (a gene required for mitochondrial function) are divergently transcribed from initiation sites only 191 bp apart. Constitutive transcription utilizes the shaded promoter elements (Struhl 1986); both genes require a poly(dA)•poly(dT) upstream element that can function in combination with the *his3* T_C (which is responsible for essentially all transcription initiated at +1) and the *pet156* T_P TATA elements. The poly(dA)•poly(dT) sequence also can function with T_R (Harbury and Struhl 1989; not shown in figure). GCN4 activation occurs only in combination with the *his3* T_R element, which by genetic and biochemical criteria is a classic TFIID-dependent TATA element (Chen and Struhl 1988; Ponticelli and Struhl 1990; Wobbe and Struhl 1990). This selectivity explains why GCN4 activates *his3* but not *pet56* transcription. In addition, *his3* transcription is activated only from the +13 site because GCN4 cannot function in combination with T_C, and T_R is too close to the +1 site for efficient initiation. The mechanism of T_C-mediated transcription is clearly distinct from the TFIID-dependent transcription from a canonical TATA element (Mahadevan and Struhl 1990; Ponticelli and Struhl 1990).

tions (Mahadevan and Struhl 1990), and it does not support transcription in yeast nuclear extracts under conditions where all known T_R-dependent phenomena can be accurately simulated (Ponticelli and Struhl 1990). The mechanism of T_C-dependent transcription is unknown, yet is clearly distinct from classic TATA- and TFIID-dependent transcription. It may involve a novel TATA factor, an effect of chromatin, or an alternative mechanism involving TFIID. Another distinction between the two *his3* TATA elements is that overproduction of GAL4 squelches transcription dependent on T_R but not T_C (Gill and Ptashne 1988). Thus, both genetic and biochemical evidence indicates that GCN4 activation is specific to TFIID-dependent transcription from the classic TATA element T_R. This specificity provides strong evidence for an interaction between GCN4 and TFIID, presumably mediated by the acidic activation domain (Struhl 1987b).

In a related set of experiments, wild-type GCN4 protein is required specifically for *his4* transcription that depends on a canonical TATA element (Pellman et al. 1990). Unlike BAS1 and BAS2, proteins that bind to the *his4* promoter and are necessary for basal transcription in the absence of this TATA element (Arndt et al. 1987), GCN4 cannot support TATA-independent transcription. Interestingly, however, GCN4 derivatives deleted for various parts of the acidic activation region stimulate low levels of TATA-independent transcription that is initiated from the correct site. Analysis of a series of GCN4 deletion mutants indicates that the discrimination between TATA-dependent and TATA-independent *his4* transcription is correlated with the strength of activation (Pellman et al. 1990). Thus, as is the case for *his3* transcription, GCN4 functions efficiently only in combination with conventional TATA elements that are TFIID interaction sites.

Functional interactions between activator proteins and TFIID have been inferred from several independent lines of evidence. First, functional distinctions between TATA elements similar to those described for T_R and T_C have been observed for a variety of different activator proteins; i.e., only certain combinations of enhancer and TATA elements are compatible for activation (Homa et al. 1988; Simon et al. 1988; Harbury and Struhl 1989). Second, functional TATA elements that support equivalent levels of basal TFIID-dependent transcription in vitro (Wobbe and Struhl 1990) respond extremely differently to GAL4-mediated activation in vivo (Harbury and Struhl 1989). Third, upstream activators and TFIID can cooperatively interact with DNA (Sawadogo and Roeder 1985; Horikoshi et al. 1988b) in a manner that may involve the acidic activation region (Horikoshi et al. 1988a). Fourth, TFIID directly and specifically interacts with the acidic activation domain encoded by the herpesvirus VP16 protein (Stringer et al. 1990). Analysis of mutant proteins indicates that the quality of the interaction in vitro is moderately correlated with the level of transcriptional stimulation in vivo (Ingles et al. 1991). This last observation suggests that the combinatorial nature of upstream activator and TATA-binding proteins may reflect direct, allosteric interactions that influence the activity of the transcription machinery. However, other lines of evidence suggest the possibility that TFIIB is the target of acidic activator proteins (Lin and Green 1991). Thus, an alternative model for TATA element specificity may involve interactions between TFIIB and TFIID that are differentially affected by the acidic activation region and the sequence of the TATA element.

In yeast, the restriction of GCN4 activation to classic TATA-dependent promoters is utilized as an important regulatory mechanism. For example, GCN4 binds about 50 bp upstream of the TATA-like elements of both the divergently transcribed *his3* and *pet56* genes, yet despite its ability to function bidirectionally, it only induces *his3* transcription (Fig. 9). The basis for this discordant regulation is that *his3* contains the T_R element that responds to GCN4 activation, whereas the *pet56* TATA-like sequence behaves like T_C and hence is not responsive to upstream activator proteins (Struhl 1986). Thus, functionally distinct TATA elements provide a mechanism for closely packed and divergently transcribed genes to be regulated independently. This may be particularly important for eukaryotic organisms, because they rely on bidirectional upstream elements that act over long distances.

Biochemical Evidence for a GCN4-RNA Polymerase II Interaction

Affinity chromatography indicates a direct and selective interaction between GCN4 and RNA polymerase II (Brandl and Struhl 1989). RNA polymerase II was selectively retained on a GCN4-Sepharose column under conditions where proteins that copurify over three or four ion-exchange columns flow through. Conversely, GCN4 binds to an RNA polymerase II column but not to control columns. Surprisingly, the GCN4 DNA-binding domain is necessary and sufficient for this interaction with RNA polymerase II. It is unlikely that this interaction reflects a trivial ionic effect because deletion of 11 carboxy-terminal residues of GCN4 has a minor effect on overall charge but eliminates the interaction.

It is tempting to believe that this selective interaction between the GCN4 DNA-binding domain and RNA polymerase II is relevant for transcription, but direct evidence is lacking. Of course, any functional role for this interaction would be mechanistically distinct from the role of the acidic activation region. In addition, it would be contrary to the commonly held view that the DNA-binding domain does not have a direct role in transcription other than targeting the protein to the promoter. However, the potential importance of DNA-binding domains in the transcription process has been implicated by studies on *E. coli* activator proteins (Hochschild et al. 1983; Irwin and Ptashne 1987; Bushman and Ptashne 1988), by the existence of glucocorticoid receptor or HAP1 derivatives that bind DNA normally but fail to activate transcription (Kim and Guarente 1989; Schena et al. 1989), and by experiments on synergistic activation to be discussed below (Oliviero and Struhl 1991).

GCN4 Can Activate Transcription When Its Binding Site Replaces the TATA Element

Although GCN4 normally activates transcription when bound upstream of a TATA element, it can stimulate transcription when bound at the position of the TATA element in a *gal-his3* promoter (Fig. 10) (Chen and Struhl 1989). This TATA-independent transcription requires the GCN4 acidic activation region, and it occurs from normal initiation sites. In contrast to normal TATA-dependent activation, the initiation pattern resembles that mediated by the T_C element, rather than the T_R element, and it does not respond to GAL4 protein. Instead, GCN4 activation from the promoter-proximal element requires at least two additional elements in the *gal* enhancer region that are distinct from the GAL4 sites and from TATA elements (Brandl and Struhl 1990). The most important of these elements, termed Q, interacts with a yeast protein (Brandl and Struhl 1990; Chasman et al. 1990) and corresponds with a nucleosome positioning sequence (Fedor et al. 1988). Consistent with (but hardly conclusive for) a potential role for nucleosome positioning, the level of transcription is significantly reduced upon small increases in the distance between Q and the GCN4 site.

These observations suggest the possibility of an alternative mechanism for transcriptional activation in which TFIID either is not required or is not directly bound to DNA. Furthermore, if TFIID is not functionally involved in this case, the requirement for the GCN4 activation region disfavors the view that TFIID is the functionally important target of acidic activation domains. Finally, these results provide additional evidence for combinatorial specificity between distal and proximal promoter elements. In particular, GAL4 can function with T_R, and Q can function with GCN4 (Fig. 10), but other combinations such as GAL4 and GCN4 or Q and T_R are nonfunctional.

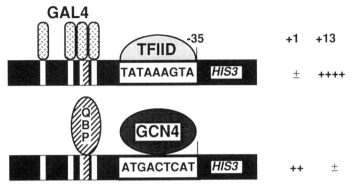

Figure 10   TATA-independent activation by GCN4. (*Top*) The *his3*-G17 promoter consists of the 365-bp *gal* enhancer fragment with four GAL4-binding sites fused to the *his3* T_R TATA element (which interacts with TFIID) and structural gene (Chen and Struhl 1988). Because transcription depends on GAL4 and the TATA element, it occurs only in galactose medium and is initiated with a very strong preference for the +13 site. (*Bottom*) The *his3*-GG1 promoter is identical to the *his3*-G17 promoter, except that the TATA element has been precisely replaced by a GCN4-binding site. Transcription from *his3*-GG1 does not involve GAL4, occurs in both glucose and galactose medium, and is initiated preferentially from the +1 site (Chen and Struhl 1989). Instead, transcription requires GCN4 (including the acidic activation region) and a distinct protein (QBP) that interacts with a site that partially overlaps one of the GAL4 sites (Brandl and Struhl 1990).

Synergistic Activation Does Not Depend on the Number of Acidic Regions

Transcriptional enhancement by activator proteins is synergistic in that promoters containing multiple protein-binding sites upstream of a TATA element are often 10–100 times more active than analogous promoters containing single binding sites. Such synergy is frequently observed when the multiple binding sites are recognized by distinct, and even evolutionarily distant, proteins. Such promiscuous synergy is a fundamental aspect of eukaryotic transcription and constitutes an important basis for the extraordinarily diverse patterns of gene expression mediated by enhancers (Struhl 1991).

Although cooperative DNA binding of transcription factors to adjacent promoter sites is likely to account for some cases of synergy (Driever et al. 1989; Schmid et al. 1989; Struhl et al. 1989; Tsai et al. 1989), the promiscuity of the phenomenon strongly suggests that there must be alternative mechanisms. In accord with this view, synergistic activation has been observed in vitro under conditions where the binding sites for a given activator protein are fully occupied (Carey et al. 1990; Lin et al. 1990). One such alternative mechanism is that acidic activation regions associated with DNA-binding proteins bound to adjacent promoter sites interact synergistically with a common target of the basic transcription machinery (for review, see Ptashne 1988). In such a model, the common target would respond in a nonlinear fashion to the number and/or quality of acidic activation regions.

To determine whether synergy depends on the number of acidic activation regions, the transcriptional activity of Fos-Jun heterodimers containing one or two GCN4 acidic regions was assayed on promoters containing one or two target sites (Fig. 8) (Oliviero and Struhl 1991). As mentioned previously, the number of GCN4 acidic regions on such heterodimers does not affect the level of transcription from promoters containing one target site. More importantly, all the heterodimer combinations and wild-type GCN4 protein stimulate transcription 10–15% more efficiently on analogous promoters containing two adjacent sites. In other words, there is a dramatic difference in transcriptional activation when two GCN4 acidic domains are located on two DNA-bound proteins, as opposed to the situation when the same two acidic regions are located on a single DNA-bound molecule. Thus, transcriptional synergy does not depend on the number of acidic activation regions, but instead on the number of proteins bound to the promoter. Although the length, quality, and probably number of acidic domains contribute to the level of transcription, they do not appear to be responsible for the synergistic effects.

The above observation argues against the prevailing view that synergy reflects a nonlinear response of a "common target" to the number and/or quality of acidic activation regions. In addition, it seems that cooperative binding may not account for synergistic activation by GCN4. Such cooperativity has not been observed in DNA-binding experiments carried out in vitro (Oliviero and Struhl 1991), and it is very likely that single binding sites are frequently occupied by GCN4 in vivo (Hope and Struhl 1986; Brandl and Struhl 1990), thus making it unlikely that cooperative binding increases promoter occupancy by a factor of 10.

The alternative explanation is that the DNA-binding domain plays a more direct role in transcription than simply targeting the protein to the promoter. This idea is supported by the existence of glucocorticoid receptor or HAP1 protein derivatives that bind DNA normally but fail to activate transcription (Kim and Guarente 1989; Schena et al. 1989) and is consistent with the interaction in vitro between the GCN4 DNA-binding domain and RNA polymerase II (Brandl and Struhl 1989). In specific models of this type, the DNA-binding domain might alter DNA structure, affect nucleosome distribution on the chromatin template (possibly to increase access of the general transcription factors and/or RNA polymerase), or interact with the basic RNA polymerase II transcriptional machinery either directly or indirectly through an adapter protein(s). By any of these models, the acidic activation region presumably would carry out a different function from the DNA-binding domain in the overall process of transcriptional enhancement.

REFERENCES

Agre, P., P.F. Johnson, and S.L. McKnight. 1989. Cognate DNA binding specificity retained after leucine zipper exchange between GCN4 and C/EBP. *Science* **246:** 922–926.

Arndt, K. and G. Fink. 1986. GCN4 protein, a positive transcription factor in yeast, binds general control promoters at all 5 ′ TGACTC 3 ′ sequences. *Proc. Natl. Acad. Sci.* **83:** 8516–8520.

Arndt, K.T., C. Styles, and G.R. Fink. 1987. Multiple global regulators control *HIS4* transcription in yeast. *Science* **237:** 874–880.

Bohmann, D., T.J. Bos, A. Admon, T. Nishimura, P.K. Vogt, and R. Tjian. 1987. Human proto-oncogene c-*jun* encodes a DNA binding protein with structural and functional properties of transcription factor AP-1. *Science* **238:** 1386–1392.

Brandl, C.J. and K. Struhl. 1989. Yeast GCN4 transcriptional activator protein interacts with RNA polymerase II *in vitro*. *Proc. Natl. Acad. Sci.* **86:** 2652–2656.

———. 1990. A nucleosome-positioning sequence is required for GCN4 to activate transcription in the absence of a TATA element. *Mol. Cell. Biol.* **10:** 4256–4265.

Brent, R. and M. Ptashne. 1985. A eukaryotic transcriptional activator bearing the DNA specificity of a prokaryotic repressor. *Cell* **43:** 729–736.

Bushman, F.D. and M. Ptashne. 1988. Turning λ Cro into a transcriptional activator. *Cell* **54:** 191–197.

Carey, M., Y.-S. Lin, M.R. Green, and M. Ptashne. 1990. A mechanism for synergistic activation of a mammalian gene by GAL4 derivatives. *Nature* **345:** 361–364.

Chasman, D.I., N.F. Lue, A.R. Buchman, J.W. LaPointe, Y. Lorch, and R.D. Kornberg. 1990. A yeast protein that influences the chromatin structure of UAS_G and functions as a powerful auxiliary gene activator. *Genes Dev.* **4:** 503–514.

Chen, W. and K. Struhl. 1988. Saturation mutagenesis of a yeast *his3* TATA element: Genetic evidence for a specific TATA-binding protein. *Proc. Natl. Acad. Sci.* **85:** 2691–2695.

———. 1989. Yeast upstream activator protein GCN4 can stimulate transcription when its binding site replaces the TATA element. *EMBO J.* **8:** 261–268.

Chen, W., S. Tabor, and K. Struhl. 1987. Distinguishing between mechanisms of eukaryotic transcriptional activation with bacteriophage T7 RNA polymerase. *Cell* **50:** 1047–1055.

Curran, T. and B.J. Franza. 1988. Fos and Jun: The AP-1 connection. *Cell* **55:** 395–397.

Driever, W., G. Thoma, and C. Nüsslein-Volhard. 1989. Determination of spatial domains of zygotic gene expression in the *Drosophila* embryo by the affinity of binding sites for the bicoid morphogen. *Nature* **340:** 363–367.

Falvey, E. and N.D.F. Grindley. 1987. Contacts between γδ resolvase and the γδ *res* site. *EMBO J.* **6:** 815–821.

Fedor, M.J., N.F. Lue, and R.D. Kornberg. 1988. Statistical positioning of nucleosomes by specific protein binding to an upstream activating sequence in yeast. *J. Mol. Biol.* **204:** 109–127.

Gartenberg, M.R., C. Ampe, T.A. Steitz, and D.M. Crothers. 1990. Molecular characterization of the GCN4-DNA complex. *Proc. Natl. Acad. Sci.* **87:** 6034–6038.

Gill, G. and M. Ptashne. 1988. Negative effect of the transcriptional activator GAL4. *Nature* **334:** 721–723.

Giniger, E. and M. Ptashne. 1987. Transcription in yeast activated by a putative amphipathic α helix linked to a DNA binding unit. *Nature* **330:** 670–672.

Glass, C.K., J.M. Holloway, O.V. Devary, and M.G. Rosenfeld. 1988. The thyroid hormone receptor binds with opposite transcriptional effects to a common sequence motif in thyroid hormone and estrogen response elements. *Cell* **54:** 313–323.

Gonzalez, G.A., K.K. Yamamoto, W.H. Fischer, D. Karr, P. Menzel, W. Biggs, W.W. Vale, and M.R. Montminy. 1989. A cluster of phosphorylation sites on the cyclic-AMP regulated nuclear factor CREB predicted by its sequence. *Nature* **337:** 749–752.

Hai, T., F. Liu, W.J. Coukos, and M.R. Green. 1989. Transcription factor ATF cDNA clones: An extensive family of leucine zipper proteins able to selectively form DNA-binding heterodimers. *Genes Dev.* **3:** 2083–2090.

Hai, T., F. Liu, E.A. Allegretto, M. Karin, and M.R. Green. 1988. A family of immunologically related transcription factors that includes multiple forms of ATF and AP-1. *Genes Dev.* **2:** 1216–1226.

Harbury, P.A.B. and K. Struhl. 1989. Functional distinctions between yeast TATA elements. *Mol. Cell. Biol.* **9:** 5298–5304.

Hill, D.E., I.A. Hope, J.P. Macke, and K. Struhl. 1986. Saturation mutagenesis of the yeast *HIS3* regulatory site: Requirements for transcriptional induction and for binding by GCN4 activator protein. *Science* **234:** 451–457.

Hinnebusch, A.G. 1984. Evidence for translational regulation of the activator of general amino acid control in yeast. *Proc. Natl. Acad. Sci.* **81:** 6442–6446.

————. 1988. Mechanisms of gene regulation in the general control of amino acid biosynthesis in *Saccharomyces cerevisiae*. *Microbiol. Rev.* **52:** 248–273.

Hochschild, A., N. Irwin, and M. Ptashne. 1983. Repressor structure and the mechanism of positive control. *Cell* **32:** 319–325.

Hoeffler, J.P., T.E. Meyer, Y. Yun, J.L. Jameson, and J.F. Haebner. 1988. Cyclic AMP-responsive DNA-binding protein: Structure based on a cloned placental cDNA. *Science* **242:** 1430–1433.

Homa, F.L., J.C. Glorioso, and M. Levine. 1988. A specific 15-bp TATA box promoter element is required for expression of a herpes simplex virus type I late gene. *Genes Dev.* **2:** 40–53.

Hope, I.A. and K. Struhl. 1985. GCN4 protein, synthesized in vitro, binds to *HIS3* regulatory sequences: Implications for the general control of amino acid biosynthetic genes in yeast. *Cell* **43:** 177–188.

————. 1986. Functional dissection of a eukaryotic transcriptional activator protein, GCN4 of yeast. *Cell* **46:** 885–894.

————. 1987. GCN4, a eukaryotic transcriptional activator protein, binds as a dimer to target DNA. *EMBO J.* **6:** 2781–2784.

Hope, I.A., S. Mahadevan, and K. Struhl. 1988. Structural and functional characterization of the short acidic transcriptional activation region of yeast GCN4 protein. *Nature* **333:** 635–640.

Horikoshi, M., M.F. Carey, H. Kakidani, and R.G. Roeder. 1988a. Mechanism of action of a yeast activator: Direct effect of GAL4 derivatives on mammalian TFIID-promoter interactions. *Cell* **54:** 665–669.

Horikoshi, M., T. Hai, Y.-S. Lin, M. Green, and R.G. Roeder. 1988b. Transcription factor ATF interacts with the TATA factor to facilitate establishment of a preinitiation complex. *Cell* **54:** 1033–1042.

Hu, J.C., E.K. O'Shea, P.S. Kim, and R.T. Sauer. 1990. Sequence requirements for coiled-coils: Analysis of repressor-GCN4 leucine zipper fusions. *Science* **250:** 1400–1403.

Ingles, C.J., M. Shales, W.D. Cress, S.J. Triezenberg, and J. Greenblatt. 1991. Reduced binding of TFIID to transcriptionally compromised mutants of VP16. *Nature* **351:** 588–590.

Irwin, N. and M. Ptashne. 1987. Mutants of the catabolite activator protein of *Escherichia coli* that are specifically deficient in the gene activation function. *Proc. Natl. Acad. Sci.* **84:** 8315–8319.

Kakidani, H. and M. Ptashne. 1988. GAL4 activates gene expression in mammalian cells. *Cell* **52:** 161–167.

Kim, K.S. and L. Guarente. 1989. Mutations that alter transcriptional activation but not DNA binding in the zinc finger of yeast activator HAP1. *Nature* **342:** 200–203.

Kouzarides, T. and E. Ziff. 1989. Leucine zippers of *fos, jun*, and GCN4 dictate dimerization specificity and thereby control DNA binding. *Nature* **340:** 568–571.

Landschulz, W.H., P.F. Johnson, and S.L. McKnight. 1988. The leucine zipper: A hypothetical structure common to a new class of DNA binding proteins. *Science* **240:** 1759–1764.

Lin, Y.-S. and M.R. Green. 1991. Mechanism of action of an acidic transcriptional activator *in vitro. Cell* **64:** 971–981.

Lin, Y.-S., M. Carey, M. Ptashne, and M.R. Green. 1990. How different eukaryotic transcriptional activators can cooperate promiscuously. *Nature* **345:** 359–360.

Ma, J. and M. Ptashne. 1987a. Deletion analysis of GAL4 defines two transcriptional activating segments. *Cell* **48:** 847–853.

———. 1987b. A new class of yeast transcriptional activators. *Cell* **51:** 113–119.

Mahadevan, S. and K. Struhl. 1990. T$_C$, an unusual promoter element required for constitutive transcription of the yeast *his3* gene. *Mol. Cell. Biol.* **10:** 4447–4455.

Murre, C., P.S. McCaw, H. Vaessin, M. Caudy, L.Y. Jan, Y.N. Jan, C.V. Cabrera, J.N. Buskin, S.D. Hauschka, A.B. Lassar, H. Weintraub, and D. Baltimore. 1989. Interactions between heterologous helix-loop-helix proteins generate complexes that bind specifically to a common DNA sequence. *Cell* **58:** 537–544.

Oakley, M.G. and P.B. Dervan. 1990. Structural motif of the GCN4 DNA binding domain characterized by affinity cleaving. *Science* **248:** 847–850.

Oliphant, A.R., C.J. Brandl, and K. Struhl. 1989. Defining sequence specificity of DNA-binding proteins by selecting binding sites from random-sequence oligonucleotides: Analysis of the yeast GCN4 protein. *Mol. Cell. Biol.* **9:** 2944–2949.

Oliviero, S. and K. Struhl. 1991. Synergistic transcriptional enhancement does not depend on the number of acidic activation domains bound to the promoter. *Proc. Natl. Acad. Sci.* **88:** 224–228.

O'Neil, K.T., R.H. Hoess, and W.F. DeGrado. 1990. Design of DNA-binding peptides based on the leucine zipper motif. *Science* **249:** 774–778.

O'Shea, E.K., R. Rutkowski, and P.S. Kim. 1989a. Evidence that the leucine zipper is a coiled coil. *Science* **243:** 538–542.

O'Shea, E.K., R. Rutkowski, W.F.I. Stafford, and P.S. Kim. 1989b. Preferential heterodimer formation by isolated leucine zippers from Fos and Jun. *Science* **245:** 646–648.

Pellman, D., M.E. McLaughlin, and G.R. Fink. 1990. Function of the TATA element at *HIS4*. *Nature* **348:** 82–86.

Ponticelli, A.S. and K. Struhl. 1990. Analysis of yeast *his3* transcription *in vitro*: Biochemical support for multiple mechanisms of transcription. *Mol. Cell. Biol.* **10:** 2832–2839.

Ptashne, M. 1988. How eukaryotic transcriptional activators work. *Nature* **335:** 683–689.

Pu, W.T. and K. Struhl. 1991a. The leucine zipper symmetrically positions the adjacent basic regions for specific binding to DNA. *Proc. Natl. Acad. Sci.* **88:** 6901–6905.

————. 1991b. Highly conserved residues in the bZIP domain of yeast GCN4 are not essential for DNA-binding. *Mol. Cell. Biol.* **11:** 4918–4926.

————. 1992. Uracil interference, a rapid and general method for defining protein-DNA interactions involving the 5-methyl group of thymines: The GCN4-DNA complex. *Nucleic Acids Res.* **20:** 771–775.

Rasmussen, R., D. Benvegnu, E.K. O'Shea, P.S. Kim, and T. Alber. 1991. X-ray scattering indicates that the leucine zipper is a coiled coil. *Proc. Natl. Acad. Sci.* **88:** 561–564.

Richardson, J.S. and D.C. Richardson. 1988. Amino acid preferences for specific locations at ends of α helices. *Science* **240:** 1648–1652.

Roesler, W.J., G.R. Vandenbark, and R.W. Hanson. 1988. Cyclic AMP and the induction of eukaryotic gene transcription. *J. Biol. Chem.* **263:** 9063–9066.

Sadler, J.R., H. Sasmor, and J.L. Betz. 1983. A perfectly symmetric *lac* operator binds the *lac* repressor very tightly. *Proc. Natl. Acad. Sci.* **80:** 6785–6789.

Sauer, R.T., D.L. Smith, and A.D. Johnson. 1988. Flexibility of the yeast α2 repressor enables it to occupy the ends of its operator, leaving the center free. *Genes Dev.* **2:** 807–816.

Sawadogo, M. and R.G. Roeder. 1985. Interaction of a gene-specific transcription factor with the adenovirus major late promoter upstream of the TATA box region. *Cell* **43:** 165–175.

Schena, M. and K.R. Yamamoto. 1988. Mammalian glucocorticoid receptor derivatives enhance transcription in yeast. *Science* **241:** 965–967.

Schena, M., L.P. Freedman, and K.R. Yamamoto. 1989. Mutations in the glucocorticoid receptor zinc finger region that distinguish interdigitated DNA binding and transcriptional enhancement activities. *Genes Dev.* **3:** 1590–1601.

Schmid, W., U. Strahle, G. Schutz, J. Schmitt, and H. Stunnenberg. 1989. Glucocorticoid receptor binds cooperatively to adjacent recognition sites. *EMBO J.* **8:** 2257–2263.

Sellers, J.W. and K. Struhl. 1989. Changing fos oncoprotein to a DNA-binding protein with GCN4 dimerization specificity by swapping "leucine zippers." *Nature* **341:** 74–76.

Sellers, J.W., A.C. Vincent, and K. Struhl. 1990. Mutations that define the optimal half-site for binding yeast GCN4 activator protein and identify an ATF/CREB-like repressor that recognizes similar DNA sites. *Mol. Cell. Biol.* **10:** 5077–5086.

Shuman, J.D., C.R. Vinson, and S.L. McKnight. 1990. Evidence of changes in protease sensitivity and subunit exchange rate on DNA binding by C/EBP. *Science* **249:** 771–774.

Simon, M.C., T.M. Fisch, B.J. Benecke, J.R. Nevins, and N. Heintz. 1988. Definition of multiple, functionally distinct TATA elements, one of which is a target in the *hsp70* promoter for E1A regulation. *Cell* **52:** 723–729.

Stringer, K.F., C.J. Ingles, and J. Greenblatt. 1990. Direct and selective binding of an acidic transcriptional activation domain to the TATA-box factor TFIID. *Nature* **345:** 783–786.

Struhl, K. 1986. Constitutive and inducible *Saccharomyces cerevisiae* promoters: Evidence for two distinct molecular mechanisms. *Mol. Cell. Biol.* **6:** 3847–3853.

————. 1987a. The DNA-binding domains of the *jun* oncoprotein and the yeast GCN4 transcriptional activator are functionally homologous. *Cell* **50:** 841–846.

————. 1987b. Promoters, activator proteins, and the mechanism of transcriptional initiation in yeast. *Cell* **49:** 295–297.

————. 1988. The JUN oncoprotein, a vertebrate transcription factor, activates transcription in yeast. *Nature* **332:** 649–650.

————. 1989. Helix-turn-helix, zinc finger, and leucine-zipper motifs for eukaryotic transcriptional regulatory proteins. *Trends Biochem. Sci.* **14:** 137–140.

————. 1991. Mechanisms for diversity in gene expression patterns. *Neuron* **7:** 177–181.

Struhl, G., K. Struhl, and P.M. Macdonald. 1989. The gradient morphogen *bicoid* is concentration-dependent transcriptional activator. *Cell* **57:** 1259–1273.

Talanian, R.V., C.J. McKnight, and P.S. Kim. 1990. Sequence-specific DNA binding by a short peptide dimer. *Science* **249:** 769–771.

Thireos, G., M.D. Penn, and H. Greer. 1984. 5′ untranslated sequences are required for the translational control of a yeast regulatory gene. *Proc. Natl. Acad. Sci.* **81:** 5096–5100.

Tsai, S.Y., M.-J. Tsai, and B.W. O'Malley. 1989. Cooperative binding of steroid hormone receptors contributes to transcriptional synergism at target enhancer elements. *Cell* **57:** 443–448.

Tzamarias, D., W.T. Pu, and K. Struhl. 1992. Mutations in the bZIP domain of yeast GCN4 that alter DNA-binding specificity. *Proc. Natl. Acad. Sci.* **89:** 2007–2011.

Umesono, K. and R.M. Evans. 1989. Determinants of target gene specificity for steroid/thyroid hormone receptors. *Cell* **57:** 1139–1146.

vanHeeckeren, W.J., J.W. Sellers, and K. Struhl. 1992. Role of the conserved leucines in the leucine zipper dimerization motif of yeast GCN4. *Nucleic Acids Res.* **20:** 3721–3724.

Vinson, C.R., P.B. Sigler, and S.L. McKnight. 1989. Scissors-grip model for DNA recognition by a family of leucine zipper proteins. *Science* **246:** 911–916.

Vogt, P.K., T.J. Bos, and R.F. Doolittle. 1987. Homology between the DNA-binding domain of the *GCN4* regulatory protein of yeast and the carboxy-terminal region of a protein coded for by the *onc* gene *jun*. *Proc. Natl. Acad. Sci.* **84:** 3316–3319.

Webster, N., J.R. Jin, S. Green, M. Hollis, and M. Chambon. 1988. The yeast UAS$_G$ is a transcriptional enhancer in human HeLa cells in the presence of the GAL4 *trans*-activator. *Cell* **52:** 169–178.

Weiss, M.A., T. Ellenberger, C.R. Wobbe, J.P. Lee, S.C. Harrison, and K. Struhl. 1990. Folding transition in the DNA-binding domain of GCN4 on specific binding to DNA. *Nature* **347:** 575–578.

Wobbe, C.R. and K. Struhl. 1990. Yeast and human TATA-binding proteins have nearly identical DNA sequence requirements for transcription *in vitro*. *Mol. Cell. Biol.* **10:** 3859–3867.

32

The Helix-Loop-Helix Motif: Structure and Function

Cornelis Murre[1,2] and David Baltimore[1,3]
[1]Whitehead Institute for Biomedical Research
Cambridge, Massachusetts 02139
[2]Department of Biology, University of California,
San Diego, La Jolla, California 92093-0116
[3]Rockefeller University
New York, New York 10021-6399

OVERVIEW

A central class of transcriptional regulatory proteins are those with an apparent helix-loop-helix (HLH) dimerization motif abutting a DNA-binding basic region. The HLH region allows for homodimerization but, more importantly, various HLH proteins can interact to form heterodimers. The heterodimers appear to be major players in determining the expression of differentiated cellular functions in various differentiated cell types.

INTRODUCTION

Control of initiation of mRNA synthesis involves the interaction of DNA-binding proteins with each other and with specific DNA sequence elements. Families of such DNA-binding proteins have been identified that are structurally related. Among these families are proteins containing a zinc finger domain, a POU/homeobox domain, and leucine zipper dimerization domains. We have recently identified a new family of proteins that have in common a conserved DNA-binding and dimerization domain, designated the HLH motif. The size of the known HLH family is large (>30 members) and growing. Protein-protein interactions can occur between various HLH members, forming hetero-oligomers. The formation of hetero-oligomers and the large size of the HLH protein family offer an enormous scope of complexity and regulation. The pur-

Transcriptional Regulation.
Copyright 1992 Cold Spring Harbor Laboratory Press 0-87969-410-6/92 $3 + 00

pose of this chapter is to survey HLH proteins and discuss their role in development.

E-BOX REGULATORY ELEMENTS

A wide variety of regulatory elements have been identified in the past decade that are involved in the control of tissue- and developmental-specific gene expression. One class of such elements, the E boxes, are interesting because they seem to be involved in the control of transcription of a number of genes, expressed in various tissues.

E boxes were first identified in the immunoglobulin gene enhancers by in vivo genomic footprinting (Church et al. 1985; Ephrussi et al. 1985). DNA-binding factors were found to protect from methylation certain sites present in the immunoglobulin heavy-chain gene enhancer in B cells but not in non-B cells. The protected sites formed a class of related sequences, termed the E boxes (consensus: CANNTG) (Sen and Baltimore 1986a). Five E-box sites are present in the immunoglobulin heavy-chain gene enhancer: They are termed $\mu E1$, $\mu E2$, $\mu E3$, $\mu E4$, and $\mu E5$. Three E-box sites are present in the immunoglobulin light-chain gene enhancer: They are termed $\kappa E1$, $\kappa E2$, and $\kappa E3$. That the E boxes are crucial for B-cell-specific gene expression became evident from mutational studies. Mutation of individual E-box sites in the immunoglobulin heavy-chain gene enhancer caused a modest yet detectable reduction in immunoglobulin heavy-chain gene enhancer activity (Lenardo et al. 1987; Kiledjian et al. 1988). However, combined mutations of various E-box sites were found to substantially reduce enhancer activity (Lenardo et al. 1987; Kiledjian et al. 1988). Mutational analysis of E boxes present in the immunoglobulin light-chain gene enhancer revealed similar results.

The most dramatic impact on immunoglobulin gene enhancer activity was observed upon mutation of sites that contain an E2-box motif (G/ACAGNTGN). This motif occurs at the $\mu E5$, $\mu E2$, and $\kappa E2$ sites. For example, a mutation in the $\kappa E2$ site reduced κ gene enhancer activity by a factor of 10 (Lenardo et al. 1987). Additionally, a single copy of $\mu E2$ is sufficient to regulate B-cell-specific transcription from a minimal promoter, whereas single or multiple copies of $\mu E1$, $\mu E3$, and $\mu E4$ sequences do not confer B-cell specificity (Cook and Neuberger 1990).

The E2 boxes are particularly interesting because they seem to be involved not only in B-cell-specific expression, but also in the regulation of muscle- and pancreas-specific genes. The E2-box element is present and important for the expression of a number of genes solely expressed in the pancreas: insulin (GCAGATGG), chymotrypsin (ACAGGTGC),

On the basis of the idea that amphipathic helices can provide a protein-protein interaction surface, we tested whether the region surrounding the HLH motif might constitute a dimerization domain. Full-length E47 protein was mixed with a truncated version of E47 and analyzed by EMSA using the E2 box as a probe. Three complexes were present binding the E2 box, indicating dimer formation (Murre et al. 1989a). That the conserved hydrophobic residues are important for dimerization was demonstrated by mutational analysis. Substitution of charged hydrophilic residues for pairs of conserved hydrophobic residues in the proposed helices disrupts dimer formation (Davis et al. 1990; Voronova and Baltimore 1990). All mutations that were observed to interfere with dimerization also abolished DNA binding (Davis et al. 1990; Voronova and Baltimore 1990).

Two proteins that contain the conserved hydrophobic residues present in the HLH region are the lamins A and C. Lamins are nuclear matrix proteins that are structurally homologous to intermediate filaments (McKeon et al. 1986). In the HLH domain there are eight identities between the lamins and, for example, E12 (Murre et al. 1989a). The amphipathic helices in the lamins have been proposed to interact to form higher order structures. A distinctive feature of the hydrophobic residues in the conserved region present in the lamins is that they contain a four-three repeat. The four-three repeat is a distinctive feature of a coiled-coil

```
CONSENSUS              R   N  ER R   ψ   F   L   ψ                          Kψ  IL  Aψ Yψ   L

AS-C/T3   Drosophila VARR---NARERNRVKQVNNGFVNLRQHL PQTVVNSLSNGGRGSSKKLS  KVDTLRIAVEYIRGLQDM

AS-C/T4   Drosophila VQRR---NARERNRVKQVNNSFARLRQHI PQSIITDLTKGGGRGPHKKLS  KVDTLRIAVEYIRSLQDL

AS-C/T5   Drosophila VIRR---NARERNRVKQVNNGFSQLRQHIPAAVIADLSNGRRGIGPGANKKLSKVSTLKMAVEYIRRLQKV

AS-C/T8   Drosophila VARR---NARERNRVKQVNNGFALLREKI PEEVSEAFEAQGAGRGASKKLS  KVSTLKMAVEYIRRLQKV


E(spl)m8 Drosophila IYQKVKKPMLERQRRARMNKCLDNLKTLVA    ELRGDDGILRMD       KAEMLESAVIFMRQQKTP

E(spl)m5 Drosophila HYLKVKKPLLERQRRARMNKCLDTLKTLVA    EFQGDDAILRMD       KAEMLEAALVFMRKQVVK

E(spl)m7 Drosophila QYRKVKKPLLERKRRARINKCLDELKDLMA    ECVAQTGDAKFE       KADILEVTVQHLRKLKES

hairy    Drosophila SDRRSNKPIMEKRRRARINNCLNELKTLIL    DATKKDPARHSKLE     KADILEKTVKHLQELQRQ


CBF1     yeast      KQRKDSHKEVERRRRENINTAINVLSDLI     PVRESS             KAAILARAAEYIQKLKET

Lc       maize      GTGTKMHVMSERKRREKLNEMFLVLKSLL     PSIHRVN            KASILAETIAYLKELQRR

Rop      E. coli    TKQEKTALNMARFIRSQALTLLEKLNELD     ADEQADIC           ESLHDHADELYRSCLARF
```

Figure 1 Proteins containing an HLH motif. Conserved residues are indicated. Solid lines mark the amphipathic helices and loop. Conserved residues present in Rop are underlined.

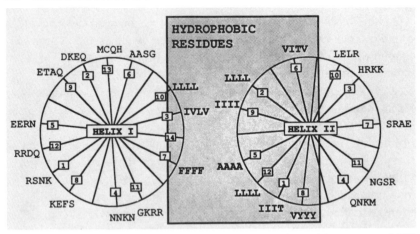

Figure 2 Helical wheel analysis of the conserved amino acid sequence of *E12*, *c-myc*, *MyoD*, and *achaete-scute*. The hydrophobic residues are presented in bold and are located in both helices on one side of the helix, whereas the hydrophilic residues are located on the other side of the the helices, forming two hypothetical amphipathic helices. The hydrophobic surface of both helices is indicated by a shaded box. (Reprinted, with permission of Cell Press, from Murre et al. 1989a.)

motif. Similarly, the three-four repeat is present in the HLH motif. Although the interaction surface of the amphipathic helices is short compared with that of many coiled-coil proteins, including the leucine zipper, we note that short coiled-coil segments can have substantial stability as dimers. An interesting structure with a short coiled coil that has weak homology with the HLH motif has been found in bacterial protein Rop (Fig. 1) (Banner et al. 1987; Gibson et al. 1991).

Rop is a repressor of plasmid replication, and although its mechanism is not exactly known, its structure has been analyzed in detail. Rop contains several of the conserved hydrophobic residues of the HLH motif (Fig. 1). Each Rop monomer consists of two helices that interact with each other and are separated by a loop (Banner et al. 1987). The loop in Rop is needed to allow the helices to bend back and interact with one another. Rop is a dimer held together by a four-helix bundle consisting of two paired coiled coils. It might be that the structure of the HLH motif is topologically similar to that of Rop and that helix I bends back to interact with helix II. These antiparallel helices could then form an interface that allows two polypeptides to dimerize (Fig. 3). There are, however, a variety of other possible models for HLH interaction, and structural analysis will be needed to determine the actual configuration. Whatever the actual structure, the loop separating helix I and helix II is probably needed for

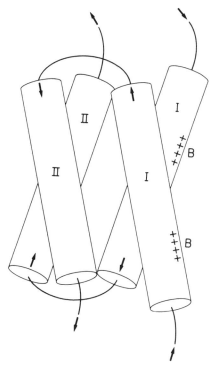

Figure 3 Model of the HLH configuration. We have drawn arbitrarily the HLH proteins in an antiparallel conformation. The basic region of the HLH proteins is marked by a plus sign and is proposed to interact with DNA. The helices are proposed to interact with each other, resulting in a four-stranded coiled coil (see text).

the helices to interact with each other. Although most mutations in the loop do not have a significant effect on dimerization and DNA binding, its length and sequence nevertheless are extremely well conserved between *Drosophila* and mammalian HLH proteins (Fig. 1). For example, the loop sequences in daughterless and E12/E47 are similar (Fig. 1). A complete deletion of the loop indeed blocks dimerization (Davis et al. 1990). Moreover, the presence of a proline in the loop of the MyoD protein is essential for dimerization (Davis et al. 1990). The loop may function to orient the helices, allowing formation of a four-stranded coiled-coil motif. Davis and co-workers (1990) have presented a model in which the helices are oriented in a parallel fashion. In Rop, the helices are oriented in an antiparallel configuration (Fig. 3). It is yet to be determined how the HLH motif is actually put together.

That the conserved basic residues are involved in contacting the DNA has been supported by mutational analysis. Even a single conservative substitution of a lysine for an arginine disrupts DNA binding (Voronova and Baltimore 1990). Recently, a new class of HLH proteins have emerged that lack a basic region, termed Id and emc (Fig. 1) (Benezra et al. 1990; Ellis et al. 1990; Garrell and Modolel 1990). Predictably, Id has been shown to lack DNA binding (Benezra et al. 1990). In addition to these proteins, another class of HLH proteins has a distinctive primary amino acid sequence. *h* protein and products of the *Enhancer of split* locus contain a proline in their basic region at a similar position (Klaembt et al. 1989; Rushlow et al. 1989). If the basic region is helical, the presence of a proline might disrupt helical continuity of the basic region and thereby inactivate DNA-binding activity. Indeed, when such a proline residue is substituted into the basic region of MyoD next to the position of its occurrence in the *h* and *Enhancer of split* proteins, MyoD DNA-binding is inhibited (Davis et al. 1990).

HLH PROTEINS FORM HETERODIMERS

The most striking feature of the HLH motif is the absolute conservation of a series of hydrophobic residues within helices I and II. One reason that these hydrophobic residues are so well conserved may be that HLH proteins form heterodimers creating the possibility for a network of inter-actions. Indeed, recent experiments have provided compelling evidence that HLH proteins form heterodimers (Murre et al. 1989b). Heterodimers can be formed between Class A proteins (daughterless, E12, E47, E2-2) and Class B proteins (achaete-scute T3, achaete-scute T5, MyoD, myogenin, myf-5). Class A molecules can interact with those of Class B and bind to the E2-box site. Class C molecules, consisting of the *myc* gene products and *lyl-1*, do not form heterodimers with either Class A or Class B proteins and do not bind, at least on their own, to the E2 box (Murre et al. 1989b). Recently, an HLH gene product that lacks the basic region, *Id*, has been shown to form heterodimers with Class A and Class B proteins, inhibiting their DNA binding (Benezra et al. 1990).

Homodimers and heterodimers of Class A and B proteins are capable of binding to the E2 box, although heterodimers bind significantly better. An exception to this general tendency is displayed by E47, which binds DNA avidly as a homodimer (Murre et al. 1989b). Thus, both HLH homodimers and heterodimers bind to DNA.

Recently, a new HLH protein (AP-4) has been found, which binds DNA only as a homodimer (Hu et al. 1990). AP-4 contains an HLH domain and two domains characterized by leucine repeats. Truncated forms of AP-4 containing only the HLH domain and basic region are able to form heterodimers with E12 and E47. However, the complete

AP-4 protein cannot form heterodimers with E12 and E47. Consequently, Hu et al. (1990) conclude that both dimerization domains containing the leucine zipper serve to prevent the formation of incorrect combinations.

Homodimers might be expected to bind to perfect palindromic sequences. However, E-box sequences are only partially symmetric. It is possible that heterodimers of HLH proteins recognize these asymmetric palindromic sequences in most cases with higher affinity than do homodimers. Indeed, HLH heterodimers do interact differently with DNA, according to methylation interference experiments. Homodimers of E47 make different contacts with DNA residues than do heterodimers of E47/MyoD and E47/AS-C (Murre et al. 1989b).

The formation of heterodimers may be the driving evolutionary force that has affected the rate of substitution of the conserved hydrophobic residues. The conserved hydrophobic residues are probably not sufficient for forming stable HLH heterodimers. For example, Class C HLH proteins such as the *myc* proteins contain the conserved hydrophobic residues, prototypical of HLH proteins, but do not form heterodimers with either Class A or Class B proteins. Such observations point to a role for the nonconserved residues located within helices I and II as well. The specificity of HLH dimerization, although not fully understood at present, is a tractable problem that lies at the heart of HLH protein function.

QUANTITATION OF HLH INTERACTIONS

E12 is very similar in its primary sequence to E47 but binds weakly to the E2-box site. However, when mixed with MyoD, E12 binds with relatively high affinity to the E2 box. No DNA sequence better suited for binding of E12, E47, and MyoD has been found relative to the E2 boxes present in the immunoglobulin and muscle creatine kinase enhancers. The question arises as to why HLH proteins with similar basic and HLH regions exhibit different DNA-binding and/or dimerization affinities. Recent quantitative experiments have addressed this issue (Sun and Baltimore 1991). The parameters for dimerization and DNA binding have shown that the E47 homodimer, and MyoD heterodimers with E12 or E47, form and bind efficiently to DNA. MyoD homodimerizes poorly but binds DNA with high affinity. Finally, E12 homodimerizes efficiently but binds weakly to DNA. Apparently, MyoD homodimers are less stable than E1*2/MyoD and E47/MyoD heterodimers, and E12 dimerization properties are very similar to those of E47. The question then arises as to why E12 binds relatively weakly to the E2 site whereas E47 binds with high affinity. Sun and Baltimore have shown by mutational analysis of the *E12* and *E47* proteins that an "inhibitory domain" is located adjacent to the basic region of E12. Such an inhibitory domain prevents E12 homodimers from binding with high affinity to the E2-box site (Sun and Baltimore 1991). It thus appears that MyoD is not optimally suited for homodimer formation and E12 has an inhibitory domain preventing it from binding efficiently to DNA. Since the E12/MyoD heterodimer binds avidly, it would appear that a dimeric molecule containing the unimpeded basic region (MyoD) and an inhibited basic region (E12) constitute an active pair.

HLH PROTEINS IN DEVELOPMENT

Among the newly discovered HLH proteins, those involved in *Drosophila* neurogenesis are particularly intriguing. Sensory organs in *Drosophila* arise within the epidermis in a precise temporal and spatial pattern. The sensory organs include a sensory neuron and accessory cells, derived from the same precursor cell (Bodmer et al. 1989; Hartenstein and Posakony 1989). Two categories of mutant phenotypes have been identified in studies of sensory organ formation in *Drosophila*. One class of mutations causes a reduction in the number of sensory organs, *AS-C* and *da* (Dambly-Chaudiere et al. 1988). Another class of mutations induces the ectopic expression of sensory organs, extramacrochaetae (*emc*) and hairy (*h*) (Moscoso del Prado and Garcia-Bellido 1984). An important feature of this group of genes is that they interact in a dosage-dependent manner. For example, increased concentrations of the *emc* gene product antagonize sensory organ formation, whereas decreased levels enhance the number of sensory structures (Garcia-Alonso and Garcia-Bellido 1988). Moreover, genetic experiments have shown that ectopic expression of sensory organs due to lower *emc* concentrations is dependent on the abundance of *achaete-scute* gene products (Moscoso del Prado and Garcia-Bellido 1984). Similarly, the ectopic appearance of sensory organs in *hairy* mutants is suppressed by heterozygosity for a deficiency of the *AS-C* genes and is increased when the *AS-C* genes are duplicated (Moscoso del Prado and Garcia-Bellido 1984). These data suggest that correct formation of the sensory organ pattern is very sensitive to the concentrations of these various gene products. Dosage-dependent genetic interactions can be easily explained by protein-protein interactions. Recent cloning of the *emc* and *hairy* genes showed that they both contain an HLH motif (Rushlow et al. 1989; Ellis et al. 1990; Garrell and Modolel 1990). Since the products of *emc* and *hairy* repress the function of *AS-C* and *da*, it might be expected that they interact via their HLH dimerization domains. Most interestingly, the *emc* gene product encodes an HLH protein that lacks a basic region (Ellis et al. 1990; Garrell et al. 1990). As discussed in the previous section, the basic region has been inferred to provide direct contact with DNA. Thus, although it is not formally proven, one can envision protein-protein interactions between emc and da or AS-C inhibiting da/AS-C DNA-binding activity and thus controlling differentiation (Ellis et al. 1990; Garrell and Modolel 1990).

Another developmental pathway in *Drosophila* that is controlled by HLH regulatory proteins is sex determination. *Drosophila* decides its sex by X/A ratio. Three gene products, da, sisterless-a (sis-a), and sisterless-b (sis-b), have been shown to be involved in sex determination (Cline 1989). *da* is contributed maternally and is likely to be present in excess. *sis-a* and *sis-b* are located on the X chromosome (Cline 1989). Although *sis-a* has not been cloned, *sis-b* maps within the *AS-C* complex. Indeed, Torres and Sanchez (1989) have shown that *AS-C T4* is *sis-b*. In situ hybridization experiments have shown that *AS-C T4* is transiently expressed in all cells (Alonso and Cabrera 1988; Cline 1989). An interesting model is that females make twice as much of *AS-C T4* as males, and only females make sufficient *da/AS-C T4* heterodimers to activate transcription from downstream genes. One of the downstream genes is *Sex-lethal (Sxl)*, a gene whose product controls sexual differentiation and dosage compensation. *Sxl* expression is off in males and on in females. In the absence of *Sxl* expression, female embryos die, whereas ectopic expression of *Sxl* in male embryos is lethal. *Sxl* is autoregulatory and needs to be activated only transiently. Recently, a series of elegant genetic experiments have further demonstrated the role of HLH proteins in sex determination (Parkhurst et al. 1990). Premature expression of the HLH protein hairy was found to interfere with the activation of the *Sxl* gene. This female lethality was rescued by a constitutive *Sxl* allele or by an excess *AS-C T4* (Parkhurst et al. 1990). These data are best explained by an interaction between hairy and other HLH proteins that control *Sxl*, possibly da and AS-C T4. Indeed, misexpression of *AS-C T4* induces ectopic expression of *Sxl*, causing male-specific lethality (Parkhurst et al. 1990). As proposed by Torres and Sanchez (1989), X chromosomes are counted by HLH proteins that together control *sex-lethal* activity, thus regulating dosage compensation and sexual differentiation.

UBIQUITOUSLY EXPRESSED HLH PROTEINS AND THEIR ROLE IN DEVELOPMENT

da is involved in at least two seemingly unrelated developmental pathways: neurogenesis and sex determination (Cline 1976; Cronmiller and Cline 1987; Caudy et al. 1988a). In sex determination, as discussed in the previous section, *da* functions as a regulatory gene that is required for the sex-determination switch gene, *sex-lethal*, to be properly expressed in female embryos. In neurogenesis, *da* function may be analogous; it may be part of a regulatory switch leading epidermal cells to take on the fate of a neuronal cell type (Caudy et al. 1988a). *da* is likely to be involved in other pathways as well.

Mammalian molecules related to da have recently been isolated and characterized. Three cDNAs have been isolated that encode E2-box DNA-binding proteins (E12, E47, and E2-2) that are highly homologous to da. E12, E47, and E2-2 are as related to da in the region surrounding the HLH domain as they are to one another (Murre et al. 1989a; Henthorn et al. 1990; Nelson et al. 1990). Relationships between the mammalian proteins and da extend beyond the HLH domain. Like da, E12, E47, and E2-2 are ubiquitously expressed (Murre et al. 1989a; Nelson et al. 1990). Thus, one might anticipate that these mammalian relatives of da are involved in various developmental pathways. Although functional data are lacking, recent results suggest that this is indeed the case (Fig. 4).

Recently, tissue-specific E2-box-binding proteins have been identified. Two muscle-specific E2-box DNA-binding proteins have been identified in EMSA assays (Buskin and Hauschka 1989; Lassar et al. 1989; Brennan and Olson 1990). These complexes contain *MyoD* and *myogenin* polypeptides. We have recently observed antibodies specific for E12/47 proteins supershift both complexes in an EMSA (Murre et al. 1991). Using the same approach, we found that two B-cell-specific complexes are present that contain E12- or E47-like subunits (Murre et al. 1991). Both B-cell-specific complexes are present in pre-B and mature B cells, but not in pro-B and other cell types. Our preliminary data indicate that these B-cell-specific E2-box DNA-binding proteins are homo-oliogmers of E47 polypeptides (Murre et al. 1991). β cells derived from the pancreas contain a tissue-specific E2-box DNA-binding protein (Whelan et al. 1990). Again, antibodies specific for E12/E47 supershift the β-cell-specific complex (R. Stein, pers. comm.). Thus, E12 and E47 molecules may function in controlling development either by associating with tissue-specific components like MyoD or a β-cell-specific subunit, or as homo-oligomers in B cells (Fig. 4). Thus, da and E12 and E47 appear to be central positive regulators of various developmental pathways.

REGULATION OF HLH INTERACTIONS

The question arises, How are HLH protein interactions regulated? One form of regulation has been discussed in previous sections. HLH pro-

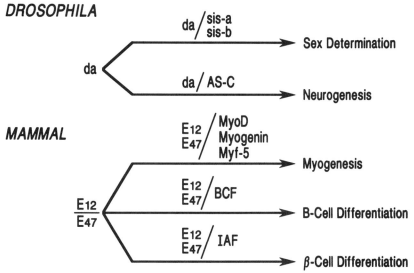

Figure 4 Diagram of ubiquitous HLH proteins (da, E12, E47) involved in *Drosophila* and mammalian development.

teins, Id and emc, have been identified that lack the basic region and therefore can inhibit DNA binding of positive regulators.

Since Id inhibits DNA binding of E12 and MyoD, it would be likely that it would inhibit muscle-specific gene expression. Consistent with this expectation, Benezra and Weintraub have shown that Id, when introduced into muscle cells, inhibits muscle creatine kinase gene expression (Benezra et al. 1990). Moreover, myoblasts, the proliferating precursors of fully differentiated muscle cells, express high levels of Id and do not express the muscle creatine kinase gene (Benezra et al. 1990). High concentrations of Id might inhibit MyoD or E12 or E47 from forming the DNA-binding-competent dimers necessary for activation of muscle-specific genes. Under conditions that facilitate muscle cell differentiation, Id levels fall, allowing E12 and/or E47 to form heterodimers with MyoD and myogenin, which in turn activates the myogenic program.

During B-cell differentiation, a similar scenario may occur. Id RNA levels are high in pro-B cells but low or absent in pre-B and mature B cells (M. Schlissel and D. Baltimore, unpubl.). Id and other related molecules are almost certainly involved in controlling various developmental pathways by regulating the activity of E12- and E47-like molecules. The *Drosophila* counterpart of *Id*, *emc*, may also be a promiscuous regulator, as its expression pattern suggests (Ellis et al. 1990; Garrell and Modolel 1990). *emc* is already known to negatively regulate both sensory organ formation and vein differentiation (Garcia-Alonso and

Garcia-Bellido 1988). Since *da* and *AS-C T4* are both involved in sex determination, it would not be surprising to find that *emc* might also play a regulatory role in this developmental pathway (Ellis et al. 1990; Garrell and Modolel 1990).

CONCLUSION

Understanding how genes are controlled in a specific manner to generate differentiated cells and tissues is an exciting challenge. One major contributor to the panoply of regulatory strategies is specific protein-protein interactions. We have described such interactions for the HLH proteins. A similar story could probably be told for proteins containing leucine zippers (Landschulz et al. 1988) and for other classes yet to be identified (the rel-homology region may be such a new class). Different combinations of developmental regulators such as HLH proteins can impart different functional properties to different tissues. The consequence of such interactions could be positive or negative regulation. The exciting challenge will be to determine just how the interactions between the various proteins result in developmental diversity and how these interactions are regulated by signals from outside the cell.

ACKNOWLEDGMENTS

We thank Jim Posakony for critical reading of the manuscript and Erin O'Shea for suggesting that we look at the possible relationship between Rop and HLH proteins. We also thank Susan Parkhurst for communicating unpublished results.

REFERENCES

Alonso, M.C. and C.V. Cabrera. 1988. The *achaete-scute* gene complex of *Drosophila melanogaster* comprises four homologous genes. *EMBO J.* 7: 2585–2591.
Alt, F.W., R.A. DePinho, K. Zimmerman, E. Legouy, K. Hutton, P. Ferrier, A. Tesfaye, G.D. Yancopoulos, and P. Nisen. 1986. The human *myc*-gene family. *Cold Spring Harbor Symp. Quant. Biol.* 51: 931–941.
Banner, D.W., M. Kokkinidis, and P. Tsernnoglou. 1987. Structure of the *ColE1 Rop* protein at 1.7 Å resolution. *J. Mol. Biol.* 196: 657–675.
Benezra, R., R.L. Davis, D. Lockshon, D.L. Turner, and H. Weintraub. 1990. The protein Id: A negative regulator of helix-loop-helix DNA binding proteins. *Cell* 61: 49–59.
Bodmer, R., S. Barbel, S. Shepherd, J.W. Jack, L.Y. Jan, and Y.N. Jan. 1989. Neurogenesis of the peripheral nervous system in *Drosophila* embryos: DNA replication patterns and cell lineages. *Neuron* 3: 21–32.
Braun, T., G. Buschhausen-Denker, E. Bober, E. Tannich, and H.H. Arnold. 1989. A

33
Structure and Function of Serum Response Factor

Richard Treisman
Transcription Laboratory
Imperial Cancer Research Fund
Lincolns Inn Fields
London WC2A 3PX, United Kingdom

OVERVIEW

Serum response factor (SRF) is a transcription factor that binds to a common regulatory element found in the promoters of many genes that are transiently activated by growth factor stimulation. In this chapter, I summarize our current knowledge of SRF as a member of a novel class of DNA-binding proteins and review current findings concerning its regulation and interactions with other proteins. Following a discussion of the function of the *Saccharomyces cerevisiae* MCM1 protein, which provides useful ideas concerning the possible molecular mechanisms of SRF function, the role of SRF in the function of the SRE is discussed.

INTRODUCTION

Stimulation of cells by growth factors or mitogens transiently activates transcription of a large family of genes, including the proto-oncogenes c-*fos*, c-*jun*, c-*myc*, and c-*rel*, without the need for prior protein synthesis. Many of these genes encode transcriptional regulatory proteins, the expression of which is presumed to determine the subsequent response of the genome, and ultimately of the cell, to growth factor stimulation (see Almendral et al. 1988; Bravo 1990). In many cases, transcriptional activation occurs immediately upon stimulation, reaches a peak within 15–30 minutes, and ceases after an hour. By analogy with the cascade of viral gene expression that occurs during lytic infection by DNA viruses, these genes have been termed cellular "immediate-early" genes.

A common *cis*-regulatory element, the serum response element (SRE; Treisman 1985, 1986; Gilman et al. 1986; Greenberg et al. 1987), has been identified that is in large part responsible for transcriptional regulation of the c-*fos* and several other cellular immediate-early genes. The

Transcriptional Regulation.
Copyright 1992 Cold Spring Harbor Laboratory Press 0-87969-410-6/92 $3 + 00

SRE acts as a basal promoter element, and its effect on transcriptional activity is rapidly and transiently increased following stimulation of cells by many different growth factors. Activation of the SRE involves signal transduction by both protein kinase C-dependent and -independent mechanisms (for reviews, see Rivera and Greenberg 1990; Treisman 1990); its activation is linked to signal pathways involving *ras* (Sassone-Corsi et al. 1989; Gauthier-Rouviere et al. 1990), *raf* (Kaibuchi et al. 1989; Jamal and Ziff 1990; Siegfried and Ziff 1990), and HTLV-I *tax* protein (Fujii et al. 1988). The down-regulation of SRE activity is achieved at least in part by an autoregulatory mechanism that involves the immediate-early gene products Fos and Jun (Sassone-Corsi et al. 1988; Schonthal et al. 1989; Wilson and Treisman 1988; Konig et al. 1989; Lucibello et al. 1989; Gius et al. 1990). The mechanism of SRE function is thus of considerable interest from the points of view of both signal transduction and transcriptional regulation.

The prototype SRE was defined in the regulatory sequences of the human c-*fos* gene and comprises a 20-bp dyad symmetry element, shown as a box in Figure 1. Two lines of evidence strongly suggest that SRE function is a fundamental property of the sequence element $CC(A/T)_6GG$ found at the center of the c-*fos* SRE. First, although a number of different proteins bind in the vicinity of the c-*fos* SRE in vivo (Fig. 1) (Herrera et al. 1989), the SRE alone can confer growth-factor-dependent transient transcriptional activation on a heterologous promoter. Sec-

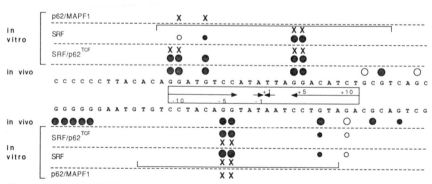

Figure 1 Protein-DNA interactions at the c-*fos* SRE. The human c-*fos* regulatory region sequence is shown with SRE shown as a box. Numbers indicate positions relative to the dyad. Filled and open circles show positions of methylation protection and enhancement, respectively; crosses indicate positions of methylation interference; brackets indicate regions protected from DNase I digestion. (Data summarized from Prywes and Roeder 1986, 1987; Treisman 1986; Schröter et al. 1987; Herrera et al. 1989; Ryan et al. 1989; Shaw et al. 1989b.)

ond, $CC(A/T)_6GG$ elements embedded in different sequence contexts, which usually lack significant dyad symmetry, act as SREs in several other immediate-early gene promoters (see Konig et al. 1989; Rivera et al. 1990; Treisman 1990). The SRE forms the binding site for a ubiquitous nuclear protein termed serum response factor (SRF), and cDNA clones encoding the protein have been isolated (Norman et al. 1988). SRE mutations that reduce or prevent SRF binding have parallel effects on the inducibility of the SRE by growth factors, suggesting that SRF plays a major role in signal transduction at the SRE.

A number of observations, however, suggest that this view may be an oversimplification. First, in addition to SRF, a number of other $CC(A/T)_6GG$-box-binding proteins have been identified in DNA-binding assays and by molecular cloning: What is the role of these proteins? For example, a protein termed p62 (Ryan et al. 1989) or MAPF1 (Walsh and Schimmel 1987) can bind to the left side of the c-*fos* SRE; like SRF, this protein contacts the DNA major groove. Several other $CC(A/T)_6GG$-box-binding activities also make close contacts in the DNA major groove at positions overlapping those made by SRF (Walsh and Schimmel 1987; Muscat et al. 1988; Gustafson and Kedes 1989; Levi et al. 1989; Quitschke et al. 1989; M. Gilman; R. Metz and E.B. Ziff, both pers. comm.): It is unlikely that SRF and these other factors can bind the SRE simultaneously. Second, SRF bound at the c-*fos* SRE forms a ternary complex with another protein, $p62^{TCF}$, which makes contacts with the DNA to the left of SRF (Fig. 1). In some cases, mutations at these positions affect growth factor activation of the SRE (Shaw et al. 1989b; Graham and Gilman 1991): What is the role of $p62^{TCF}$ in SRE function? Third, $CC(A/T)_6GG$ boxes are essential promoter elements found in a number of muscle-specific promoters (Minty and Kedes 1986; Miwa and Kedes 1987; Muscat et al. 1988; Walsh and Schimmel 1988; Mohun et al. 1989b; Chow and Schwartz 1990), which can also bind SRF (Boxer et al. 1989; Gustafson et al. 1989b; Taylor et al. 1989). These muscle gene $CC(A/T)_6GG$ boxes exhibit preferential activity in muscle cells but can function as effective SREs in nonmuscle cells (Taylor et al. 1989; Walsh 1989; Tuil et al. 1990): Are the same proteins involved in both muscle-specific and growth-factor-regulated transcription?

At present, the answers to these questions are not clear. In this review, I summarize our current knowledge of SRF as a member of a novel class of DNA-binding proteins and review current findings concerning its regulation and interactions with other proteins. Following a discussion of the function of the *S. cerevisiae* MCM1 protein, which provides useful ideas concerning the possible molecular mechanisms of SRF function, I address possible models for the role of SRF in the function of the SRE.

STRUCTURE AND FUNCTION OF SRF

SRF and SRF-related Proteins

SRF purified from growing HeLa cells by DNA affinity chromatography is a 62–67-kD polypeptide, in agreement with molecular-weight estimates from photoactivated protein-DNA cross-linking and SDS gel elution-renaturation experiments (Prywes and Roeder 1987; Schröter et al. 1987; Treisman 1987). Partial peptide sequence information was used to generate oligonucleotide probes that allowed the isolation of SRF cDNA clones (Norman et al. 1988). In humans, the protein is encoded by a single copy gene, which specifies two mRNAs, differing in the lengths of their 3′-untranslated regions. The open reading frame encodes a protein of 508 amino acids (predicted M_r 51,593), rich in serine (12.5%), threonine (11.6%), proline (7.3%), and glutamine (5.5%) (Fig. 2). The amino-terminal region of the protein, residues 1–141, contains a consensus recognition site for casein kinase II (CKII) (SGSEGDSES-GEEEEL, residues 77–91; Cohen 1988). The region of SRF required for DNA binding comprises residues 133–222 and contains an 81-amino-acid region related to several other DNA-binding proteins (residues 142–223; see Fig. 3). The DNA-binding domain also contains potential recognition sites for protein kinase A (RRYT and KRKT, residues 159 and 166, respectively; Cohen 1988) and calmodulin-dependent multi-

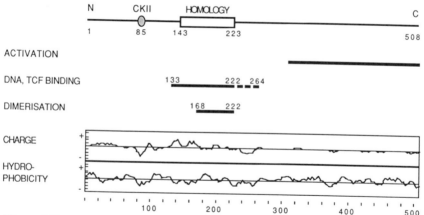

Figure 2 Features of SRF. Structural and functional features of SRF are shown above the charge and hydrophobicity profiles of the protein. At the top are shown the positions of the major amino-terminal CKII site and the homology with the *S. cerevisiae* regulators MCM1 and ARG80. Below are shown regions of the protein required for transcriptional activation, DNA and p62^{TCF} binding, and dimerization. (Data summarized from Norman et al. 1988; Manak et al. 1990; Schröter et al. 1990; Marais et al. 1992).

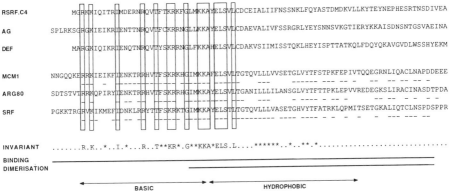

Figure 3 SRF-related proteins. The sequences of the SRF-related proteins RSRF.C4, AG, DEF, MCM1, and ARG80 are shown aligned with the SRF DNA-binding domain, with invariant amino acids boxed. These invariant residues are shown below the sequences, together with highly conserved residues indicated by asterisks. The identities between SRF, MCM1, and ARG80 are shown by dashes. Two further SRF-related proteins, RSRF.R2 and RSRF.C9, contain DNA-binding domains 90% identical to RSRF.C4, but diverge outside the region shown. Regions of SRF involved in DNA binding and dimerization are shown at the bottom. For discussion see text. (Data from Norman et al. 1988; Passmore et al. 1988; Sommer et al. 1990; Yanofsky et al. 1990; Pollock and Treisman 1991).

protein kinase (RRYTT, residue 158; Cohen 1988). The carboxy-terminal region, predicted to be rich in β-sheet structure, is predominantly uncharged apart from the segment next to the homology region, which contains a poorly matched potential CKII recognition site (SESDSSGETKD, residues 251–261).

SRF homologs have also been isolated from *Xenopus laevis* (Mohun et al. 1991) and *Drosophila melanogaster* (M. LaRosa et al., pers. comm.). The amino-terminal region of the *Xenopus* protein is very divergent from the human (85 vs. 130 residues; 49% identity) but retains a CKII site (SGSSGSSESGEEEDP, residues 39–53); the *Xenopus* and human proteins are virtually identical within the DNA-binding domain and 82% conserved in the carboxy-terminal portion.

A number of SRF-related proteins have been identified that contain regions of high similarity to the SRF DNA-binding domain (see Fig. 3). The two *S. cerevisiae* proteins ARG80 and MCM1 are 70% identical to SRF over the entire 80-amino-acid DNA-binding domain (Dubois et al. 1987; Norman et al. 1988; Passmore et al. 1988; Ammerer 1989). The functions and properties of the MCM1 protein suggest possible mechanisms of SRF function and are considered in detail below. A family of human SRF-related proteins, each comprising a common highly conserved amino-terminal SRF-type DNA-binding domain joined to one of three alternative carboxy-terminal domains, has been identified by oligonucleotide screening (RSRFs; Pollock and Treisman 1991). Plants contain a number of genes that contain similarities to the SRF DNA-binding domain, including two homeotic genes involved in flower formation, the *Antirrhinum majus Deficiens (Def)* and the *Arabidopsis thaliana Agamous (Ag)* (Sommer et al. 1990; Yanofsky et al. 1990; for review, see Schwarz-Sommer et al. 1990).

SRF as a DNA-binding Protein

SRF is a member of a novel class of DNA-binding proteins apparently unrelated to previously characterized DNA recognition structures. In this section, I consider the DNA-binding properties of SRF and other proteins in the family. The SRF-binding site is defined by the core sequence $CC(A/T)_6GG$. The protein binds as a dimer and makes close contacts with the DNA at the CG base pairs of this sequence, one DNA helical turn apart (Gilman et al. 1986; Prywes and Roeder 1986; Treisman 1986; Greenberg et al. 1987). A reasonable assumption is that this reflects contacts by the two subunits. SRF binds the c-*fos* SRE with an apparent K_d of 0.5×10^{11} M to 3×10^{11} M (Prywes and Roeder 1987; Schröter et al. 1990), similar to other eukaryotic sequence-specific DNA-binding proteins, and some 10^5-fold greater than its affinity for nonspecific DNA (Prywes and Roeder 1987). Experiments in which an SRF-binding site is located at different positions along a DNA fragment suggest SRF binding bends the DNA (Gustafson et al. 1989b).

The SRF DNA-binding Domain

The minimal SRF DNA-binding domain, mapped using deleted derivatives of the protein produced by cell-free translation, corresponds to the 80-amino-acid region of homology with the MCM1 and ARG80 proteins; the carboxy-terminal two-thirds of this domain is required for stable dimer formation (Fig. 3) (Norman et al. 1988). It contains no sequences previously associated with sequence-specific DNA-binding structures or motifs, such as helix-turn-helix (Harrison; Sigler; both this volume), zinc finger (Schmidt and Berg; Wright; both this volume), basic zipper (Curran and Vogt; McKnight; both this volume), basic helix-loop-helix (Murre and Baltimore, this volume), Ets domain (Karim et al. 1990), or HMG box (see Sinclair et al. 1990).

Sequences common to the entire family of SRF-like proteins lie within the amino-terminal two-thirds of the SRF DNA-binding domain (see Fig. 3). These common sequences, which have been referred to as the "MADS box" (Schwarz-Sommer et al. 1990), comprise a highly conserved amino-terminal region rich in basic residues (11 or 12/30) and a carboxy-terminal segment rich in hydrophobic residues, distinguished by a run of six (VLLLVA in SRF). Structural predictions by multiple methods using the algorithm of Eliopoulos et al. (1982) suggest that the basic region comprises two helical segments separated by regions of turn and β-sheet. The remaining third of the SRF DNA-binding domain is homologous to the ARG80 and MCM1 proteins but diverges considerably from other proteins in the family. However, two lines of evidence suggest that this region forms part of the DNA-binding domain in the entire group of proteins. First, truncations of SRF, MCM1, and RSRF proteins that impinge on these carboxy-terminal sequences abolish DNA binding (Ammerer 1989; Pollock and Treisman 1991). Second, the MCM1-1 mutation (a P→L change at position 97; Passmore et al. 1988) is defective in dimerization (M. Primig and G. Ammerer, pers. comm.).

Although the SRF DNA-binding domain includes sequences required for both sequence-specific DNA binding and subunit dimerization, the two functions are to some extent separable. For example, deletions within the highly conserved amino-terminal basic region block DNA binding but allow dimerization, and the basic regions of RSRF.C4 and SRF can be exchanged with a resulting precise exchange of sequence specificity between the proteins (Pollock and Treisman 1991). However, the carboxy-terminal border of the DNA-binding domain coincides with the carboxy-terminal border of the dimerization region. Since SRF will form heterodimers with MCM1 but not with RSRF.C4 (Pollock and Treisman 1991), perhaps the divergent carboxy-terminal half of the dimerization domain governs dimerization specificity.

Sequence Specificity of SRF

The sequence-specific DNA-binding properties of SRF have mainly been deduced from study of the effects of SRE mutations on SRF binding affinity. The conclusions drawn from these studies have been confirmed and extended by use of SRF to affinity-select binding sites from populations of random sequence DNA. These studies show that SRF-binding sites are basically defined by the consensus $CC(A/T)_6GG$, and that three factors affect the affinity of SRF for individual $CC(A/T)_6GG$ elements: first, the integrity of the GC base pairs at positions ±4 and ±5 relative to the dyad, which are virtually invariant in naturally occurring sites; second, the sequence of the intervening six AT-rich base pairs, perhaps to facilitate DNA bending in the SRF:DNA complex; third, the sequences flanking an individual $CC(A/T)_6GG$ box. It has been suggested that the symmetric elements of the c-*fos* SRE act to increase binding affinity (Rivera et al. 1990), but high-affinity SRF-binding sites selected from random sequence DNA are asymmetric, suggesting that the free energy of SRF binding can be maximized by increased contacts with one half-site (Pollock and Treisman 1990).

Methylation interference studies suggest that SRF makes close contacts with the DNA at the GC base pairs at positions ±4 and ±5 relative to the dyad (Gilman et al. 1986; Prywes and Roeder 1986; Treisman 1986; Greenberg et al. 1987). Symmetrically placed mutations at these positions, or deletions encompassing them, block binding entirely (Greenberg et al. 1987; Treisman 1987; Gilman 1988). In the c-*fos* SRE, single mutations at these positions reduce binding affinity more than tenfold but do not necessarily prevent binding (Leung and Miyamoto 1989).

Deletion of an AT base pair from the AT-rich center of the $CC(A/T)_6GG$ box in the center prevents binding (Phan-Dinh Tuy et al. 1988; Christy and Nathans 1989; Subramanian et al. 1989), whereas substitutions of C or G residues reduce affinity (Leung and Miyamoto 1989). Nevertheless, several naturally occurring SRF-binding sites in muscle-specific promoters contain C or G substitutions within the AT-rich sequence (Minty and Kedes 1986). Binding affinity is at least partly determined by the sequence of AT base pairs: In particular, the central AT dinucleotide is important for high-affinity binding (Leung and Miyamoto 1989; Taylor et al. 1989; Pollock and Treisman 1990).

Several experiments confirm that the context of a $CC(A/T)_6GG$ box affects SRF binding affinity. First, the location of identical $CC(A/T)_6GG$ boxes in different sequence contexts, or mutations of the flanking sequences in the c-*fos* SRE, result in sites of different affinities (Norman and Treisman 1988; Fredrickson et al. 1989; Leung and Miyamoto 1989; Shaw et al. 1989b; Rivera et al. 1990). Second, methylation of base pairs outside the $CC(A/T)_6GG$ in several SRF-binding sites interferes with SRF binding (Mohun et al. 1987; Gustafson et al. 1988; Gustafson and Kedes 1989; Taylor et al. 1989). Third, when high-affinity SRF sites are selected from random sequence DNA, clear sequence preferences are observed outside the $CC(A/T)_6GG$ sequence (Pollock and Treisman 1990).

Sequence Specificity of SRF-like Proteins

As might be expected from the degree of sequence identity within their DNA-binding domains, the binding specificities of the SRF and MCM1 are related. Many MCM1 sites contain the core sequence $CC(A/T)_6GG$

(Hayes et al. 1988; Jarvis et al. 1989; Passmore et al. 1989), and MCM1 protein can bind the c-*fos* SRE in vivo and in vitro (Hayes et al. 1988; Passmore et al. 1989). However, not all MCM1 operators can bind SRF, and vice versa (J. Wynne and R. Treisman, in prep.). Partial proteolytic degradation experiments suggest that MCM1 adopts different conformations according to the sequence of the operator, which might influence its properties as a transcriptional activator (Tan and Richmond 1990); it will be interesting to see if this is also true of SRF.

The mammalian SRF-related protein RSRF.C4 binds sites containing the sequence C/TTA(A/T)$_4$TAA/G. Unlike SRF sites, these sites show absolute conservation of sequence at base pairs at ±3 and ±4 relative to the dyad, presumably reflecting sequence differences within the amino-terminal basic region of its DNA-binding domain (Pollock and Treisman 1991).

Posttranslational Modifications of SRF

Phosphorylation

Since many of the agents that stimulate the activity of the SRE lead to increases in the activity of cellular kinases, it is of special interest to see if the susceptibility of SRF to phosphorylation can be correlated with changes in SRE activity. SRF is a phosphosprotein (Prywes et al. 1988b; Ryan et al. 1989; Schalasta and Doppler 1990; D. Hancock et al., unpubl.) containing multiple phosphorylated serine residues (Prywes et al. 1988b; Manak et al. 1990). Stimulation of A431 cells, but not HeLa cells, results in increased phosphorylation of the protein (Schalasta and Doppler 1990; Prywes et al. 1988b). In A431 cells, epidermal growth factor (EGF) stimulation and SRF phosphorylation can be partially inhibited by treatment with phospholipase C inhibitors, implicating a protein-kinase-C-dependent pathway in both processes (Schalasta and Doppler 1990). It is not clear whether this increased phosphorylation mediates the increase in SRF DNA-binding activity that has previously been observed in these cells (Prywes and Roeder 1986; Prywes et al. 1988b; Manak et al. 1990).

SRF cDNA has been expressed in bacteria (Manak et al. 1990) or insect cells (Marais et al. 1992), and the ability of the purified protein to act as a substrate for purified kinases or cell extracts has been evaluated. Both cell extracts and purified CKII efficiently phosphorylate the protein at the major amino-terminal CKII consensus site, which is also phosphorylated in vivo (Fig. 2) (Manak et al. 1990; Marais et al. 1992). This phosphorylation potentiates DNA-binding activity by an unknown mechanism and is discussed in detail below. The protein is not a good in vitro substrate for protein kinase C α or β, protein kinase A, or glycogen synthase kinase III (Marais et al. 1992). It remains possible that transcriptional activation by SRF can be regulated by changes in phosphorylation.

Glycosylation

Many transcription factors involved in the regulation of genes transcribed by RNA polymerase II are modified by O-linked glycosylation (Jackson and Tjian 1988), and SRF is no exception (Schröter et al. 1990). The HeLa protein is quantitatively retained on wheat germ agglutinin columns, can be eluted with *N*-acetylglucosamine, and acts as a substrate for galactosyl transferase, suggesting that the molecule is modified by at least one *N*-acetylglucosamine moiety. Analysis of recombinant human SRF produced in insect cells reveals at least four different sites for addition of single *N*-acetylglucosamine moieties in the carboxy-terminal portion of the molecule (A. Reason et al., in prep.). The effect of glycosylation on SRF function is as yet obscure: Such modifications may act to regulate the availability of potential phosphorylation sites, target SRF to specific intracellular sites, increase SRF solubility, or potentiate its transcriptional activation properties.

Regulation of SRF DNA-binding Activity

An obvious way in which SRE activity could be regulated is at the level of SRF DNA-binding activity. However, although it is clear that SRF DNA-binding affinity can be modulated by phosphorylation, two lines of evidence suggest that this is not a major pathway by which SRE activity is regulated upon growth factor stimulation. First, in many cell types, the amount of extractable SRE-binding activity remains constant regardless of whether or not the cells are growth-factor-stimulated (Gilman et al. 1986; Prywes and Roeder 1986; Treisman 1986; Greenberg et al. 1987). Second, an SRF-like genomic footprint is present on the c-*fos* SRE before, during, and after growth factor stimulation (Herrera et al. 1989). Two apparent exceptions to this have been reported: a three- to tenfold increase in SRF DNA-binding activity upon treatment of an A431 cell line with EGF (Prywes and Roeder 1986; Prywes et al. 1988b) and a decrease in SRF-binding activity upon prolonged treatment of a Jurkat cell line with phorbol ester (Toledano et al. 1990).

Experiments using purified recombinant SRF have demonstrated that phosphorylation at the amino-terminal CKII site causes a large increase in the rate of SRF-DNA exchange, but has very little effect on equilibrium DNA-binding affinity (Janknecht et al. 1992; Marais et al. 1992). Although CKII activity in several cell types increases upon growth factor stimulation (Sommercorn et al. 1987), as discussed above, the relation of this activation to SRE activation remains unclear. The mechanism by which this phosphorylation regulates SRF DNA binding is unknown. Perhaps phosphorylation acts to facilitate a transient conformational change that is required for SRF to form a stable complex with the SRE. Curiously, the sequences surrounding the amino-terminal CKII site are the least conserved between the human and *Xenopus* SRF. Regulation of binding affinity by remote CKII sites has also been observed in the product of the c-*myb* proto-oncogene, although in this case its effect is to decrease DNA-binding affinity (Luscher et al. 1990).

SRF derivatives lacking the major CKII site produced by cell-free translation or by bacterial or insect cell expression systems exhibit readily detectable SRE-binding activity (Norman et al. 1988; Manak et al. 1990; Janknecht et al. 1992; Marais et al. 1992); conversely, phosphatase treatment of highly fractionated or pure protein reduces but does not destroy binding (Prywes et al. 1988b; R. Marais and R. Treisman, in prep.). Thus, phosphorylation is not necessary for binding per se. However, treatment of SRF in crude extracts with phosphatase causes virtually complete loss of DNA-binding activity (Prywes et al. 1988b; Boxer et al. 1989; Schalasta and Doppler 1990). The reasons for this apparent contradiction are not clear: Possibly an additional factor present in crude cell extracts blocks SRE binding by dephosphorylated SRF; alternatively, dephosphorylation may activate an inhibitory factor. Further studies are necessary to resolve this issue.

Regulation of SRF Gene Expression

In addition to regulation of its DNA-binding activity, SRF expression is also regulated by changes in gene expression following growth factor stimulation. In human cells, SRF mRNAs are transcribed from a single copy gene 12 kb in length (R. Pollock and R. Treisman, unpubl.). The SRF gene is itself a cellular immediate-early gene, with serum stimulation of HeLa cells resulting in a five- to tenfold increase in the abundance of SRF mRNA and with transient accumulation of two presumptive precursor RNAs between 15 and 30 minutes after stimulation (Norman et al. 1988). The 5'-flanking sequences of the SRF gene include two $CC(A/T)_6GG$ sequences, one of which binds SRF in vitro, and which presumably mediate the response of the gene to growth factor stimulation (R. Pollock and R. Treisman, in prep.).

Although SRF mRNA is readily detectable in growing cultured cells, the SRF synthetic rate is very low, and the protein is very stable with an apparent half-life of more than 6 hours (Misra et al. 1991; D. Hancock et al., unpubl.). However, substantially increased rates of SRF protein synthesis are observed in serum-stimulated mouse 3T3 cells. Under these conditions, the protein is first synthesized as a polypeptide of M_r 63,000, which with time increases to 67,000. This apparent change presumably results from posttranslational modifications (Misra et al. 1991). It remains possible that the regulation of SRF synthesis upon growth factor stimulation involves translational as well as transcriptional control.

The role of the changes in SRF gene expression upon growth factor stimulation remains unclear. Since SRF mRNA level, protein synthetic rate, and specific binding activity all appear to change, it may be necessary to reevaluate early studies that examined the effects of growth factor stimulation on SRF DNA-binding activity. For example, the measurement of total binding activity in cell extracts may mask the appearance of stimulation of SRF subpopulations with lowered or elevated DNA-binding affinity.

Transcriptional Activation by SRF

Two kinds of approaches have been used to examine the role of SRF in SRE function. In the first, the basal promoter activity of the SRE can be exploited to develop SRF-dependent in vitro transcription systems. The second approach has been to use transfection of SRF cDNA expression plasmids into cultured cells to study the transcriptional activation properties of SRF in vivo.

When SRE elements are placed upstream of the human c-*fos* or *Xenopus* type 5 cytoskeletal actin gene TATA boxes, they activate transcription in an SRF-dependent manner in soluble extracts derived from HeLa cells (Norman and Treisman 1988; Norman et al. 1988; Prywes et al. 1988a). Mutation of the SRE, or removal of SRF from these extracts by DNA affinity chromatography, reduces transcription to basal levels. In SRF-depleted extracts, activity can be restored to maximal levels by addition of exogenous SRF either purified from HeLa cells, produced by in vitro translation of SRF cRNA, or expressed in insect or bacterial cells (Norman and Treisman 1988; Norman et al. 1988; Prywes et al. 1988a; Manak et al. 1990; R. Marais et al., in prep.). Analysis of SRF deletion mutants produced by translation in vitro shows that carboxy-terminal deletions destroy transcriptional activation by SRF and that the minimal

the STE3 UAS is also pheromone-responsive and STE12-dependent, although it lacks a clear STE12 consensus: Perhaps MCM1 also acts to recruit STE12 to this site (Jarvis et al. 1988; Dolan and Fields 1991; P. Sengupta and B. Cochran, pers. comm.). As with the MATα proteins, the DNA-binding domain of MCM1 is sufficient to allow STE12 recruitment (M. Primig and G. Ammerer, pers. comm.).

Given the wealth of information about the role of MCM1 in gene regulation, it is tempting to speculate that the structural homology between the DNA-binding domains of SRF and MCM1 may reflect a functional homology between the two proteins. First, they are involved in similar processes; second, the function of both proteins is modified by their interaction with other factors; third, these interactions occur through their DNA-binding domains.

The Role of SRF in Growth-factor-regulated Transcription

Evidence has been presented in the preceding sections that the sequence specificity of SRF defines an SRE, that SRF can recruit the p62^{TCF} protein to the SRE, and that SRF contains a transcriptional *trans*-activation domain. Genomic footprinting indicates that at least at the c-*fos* SRE, proteins of specificity similar to the SRF:p62^{TCF} complex are bound to the SRE before, during, and after growth factor stimulation. A simple model for SRE function is thus that SRF remains bound to the SRE throughout the induction process and that SRE activity is modulated by posttranslational modification of either SRF or proteins with which it interacts. Such modifications might be expected either to regulate the association of SRF with accessory proteins or to modify the activity of a preexisting complex. Down-regulation of the SRE would be achieved by indirect interaction of Fos/Jun with the SRE via their interaction with SRF. This "recruitment model" has the obvious attraction of analogy with the function of the *S. cerevisiae* MCM1 protein, although it should be emphasized that proof of an exact functional homology between the two systems is lacking.

According to this view, the activity of a particular SRF-binding site with respect to different signaling pathways would be affected by at least three variables. First, the sequence context of a $CC(A/T)_6GG$ box could affect the ability of SRF to recruit accessory factors required for transduction of particular signals. Such a mechanism has been invoked to explain the requirement for p62^{TCF} binding to the SRF:SRE complex for the response to protein kinase C activators but not for the response to serum factors (Graham and Gilman 1991). Second, the availability of particular accessory factors could vary according to cell type. Thus, the activity of a particular $CC(A/T)_6GG$ box might be modulated in a cell-specific manner, and the same stimulus might produce different effects in different cell types. Third, it is possible that the conformation of SRF itself is influenced by the primary sequence of its binding site, as has been proposed in the case of the *S. cerevisiae* MCM1 protein. Such "DNA effected allostery" might affect either the ability of SRF to recruit particular accessory proteins or its interaction with other components of the transcription apparatus.

An alternative view is that the protein complex at the SRE undergoes protein exchange during the induction process, either with modified SRF or with other SRE-binding proteins. If such exchanges occur very rapidly, they might not be detectable in genomic footprinting analysis, especially if they involved proteins of similar specificity to those bound before stimulation. A number of variations of this theme can be envisaged. For example, SRF (and $p62^{TCF}$) might regulate basal transcription levels and, upon growth factor stimulation, be replaced by a different, activated, complex; Fos and Jun would then act either to down-regulate the active complex or to generate a form of SRF that could replace it. This kind of model would provide potential roles for other $CC(A/T)_6GG$-box-binding proteins, such as p62/MAPF1, or proteins with similar DNA-binding specificities to SRF.

Neither of these models provides a rationale for why SRF is itself an immediate-early gene. Perhaps SRF is somehow inactivated or destroyed upon induction, and newly synthesized protein is required to suppress SRE activity; fresh synthesis of SRF might also allow binding at lower affinity sites inaccessible before stimulation. An alternative, speculative view is that newly synthesized SRF acts to antagonize other immediate-early gene products in a manner reminiscent of the interactions between the glucocorticoid receptor and the Fos/Jun complex.

The role of SRF in Muscle-specific Gene Expression

The involvement of similar promoter elements in both growth-factor-responsive and muscle-specific promoters remains poorly understood. The muscle specificity of $CC(A/T)_6GG$ boxes from muscle-specific genes appears to reflect their lower activity in nonmuscle cells, rather than their increased activity in muscle cells (Walsh 1989; Tuil et al. 1990); in nonmuscle cells, however, these $CC(A/T)_6GG$ boxes can function as effective SREs (Taylor et al. 1989; Walsh 1989; Tuil et al. 1990). Muscle-specific $CC(A/T)_6GG$ box activity depends on both sets of SRF close contact points (Walsh 1989), and muscle cells contain SRF (Boxer et al. 1989; Taylor et al. 1989). A simple model is that SRF mediates

$CC(A/T)_6GG$ box activity in both cell types. Several questions follow from these findings. Do the same proteins, particularly SRF, participate in both muscle and nonmuscle $CC(A/T)_6GG$ box activity? What determines the muscle-restricted activity of the muscle-specific $CC(A/T)_6GG$ boxes? Are $CC(A/T)_6GG$ boxes always growth factor responsive? How do $CC(A/T)_6GG$-box-binding proteins interact with other muscle-specific activator proteins such as MyoD1 (see Sartorelli et al. 1990)? The answers to these questions are not clear and will require further study of the properties of both growth-factor-regulated and muscle-specific promoters in muscle cells.

CONCLUSIONS AND PERSPECTIVES

SRF is a member of a novel class of DNA-binding proteins. The SRF-binding site is involved in both growth-factor-responsive and tissue-specific gene expression, and although it is likely that SRF itself is involved in the signal transduction process, its precise role in the process remains unclear. Future studies of SRF must concentrate on three areas: first, its involvement in the various signaling pathways acting through the SRE; second, its relevance to cell-specific transcription; and third, the identification, cloning, and functional analysis of proteins that interact with SRF. Since two members of the family of proteins with SRF-related DNA-binding domains act to recruit accessory proteins to their binding sites, it will be of interest to determine if this is a general property of this class of DNA-binding proteins.

ACKNOWLEDGMENTS

I thank workers in the c-*fos* and immediate-early gene field for communication of data and manuscripts prior to publication, and members of my laboratory for helpful comments on the manuscript.

REFERENCES

Almendral, J.M., D. Sommer, H. Macdonald-Bravo, J. Burckhardt, J. Perera, and R. Bravo. 1988. Complexity of the early genetic response to growth factors in mouse fibroblasts. *Mol. Cell. Biol.* **8:** 2140–2148.

Ammerer, G. 1989. Identification, purification and cloning of a polypeptide (PRTF/GRM) that binds to mating-specific promoter elements in yeast. *Genes Dev.* **4:** 299–312.

Ballard, D.W., E. Bohnlein, J.A. Hoffman, H.P. Bogerd, E.P. Dixon, B.R. Franza, and W.C. Greene. 1989. Activation of the interleukin-2 receptor α gene: Regulatory role for DNA-protein interactions flanking the κ B enhancer. *New Biol.* **1:** 83–92.

Bender, A. and G.F. Sprague. 1987. MATα1 protein, a yeast transcription activator, binds synergistically with a second protein to a set of celltype specific genes. *Cell* **50:** 681–691.

Berkowitz, L., K.T. Riabowol, and M.Z. Gilman. 1989. Multiple sequence elements of a single functional class are required for cyclic AMP responsiveness of the mouse c-*fos* promoter. *Mol. Cell. Biol.* **9:** 4272–4281.

Boxer, L.M., R. Prywes, R.G. Roeder, and L. Kedes. 1989. The sarcomeric actin CArG-binding factor is indistinguishable from the c-*fos* serum response factor. *Mol. Cell. Biol.* **9:** 515–522.

Bravo, R. 1990. Genes induced during the G0/G1 transition in mouse fibroblasts. In *Seminars in cancer biology* (ed. N. Jones), vol. 1, p. 37–46. W.B. Saunders, Philadelphia.

Chow, K-L. and R.J. Schwartz. 1990. A combination of closely associated positive and negative promoter elements regulates transcription of the skeletal α actin gene. *Mol. Cell. Biol.* **10:** 528–538.

Christy, B. and D. Nathans. 1989. Functional serum response elements upstream of the growth factor inducible zif268. *Mol. Cell. Biol.* **9:** 4889–4895.

Cohen, P. 1988. Protein phosphorylation and hormone action. *Proc. R. Soc. Lond. B Biol. Sci.* **234:** 115–144.

Courey, A.J. and R. Tjian. 1988. Analysis of Sp1 in vivo reveals multiple transcriptional domains including a novel glutamine-rich activation motif. *Cell* **59:** 827–836.

Dalton, S. and R. Treisman. 1992. Characterisation of SAP-1, a protein recruited by serum response factor to the c-*fos* serum response element. *Cell* **68:** 597–612.

Dolan, J. and S. Fields. 1991. Cell-type specific transcription in yeast. *Biochim. Biophys. Acta* **1088:** 155–169.

Dolan, J., C. Kirkman, and S. Fields. 1989. The yeast STE12 protein binds to the DNA sequence mediating pheromone induction. *Proc. Natl. Acad. Sci.* **86:** 5703–5707.

Dubois, E., J. Bercy, F. Descamps, and F. Messenguy. 1987. Characterisation of two new genes essential for vegetative growth of *Saccharomyces cerevisiae*: Nucleotide sequence determination and chromosome mapping. *Gene* **55:** 265–275.

Eliopoulos, E.E., A.J. Geddes, M. Brett, D.J.C. Pappin, and J.B.C. Findley. 1982. A structural model of the chromophore binding domain of ovine rhodopsin. *Int. J. Biol. Macromol.* **4:** 263–268.

Errede, B. and G. Ammerer. 1989. STE12, a protein involved in cell-type-specific transcription and signal transduction in yeast. *Genes Dev.* **3:** 1349–1361.

Fields, S., D.A. Chaleff, and G.F. Sprague, Jr. 1988. Yeast STE7, STE11 and STE12 genes are required for expression of cell-type specific genes. *Mol. Cell. Biol.* **8:** 551–556.

Fisch, T.M., R. Prywes, and R.G. Roeder. 1988. Multiple sequence elements in the c-*fos* 5′ flanking region mediate induction by cAMP. *Genes Dev.* **2:** 391–405.

Frederickson, R.M., M.R. Micheau, A. Iwamoto, and N.G. Miyamoto. 1989. 5′ Flanking and first intron sequences of the human β actin gene required for efficient promoter activity. *Nucleic Acids Res.* **17:** 253–270.

Fujii, K., P. Sassone-Corsi, and I.M. Verma. 1988. c-*fos* promoter transactivation by the tax1 protein of human T cell leukemia virus type 1. *Proc. Natl. Acad. Sci.* **85:** 8526–8530.

Fujiwara, K.T., K. Ashida, H. Nishina, H. Iba, N. Miyajima, M. Nishizawa, and S. Kawai. 1987. The chicken fos gene: Cloning and nucleotide sequence analysis. *J. Virol.* **61:** 4012–4018.

Gauthier-Rouvière, C., A. Fernandez, and N.J.C. Lamb. 1990. *ras*-induced c-*fos* expression and proliferation in living rat fibroblasts involves C-kinase activation and the serum response element pathway. *EMBO J.* **9:** 171–180.

Gauthier-Rouviere, C., M. Basset, J.-M. Blanchard, J.-C. Cavadore, A. Fernandez, and N.J.C. Lamb. 1991. Casein kinase II induces c-*fos* expression via the serum response element pathway and p67/SRF phosphorylation in living fibroblasts. *EMBO J.* **10:** 2921–2930.

Gilman, M.Z. 1988. The c-*fos* SRE responds to protein kinase C dependent and independent signals but not to cyclic AMP. *Genes Dev.* **2:** 394–402.

Gilman, M.Z., R.N. Wilson, and R.A. Weinberg. 1986. Multiple protein binding sites in the 5′ flanking region regulate c-*fos* expression. *Mol. Cell. Biol.* **6:** 4305–4314.

Gius, D., X. Cao, F.J. Rauscher III, D.R. Cohen, T. Curran, and V.P. Sukhatme. 1990. Transcriptional activation and repression by Fos are independent functions: The C-terminus represses immediate-early gene expression via CArG elements. *Mol. Cell. Biol.* **10:** 4243–4255.

Graham, R. and M.Z. Gilman. 1991. Distinct protein targets for signals acting at the c-*fos* serum response element. *Science* **251:** 189–192.

Greenberg, M.E., Z. Siegfried, and E.B. Ziff. 1987. Mutation of the c-*fos* dyad symmetry element inhibits inducibility in vivo and the nuclear regulatory factor binding in vitro. *Mol. Cell. Biol.* **7:** 1217–1225.

Gustafson, T.A. and L.J. Kedes. 1989. Identification of multiple factors that interact with the functional regions of the human cardiac α-actin promoter. *Mol. Cell. Biol.* **9:** 3269–3283.

Gustafson, T.A., A. Taylor, and L. Kedes. 1989. DNA bending is induced by a transcription factor that interacts with the human c-*fos* and α-actin promoters. *Proc. Natl. Acad. Sci.* **86:** 2162–2166.

Gustafson, T.A., T. Miwa, L. Boxer, and L. Kedes. 1988. Interaction of nuclear proteins with muscle-specific regulatory sequences of the human cardiac actin promoter. *Mol. Cell. Biol.* **8:** 4110–4119.

Hayes, T.E., P. Sengupta, and B.H. Cochran. 1988. The human serum response factor and the yeast factors GRM/PRTF have related DNA binding specificities. *Genes Dev.* **2:** 1713–1722.

Herrera, R.E., P.E. Shaw, and A. Nordheim. 1989. Occupation of the c-*fos* serum response elements in vivo by a multiprotein complex is unaltered by growth factor induction. *Nature* **340:** 68–70.

Herskowitz, I. 1989. A regulatory hierarchy for cell specialization in yeast. *Nature* **342:** 749–757.

Hipskind, R.A., V.N. Rao, C.G.F. Mueller, E.P. Reddy, and A. Nordheim. 1991. Ets-related protein Elk-1 is homologous to the c-*fos* regulatory factor p62TCF. *Nature* **354:** 531–534.

Hope, I.A., S. Mahadevan, and K. Struhl. 1988. Structural and functional analysis of the short acidic transcriptional activating region of yeast GCN4 protein. *Nature* **333:** 635–640.

Jackson, S.P. and R. Tjian. 1988. Unexpected O-glycosylation of eukaryotic transcription factors: Implications for mechanisms of transcriptional regulation. *Cell* **55:** 125–133.

Jamal, S. and E.B. Ziff. 1990. Transactivation of c-*fos* and β actin genes by *raf* as a step in the early response to transmembrane signals. *Nature* **344:** 463–466.

Janknecht, R., R.A. Hipskind, T. Houthaeve, A. Nordhein, and H.G. Stunnenberg. 1992. Identification of multiple SRF N terminal phosphorylation sites affecting DNA binding properties. *EMBO J.* **11:** 1045–1054.

Jarvis, E.E., K.L. Clark, and G.F. Sprague, Jr. 1989. The yeast transcription activator

PRTF, a homolog of the mammalian serum response factor, is encoded by the MCM1 gene. *Genes Dev.* **3:** 936–945.

Jarvis, E.E., D.C. Hagen, and G.F. Sprague, Jr. 1988. Identification of a DNA segment that is necessary and sufficient for α-specific gene control in *S. cerevisiae*: Implications for regulation of α-specific and a-specific genes. *Mol. Cell. Biol.* **8:** 308–320.

Kaibuchi, K., Y. Fukumoto, N. Oku, Y. Hori, T. Yamamoto, K. Toyoshima, and Y. Takai. 1989. Activation of the serum response element and 12-*O*-tetradecanoylphorbol-13-acetate response element by the activated c-raf-1 protein in a manner independent of protein kinase C. *J. Biol. Chem.* **264:** 20855–20858.

Karim, F.D., L.D. Urness, C.S. Thummel, M.S. Klemscz, S.D. McKercher, A. Celada, C. van Beveren, R.A. Maki, C.V. Gunther, J.A. Nye, and B.J. Graves. 1990. The ets-domain: A new DNA binding motif that recognizes a purine rich core DNA sequence. *Genes Dev.* **4:** 1451–1453.

Keleher, C.A., C. Gouette, and A.D. Johnson. 1988. The yeast cell-type-specific repressor α2 acts cooperatively with a non cell-type-specific protein. *Cell* **53:** 927–936.

Konig, H., H. Ponta, U. Rahmsdorf, M. Buscher, A. Schontal, H.J. Rahmsdorf, and P. Herrlich. 1989. Autoregulation of Fos: The dyad symmetry element as the major target of repression. *EMBO J.* **8:** 2559–2566.

Kronstad, J.W., J.A. Holly, and V.L. MacKay. 1987. A yeast operator overlaps an upstream activation site. *Cell* **50:** 369–377.

Leung, S. and N.G. Miyamoto. 1989. Point mutational analysis of the human c-*fos* serum response factor binding site. *Nucleic Acids Res.* **17:** 1177–1195.

Levi, B.-Z., J.W. Kasik, P.A. Burke, R. Prywes, R.G. Roeder, E. Appella, and K. Ozato. 1989. Neonatal induction of a protein that binds to the c-*fos* enhancer. *Proc. Natl. Acad. Sci.* **86:** 2262–2266.

Lucibello, F., C. Lowag, M. Neuberg, and R. Muller. 1989. Trans-repression of the mouse c-*fos* promoter: A novel mechanism of Fos-mediated trans-regulation. *Cell* **59:** 999–1007.

Luscher, B., E. Christenson, D.W. Litchfield, E.G. Krebs, and R.N. Eisenman. 1990. Myb DNA binding inhibited by phosphorylation at a site deleted during oncogenic activation. *Nature* **344:** 517–522.

Ma, J. and M. Ptashne. 1987a. Deletion analysis of GAL4 defines two transcription activating segments. *Cell* **48:** 847–853.

———. 1987b. A new class of transcription activators. *Cell* **51:** 113–119.

Manak, J.R., N. de Bisschop, R.M. Kris, and R. Prywes. 1990. Casein kinase II enhances the DNA binding activity of serum response factor. *Genes Dev.* **4:** 955–967.

Marais, R.M., J.J. Hsuan, C.M. McGuigan, J. Wynne, and R. Treisman. 1992. Casein kinase II phosphorylation increases the rate of serum response factor-binding site exchange. *EMBO J.* **11** 97–105.

Mermod, J., E.A. O'Neill, T.J. Kelly, and R. Tjian. 1989. The proline rich activator of CTF/NF1 is distinct from the replication and DNA binding domain. *Cell* **58:** 741–753.

Minty, A. and L.J. Kedes. 1986. Upstream regions of the human cardiac actin gene that modulate its transcription in muscle cells: Presence of an evolutionarily conserved regulatory motif. *Mol. Cell. Biol.* **6:** 2125–2136.

Misra, R.P., V.M. Rivera, J.M. Wang, P.D. Fan, and M.E. Greenberg. 1991. The serum response factor is extensively modified by phosphorylation following its synthesis in serum-stimulated fibroblasts. *Mol. Cell. Biol.* **11:** 4545–4554.

Miwa, T. and L.J. Kedes. 1987. Duplicated CarG box domains have positive and mutually dependent regulatory roles in expression of the human α cardiac actin gene.

Mohun, T.J., N. Garrett, and M.J. Taylor. 1989a. Temporal and tissue specific expression

34
Heat Shock Factor

John Lis
Section of Biochemistry,
Molecular and Cell Biology
Cornell University
Ithaca, New York 14853

Carl Wu
Laboratory of Biochemistry
National Cancer Institute
National Institutes of Health
Bethesda, Maryland 20892

OVERVIEW

The transcriptional activation of genes encoding the heat shock proteins is mediated by the binding of heat shock factor (HSF) to specific DNA sequence elements (heat shock elements [HSEs]). The canonical HSE is a continuous array of three, alternately oriented nGAAn units. However, the number of repeating pentanucleotide units in an HSE can vary, and the unusual multimeric nature of HSF allows it to bind efficiently HSEs of different lengths. HSF activity is regulated by heat shock at the level of both DNA binding and transcriptional activation. The binding activity of HSF is dependent on its multimeric state, whereas transcriptional activity correlates with its heat-shock-induced phosphorylation. Complementary DNAs for yeast and *Drosophila* HSF have been cloned. Although heat shock proteins exhibit strong sequence conservation among many species, the sequences of *Drosophila* and yeast HSF are divergent, except in regions important for DNA binding and multimerization.

In uninduced cells, heat shock promoters are organized in nuclease-hypersensitive chromatin structures. These hypersensitive sites apparently possess bound transcription factor IID (TFIID) and a transcriptionally engaged but arrested RNA polymerase molecule. The heat shock promoter is thus primed or potentiated for activity in the absence of heat shock. Binding of HSF upon heat induction leads to increased transcription by unknown mechanisms, possibly involving both the release of the arrested RNA polymerase and the recruitment of additional polymerase molecules to the promoter itself.

INTRODUCTION

The heat shock gene regulatory circuit has several features that make it an attractive model for investigating the activation of transcription. First, the frequency with which RNA polymerase II transcribes the major heat shock genes can be increased more than 100-fold upon heat shock (Gilmour and Lis 1985). This large stimulation enhances the detection of specific regulatory components and allows a quantitative analysis of the role of these components to be accurately made. Second, the rapidity of the response, which is mediated by proteins that are present in uninduced cells (Kingston et al. 1987; Zimarino and Wu 1987), facilitates kinetic and mechanistic investigations of the activation of these genes. Third, comprehensive studies from many laboratories provide a strong foundation of information on the primary structure of these genes, the DNA sequence elements and protein factors that participate in the regulation of their transcription, and their assembly into chromatin (for reviews, see Eissenberg et al. 1985; Bienz and Pelham 1987; Nover 1987). Finally, heat shock promoters are composed of elements similar to those of other genes; therefore, at least some of the principles identified in the study of transcription of heat shock genes are likely to be of general relevance to transcriptional regulation.

Several independent studies demonstrate that the regulatory elements and proximal promoter elements (the TATA box and transcription start regions) of heat shock genes are compatible with those of non-heat-shock genes. The fat body enhancer element of the YP1 gene is effective in stimulating expression from an hsp70 promoter when placed either upstream or downstream from this heat shock gene (Garabedian et al. 1986), and the hsp70 proximal promoter sequences can substitute for those of the *Drosophila Sgs-3* gene (Martin et al. 1989). In addition, a well-characterized transcriptional activator from yeast, the GAL4 protein, when expressed in *Drosophila*, will induce an hsp70 gene that has been modified to contain DNA sequences that bind GAL4 (Fischer et al. 1988). Likewise, HSEs found upstream of *Drosophila* heat shock genes can mediate positive transcriptional regulation from proximal promoter sequences of genes that are not normally induced by heat shock. For example, the fusion of a DNA segment containing the hsp70 HSEs to a site immediately upstream of the TATA box of the herpesvirus thymidine kinase gene results in heat-inducible expression of this gene in transfected monkey COS cells (Pelham 1982). Therefore, information on the mechanism of regulation of the heat shock promoters should prove generally useful in understanding the regulation of promoters that respond to metabolic or developmental cues.

Heat shock genes usually possess multiple HSEs, and these elements have been shown to be required for the stress-induced transcription of these genes. In response to heat shock in higher eukaryotes, a transcriptional activator, HSF, is rapidly converted to a form that binds tightly to the HSE. In this chapter, we describe the properties of HSEs and HSF, and their interactions, focusing primarily on the heat shock system in *Drosophila*. We conclude by speculating on how the complexes of HSE-HSF formed during heat shock may influence the frequency of transcription of heat shock genes by RNA polymerase II.

HSE

Pelham (1982) and Mirault et al. (1982) reported the first functional analyses of the regulatory region of the *Drosophila* hsp70 gene by examining the expression of a series of deletion mutations that were transfected into monkey COS cells. Pelham showed that sequences between nucleotides –66 to –47 upstream of the hsp70 gene are necessary for heat-induced expression and identified a 14-bp consensus sequence (5′-CnGAAnnTTCnnG-3′) that is found upstream of all *Drosophila* heat shock genes. The importance of specific DNA sequences in and around this consensus has recently been examined in detail by studies on the *Drosophila* hsp70 gene (Amin et al. 1988; Xiao and Lis 1988). These studies demonstrate that sequences within and, more surprisingly, sequences flanking the 14-bp consensus are critical for heat-induced expression. In particular, a single base mutation at a site 2 bp downstream from the promoter-proximal consensus reduces heat-shock-induced expression of a transfected hsp70 gene by 1 order of magnitude (Amin et al. 1988). These results, together with an inspection of the genetically defined regulatory regions of a variety of *Drosophila* heat shock genes, have led to a reevaluation of the structure of the HSE. All HSEs possess a simple, repeating 5-bp sequence, 5′-nGAAn-3′, where the repeats are contiguous but arranged in alternating orientations, i.e., 5′-nGAAnnTTCnnGAAn-3′. These repeats include the originally defined 14-bp consensus and also the critical nucleotides that flank the consensus (Amin et al. 1988; Xiao and Lis 1988).

The number of 5-bp units in a functional heat shock element can vary. For example, the four HSEs upstream of the hsp70 gene each contain either three or four 5-bp units, whereas the single hsp83 HSE can be viewed as having seven or eight contiguous 5-bp units, depending on the stringency used to define the 5-bp unit (Fig. 1). The start of the HSE can vary, beginning with either a 5'-nCAAn-3' (→) repeat or its complement 5'-nTTCn-3' (←) (Fig. 1). In addition, an HSE can tolerate a 5-bp insertion between repeating units, provided the phase of the repeating units (→--→) is maintained (Amin et al. 1988). Thus, the HSE can be viewed as a contiguous array of the 5-bp module 5'-nGAAn-3', where each module is inverted relative to the immediately adjacent modules.

(A)

```
                        ──►◄──►──►
                cgcCtcGAAtgTTCgcGAAa      -46        hsp70
                aTTCtcGttgcTTCgaGAga      -69 (H8)
                gcTCtcGttggTTCgaGAga      -69 (E3)
            aGAAaacTCgaGAAatTTCt          -182
                cGAAtaTTCtaGAAt           -247 (H8)
                aGAAtaTTCtaGAAt           -247 (E3)
   caTCcaGAAgccTCtaGAAgtTTCtaGAgacTTCcaGttc  -49    hsp83
     gTgCcaGAAagagCcaGAAgaTgCgaGAga        -270      hsp27
     aGAAatgTCaaGAAgtTTCtgGttc             -328
            aGAAacTcCcaGAAa               -353
            tTTCcgGActcTTCtaGAAa          -45        hsp26
            tcTCtaGAAacTTCg               -338
   aGAAaaTTCgaGAgagTgCcgGtAttTTCtaGAtt    -59        hsp22
        aGAgagccCcaGAAacTTCc              -185
   gccCgaGAAgtTTCgtGtcccTTCtcGtgt         -232       hsp23
   tgTCtcGAAgtTTCgcGAAttTaCt              -391
```

(B)

	Base Usage at Each Position of the 5 bp Unit				
	1A	2G	3A	4A	5A
A	49	0	68	58	36
T	2	0	8	7	18
G	12	85	5	14	19
C	22	0	4	6	12

Figure 1 The 5-bp unit is repeated in genetically defined HSEs. (*A*) Nucleotide sequences containing the conserved 5-bp repeating unit in the upstream regions of *D. melanogaster* heat shock genes. Bases that match the three conserved nucleotides TTC or GAA of the 5-bp unit are in capital letters. The position of the last nucleotide is indicated to the right of each sequence, and the numbering used is from the original publications. H8 indicates sequences of the hsp70 variant from cytological locus 87A, and E3 indicates sequences of the hsp70 variant from 87C. Only those elements that have been demonstrated to be functional are shown (see citations in Fig. 3 of Lis et al. 1990). (*B*) Base frequency at each position of the 5-bp unit. The most frequent base at each position (1–5) is assigned as the consensus base and is shown on the top row of the table. The numbers below indicate the occurrence of each base at each of the five positions. (Adapted, with permission, from Lis et al. 1990.)

35
GAL11, GAL11P, and the Action of GAL4

Alexander A.F. Gann, Howard J. Himmelfarb, and Mark Ptashne
Department of Biochemistry and Molecular Biology
Harvard University, Cambridge, Massachusetts 02138

OVERVIEW

A transcriptional activator binds to DNA through a DNA-binding domain and activates transcription of a nearby gene through a separate activating region. According to the simplest version of this picture, both domains are located on a single polypeptide, but it is now clear that this is not always the case; we know of activators whose DNA-binding and activating regions, although working within the framework outlined above, are located on separate proteins which must both be present to activate transcription. Examples of activators with this and even more elaborate arrangements are discussed. In particular, we present a model for how the yeast activator GAL4 works in collaboration with GAL11 to produce a strong activator.

INTRODUCTION

GAL4 is an 881-amino-acid protein found in yeast that binds to specific DNA sequences and activates transcription of nearby genes. It contains a type of Zn-dependent DNA-binding domain at its amino-terminal end (Keegan et al. 1986; Johnston 1987; Pan and Coleman 1990) and two acidic activating regions (designated I and II in Fig. 1), either of which can activate transcription when fused to the DNA-binding domain (Ma and Ptashne 1987a). In yeast, the DNA-binding domain of GAL4 alone can bind to DNA but cannot activate transcription (Keegan et al. 1986; Ma and Ptashne 1987a; Sadowski et al. 1988; Gill et al. 1990), and a fusion protein bearing the activating regions of GAL4 attached to a heterologous DNA-binding domain, that of the bacterial repressor protein LexA, activates transcription when bound to Lex sites (Brent and Ptashne 1985; J. Ma and M. Ptashne, unpubl.). GAL4 activates transcrip-

Transcriptional Regulation.
Copyright 1992 Cold Spring Harbor Laboratory Press 0-87969-410-6/92 $3 + 00

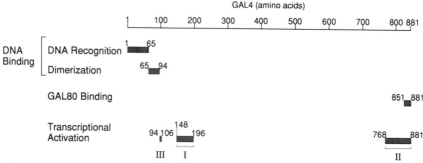

Figure 1 Functional regions of GAL4. The figure illustrates the components of GAL4, including the regions required for dimerization and site-specific DNA binding, the activating regions of GAL4, and the carboxy-terminal target of the GAL4-specific inhibitory protein GAL80 (Ma and Ptashne 1987b). See the legend to Fig. 4 for definition of activation region III.

tion in a wide array of eukaryotic cells and is therefore called a universal activator (Fischer et al. 1988; Kakidani and Ptashne 1988; Ma et al. 1988; Webster et al. 1988; Gill et al. 1990). These and other observations have led to a general picture of how at least some activators are designed and function: A DNA-binding domain brings an acidic activating region to the DNA in the vicinity of a gene, and the interaction of this activating region with a conserved target protein (presumably part of, or associated with, the basic transcription machinery) activates transcription (for review, see Ptashne 1988).

We describe recent observations suggesting that in yeast, GAL4 ordinarily functions as part of a complex with the coactivator GAL11. We begin by discussing two issues relevant to the function of GAL11: The first concerns the use of the term "transcriptional activator," and the second, ways in which multiple activators might work together to activate transcription.

ACTIVATORS AND ACTIVATING REGIONS

The term transcriptional activator refers to a protein that must be tethered to DNA to activate transcription. This definition excludes enzymes that regulate the activities of transcription factors through modification or the production of cofactors, but it includes a number of previously characterized proteins that function in different ways within the framework outlined above for acidic activators. Among these the following classes can be distinguished:

Class I: Universal activators that fit the picture outlined above in its simplest form and contain, on a single polypeptide, a DNA-binding domain and an acidic activating region

Class II: Proteins that bind DNA but do not contain acidic activating regions and which function as activators only when complexed with a second protein that contains an acidic activating region (class III)

Class III: Proteins that contain an acidic activating region but alone cannot efficiently bind to DNA and which function as activators only when tethered to the DNA through interaction with a DNA-bound protein

Class IV: Proteins that link class II and class III proteins but themselves contain neither a DNA-binding domain nor an acidic activating region

As we have noted, GAL4 exemplifies class I (Fig. 2a). Examples of both class II and class III are found in the Oct-1/VP16 complex (Fig. 2b). Oct-1 is a DNA-binding protein found in many mammalian cells that has no acidic activating region and does not alone activate transcription of a typical polymerase II gene (Tanaka et al. 1988). Oct-1 interacts with the herpes simplex virus protein VP16 (Stern et al. 1989), a protein bearing an acidic activating region that cannot bind to DNA efficiently (O'Hare and Goding 1988; Preston et al. 1988; Triezenberg et al. 1988a,b). It has been claimed that purified VP16 can bind to DNA in vitro, but the affinity of this binding is too low to allow significant binding in vivo at

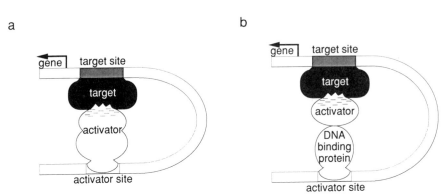

Figure 2 Acidic activators comprising one or more polypeptides. (*a*) Universal activators bear on a single polypeptide a DNA-binding domain and an acidic activating region. The activator, bound at its cognate site, brings to the DNA and/or changes the conformation of, a "universally" conserved target protein that binds near the 5' end of the gene, the intervening DNA looping out to accommodate the interaction. GAL4 is an example of such an activator. (*b*) An acidic activating region and a DNA-binding domain are carried on separate molecules, and both molecules are required for activation. Oct-1/VP16 is an example.

physiological concentrations (Kristie and Sharp 1990). Thus, when Oct-1 and VP16 are present in the same cell, they combine (perhaps along with other cellular factors [Kristie et al. 1989; Katan et al. 1990]) to form an activator that binds to DNA (through the Oct-1 polypeptide) and activates transcription (through the activating region in VP16). Neither protein can activate transcription alone because each contains only one of the two properties required. VP16 is transformed into a universal activator when fused to a DNA-binding domain, e.g., that of GAL4 or LexA (see Sadowski et al. 1988; Chasman et al. 1989; Driever et al. 1989; Carey et al. 1990a). It is not surprising that neither Oct-1 nor VP16 alone activates transcription in heterologous cell types, e.g., yeast; presumably the presence of both components would be required for activation.

Potential class IV proteins have not been as well characterized as have class II and III. There are, however, at least two possible candidates, one being the yeast HAP3 protein. HAP3 links the DNA-bound HAP2 protein to HAP4, which contains an acidic activating region (Olesen et al. 1987; Forsburg and Guarente 1989; Olesen and Guarente 1990), and thus all three proteins must be present in a cell to form a complex able to bind to DNA and activate transcription. HAP3 also appears to help HAP2 bind DNA; whether HAP3 possesses some DNA-binding potential itself or only works through HAP2 is not known. Another candidate for a class IV molecule is the adenovirus protein E1A (see Berk 1986). This protein interacts with the DNA-binding protein ATF-2 through one surface (Liu and Green 1990), and through another is proposed to interact with a second protein required for activation (Martin et al. 1990). It is possible, although there is no evidence to support this, that this second protein bears an acidic activating region.

The mammalian transcription factor Sp1 (Mitchell and Tjian 1989) may or may not conform to our description of a class II molecule: It binds to DNA but does not have an acidic activating region and activates transcription in mammalian cells (Dynan and Tjian 1983) but not in yeast (G. Gill et al., unpubl.). Thus, Sp1 might be analogous to Oct-1, binding to DNA and interacting with an (as-yet-unidentified) second protein bearing an acidic activating region. It is also possible, however, that Sp1 works through an alternative pathway that does not involve an acidic activating region; according to this scenario, Sp1, either directly or through an intermediary, would contact a part of the transcription machinery different from that contacted by acidic activating regions.

Two proteins, TFIIB and TFIID, have been shown to interact with acidic activating regions in vitro, and both interactions have been proposed to mediate transcriptional activation (Horikoshi et al. 1988a,b;

Stringer et al. 1990; Lin and Green 1991). TFIIB and TFIID are part of a group of proteins, including RNA polymerase II itself, that together direct a low (i.e., basal) level of transcription in vitro in the absence of an activator (see Buratowski et al. 1989; Van Dyke et al. 1988). Other experiments have suggested that some as-yet-unidentified protein, in addition to those required for basal transcription, is required for response to activators (Berger et al. 1990; Kelleher et al. 1990; Pugh and Tjian 1990; see also Lewin 1990; Ptashne and Gann 1990). Whether this additional component also (or exclusively) contacts activating regions is not known.

To reiterate, perhaps the reason activators of class I (e.g., GAL4) work universally is that their target protein, whatever its identity, is highly conserved among all eukaryotes, whereas nonacidic activators do not work universally because either an essential class III molecule or an alternative target protein is not universally conserved.

STRENGTHS OF ACTIVATING REGIONS AND THE STRUCTURE OF ENHANCERS

The model outlined at the beginning of this chapter requires that the DNA between an activator and the target protein bound near the beginning of the gene be looped out to accommodate the necessary protein-protein interaction. The model anticipates, moreover, that different activating regions would differ in the avidities with which they interact with their targets, with stronger interactions inducing higher levels of transcription. Indeed, a family of activators can be constructed bearing a common DNA-binding domain (e.g., that of GAL4) and different activating regions that differ over a wide range in their activities. GAL4-AH, for example, which bears a weak acidic activating region attached to the DNA-binding domain of GAL4 (Giniger and Ptashne 1987), activates a given gene in mammalian cells much more weakly than does the corresponding molecule bearing the acidic activating region of VP16 (Sadowski et al. 1988). However, as the following discussion indicates, a systematic comparison of activating region strengths requires that we specify in each case two aspects of the reporter gene: the number of sites to which the activator can bind and the distance of these sites from the gene. The model under discussion predicts that, for a given activator, the level of activation will decrease as the distance of its binding sites from the gene increases and will increase as the number of sites to which it can bind increases. The former prediction follows from the plausible notion that more energy is required for efficient activator-target interaction at larger separations. The latter prediction stems from the idea that multiple activators would increase the likelihood of having an activator-target interaction at any given time: Activators sampled singly by the target protein would work roughly additively, whereas were the target to interact with multiple activators simultaneously, those activators might work synergistically (cooperatively). It follows that, assuming there is a maximum level to which a gene can be activated, a weak activator will tend to elicit the same level of activation as does a strong activator on a template bearing binding sites close to the gene and/or a large number of sites. Some of these predictions have been realized in a series of experiments performed in vitro comparing GAL4-derived activators of different strengths on templates with varying numbers of GAL4-binding sites placed at different distances from the gene (Carey et al. 1990a,b; Lin et al. 1990). These experiments also confirmed an additional prediction of our model concerning how unrelated activators can work synergistically to activate transcription as described in the following paragraph.

Experiments performed in vivo have shown that unrelated activators (e.g., GAL4 and the dexamethasone receptor) can together elicit a level of transcription well in excess of the sum of the levels elicited by each working independently on a template bearing binding sites for both activators (Kakidani and Ptashne 1988; see also Lin et al. 1988; Webster et al. 1988; Schatt et al. 1990). It is difficult to imagine that these two proteins interact directly to help each other bind DNA as do, for example, two bacteriophage λ repressors (see Ptashne 1986). It has been proposed, rather, that the activating regions of each simultaneously touch the transcription machinery (directly or through intermediaries) (see Fig. 3). This idea is distinguished from the λ case in that it makes the following prediction: Under conditions of activator excess, i.e., under conditions where their respective binding sites are filled regardless of the number of such sites, two or more DNA-bound activators would work synergistical-

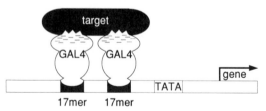

Figure 3 Schematic representation of multiple activators simultaneously contacting a common target. Two molecules of GAL4, bound to adjacent sites on DNA, simultaneously contact an as-yet-unidentified target protein. The interaction energies would add, leading to an exponential increase in the affinity of the target for multiple activators; the exponential increase in affinity would generate a synergistic increase in transcription. The target is shown as a single molecule, although there may be multiple targets that interact with one another.

ly to activate transcription, a prediction confirmed by the experiments performed in vitro alluded to above. The details of the process remain obscure; for example, we do not know how many activators can work synergistically (as opposed to additively) to activate transcription and whether this number might be different for different activators. This is not to say that all cases of synergy between eukaryotic activators will necessarily work according to this description of GAL4; for example, the yeast proteins α1 and MCM1 (GRM, PRTF) interact with each other directly and as a result bind to DNA cooperatively (Bender and Sprague 1987). Similarly, the yeast repressor protein α2 depends on a direct interaction either with MCM1 or with α1 to bind to one or the other of its two defined operator sites (Keleher et al. 1988, 1989; Dranginis 1990).

Natural "enhancers" typically contain multiple binding sites for various activators that together produce potent activation (for review, see Maniatis et al. 1987; Atchison 1988; Jones et al. 1988; Johnson and McKnight 1989; Mitchell and Tjian 1989), and in some cases it has been shown that isolated activator binding sites from within an enhancer cannot substitute for the entire enhancer, whereas multiple copies of such sites can (Dignam et al. 1983; Fromenthal et al. 1988; Ondek et al. 1988; Schaffner et al. 1988). According to our picture, we imagine that each site within a typical enhancer binds a weak activator and that together these activators produce a strong effect.

Why is a typical enhancer designed in this way, containing several sites for weak activators rather than a single site for a strong activator? Perhaps a larger number of regulatory proteins acting on a given gene allows a greater flexibility of response to changing environmental and developmental signals (see, e.g., Maniatis et al. 1987). Another reason that has been proposed is that very strong activators cannot be accommodated in the cell because of the "squelching" problem (Gill and Ptashne 1988; see Ptashne 1988). According to this idea, the interaction between an activator and its target, which on DNA leads to activation, can occur off the DNA as well, and when it does so, it inhibits (squelches) transcription generally, presumably because the target is sequestered. Following this line of argument, we would expect that high concentrations of a strong activator would be required in order for squelching to occur. Indeed, we have found that squelching is typically seen when an activator is expressed at levels higher than those normally found in the cell; consistent with the idea that stronger activating regions have a higher affinity for the target, they squelch at lower concentrations than do weaker activating regions (Gill and Ptashne 1988; Triezenberg et al. 1988a; Martin et al. 1990). Thus, there may be a limit to the strength of an activator that can be accommodated in a cell, even at the relatively low concentrations at which activators are normally found. Indeed, the strongest activators described to date, e.g., VP16, are produced by viruses during lytic growth when presumably no consideration is given to maintaining the health of the cell.

Avoiding the problem of squelching is therefore one possible explanation for why a given gene is typically activated by a number of weak activators rather than by a single potent activator. None of these weak activators is sufficiently strong to cause squelching, but, when brought together on the DNA close to a gene, they can activate transcription to a high level. An alternative solution to the squelching problem might be to divide the activating potential of a strong activator between two proteins which form a complex only when bound to the DNA. This would allow strong activators to be "constructed" on the DNA but not to exist off the DNA where they might squelch. We believe that GAL4 employs this strategy, as we now describe.

GAL11

Genetic experiments suggest that the DNA-binding domain of GAL4 brings to the DNA, in addition to its contiguous acidic activating regions, a separate polypeptide encoded by the *GAL11* gene. The following observations are relevant to our discussion (for examples of the data see Figs. 4 and 5, columns marked "*GAL11+*" and "*gal11−*"; for full details, see Himmelfarb et al. 1990; see also Suzuki et al. 1988; Nishizawa et al. 1990).

1. Deletion of the *GAL11* gene reduces, but does not eliminate, activation by GAL4.
2. In the absence of GAL4, GAL11 cannot activate transcription from a GAL4 site.
3. When fused to the DNA-binding domain of LexA, GAL11 activates transcription from LexA operator sites even in the absence of GAL4.
4. GAL11 helps activation by another yeast activator (PPR1; see Kammerer et al. 1984), which has a DNA-binding domain homologous to that of GAL4. GAL11 does not, however, increase activation by activators containing the unrelated DNA-binding domains of either LexA or GCN4.
5. Even in the presence of GAL11, the DNA-binding domain of GAL4 bearing no activating region cannot activate transcription.

From these and other observations, we believe that a complex of GAL4 and GAL11 functions as a strong activator, with both GAL4 and GAL11 simultaneously interacting with the transcription machinery (see Fig. 6)

226bp

| UAS_G | TATA | GAL1 -lacZ |

Activator	β-Galactosidase Activity		
	GAL11+	GAL11P	gal11-
none	<0.2	<0.2	<0.2
GAL4(1-93)	<0.2	<0.2	<0.2
(1-147)	<0.2	7	<0.2
(1-147)+AH	72	928	16
(1-147)+ II	525	1,230	105
(1-881)	1,160	1,220	180
LexA(1-87)+GAL4(1-147)+AH	33	281	10

Figure 4 The effect of GAL11 and GAL11P on GAL4-derived activators. The table shows the activities of a number of GAL4-derived proteins in wild-type (GAL11+), potentiator (GAL11P), and gal11 null mutant (gal11-) cells. The yeast strains carried a single integrated copy of a plasmid bearing the reporter construct shown above. *GAL11+* cells harbor the wild-type *GAL11* gene; *GAL11P* cells carry the mutant *GAL11P* allele; and *gal11-* cells harbor a *GAL11* gene deletion. Cells were transformed with multicopy plasmids expressing the indicated GAL4 derivatives. Activity is given in units of β-galactosidase activity per microgram of protein in a whole-cell extract. GAL4(1-93) contains the DNA binding and dimerization domains of GAL4 but no activating region (M. Carey and M. Ptashne, unpubl.). GAL4(1-147) contains, in addition to the DNA-binding and dimerization domains, the weak activating region III (see Fig. 1). This activating region is too weak to detect in wild-type yeast and was originally defined by its (low) activity in a mammalian system in vitro (Lin et al. 1988; M. Carey and M. Ptashne, unpubl.). GAL4(1-147)+AH bears the weak activating region AH described by Giniger and Ptashne (1987). GAL4(1-147)+II bears the activating region II of GAL4 shown in Fig. 1 (Ma and Ptashne 1987a). GAL4 (1-881) is the full-length wild-type GAL4 molecule.

(Nishizawa et al. 1990; Himmelfarb et al. 1990). According to this picture, GAL11 recognizes (at least) a region of the DNA-binding domain of GAL4, but the interaction is weak. The complex forms efficiently only if, in addition, GAL4 bears an acidic activating region: We believe that the binding of GAL11 to both GAL4 and the transcription machinery is stabilized by a simultaneous interaction between GAL4 and the transcription machinery, formation of the complex being a concerted reaction (Himmelfarb et al. 1990).

We have considered alternative models for GAL11 function: e.g., GAL11 might be an enzyme that modifies GAL4. This model is not favored because, as we have noted, GAL11 itself activates transcription in yeast in the absence of GAL4 when tethered to DNA through the DNA-binding domain of LexA, and preliminary deletion analysis suggests a strong correlation between this activating potential and GAL11 function (J. Pearlberg and M. Ptashne, unpubl.). Another possibility would be that GAL11 is the "target" of the acidic activating regions of GAL4. This is inconsistent with the observation that deleting GAL11 leads to only a fivefold decrease in GAL4 activity and not to its complete elimination, as such a model would predict. In addition, a model in which GAL11 is imagined to be the target of the acidic activating regions is complicated by the observation that deleting GAL11 has no effect on activation by other acidic activators bearing DNA-binding domains unrelated to that of GAL4 (e.g., GCN4 or LexA); salvaging this model would demand the existence of multiple target proteins, each specific for acidic activating regions attached to a particular DNA-binding domain.

According to our favored model, GAL11 evidently does not fit any of the categories described earlier in this chapter. In some respects, it is similar to VP16 and HAP4; it is unable to bind to DNA alone, but once brought to the DNA (either by fusion to LexA or, according to our model, by interaction with GAL4), it can activate transcription. Unlike VP16 or HAP4, however, GAL11 has no obvious acidic activating region. GAL11 does not work universally, even when provided with a DNA-binding domain: e.g., GAL11 fused to LexA does not activate from Lex sites in mammalian cells (P. Broad and M. Ptashne, unpubl.). As with other nonacidic activators that do not work universally, we assume that GAL11, either directly or through an intermediary, interacts with a nonconserved region of the transcription machinery or, alternatively, works through a yeast-specific adapter bearing an acidic activat-

Lex Sites		
83bp		
TATA	GAL1-lacZ	

	β–Galactosidase Activity		
LexA-derivative	GAL11 +	GAL11P	gal11 -
LexA (1-87)	<0.2	<0.2	<0.2
+AH	14	12	16
+GAL4(1-147)+AH	12	60	15

Figure 5 The effect of GAL11[+] and GAL11P on activators bearing the DNA-binding domain of LexA. The *GAL11[+]*, *GAL11P*, and *gal11[-]* yeast strains are described in the legend to Fig. 4. Activity is given in units of β-galactosidase per microgram of whole-cell extract. Each strain carried a single integrated copy of a plasmid bearing the reporter construct shown; the shaded boxes indicate LexA-binding sites. Cells were transformed with multicopy plasmids expressing the indicated LexA derivatives. The results for LexA(1-87)+AH protein have been confirmed by primer extension analysis (data not shown).

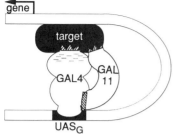

Figure 6 A model for GAL11 action. The shaded bar represents the DNA template; the UAS_G and the transcription start site are indicated. The dashed lines indicate GAL4's negatively charged activating region II. Proposed sites of contact between GAL4, GAL11, and their target protein(s) are indicated by the striped boxes.

ing region. The evident difference between GAL11 and any of the classes of proteins described earlier, however, is that in the GAL4/GAL11 complex both the GAL4 and GAL11 polypeptides contribute to its activating potential and, as we discuss in the next section, we believe that this explains why a cell chooses to maintain GAL4 and GAL11 as separate polypeptides.

WHY HAVE GAL11?

We have seen previously how efficient activation of appropriate genes can be ensured, and the problem of squelching can be avoided, by arranging for the binding sites for several weak activators to be located upstream of a gene. As discussed, we believe that GAL11 and GAL4 form a complex preferentially when GAL4 is bound to DNA and that this is an example of an alternative strategy designed to achieve the same end: construction of a strong activator on the DNA but not off it. Further evidence in support of this idea comes from a mutant GAL11 that appears to bind to GAL4 more tightly than does the wild type.

The mutant, called *GAL11P*, bears a single point mutation in the *GAL11* gene (Himmelfarb et al. 1990). It was found that in a cell expressing GAL11P, a weak activator, comprising the DNA-binding domain of GAL4 fused to a weak acidic activating region, activates about tenfold more strongly than it does in the presence of wild-type GAL11 (compare columns marked "*GAL11+*" and "*GAL11P*" in Fig. 4). We believe that the mutation in *GAL11P* produces its effect by enhancing the interaction between GAL11 and GAL4, either by introducing a new contact or by strengthening an existing contact. An alternative explanation would be that the mutation increases the strength of the activating region of GAL11; we believe this not to be the case, however, because when fused to LexA, GAL11P activates to approximately the same extent as does wild-type GAL11 fused to LexA. In addition, a single amino acid substitution in the DNA-binding domain of GAL4 specifically disrupts the interaction between GAL4 and GAL11P, although apparently not affecting the interaction between GAL4 and wild-type GAL11 (Himmelfarb et al. 1990). We believe, therefore, that the products of these two *GAL11* alleles differ in their interactions with GAL4.

Two further observations are consistent with our description of the GAL11P phenotype and are also consistent with our proposed explanation for the presence of a GAL11 protein in cells (see Himmelfarb et al. 1990).

1. A tripartite protein was constructed that contains three different domains: the DNA-binding domain of LexA, the DNA-binding domain of GAL4, and the weak acidic activating region AH. This protein activates transcription from either Lex sites or GAL4 sites. GAL11 increases the activity of the fusion protein bound to GAL4 sites; when the fusion protein is bound at Lex sites, however, wild-type GAL11 has no effect (see Fig. 5). In contrast, GAL11P potentiates activation by this fusion protein when the latter is bound at either GAL4 sites or Lex sites (compare Figs. 4 and 5).

2. GAL4(1-147)+AH, an activator comprising the DNA-binding domain of GAL4 fused to a weak acidic activating region, does not squelch in wild-type cells, even when expressed at very high levels. When overexpressed in *GAL11P* cells, however, it does squelch (Himmelfarb et al. 1990).

These experiments suggest that wild-type GAL11 is unable to interact efficiently with GAL4 when GAL4 is not bound to DNA, and as a result, the two halves of a strong activating region are kept apart except when GAL4 is bound to DNA and actually involved in activation. Strengthening the interaction between GAL4 and GAL11 (as a result of the *GAL11P* mutation) enables the proteins more efficiently to interact off the DNA, as evidenced by the potentiating effect GAL11P has on the Lex-GAL4 fusion bound to Lex sites. Consistent with this observation, we see that the interaction between GAL4 and GAL11P off the DNA increases the potential of weak activators to squelch.

What might be the physical basis for the interaction between GAL11 and GAL4 preferentially occurring when GAL4 is bound to DNA? At present, all we know about the proposed interaction is that it appears to involve GAL11 recognizing some aspect of the DNA-binding domain of GAL4. There are two obvious ways in which DNA binding by GAL4 could be important to the recognition. For example, GAL11 might only interact efficiently with a conformation of the GAL4 DNA-binding domain formed when it is bound to DNA. It has been reported that a number of transcriptional activators undergo some change in the conformation of their DNA-binding domains when they bind to their specific sites on DNA (Patel et al. 1990; Shuman et al. 1990; Weiss et al. 1990). Alternatively, GAL11 might bind weakly to some part of the GAL4 DNA-binding site as well as interacting with GAL4. Whatever the details of the mechanism, the enhanced interaction between GAL4 and GAL11 produced by the potentiator mutation presumably allows the complex to form efficiently even in the absence of DNA.

REFERENCES

Atchison, M.L. 1988. Enhancers: Mechanisms of action and cell specificity. *Annu. Rev. Cell Biol.* **4:** 127–153.

Bender, A. and G.F. Sprague, Jr. 1987. MATα2 protein, a yeast transcriptional activator, binds synergistically with a second protein to a set of cell-type-specific genes. *Cell* **50:** 681–691.

Berger, S.L., W.D. Cress, A. Cress, S.J. Triezenberg, and L. Guarente. 1990. Selective inhibition of activated but not basal transcription by the acidic activating domain of VP16: Evidence for transcriptional adaptors. *Cell* **61:** 1199–1208.

Berk, A.J. 1986. Adenovirus promoters and E1a transactivation. *Annu. Rev. Genet.* **20:** 45–79.

Brent, R. and M. Ptashne. 1985. A eukaryotic transcriptional activator bearing the DNA binding specificity of a prokaryotic repressor. *Cell* **43:** 729–736.

Buratowski, S., S. Hahn, L. Guarente, and P.A. Sharp. 1989. Five intermediate complexes in transcription initiation by RNA polymerase II. *Cell* **56:** 549–561.

Carey, M.F., J. Leatherwood, and M. Ptashne. 1990a. A potent GAL4 derivative activates transcription at a distance in vitro. *Science* **247:** 710–712.

Carey, M.F., Y.S. Lin, M.R. Green, and M. Ptashne. 1990b. A mechanism for synergistic activation of a mammalian gene by GAL4-derivatives. *Nature* **345:** 361–364.

Chasman, D.I., J. Leatherwood, M. Carey, M. Ptashne, and R.D. Kornberg. 1989. Activation of yeast polymerase II transcription by herpesvirus VP16 and GAL4 derivatives in vitro. *Mol. Cell. Biol.* **9:** 4746–4749.

Dignam, J.D., P.L. Martin, B.S. Shastry, and R.G. Roeder. 1983. Eukaryotic gene transcription with purified components. *Methods Enzymol.* **101:** 582–598.

Dranginis, A.M. 1990. Binding of yeast a1 and α2 as a heterodimer to the operator DNA of a haploid-specific gene. *Nature* **347:** 682–685.

Driever, W., J. Ma, C. Nüsslein-Volhard, and M. Ptashne. 1989. Rescue of bicoid mutant *Drosophila* embryos by bicoid fusion proteins containing heterologous activating sequences. *Nature* **342:** 149–154.

Dynan, W.S. and R. Tjian. 1983. The promoter specific transcription factor Sp1 binds to upstream sequences in the SV40 early promoter. *Cell* **35:** 79–87.

Fischer, J.A., E. Giniger, T. Maniatis, and M. Ptashne. 1988. GAL4 activates transcription in *Drosophila*. *Nature* **332:** 853–856.

Forsburg, S.L. and L. Guarente. 1989. Identification and characterization of HAP4: A third component of the CCAAT-bound HAP2/HAP3 heteromer. *Genes Dev.* **3:** 1166–1178.

Fromenthal, C., M. Kanno, H. Nomiyama, and P. Chambon. 1988. Cooperative and hierarchical levels of functional organization in the SV40 enhancer. *Cell* **54:** 943–953.

Gill, G. and M. Ptashne. 1988. Negative effect of the transcriptional activator GAL4. *Nature* **334:** 721–724.

Gill, G., I. Sadowski, and M. Ptashne. 1990. Mutations that increase the activity of a transcriptional activator in yeast and mammalian cells. *Proc. Natl. Acad. Sci.* **87:** 2127–2131.

Giniger, E. and M. Ptashne. 1987. Transcription in yeast activated by a putative amphipathic alpha helix linked to a DNA binding unit. *Nature* **330:** 670–672.

Himmelfarb, H.J., J. Pearlberg, D.H. Last, and M. Ptashne. 1990. GAL11P: A yeast mutation that potentiates the effect of weak GAL4-derived activators. *Cell* **63:** 1299–1309.

Horikoshi, M., M.F. Carey, H. Kakidani, and R.G. Roeder. 1988a. Mechanism of action of a yeast activator: Direct effect of GAL4 derivatives on mammalian TFIID-promoter interactions. *Cell* **54:** 665–666.

Horikoshi, M., T. Hai, Y.S. Lin, M.R. Green, and R.G. Roeder. 1988b. Transcription factor ATF interacts with the TATA binding factor to facilitate establishment of a preincubation complex. *Cell* **54:** 1033–1042.

Johnson, P.F. and S.L. McKnight. 1989. Eukaryotic transcriptional regulatory proteins. *Annu. Rev. Biochem.* **58:** 799–839.

Johnston, M. 1987. Genetic evidence that zinc is an essential co-factor in the DNA binding domain of GAL4 protein. *Nature* **328:** 353–355.

Jones, N.C., W.J. Rigby, and E.B. Ziff. 1988. *Trans*-acting protein factors and the regulation of eukaryotic transcription: Lessons from studies on DNA tumour viruses. *Genes Dev.* **2:** 267–281.

Kakidani, H. and M. Ptashne. 1988. GAL4 activates gene expression in mammalian cells. *Cell* **52:** 161–167.

Kammerer, B., A. Guyounvarch, and J.C. Hubert. 1984. Yeast regulatory gene *PPR1*. I. Nucleotide sequence, restriction map and codon usage. *J. Mol. Biol.* **180:** 239–250.

Katan, M., A. Haigh, C.P. Verrijzer, P.C. van der Vliet, and P. O'Hare. 1990. Characterization of a cellular factor which interacts functionally with Oct1 in the assembly of a multicomponent transcription complex. *Nucleic Acids Res.* **18:** 6871–6880.

Keegan, L., G. Gill, and M. Ptashne. 1986. Separation of DNA binding from the transcription-activation function of a eukaryotic regulatory protein. *Science* **231:** 699–704.

Keleher, C.A., C. Goutte, and A.D. Johnson. 1988. The yeast cell-type-specific repressor α2 acts cooperatively with a non-cell-type-specific protein. *Cell* **53:** 927–936.

Keleher, C.A., S. Passmore, and A.D. Johnson. 1989. Yeast repressor α2 binds to its operator cooperatively with yeast protein MCM1. *Mol. Cell. Biol.* **9:** 5228–5230.

Kelleher, R.J., P.M. Flanagan, and R.D. Kornberg. 1990. A novel mediator between activator proteins and the RNA polymerase transcription apparatus. *Cell* **61:** 1209–1215.

Kristie, T.M. and P.A. Sharp. 1990. Interactions of the Oct-1POU subdomain with specific DNA sequences and with the HSV α-*trans*-activator protein. *Genes Dev.* **4:** 2383–2396.

Kristie, T.M., J.H. LeBowitz, and P.A. Sharp. 1989. The octamer binding proteins form multi-protein-DNA complexes with the HSV αTIF regulatory protein. *EMBO. J.* **8:** 4229–4238.

Lewin, B. 1990. Commitment and activation at Pol II promoters: A tail of protein-protein interactions. *Cell* **61:** 1161–1164.

Lin, Y.S. and M.R. Green. 1991. Mechanism of action of an acidic transcriptional activator in vitro. *Cell* **64:** 971–981.

Lin, Y.S., M.F. Carey, M. Ptashne, and M.R. Green. 1988. GAL4 derivatives function alone and synergistically with mammalian activators in vitro. *Cell* **54:** 659–664.

———. 1990. How different eukaryotic transcriptional activators can cooperate promiscuously. *Nature* **345:** 359–361.

Liu, F. and M.R. Green. 1990. A site specific member of the ATF transcription factor family can mediate transcription activation by the adenovirus E1a protein. *Cell* **61:** 1217–1224.

Ma, J. and M. Ptashne. 1987a. Deletion analysis of GAL4 defines two transcriptional activating segments. *Cell* **48:** 847–853.

———. 1987b. The carboxy-terminal 30 amino acids of GAL4 are recognized by GAL80. *Cell* **50:** 137–142.

Ma, J., E. Przbilla, J. Hu, L. Bogorad, and M. Ptashne. 1988. Yeast activators stimulate plant gene expression. *Nature* **334:** 631–633.

Maniatis, T., S. Goodburn, and J.A. Fischer. 1987. Regulation of inducible and tissue-specific gene expression. *Science* **236:** 1237–1245.

Martin, K.J., J.W. Lillie, and M.R. Green. 1990. Evidence for interaction of different eukaryotic transcriptional activators with distinct cellular targets. *Nature* **346:** 147–152.

Mitchell, P.J. and R. Tjian. 1989. Transcriptional regulation in mammalian cells by sequence specific DNA binding proteins. *Science* **245:** 371–378.

Nishizawa, M., Y. Suzuki, Y. Nogi, K. Matsumoto, and T. Fukasawa. 1990. Yeast GAL11 protein mediates the transcriptional activation signal of two different transacting factors, GAL4 and general regulatory factor I/repressor/activator site binding protein I/translation upstream factor. *Proc. Natl. Acad. Sci.* **87:** 5373–5377.

O'Hare, P. and C.R. Goding. 1988. Herpes simplex virus regulatory elements and the immunoglobulin octamer domain bind a common factor and are both targets for virion transactivators. *Cell* **52:** 435–445.

Olesen, J.T. and L. Guarente. 1990. The HAP2 subunit of yeast CCAAT transcriptional activator contains adjacent domains for subunit association and DNA recognition: Model for the HAP2/3/4 complex. *Genes Dev.* **4:** 1714–1729.

Olesen, J.T., S. Hahn, and L. Guarente. 1987. Yeast HAP2 and HAP3 activators both bind to CYC1 upstream activation site, UAS2, in an interdependent manner. *Cell* **51:** 953–961.

Ondek, B., L. Gloss, and W. Herr. 1988. The SV40 enhancer contains two distinct levels of organization. *Nature* **333:** 40–45.

Pan, T. and J.E. Coleman. 1990. GAL4 transcription factor is not a "zinc finger" but forms a $Zn(II)_2Cys_6$ binuclear cluster. *Proc. Natl. Acad. Sci.* **87:** 2077–2081.

Patel, L., C. Abate, and T. Curran. 1990. Altered protein conformation on DNA binding by Fos and Jun. *Nature* **347:** 572–575.

Preston, M., M.C. Frame, and M.E.M. Campbell. 1988. A complex formed between cell components and an HSV structural polypeptide binds to a virion immediate early gene regulatory DNA sequence. *Cell* **52:** 425–434.

Ptashne, M. 1986. *A genetic switch.* Cell Press, Palo Alto, California and Blackwell Publishing, Oxford.

———. 1988. How eukaryotic activators work. *Nature* **335:** 683–689.

Ptashne, M. and A.A.F. Gann. 1990. Activators and targets. *Nature* **346:** 329–331.

Pugh, B.F. and R. Tjian. 1990. Mechanism of transcriptional activation by Sp1: Evidence for coactivators. *Cell* **61:** 1187–1197.

Sadowski, I., J. Ma, S. Triezenberg, and M. Ptashne. 1988. GAL4-VP16 is an unusually potent transcriptional activator. *Nature* **335:** 563–564.

Schatt, M.D., S. Rusconi, and W. Schaffner. 1990. A single DNA-binding transcription factor is sufficient for activation from a distant enhancer and/or from a promoter position. *EMBO J.* **9:** 481–487.

Schaffner, G., S. Schrim, B. Muller-Baden, F. Weber, and W. Schaffner. 1988. Redundancy of information in enhancers as a principle of mammalian transcriptional control. *J. Mol. Biol.* **201:** 81–90.

Shuman, J.D., C.R. Vinson, and S.L. McKnight. 1990. Evidence of changes in protease sensitivity and subunit exchange rate on DNA binding by C/EBP. *Science* **248:** 771–774.

Stern, S., M. Tanaka, and W. Herr. 1989. The Oct-1 homeodomain directs formation of a multiprotein-DNA complex with the HSV transactivator VP16. *Nature* **341:** 624–630.

Stringer, K.F., C.J. Ingles, and J. Greenblatt. 1990. Direct and selective binding of an acidic transcriptional activation domain to the TATA-box factor TFIID. *Nature* **345:** 783–786.

Suzuki, Y., Y. Nogi, A. Abe, and T. Fukasawa. 1988. GAL11 protein, an auxiliary transcription activator for genes encoding galactose-metabolizing enzymes in *Saccharomyces cerevisiae. Mol. Cell Biol.* **8:** 4991–4999.

Tanaka, M., U. Grossniklaus, W. Herr, and S. Hernandez. 1988. Activation of the U2 snRNA promoter by the octamer motif defines a new class of polymerase II enhancer elements. *Genes Dev.* **2:** 1764–1778.

Triezenberg, S.J., R.C. Kingsbury, and S.L. McKnight. 1988a. Functional dissection of VP16, the *trans*-activating of herpes simplex immediate early gene expression. *Genes Dev.* **2:** 718–729.

Triezenberg, S.J., K.L. LaMarco, and S.L. McKnight. 1988b. Evidence of DNA:protein interactions that mediate HSV-1 immediate early gene activation by VP16. *Genes Dev.* **2:** 730–742.

Van Dyke, M.W., R.G. Roeder, and M. Sawadogo. 1988. Physical analysis of transcription preinitiation complex assembly on a class II gene promoter. *Science* **241:** 1335–1338.

Webster, N., J.R. Jin, S. Green, M. Hollis, and P. Chambon. 1988. The yeast UASG is a transcriptional enhancer in human HeLa cells in the presence of the GAL4 *trans*-activator. *Cell* **52:** 169–178.

Weiss, M.A., T. Ellenberger, C.R. Wobbe, J.P. Lee, S.C. Harrison, and K. Struhl. 1990. Folding transition in the DNA binding domain of GCN4 on specific binding to DNA. *Nature* **347:** 575–578.

Regulatory Networks

36

Integration of Multiple Regulatory Inputs in the Control of *HO* Expression in Yeast

Ira Herskowitz, Brenda Andrews,[1] Warren Kruger,
Joseph Ogas,[2] Anita Sil, Cara Coburn, and Craig Peterson[3]
Programs in Genetics and Cell Biology
Department of Biochemistry and Biophysics
University of California
San Francisco, California 94143-0448

OVERVIEW

The *HO* gene of the yeast *Saccharomyces cerevisiae* is subject to multiple forms of regulation–expressed only in certain cell types, only in one phase of the cell cycle, and only in certain cells of a mitotic cell lineage. These different modes of regulation are individually of considerable interest, but it is perhaps of special interest to understand how they are coordinated with each other. This coordination takes place in an upstream regulatory region of 1500 base pairs that is governed by at least eight *SWI* and *SNF* genes required for transcription of *HO* and at least five *SIN* genes, which mediate some type of negative regulation. Many of these regulatory proteins play roles in transcription of several other yeast genes, including G1 cyclins. Some are known to be components of chromatin; others identify a regulatory activity ("SWI1, 2, 3") that appears to be present in other organisms, including *Drosophila* and vertebrates.

INTRODUCTION

The yeast *HO* gene is subject to three different modes of regulation that are coordinated with each other. The upstream region of *HO* can be viewed as a "regulatory ganglion" where multiple inputs are integrated to generate an output signal, transcription of the *HO* gene. There are three inputs, one concerned with monitoring cell type, the second with position in the cell cycle, and the third with cell lineage. *HO* is transcribed only when the three inputs are appropriate.

Present addresses: [1]Department of Medical and Molecular Genetics, University of Toronto, Toronto, Ontario M5S 1A8 Canada; [2]Department of Energy Plant Research Laboratory, Michigan State University, East Lansing, Michigan 48824; [3]Program in Molecular Medicine, University of Massachusetts Medical School, 373 Plantation Street, Worcester, Massachusetts 01605.

Many products required for transcription of *HO* have been identified, primarily on the basis of mutant isolation but increasingly from biochemical routes. At least eight genes (*SWI1–SWI6, SNF5, SNF6*) are required for transcription of *HO*. Another five genes (*SIN1–SIN5*) behave in some respects as negative regulators of *HO*. Studies on these regulators have led to several new thoughts on how regulatory proteins function and how they are regulated. Some of the highlights are:

1. Genetic evidence indicates that Swi1p, Swi2p, and Swi3p activate transcription by antagonizing Sin1p and Sin2p.
2. Sin1p and Sin2p appear to affect chromatin: *SIN1* encodes a protein that is similar to an HMG protein, and *SIN2* encodes histone H3. Studies of regulation by SIN1, SIN2 (histone H3), and histone H4 thus may provide insights into how chromatin structure influences gene expression.
3. A functional link has been found between *SIN1* and *SIN2* genes and the large subunit of RNA polymerase II, which leads to some specific hypotheses for the roles of the conserved carboxy-terminal domain of RNA polymerase and Swi1p, Swi2p, and Swi3p.
4. Swi4p and Swi6p are components of a DNA-binding transcription factor that is responsible for cell-cycle-dependent transcription and may be a substrate for the *CDC28* protein kinase. Both Swi4p and Swi6p contain a motif of 33 amino acids (the Swi6p-cdc10p motif) that is present in many other proteins. Studies of this motif in Swi4p and Swi6p may shed light on its function.
5. The activity of Swi5p, a zinc finger protein, is governed in part by controlling its nuclear localization.
6. Sin3p may be a helix-loop-helix protein and participate in a protein interaction chain that ultimately represses *HO*.

The *SWI* and *SIN* genes are of interest beyond their role in *HO* regulation. The first indication of their importance outside the confines of *HO* transcription was that mutants defective in some of the *SWI* genes exhibit slow growth and other phenotypes and are inviable under some conditions. It has subsequently been found that *SWI1, SWI2,* and *SWI3* are necessary for transcription of a wide variety of yeast genes, including *INO1, SUC2,* and *GAL10*. As described below, it is likely that these *SWI* gene products play a role in transcription in many organisms. The *SWI4* and *SWI6* genes have recently been found to control transcription of two groups of genes that are expressed specifically in the G1 phase of the cell cycle–G1 cyclins (*CLN1, CLN2,* and *HCS26*) and genes involved in DNA synthesis.

In this review, we describe specific aspects of these regulatory proteins and how they are proposed to function together to regulate *HO* transcription. Studies of the regulators of *HO* thus should provide information of general significance in understanding molecular mechanisms of gene control.

BIOLOGY OF *HO* AND ITS MULTIPLE MODES OF REGULATION

Before considering how *HO* transcription is regulated, we first describe the *HO* gene itself, its function, and the role that it plays in the organism. We also describe the three different types of regulation and the roles that they might play in yeast. *HO* codes for a site-specific endonuclease that initiates the process of mating-type interconversion (Kostriken et al. 1983). Haploid yeast cells can be either of two types, a or α, depending on whether they have the **a** or α allele of the mating-type locus (*MAT*). *MAT*α and *MAT*a code for regulatory proteins that determine cell type (for review, see Herskowitz and Oshima 1981; Herskowitz 1989; Herskowitz et al. 1992). The *HO* gene product catalyzes the switching of cells from **a** to α or from α to **a** and thus can be viewed as a regulator of *MAT*. Strains with the inactive version of *HO* (*ho*, "heterothallic" strains) have a stable mating type. In strains with *HO* ("homothallic" strains), a cell that is, for example, initially α rapidly gives rise to cells of opposite mating type (Fig. 1). This change occurs because the *HO* gene product cleaves *MAT*α DNA to produce a double-strand break, thereby setting in motion a repair process that culminates in replacement of the *MAT*α information by *MAT*a (Strathern et al. 1982). The **a** cells produced in this way then mate with α siblings to form an **a**/α diploid cell. This cell no longer exhibits mating-type switching, because transcription of *HO* is turned off in **a**/α cells (Jensen et al. 1983). The end result of mating-type switching is therefore the production of stable diploids from haploids: *HO* is responsible for diploidization (Fig. 1).

Mating-type interconversion should be viewed as a layer of regulation governing the master regulators of cell type coded by the mating-type locus. The process of mating-type switching is itself regulated exquisitely, being controlled with respect to cell type, cell lineage, and cell cycle. In each case, regulation of the *HO* gene is responsible for the type of regulation.

Cell-type Regulation

HO is expressed only in haploid cells (**a** or α) and not in **a**/α diploids (Jensen et al. 1983). As noted above, this mode of regulation results in production of stable diploids and is an example of feedback repression.

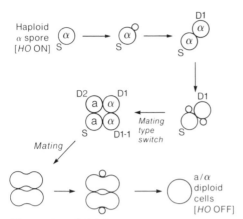

Figure 1 Diploidization and negative feedback control of mating-type inter-conversion. The end product of mating-type interconversion is formation of stable **a**/α diploid cells. The diagram shows the first two cell divisions of a spore that is initially *MAT*α and that carries the *HO* gene. After two cell divisions, it is frequently observed that two of the four cells have changed to **a** mating type, whereas the other cells remain as α. These siblings mate to form two **a**/α diploid zygotes, which give rise to further **a**/α cells by mitotic divisions. These **a**/α cells do not undergo further changes in mating type (to **a**/**a** or to α/α) because transcription of the *HO* gene is turned off in **a**/α cells because of the presence of the novel repressor **a**1-α2. The *HO* gene remains repressed until cells become haploid again (which occurs after the **a**/α cell undergoes meiosis). The S, D1, D2, and D1-1 cells are described further in Fig. 2. (Reprinted, with permission, from Herskowitz 1988.)

The expression pattern of *HO* is representative of a group of genes ("haploid-specific genes"), which are expressed only in haploid cells (Herskowitz 1989). Repression of haploid-specific genes results from the presence of the regulatory protein Mata1p-Matα2p, which is present only in **a**/α cells (Goutte and Johnson 1988; Dranginis 1990).

The two other modes of regulation of mating-type interconversion were revealed by studying the pattern of switching in mitotic cell lineages (Hicks and Herskowitz 1976; Strathern and Herskowitz 1979). Two rules were derived from the cell lineages (Fig. 2): (1) Cells always switch in pairs: an α cell gives rise to two **a** cells and not to one **a** and one α cell. (2) Cells differ in their ability to switch: Only cells that have undergone at least one cell division cycle ("mother" cells or "experienced" cells) are able to switch. The first of these rules reflects expression of the *HO* gene in a cell-cycle-dependent manner, only in late G1. The second of these rules reflects expression of the *HO* gene only in mother cells and not in daughter cells.

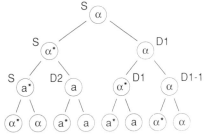

Figure 2 The switching pattern of homothallic yeast, a mitotic lineage of yeast cells that are able to switch mating type. Asterisks indicate cells that are competent to switch mating type in their next cell division. As described in the text, only cells that have previously budded are competent. The initial cell (S) is a spore that carries *HO* and can thus exhibit high frequency of mating-type interconversion. This cell germinates and after its first cell division yields two cells (S and its first daughter, D1), which are invariably α. In the next cell division, the S cell typically (in ~75% of its cell divisions) gives rise to two cells (S and D2) that have switched to **a**. The D1 cell at the two-cell stage invariably gives rise to two α cells, but in its next division (to produce cells D1 and D1-1), it can yield **a** cells. (Modified from Strathern and Herskowitz 1979.)

Cell-cycle Regulation

HO is expressed only in a brief window of the cell cycle, during late G1, just before the initiation of DNA synthesis (Nasmyth 1985b). Many genes involved in DNA synthesis and repair (e.g., the genes coding for DNA polymerase I, DNA ligase, and ribonucleotide reductase) are also expressed at this time (for review, see Andrews and Herskowitz 1990). Restriction of *HO* transcription to this period may reflect caution by the yeast cell: Because mating-type interconversion is initiated by a DNA-damaging event, expression of *HO* may have evolved to be coordinated with that of genes whose products are involved in DNA repair.

Mother-Daughter Regulation

HO is expressed in only half of the cells of a population: Mother cells transcribe *HO*; daughter cells do not (Nasmyth 1983). Expression of *HO* in daughter cells from the *GAL1–GAL10* regulatory region allows daughter cells to switch (Jensen and Herskowitz 1984; Nasmyth 1987). Because *HO* is transcribed only in mother cells, microcolonies of yeast always contain both **a** and α cells (see Strathern and Herskowitz 1979) and can thus form **a**/α diploid cells.

IDENTIFICATION OF GENES THAT REGULATE *HO* AND
DEFINITION OF THREE REGULATORY ACTIVITIES

The *SWI* genes were identified initially in mutants defective for switching of mating types (hence the name, *SWI*, "required for mating-type *swi*tching") (Table 1) (Haber and Garvik 1977; Stern et al. 1984). These genes, *SWI1–SWI5*, are required for transcription of *HO* (Stern et al. 1984). A subsequent mutant hunt by Breeden and Nasmyth (1987a) used an *HO-lacZ* fusion to isolate mutants that were specifically defective in *HO* expression as β-galactosidase-deficient strains. These studies identified an additional gene, *SWI6*. More recent studies (Peterson and Herskowitz 1992) have shown that the *SNF5* and *SNF6* genes are also required for transcription of *HO*. K. Nasmyth (pers. comm.) has observed that the *SWI2* gene is identical to the *SNF2* gene (Laurent et al. 1991) and that the *SWI10* gene described by Breeden and Nasmyth (1987a) corresponds to the *SNF5* gene (see Johnston and Carlson 1992).

The *SIN* genes were identified because mutations in these genes bypass the need for specific *SWI* genes for transcription of *HO*. Beginning with mutants defective in genes *SWI1–SWI5*, Sternberg et al. (1987) isolated mutants that allowed expression of *HO* (using an *HO-lacZ* hybrid gene). These studies identified five *SIN* genes (*SIN*, "*SWI INdependent*"). (The *SIN6* gene described by Sternberg et al. [1987] proved to be a nonsense suppressor [B. Andrews, unpubl.].) The *SDI1* gene was identified in a similar manner (Nasmyth et al. 1987b) and corresponds to *SIN3* (Wang et al. 1990). The salient properties of the *SIN* genes can be demonstrated by the behavior of mutations in *SIN1*: Deletion of *SIN1* greatly increases transcription of *HO* to mutants deleted for the *SWI1* gene (as well as to mutants defective in several other *SWI* genes). Thus, Swi1p is not needed if Sin1p is absent. It is therefore proposed that Sin1p inhibits transcription of *HO* and that Swi1p activates transcription by inhibiting Sin1p (Sternberg et al. 1987).

The *SWI* genes define three regulatory activities, as deduced from the phenotypes of the *swi* mutants (see also Table 1). In particular, the *SWI1*, *SWI2*, and *SWI3* genes comprise a related group; mutants defective in these genes exhibit all of the same secondary phenotypes (altered colony morphology, lethality when combined with *swi4* mutations, etc.; Stern et al. 1984). We therefore speak of the activity coded by these genes as Swi1,2,3p. In the same manner, *SWI4* and *SWI6* comprise another group, which constitutes an activity that can be called Swi4,6p. *SWI5* defines a third, distinct regulatory component. The suppression profile of mutations in the different *SIN* genes (the ability of a *sin* mutation to suppress different *swi* mutations; see Tables 1 and 2) supports this classification.

THE UPSTREAM REGULATORY REGION, SITES OF
SWI AND SIN PRODUCT ACTION, AND AN
OVERVIEW OF *HO* REGULATION

Regulatory Sites

The upstream regulatory region of *HO* is large by yeast standards (1500 bp) and has been divided into two regions, URS1 and URS2 (Fig. 3) (Nasmyth 1985a). URS1 extends from position –900 to –1500 and is essential for transcription, as demonstrated by producing deletions in vitro and then replacing the corresponding wild-type regions in vivo. URS1 functions as an upstream activating sequence (UAS) in a test plasmid, where it requires Swi1p, Swi2p, Swi3p, and Swi5p, and is regulated by Sin3p, and by Mata1p-Matα2p. The URS1 region thus is necessary and sufficient for UAS activity and appears to be the ultimate site of action for Swi1,2,3p, Swi5p, Sin3p, and Mata1p-Matα2p. URS1 contains two binding sites for Swi5p, a zinc finger protein (Nagai et al. 1988; Stillman et al. 1988), and contains three putative sites for binding of Mata1p-Matα2p (Fig. 3). Swi5p has been argued to play a role in mother-daughter control (see below).

The URS2 region extends from position –200 to –900. Deletion of URS2 does not inactivate *HO* transcription but causes it to become independent of cell-cycle regulation (Nasmyth 1985a,b). Thus, this region is responsible for mediating cell-cycle control. The URS2 region does not function well as a UAS in a test plasmid, for reasons discussed below. URS2 contains ten repeats of a sequence (originally called the "cell-cycle box" and now called the *SWI4/SWI6*-dependent cell-cycle box, or SCB) that is necessary and sufficient for cell-cycle regulation (Nasmyth 1985b; Breeden and Nasmyth 1987a). A protein has been identified that binds to the cell-cycle box, and it contains Swi4p (Andrews and Herskowitz 1989a,b) and Swi6p (Ogas et al. 1991; Taba et al. 1991). Swi1,2,3p does not act on these sites (Andrews and Herskowitz 1989a) but does act elsewhere in URS2 (Sternberg et al. 1987). Thus, URS2 is responsible for cell-cycle control and contains sites of action for Swi1,2,3p and Swi4,6p. Nine sites that match the consensus sequence for regulation by Mata1p-Matα2p are dispersed throughout URS2 (Miller et al. 1985).

Regulatory Overview

One goal in studying *HO* regulation is to understand how the three types of regulation are coordinated: What is the mechanism that allows *HO* to be transcribed only when three conditions are satisfied—only in particular cell types (**a** and α), only in G1, and only in mother cells? An overview of this process is presented here; additional information is given be-

Table 1 Genes that regulate transcription of *HO*

(a) Genes required for transcription of *HO*

	Synonym	Properties of ORF	Comments	Reference for nucleotide sequence
SWI1	ADR6	148 kD	component of global activator (Swi1,2,3p)	Taguchi and Young (1987)
SWI2	SNF2	194 kD	component of global activator (Swi1,2,3p); has motifs found in DNA helicases	Laurent et al. (1992); K. Nasmyth (pers. comm.)
SWI3		99 kD	component of global activator (Swi1,2,3p)	Peterson and Herskowitz (1992)
SNF5	SWI10	102.5 kD	component of global activator (Swi1,2,3p); originally identified as required for sucrose fermentation	Laurent et al. (1991)
SNF6		38 kD	component of global activator (Swi1,2,3); originally identified as required for sucrose fermentation	Estruch and Carlson (1990)
SWI4		124 kD	necessary for cell-cycle control of *HO* transcription; binds to sites in URS2; component of SCBF (Swi4,6p cell-cycle box factor); also regulates G1 cyclins (*CLN1* and *CLN2*); contains two Swi6p-cdc10p motifs	Andrews and Herskowitz (1989b)
SWI6		91 kD	necessary for cell-cycle control of *HO* transcription; binds to sites in URS2; component of SCBF (Swi4/6 cell-cycle box factor); also regulates G1 cyclins (*CLN1* and *CLN2*) and DNA metabolism genes; contains two Swi6p-cdc10p motifs	Breeden and Nasmyth (1987b)
SWI5		85 kD	necessary for mother-daughter control of *HO* transcription; contains two zinc fingers; binds to two sites in URS1	Stillman et al. (1988)

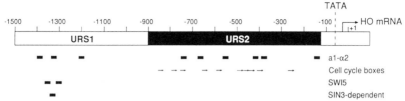

Figure 3 The upstream regulatory region of *HO*. The *HO* upstream regulatory region is drawn to approximate scale. The two major subdivisions are the URS1 region, which is essential for transcription of *HO* and which has UAS activity, and the URS2 region, which is essential for cell-cycle regulation. Deletion of URS2 removes *HO* transcription from cell-cycle regulation (it no longer requires *CDC28*). The approximate positions of binding sites are indicated. (a1-α2) Binding sites for Mata1p-Matα2p; (cell-cycle boxes) binding sites for Swi4p/Swi6p-dependent binding activity; (SWI5) binding sites for *SWI5*-dependent activity; (SIN3) binding site for *SWI3*-dependent activity. Data are from Nasmyth (1985a,b), Stillman et al. (1988), and Andrews and Herskowitz (1989a).

Just as mother-daughter control is mediated by controlling activity of Swi5p, cell-cycle-dependent regulation is thought to be mediated by regulating activity of SCBF. A working hypothesis is that SCBF is phosphorylated by the *CDC28* protein kinase, whose activity is necessary for transcription of *HO* and which is necessary for progression of the cell cycle from G1 to S. In summary, Swi5p lifts repression in URS1 in mother cells, which allows a signal to propagate into URS2, where the transcription factor SCBF–activated in some appropriate manner–is then able to bind to its site and stimulate transcription.

One key piece of information leading to this overview is the spectrum of suppression by *sin1* mutations: Inactivation of *SIN1* suppresses mutations in *SWI1*, *SWI2*, *SWI3*, and *SWI5* but not in *SWI4* or *SWI6* (Sternberg et al. 1987).

MODES OF *HO* REGULATION

Cell-type Control

As noted above, the *HO* regulatory region contains nine consensus sites for binding of Mata1p-Matα2p, and segments of these regions have been shown to confer regulation by Mata1p-Matα2p (Miller et al. 1985; Russell et al. 1986). Several of these sites bind Mata1p-Matα2p in vitro (B. Andrews and C. Goutte, unpubl.). It is thus likely that Mata1p-Matα2p represses *HO* transcription by directly binding in its upstream regulatory region.

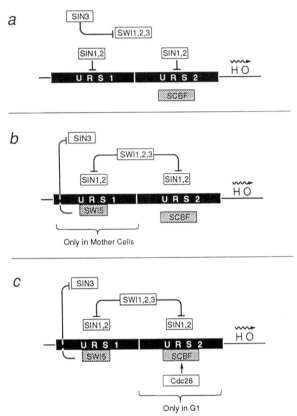

Figure 4 Sequential activation scheme for regulation of *HO*. To activate transcription of *HO*, two independent events must occur: one in URS1, which occurs
only in mother cells, and another in URS2, which occurs only in G1. Lines with
blunt arrowheads indicate inhibition; lines with pointed arrowheads indicate
stimulation. Panel *a* shows the upstream region in a daughter cell, in which it is
proposed that two factors, Sin3p and Sin1p/Sin2p, keep the *HO* gene silent. As
described in the text, Sin1p/Sin2p is composed of known or likely components
of chromatin. It is proposed that Sin1p/Sin2p prevents Swi4p/Swi6p (part or all
of the SCB-binding factor) from binding to the SCB elements in the URS2
region (see Fig. 3 for details). Panels *b* and *c* show how the *HO* gene is activated. First, Swi5p inhibits Sin3p (an event that occurs only in mother cells).
This allows Swi1,2,3p to relieve the inhibition exerted by Sin1p/Sin2p. As a
result, the SCB factor (SCBF) can bind to the SCB and trigger transcription of
HO. SCBF is proposed to be active only in the G1 phase of the cell cycle because it must be phosphorylated by the G1-specific *CDC28* protein kinase. The
overview presented in this diagram is highly speculative and is justified in the
text.

In general, the Mata1p-Matα2p sites are adjacent to binding sites for other known proteins (Fig. 3), adjacent to Swi5p binding sites in URS1 and adjacent to SCBF binding sites in URS2. Thus Mata1p-Matα2p may function by preventing binding of Swi5p or SCBF. Another possibility is that Mata1p-Matα2p provides a binding site for Ssn6p-Tup1p, which then represses transcription (Keleher et al. 1992). Mata1p-Matα2p does not block *HO* transcription by repressing synthesis of the *SWI* gene products (*SWI1*, *SWI3–SWI6* have been analyzed; Stern 1985; C. Peterson; B. Andrews; both unpubl.; see also Sternberg et al. 1987).

Mother-Daughter Control

Two primary pieces of evidence indicate that Swi5p plays a crucial role in mother-daughter control. First, daughter cells are able to switch if they are defective in *SIN3* (Nasmyth et al. 1987a; Sternberg et al. 1987). Second, daughter cells that express *SWI5* under galactose-inducible control are able to switch (Nasmyth et al. 1987a). The first observation indicates that Sin3p is responsible for keeping *HO* silent in daughter cells. Because Swi5p is an antagonist of Sin3p, the difference between mother and daughter cells could be explained in two ways: (1) Daughter cells might have a higher level of Sin3p than mother cells or (2) mother cells might have a higher level of Swi5p than daughter cells. The observations with pGAL-*SWI5* support the latter view.

Two types of explanations have been proposed for the difference in Swi5p activity between mother and daughter cells. In one scenario, the Swi5p protein is segregated asymmetrically, to mother cells and not to daughter cells. According to another model, Swi5p is present in both mother and daughter cells, but its activity is reduced in daughter cells for some other reason. Because daughter cells are smaller than mother cells, they must increase in size before they reach the position in the cell cycle where *HO* transcription is activated. If Swi5p is unstable, its level may be too low at the point in the cell cycle when it is needed to activate *HO*. Immunofluorescence localization studies indicate that Swi5p is present in both daughter and mother cells (Nasmyth et al. 1990) and thus argue against the asymmetric distribution model. As a test of the stability explanation, Nasmyth has treated cells with hydroxyurea, which allows production of daughter cells that are the same size as mother cells (Nasmyth et al. 1987a). Despite their increased size (which presumably allows them to activate *HO* transcription without needing to grow larger), the daughter cells do not exhibit mating-type switching. Thus, although Swi5p has been argued to be a key determinant responsible for the difference between mother and daughter cells, this hypothesis remains to be proven. Possibly another protein, e.g., one that affects activity of Swi5p, is responsible for the difference between mother and daughter cells.

The *SWI5* gene and its product are under intensive study. First of all, transcription of *SWI5* is cell-cycle-regulated, occurring in S phase and continuing until the end of M (Nasmyth et al. 1987a). Transcription of *SWI5* requires Mcm1p and a novel protein termed "Sffp" coded by the *SFF* gene (Lydall et al. 1991). The cellular location of Swi5p–in the cytoplasm as opposed to the nucleus–is also regulated: Swi5p does not enter the nucleus until late anaphase (Nasmyth et al. 1990). This change in location apparently results from dephosphorylation of the nuclear localization signal of Swi5p at the end of M (Moll et al. 1991). Thus, Swi5p is synthesized in the cell cycle preceding the cell cycle in which it functions. It is distributed initially to both mother and daughter cells but functions only in the mother cell. The segment of Swi5p containing the zinc fingers is sufficient for DNA binding (Nagai et al. 1988).

Sin3p is proving to have its own set of mysteries and fascinations. Nasmyth et al. (1987b) observed a *SIN3*-dependent binding activity in URS1 of *HO* that overlaps a Swi5p binding site (Fig. 3). Recent biochemical work (Wang and Stillman 1991) shows that the binding protein is not Sin3p but rather another protein termed SDP1. The ability of this protein to bind to DNA is controlled by another protein termed I-SDP1, and it is thought that Sin3p binds to I-SDP1 and thereby allows binding of SDP1 to DNA. The nucleotide sequence of *SIN3* may provide some clues to its function. Most notably, the deduced polypeptide (which is enormous, 175 kD; Wang et al. 1990) contains four paired amphipathic helices in which each helix of a pair is separated by 20 amino acid residues. These segments do not bear any resemblance to the helices found in the helix-loop-helix motif of Myc and related proteins (Murre et al. 1989) or to the yeast TPR repeats (Sikorski et al. 1990), but may serve a similar function, association with other proteins. The intrigue of *SIN3* is further enhanced by the recent finding that it is identical to several genes identified by other criteria–*UME4*, *RPD1*, and *CPE1* (Strich et al. 1989; Vidal et al. 1990, 1991; K. Hudak and S. Henry, pers. comm.). Sin3p is thus involved in regulating several genes in addition to *HO*. The *SIN4* gene has recently been cloned and its nucleotide sequence has been determined (Jiang and Stillman 1992). The diversity of its phenotypes leads to the suggestion that Sin4p may affect chromatin structure (Jiang and Stillman 1992).

Cell-cycle Control

As described above, cell-cycle control is dependent on *SWI4* and *SWI6* and the cell-cycle box elements in URS2. A key observation in studies of cell-cycle regulation is the finding that the SCB element functions as a UAS in a test plasmid (Breeden and Nasmyth 1987a). These studies showed, furthermore, that activation of transcription via the SCB sequences is periodic in the cell cycle and dependent on passage through START (in particular, requiring *CDC28*). The *SWI4* and *SWI6* genes are required for utilization of the SCB as a UAS (Breeden and Nasmyth 1987a; Andrews and Herskowitz 1989a). As noted above, a protein activity, SCBF, which binds to the cell cycle boxes, contains Swi4p and Swi6p by gel-shift experiments using antibodies against Swi4p and Swi6p (Andrews and Herskowitz 1989b; Ogas et al. 1991; Taba et al. 1991).

Cell-cycle-dependent transcription of *HO* may result from two factors. First, transcription of *SWI4* increases sharply in late G1; expression throughout the cell cycle leads to constitutive transcription of *HO* (Breeden and Mikesell 1991). A second contribution to G1-specific expression may be that activity of Swi4p and/or Swi6p is governed by phosphorylation. This hypothesis is motivated in part by the finding that both Swi4p and Swi6p contain potential phosphorylation sites for *CDC28* protein kinase (Breeden and Nasmyth 1987b; Andrews and Herskowitz 1989b). At least one of the sites in Swi4p is essential for Swi4p function (B. Andrews, unpubl.).

Swi4p and Swi6p contain two copies of an evolutionarily conserved 33-amino acid motif (the "Swi6p-cdc10p" motif; Breeden and Nasmyth 1987b; Andrews and Herskowitz 1989b), within which some of the potential phosphorylation sites are located. This motif was originally identified as a segment conserved in Swi6p and *Schizosaccharomyces pombe* cdc10p (Breeden and Nasmyth 1987b) and has subsequently been found in *Drosophila* Notch, nematode glp-1, lin-12, and fem-1, and in vertebrate proteins ankyrin, bcl-3, and NF-κB proteins (Kieran et al. 1990; for review, see Andrews and Herskowitz 1990). This motif is present in the mammalian GABP protein β subunit, where it appears to be involved in protein-protein interactions (Thompson et al. 1991). The Swi6p-cdc10p motif is not necessary for association between Swi4p and Swi6p (Andrews and Moore 1992; see also Primig et al. 1992).

Several lines of evidence indicate that *SWI4* and *SWI6* are necessary for transcription of essential genes. The first indication is the observation that *swi4* strains are inviable if they are also deficient in *SWI1*, *SWI2*, or *SWI3* (Stern et al. 1984). These observations suggest that Swi4p and Swi1,2,3p serve a redundant function in activating some essential gene. It was subsequently shown that *swi4 swi6* double mutants are also inviable (Breeden and Nasmyth 1987b). Recently, it has been found that strains defective only in *SWI4* are inviable under two conditions, at high temperature and in a/α strains (Ogas et al. 1991). Recent studies (Nasmyth and Dirick 1991; Ogas et al. 1991) reveal that *SWI4* and *SWI6* are required for full-level transcription of G1 cyclins, *CLN1* and *CLN2*. The essential role of *SWI4* and *SWI6* appears to be for transcription of these genes, as indicated by the observation that expression of these genes under *GAL* control or on high copy number plasmid bypasses the requirement of *SWI4* and *SWI6*. Swi4p and Swi6p appear to play a role in a positive feedback loop by which Cln1p and Cln2p stimulate their own synthesis (Nasmyth and Dirick 1991; Ogas et al. 1991). Swi6p also plays a role in regulating the group of DNA metabolism genes that is expressed in G1 (Dirick et al. 1992; Lowndes et al. 1992). Expression of these genes is under control of the "*Mlu*I motif" (now called "MCB", "*Mlu*I cell-cycle box"); use of this motif as a UAS requires *SWI6* (Dirick et al. 1992; Lowndes et al. 1992; Verma et al. 1992).

ROLES OF Swi1p, Swi2p, Swi3p, Sin1p, AND Sin2p IN *HO* REGULATION AND OTHER PROCESSES

Sin1p (an HMG1-like Protein) and Sin2p (Histone H3) Are Proposed to Govern Use of Sites in URS2

The amino acid composition (45% charged residues) and sequence of Sin1p indicate that it is a member of the HMG class of proteins, non-histone chromosomal proteins of unknown function that are highly charged (Kruger and Herskowitz 1991). Consistent with this view of Sin1p, we have found that it is located in the nucleus and binds nonspecifically to DNA in vitro (Kruger and Herskowitz 1991). The nucleotide sequence of the *SIN2-1* mutation (Kruger 1991) shows that it is an alteration of one of the two histone H3 genes (*HTH1*) (Smith and Andresson 1983), a change from arginine to histidine at position 116. A similar mutation produced in the other histone H3 gene, *HTH2*, also causes a Sin⁻ phenotype. These mutations appear to create special forms of histone H3 that alter the chromatin conformation in a particular manner rather than being simple inactivations of these genes. In fact, simple deletion of either *HTH* gene has no phenotype (Smith and Stirling 1988). In contrast, the *SIN2-1* mutation is dominant to wild-type. Changes from glutamic acid to lysine at position 105 (in the *hht2-2* mutation) and from threonine to isoleucine at position 118 (in the *hht2-3* mutation) also cause Sin⁻ mutant phenotypes. One possibility is that these alterations allow selective disassembly of a histone octamer in the nucleosome and thereby alter gene expression. Another possibility is that these mutations alter specific interactions with certain regulatory proteins. Mutations affecting histone H4 that confer a Sin⁻ phenotype have also been identified (A. Sil et al., unpubl.).

It is hypothesized that Sin1p and Sin2p prevent use of CCB elements as UASs until the appropriate time. The ability of URS2 to function as a UAS is regulated by *SIN1*: A segment of URS2 exhibits tenfold higher activity in a *sin1 swi1* strain than in a *SIN1 swi1* strain (Kruger 1991). As noted earlier, we believe that Swi1,2,3p activates transcription by inhibiting Sin1p and Sin2p.

Mutations in *SIN1* also relieve transcriptional defects of genes other than *HO*. Cloning of *SIN1* revealed that it is the same as the *SPT2* gene (Roeder et al. 1985; see also Winston and Carlson 1992), identified because *spt2* mutations allow expression of *HIS4* or *LYS2* in mutants containing δ insertions in their regulatory regions. The *spt2* mutations appear to function by allowing a low level of transcription from these genes to be increased (Silverman and Fink 1984).

Mutations in *SIN1* and *SIN2* also reverse the reduced transcription observed for *INO1* and other genes which results from mutations that enfeeble RNA polymerase. RNA polymerase II from a wide variety of eukaryotes contains a carboxy-terminal domain (CTD) containing repeats of a heptapeptide; its function is unknown. The *S. cerevisiae* CTD contains 26 or 27 such repeats. Elimination of this domain leads to inviability; truncation to ten repeats leads to a defect in *INO1* transcription and to growth defects at high and low temperatures (Nonet et al. 1987; Nonet and Young 1989). Mutations of *SIN1* or *SIN2* partially relieve the transcriptional defect for the *INO1* gene and greatly improve growth at low temperature (Peterson et al. 1991). These observations can be explained by proposing that one function of the CTD is to antagonize Sin1p and Sin2p (see discussion by Peterson et al. 1991). Because mutants lacking *SWI1*, *SWI2*, or *SWI3* exhibit phenotypes similar to the CTD partial truncations (see below), it has been suggested that Swi1,2,3p assists the CTD in antagonizing Sin1p and Sin2p. Mutations in *SIN1* also cause increased loss of chromosome III and decreased expression of some genes (Kruger and Herskowitz 1991). These observations indicate that Sin1p plays a widespread role in transcription, perhaps by setting the context for correct transcription, and also influences chromosome behavior in general.

The discovery of a functional interaction between RNA polymerase and *SIN* genes provides an explanation for why some genes (e.g., *INO1* and *GAL1*) are affected by CTD mutations, whereas many others (e.g., *HIS4*, *ACT1*, and *URA3*) are not (Scafe et al. 1990). The differences between these genes may reside in subtle differences in affinity by Sin1p or the probability that a gene is associated with nucleosomes. Thus, it is possible that the regulatory region of *INO1* is preferred by Sin1p and hence requires a full-length CTD for its transcription.

Swi1p, Swi2p, and Swi3p Comprise a General
Transcription Factor

The pleiotropic consequences of mutations in *SWI1*, *SWI2*, and *SWI3* led to the suggestion (Stern et al. 1984) that these genes were generally involved in transcription. *SWI1*, *SWI2*, and *SWI3* are also required for transcription of *INO1* (Peterson et al. 1991); this requirement is relieved by a mutation in *SIN1* or *SIN2*. It is thus argued that Swi1,2,3p is required for transcription of *INO1* because it antagonizes Sin1p and Sin2p.

Swi1,2,3p is required for transcription of many more genes, including *ADH1*, *ADH2*, *SUC2*, and for high-level transcription of *GAL1* and *GAL10* (Peterson and Herskowitz 1992; Winston and Carlson 1992). The effect of a *swi1* mutation on transcription of *GAL1* is modest (~4-fold in a *GAL4* strain), but is much greater (>20-fold) in a strain that contains only one of the two Gal4p activation domains (C. Peterson, unpubl.). The sequence of *SWI1* (Peterson and Herskowitz 1992) revealed that it is identical to the *ADR6* gene, identified by its requirement for transcription of *ADH1* (Taguchi and Young 1987). As noted above, *SWI2* is identical to *SNF2*, which is one of a group of genes (including *SNF5* and *SNF6*) required for transcription of *SUC2* (Laurent et al. 1991; Johnston and Carlson 1992; Winston and Carlson 1992). *SNF5* and *SNF6* are required also for transcription of *HO* (Peterson and Herskowitz 1992).

Swi1,2,3p is also required for functioning of the mammalian glucocorticoid receptor (Yoshinaga et al. 1992) and the *Drosphila* ftz protein in yeast (Peterson and Herskowitz 1992). It is suggested that Swi1,2,3p is a general activator protein (a "global activator") that assists gene-specific ("dedicated") regulatory proteins Adr1p, Swi5p, Gal4p, etc. There are several ways in which Swi1,2,3p might act. For example, Swi1,2,3p might help these dedicated activator proteins bind to the DNA or it might help them to function after they have bound. In the latter case, it might help the bound activator protein communicate with RNA polymerase II or factors bound to the TATA element. More specifically, antagonism of chromatin structure (inhibition of Sin1p and Sin2p) by Swi1,2,3p could facilitate binding of the dedicated activator to allow DNA looping and thereby facilitate communication between segments of a regulatory region.

The nucleotide sequence of *SWI2* (*SNF2*) shows that its open reading frame (ORF) (Laurent et al. 1991) has similarities to DNA helicases (Davis et al. 1992; Laurent et al. 1992). An exciting hypothesis is that Swi2p untwists DNA to cause a change in chromatin structure. The nucleotide sequences of *SWI1*, *SWI3*, *SNF5*, and *SNF6* contain ORFs of 148, 99, 103, and 38 kD, respectively (see Table 1) and do not reveal any known DNA-binding domains. These proteins may function along with

Swi2p as a complex, although direct experiments remain to be carried out (see Peterson and Herskowitz 1992). Recent work (Yoshinaga et al. 1992) indicates that at least Swi3p is associated with the glucocorticoid receptor in yeast. The hypothetical Swip/Snfp complex may thus be tethered to DNA by association with DNA-binding proteins.

Activities related to Swi1,2,3p are likely to be conserved in multicellular eukaryotes. The *Drosophila Brahma* gene product, thought to be a positive regulator of homeotic genes, shares extensive identity with Swi2p (Tamkun et al. 1992). *Drosophila* and mammalian extracts contain material that cross-reacts with antibodies against Swi1p (Adr6p) and Swi3p (C. Peterson and S. Yoshinaga, unpubl.).

ORIGIN OF A COMPLEX UPSTREAM REGION:
COUPLING OF URS1 AND URS2

To conclude this chapter, we return to a discussion of one of the major goals of these studies, to understand how the yeast cell creates the combinatorial requirement for limiting transcription of *HO* only to mother cells in the G1 phase of the cell cycle. We have proposed that an event in URS1, which occurs only in mother cells, sets the stage for an event in URS2–"activation" of the UAS elements in this region. As discussed earlier, we propose that Sin1p is responsible for maintaining the UAS elements in URS2 in an inactive state until the appropriate circumstances. Activation is initiated in a mother cell, where Swi5p can antagonize Sin3p, which then allows Swi1,2,3p to do its job (Fig. 4). Swi1,2,3p then lifts repression exerted by Sin1p, to allow activated SCBF to bind to the cell-cycle boxes and stimulate transcription.

We have seen that the upstream region of *HO* can be viewed as a composite: both URS1 and URS2 can function separately as UAS elements. URS1 can function in wild-type hosts; URS2 functions optimally only when *SIN1* and *SWI1* are mutated. We suggest that the present-day *HO* regulatory region may have been created by joining two independent regulatory regions, each with its own specific regulatory proteins: one region regulated by Swi5p and corresponding to URS1 and the other regulated by Swi4,6p and corresponding to URS2 (at least to the CCB elements of URS2). Subsequently, the entire region came under control of nonspecific DNA-binding proteins, Sin1p and Sin2p (and, by extension, nucleosomes), which served to couple the events in these two previously autonomous regions. Upstream regulatory regions are frequently found to be composites of individual regulatory sequences (Dynan 1989). *HO* may provide an example of how these different elements become pasted together in a coherent, coordinated form.

CONCLUSIONS AND PERSPECTIVES

Biochemistry on the Horizon

One of the most striking and bewildering observations to come from recent molecular analysis on gene regulation is that regulatory regions are typically studded with binding sites for several different proteins. This complexity poses considerable problems for molecular analysis because the number of possible interactions among these proteins is enormous. Although a biochemical characterization of DNA-binding sites has not yet been reported for the *HO* regulatory region, it is clear that its upstream region is like that of many mammalian gene regulatory regions, with two binding sites for Swi5p, nine putative binding sites for Mata1p-Matα2p, and ten putative binding sites for SCBF. These DNA-binding activities have been identified genetically and then shown to have the particular DNA-binding properties. In the immediate future, we can expect to see this approach complemented by that typical for mammalian systems: identification of important activities first by biochemical methods. The work of Wang and Stillman (1991) is a harbinger of things to come, in the sense that they are studying the role of an activity (SDP1) that was originally identified by its DNA-binding ability (Stillman et al. 1988). It is, of course, crucial in both yeast and other studies to validate the biological relevance of such a protein, for example, by inactivating the corresponding gene.

Perils and Rewards of Analyzing Sequence Elements Out of Context

A strategy often employed in analysis of upstream regulatory regions is to remove a segment from its native position and study its properties in isolation. In the case of yeast, one strength of this strategy is that a small segment can be identified that is sufficient to confer UAS activity and that this UAS activity requires certain genes in order to function. This strategy has shown that Swi5p functions in URS1 and that Swi1,2,3p functions in both URS1 and URS2.

It is important, however, to be aware that the properties of a regulatory segment can change by removing it from its native position. Analysis of the *HO* regulatory region demonstrates some of the potential uncertainties that can result. The URS1 region behaves as a UAS by two standard criteria: (1) It is necessary for transcription of *HO*–deletion inactivates transcription; and (2) it is sufficient for transcription of *HO*–as assayed both on test plasmids and in the chromosome (e.g., in a URS2 deletion strain). Our studies, however, indicate that the "real" UAS–the

UAS that ultimately drives transcription–comprises the CCB elements within URS2. This view of *HO* regulation was launched because of a disparity between the behavior of the CCB element studied in isolation versus in its native position: The cell-cycle box element is sufficient to function as a UAS in a test plasmid (Breeden and Nasmyth 1987a) but is not sufficient to do so in its chromosomal position (e.g., when URS1 is deleted). We explain this disparity by proposing that use of the cell-cycle box elements in the chromosome is regulated by adjacent sites, by Sin1p and Sin2p, and by events in URS1. Thus, although we initially thought that the ability of the CCB elements to function as a UAS in test plasmids might be artificial, in fact, this finding has proved to be critically important.

This hypothesis makes good logical sense, but it is worth looking once again at the original behavior of URS1: If it is not the "real" UAS, why does it function as a UAS on a test plasmid? This is somewhat troubling, but we can fall back on the dilemma that is faced by everyone working on transcriptional regulation: We do not know in molecular terms what is meant by a UAS. Another possible formal explanation for the dual roles of URS1 and URS2 is that they comprise a "composite" UAS, in which both parts are necessary to make a functional UAS.

A Special Property of Eukaryotic Transcription Machinery?

The functional interaction between the CTD and Sin1p and Sin2p (or, more accurately, between mutant forms of the CTD, Sin1p, and Sin2p) provides a rationale for the existence of the CTD, which is highly conserved in eukaryotes but absent from prokaryotes. This evolutionary conservation may reflect an additional constraint on transcriptional activation in eukaryotes, where sites essential for gene activation are often located far from the RNA polymerase binding site. Interactions between activator proteins bound at these sites with the rest of the transcriptional machinery require DNA looping. In prokaryotes, regulatory sites are generally close to the RNA polymerase binding site (McClure 1985). Regulation of the *Klebsiella pneumoniae nifHDK* promoter by NifAp, which acts at a considerable distance from the promoter, is an exception to the general rule and is instructive. In this case, efficient interaction between NifAp and RNA polymerase requires action of the IHF protein, which induces bending of the DNA between the binding sites for NifAp and RNA polymerase (Hoover et al. 1990). Perhaps the CTD of eukaryotic RNA polymerases is analogous to IHF in that it ultimately facilitates DNA looping or bending.

The *HO* Regulatory Team

Studies of *HO* regulation have identified at least 15 regulators (*SWI1–SWI6, SNF5, SNF6, SIN1–SIN5, MATa1*, and *MATα2*). Our understanding of these regulators is rapidly interfacing, both literally and figuratively, with transcriptional components and motifs that are widely distributed. Studies of Swi4p and Swi6p are providing insights into regulation of the cell cycle. We can expect to learn in the near future about the function of their Swi6p-cdc10p motif, and we should soon know whether Swi4p and Swi6p are indeed substrates for the regulatory protein kinase Cdc28p. Studies of *HO* have led us into learning how chromatin structure interfaces with gene regulation and have led to identification of a general transcription factor, Swi1,2,3p/Snf5,6p, which has a broad role in yeast and appears to be found in other organisms as well. We hope that this review has provided a guide to the facts and hypotheses concerned with *HO* regulation and will help reveal ways in which transcription is regulated at the molecular level.

ACKNOWLEDGMENTS

Research from the Herskowitz laboratory described in this chapter was supported by a research grant from the National Institute of Allergy and Infectious Diseases (to I.H.) and by predoctoral and postdoctoral fellowships from the Markey Foundation, the Medical Research Council of Canada, the National Science Foundation, and the Helen Hay Whitney Foundation. This manuscript was modified from Herskowitz et al. (1992). We thank Kerrie Andow for preparation of the figures.

REFERENCES

Andrews, B.J. and I. Herskowitz. 1989a. Identification of a DNA binding factor involved in cell-cycle control of the yeast *HO* gene. *Cell* 57: 21–29.

————. 1989b. The yeast SWI4 protein contains a motif present in developmental regulators and is part of a complex involved in cell-cycle-dependent transcription. *Nature* 342: 830–833.

————. 1990. Regulation of cell cycle-dependent gene expression in yeast. *J. Biol. Chem.* 265: 14057–14060.

Andrews, B.J. and L.A. Moore. 1992. Interaction of the yeast Swi4 and Swi6 cell cycle regulatory proteins *in vitro. Proc. Natl. Acad. Sci.* 89: 11852–11856..

Breeden, L. and G.E. Mikesell. 1991. Cell cycle-specific expression of the *SWI4* transcription factor is required for the cell cycle regulation of *HO* transcription. *Genes Dev.* 5: 1183–1190.

Breeden, L. and K. Nasmyth. 1987a. Cell cycle control of the yeast *HO* gene: *cis*- and *trans*-acting regulators. *Cell* **48:** 389–397.

————. 1987b. Similarity between cell-cycle genes of budding yeast and fission yeast and the *Notch* gene of *Drosophila*. *Nature* **329:** 651–654.

Davis, J.L., R. Kunisawa, and J. Thorner. 1992. A presumptive helicase (*MOT1* gene product) affects gene expression and is required for viability in the yeast *Saccharomyces cerevisiae*. *Mol. Cell. Biol.* **12:** 1879–1892.

Dirick, L., T. Moll, H. Auer, and K. Nasmyth. 1992. A central role for *SWI6* in modulating cell cycle Start-specific transcription in yeast. *Nature* **357:** 508–513.

Dranginis, A.M. 1990. Binding of yeast a1 and α2 as a heterodimer to the operator DNA of a haploid-specific gene. *Nature* **347:** 682–685.

Dynan, W.S. 1989. Modularity in promoters and enhancers. *Cell* **58:** 1–4.

Estruch, F. and M. Carlson. 1990. *SNF6* encodes a nuclear protein that is required for expression of many genes in *Saccharomyces cerevisiae*. *Mol. Cell. Biol.* **10:** 2544–2553.

Goutte, C. and A.D. Johnson. 1988. a1 protein alters the DNA binding specificity of α2 repressor. *Cell* **52:** 875–882.

Haber, J.E. and B. Garvik. 1977. A new gene affecting the efficiency of mating type interconversion in homothallic strains of *Saccharomyces cerevisiae*. *Genetics* **87:** 33–50.

Herskowitz, I. 1988. Life cycle of the budding yeast *Saccharomyces cerevisiae*. *Microbiol. Rev.* **52:** 536–553.

————. 1989. A regulatory hierarchy for cell specialization in yeast. *Nature* **342:** 749–757.

Herskowitz, I. and Y. Oshima. 1981. Control of cell type in *Saccharomyces cerevisiae*: Mating type and mating type interconversion. In *The Molecular biology of the yeast Saccharomyces: Life cycle and inheritance* (ed. J.N. Strathern et al.), pp. 181–209. Cold Spring Harbor Laboratory, Cold Spring Harbor, New York.

Herskowitz, I., J. Rine, and J. Strathern. 1992. Mating-type determination and mating-type interconversion in *Saccharomyces cerevisiae*. In *The molecular and cellular biology of the yeast* Saccharomyces: *Gene expression* (ed. E.W. Jones et al.), vol. 2. Cold Spring Harbor Laboratory Press, Cold Spring Harbor. (In press.)

Hicks, J.B. and I. Herskowitz. 1976. Interconversion of yeast mating types. I. Direct observations of the action of the homothallism *(HO)* gene. *Genetics* **83:** 245–258.

Hoover, T.R., E. Santero, S. Porter, and S. Kustu. 1990. The integration host factor stimulates interaction of RNA polymerase with NIFA, the transcriptional activator for nitrogen fixation operons. *Cell* **63:** 11–22.

Jensen, R.E. and I. Herskowitz. 1984. Directionality and regulation of cassette substitution in yeast. *Cold Spring Harbor Symp. Quant. Biol.* **49:** 97–104.

Jensen, R., G. Sprague, Jr., and I. Herskowitz. 1983. Regulation of yeast mating-type interconversion: Feedback control of *HO* gene expression by the yeast mating-type locus. *Proc. Natl. Acad. Sci.* **80:** 3035–3039.

Johnston, M. and M. Carlson. 1992. Regulation of carbon and phosphate utilization. In *The molecular and cellular biology of the yeast* Saccharomyces: *Gene expression* (ed. E.W. Jones et al.), vol. 2, pp. 193–281. Cold Spring Harbor Laboratory Press, Cold Spring Harbor, New York.

Jiang, Y.W. and D.J. Stillman. 1992. Involvement of the *SIN4* global transcriptional regulator in the chromatin structure of *Saccharomyces cerevisiae*. *Mol. Cell. Biol.* **12:** 4503–4514.

Keleher, C.A., M.J. Redd, J. Schultz, M. Carlson, and A.D. Johnson. 1992. Ssn6/Tup1 is a general repressor of transcription in yeast. *Cell* **68:** 709–719.

Kieran, M., V. Blank, F. Logeat, J. Vandeherckhove, F. Lottspeich, O. Le Bail, M.B. Urban, P. Kourilsky, P.A. Baeuerle, and A. Israël. 1990. The DNA binding subunit of NF-κB is identical to factor KBF1 and homologous to the *rel* oncogene product. *Cell* 62: 1007–1018.

Kostriken, R., J.N. Strathern, A.J.S. Klar, and F. Heffron. 1983. A site-specific endonuclease essential for mating-type switching in *Saccharomyces cerevisiae*. *Cell* 35: 167–174.

Kruger, W.D. 1991. "Analysis of the *SIN1* and *SIN2* gene products and their role in transcriptional regulation in *Saccharomyces cerevisiae*." Ph.D. thesis, University of California, San Francisco.

Kruger, W. and I. Herskowitz. 1991. A negative regulator of *HO* transcription, SIN1 (SPT2), is a nonspecific DNA-binding protein related to HMG1. *Mol. Cell. Biol.* 11: 4135–4146.

Laurent, B.C., M.A. Treitel, and M. Carlson. 1991. Functional interdependence of the yeast SNF2, SNF5, and SNF6 proteins in transcriptional activation. *Proc. Natl. Acad. Sci.* 88: 2687–2691.

Laurent, B.C., X. Yang, and M. Carlson. 1992. An essential *Saccharomyces cerevisiae* gene homologous to *SNF2* encodes a helicase-related protein in a new family. *Mol. Cell. Biol.* 12: 1893–1902.

Lowndes, N.F., A.L. Johnson, L. Breeden, and L.H. Johnston. 1992. *SWI6* protein is required for transcription of the periodically expressed DNA synthesis genes in budding yeast. *Nature* 357: 505–508.

Lydall, D., G. Ammerer, and K. Nasmyth. 1991. A new role for MCM1 in yeast: Cell cycle regulation of *SWI5* transcription. *Genes Dev.* 5: 2405–2419.

McClure, W.R. 1985. Mechanism and control of transcription initiation in prokaryotes. *Annu. Rev. Biochem.* 54: 171–204.

Miller, A.M., V.L. MacKay, and K.A. Nasmyth. 1985. Identification and comparison of two sequence elements that confer cell-type specific transcription in yeast. *Nature* 314: 598–603.

Moll, T., G. Tebb, U. Surana, H. Robitsch, and K. Nasmyth. 1991. The role of phosphorylation and the CDC28 protein kinase in cell cycle-regulated nuclear import of the *S. cerevisiae* transcription factor SWI5. *Cell* 66: 743–758.

Murre, C., P.S. McCaw, and D. Baltimore. 1989. A new DNA binding and dimerization motif in immunoglobulin enhancer binding, daughterless, MyoD, and myc proteins. *Cell* 56: 777–783.

Nagai, K., Y. Nakaseko, K. Nasmyth, and D. Rhodes. 1988. Zinc-finger motifs expressed in *E. coli* and folded *in vitro* direct specific binding to DNA. *Nature* 332: 284–286.

Nasmyth, K. 1983. Molecular analysis of a cell lineage. *Nature* 302: 670–676.

———. 1985a. At least 1400 base pairs of 5′-flanking DNA is required for the correct expression of the *HO* gene in yeast. *Cell* 42: 213–223.

———. 1985b. A repetitive DNA sequence that confers cell-cycle START (CDC28)-dependent transcription of the *HO* gene in yeast. *Cell* 42: 225–235.

———. 1987. The determination of mother cell-specific mating type switching in yeast by a specific regulator of *HO* transcription. *EMBO J.* 6: 243–248.

Nasmyth, K. and L. Dirick. 1991. The role of *SWI4* and *SWI6* in the activity of G1 cyclins in yeast. *Cell* 66: 995–1013.

Nasmyth, K., A. Seddon, and G. Ammerer. 1987a. Cell cycle regulation of *SWI5* is required for mother-cell-specific *HO* transcription in yeast. *Cell* 49: 549–558.

Nasmyth, K., D. Stillman, and D. Kipling. 1987b. Both positive and negative regulators of *HO* transcription are required for mother-cell-specific mating-type switching in yeast. *Cell* 48: 579–587.

Nasmyth, K., G. Adolf, D. Lydall, and A. Seddon. 1990. The identification of a second cell cycle control on the *HO* promoter in yeast: Cell cycle regulation of SWI5 nuclear entry. *Cell* **62:** 631–647.

Nonet, M.L. and R.A. Young. 1989. Intragenic and extragenic suppressors of mutations in the heptapeptide repeat domain of *Saccharomyces cerevisiae* RNA polymerase II. *Genetics* **123:** 715–724.

Nonet, M., D. Sweetser, and R.A. Young. 1987. Functional redundancy and structural polymorphism in the large subunit of RNA polymerase II. *Cell* **50:** 909–915.

Ogas, J., B.J. Andrews, and I. Herskowitz. 1991. Transcriptional activation of *CLN1*, *CLN2*, and a putative new G1 cyclin (*HCS26*) by SWI4, a positive regulator of G1-specific transcription. *Cell* **66:** 1015–1026.

Peterson, C.L. and I. Herskowitz. 1992. Characterization of the yeast *SWI1*, *SWI2*, and *SWI3* genes, which encode a global activator of transcription. *Cell* **68:** 573–583.

Peterson, C., W. Kruger, and I. Herskowitz. 1991. A functional interaction between the C-terminal domain of RNA polymerase II and the negative regulator SIN1. *Cell* **64:** 1135–1143.

Primig, M., S. Sockanathan, H. Auer, and K. Nasmyth. 1992. Anatomy of a transcription factor important for the start of the cell cycle in *Saccharomyces cerevisiae*. *Nature* **358:** 593–597.

Roeder, G.S., C. Beard, M. Smith, and S. Keranen. 1985. Isolation and characterization of the *SPT2* gene, a negative regulator of Ty-controlled yeast gene expression. *Mol. Cell. Biol.* **5:** 1543–1553.

Russell, D.W., R. Jensen, M.J. Zoller, J. Burke, B. Errede, M. Smith, and I. Herskowitz. 1986. Structure of the *Saccharomyces cerevisiae HO* gene and analysis of its upstream region. *Mol. Cell. Biol.* **6:** 4281–4294.

Scafe, C., D. Chao, J. Lopes, J.P. Hirsch, S. Henry, and R.A. Young. 1990. RNA polymerase II C-terminal repeat influences response to transcriptional enhancer signals. *Nature* **347:** 491–494.

Sikorski, R.S., M.S. Boguski, M. Goebl, and P. Hieter. 1990. A repeating amino acid motif (TPR) in CDC23 defines a family of proteins and a new relationship among genes required for mitosis and RNA synthesis. *Cell* **60:** 307–317.

Silverman, S.J. and G.R. Fink. 1984. Effects of Ty insertions on *HIS4* transcription in *Saccharomyces cerevisiae*. *Mol. Cell. Biol.* **4:** 1246–1251.

Smith, M.M. and O.S. Andresson. 1983. DNA sequences of yeast H3 and H4 histone genes from the two non-allelic gene sets encode identical H3 and H4 proteins. *J. Mol. Biol.* **169:** 663–690.

Smith, M.M. and V.B. Stirling. 1988. Histone H3 and H4 gene deletions in *Saccharomyces cerevisiae*. *J. Cell Biol.* **106:** 557–566.

Stern, M. 1985. "Genes controlling the expression of the *HO* gene in yeast." Ph.D. thesis. University of California, San Francisco.

Stern, M., R. Jensen, and I. Herskowitz. 1984. Five *SWI* genes are required for expression of the *HO* gene in yeast. *J. Mol. Biol.* **178:** 853–868.

Sternberg, P.W., M.J. Stern, I. Clark, and I. Herskowitz. 1987. Activation of the yeast *HO* gene by release from multiple negative controls. *Cell* **48:** 567–577.

Stillman, D.J., A.T. Bankier, A. Seddon, E.G. Groenhout, and K.A. Nasmyth. 1988. Characterization of a transcription factor involved in mother cell specific transcription of the yeast *HO* gene. *EMBO J.* **7:** 485–494.

Strathern, J.N. and I. Herskowitz. 1979. Asymmetry and directionality in production of new cell types during clonal growth: The switching pattern of homothallic yeast. *Cell* **17:** 371–381.

Strathern, J.N., A.J. Klar, J.B. Hicks, J.A. Abraham, J.M. Ivy, K.A. Nasmyth, and C.

McGill. 1982. Homothallic switching of yeast mating type cassettes is initiated by a double-stranded cut in the *MAT* locus. *Cell* **31:** 183–192.

Strich, R., M.R. Slater, and R.E. Esposito. 1989. Identification of negative regulatory genes that govern the expression of early meiotic genes in yeast. *Proc. Natl. Acad. Sci.* **86:** 10018–10022.

Taba, M.R., I. Muroff, D. Lydall, G. Tebb, and K. Nasmyth. 1991. Changes in a SWI4,6-DNA-binding complex occur at the time of *HO* gene activation in yeast. *Genes Dev.* **5:** 2000–2013.

Taguchi, A.K.W. and E.T. Young. 1987. The identification and characterization of *ADR6*, a gene required for sporulation and for expression of the alcohol dehydrogenase II isozyme from *Saccharomyces cerevisiae*. *Genetics* **116:** 523–530.

Tamkun, J.W., R. Deuring, M.P. Scott, M. Kissinger, A.M. Pattatucci, T.C. Kaufman, and J.A. Kennison. 1992. brahma: A regulator of *Drosophila* homeotic genes structurally related to the yeast transcriptional activator SNF2/SWI2. *Cell* **68:** 561–572.

Thompson, C.C., T.A. Brown, and S.L. McKnight. 1991. Convergence of Ets- and Notch-related structural motifs in a heteromeric DNA binding complex. *Science* **253:** 762–768.

Verma, R., J. Smiley, B. Andrews, and J.L. Campbell. 1992. Regulation of the yeast DNA replication genes through the *Mlu*I cell cycle box is dependent on *SWI6*. *Proc. Natl. Acad. Sci.* **89:** 9479–9483.

Vidal, M., A.M. Buckley, F. Hilger, and R.F. Gaber. 1990. Direct selection for mutants with increased K^+ transport in *Saccharomyces cerevisiae*. *Genetics* **125:** 313–320.

Vidal, M., R. Strich, R.E. Esposito, and R.F. Gaber. 1991. *RPD1* (*SIN3/UME4*) is required for maximal activation and repression of diverse yeast genes. *Mol. Cell. Biol.* **11:** 6306–6316.

Wang, H. and D.J. Stillman. 1991. *In vitro* regulation of a *SIN3*-dependent DNA-binding activity by stimulatory and inhibitory factors. *Proc. Natl. Acad. Sci.* **87:** 9761–9765.

Wang, H., I. Clark, P.R. Nicholson, I. Herskowitz, and D.J. Stillman. 1990. The *Saccharomyces cerevisiae SIN3* gene, a negative regulator of *HO*, contains four paired amphipathic helix motifs. *Mol. Cell. Biol.* **10:** 5927–5936.

Winston, F. and M. Carlson. 1992. Yeast SNF/SWI transcriptional activators and the SPT/SIN chromatin connection. *Trends Genet.* **8:** 387–391.

Yoshinaga, S.K., C.L. Peterson, I. Herskowitz, and K.R. Yamamoto. 1992. Roles of the SWI1, SWI2, and SWI3 proteins for transcriptional enhancement by steroid receptors. *Science* **258:** 1598–1604.

37

A Combinatorial Regulatory Circuit in Budding Yeast

Alexander Johnson
Department of Microbiology and Immunology
University of California, San Francisco, California 94143

OVERVIEW

In budding yeast, three negative regulators of transcription ($\alpha 2$, $\mathbf{a}1$, and MCM1) participate in combinatorial control circuits that specify cell type. Studies of these regulatory proteins have revealed the features that account for their abilities to act in various combinations. These studies have also provided insights into the way these regulatory proteins direct transcriptional repression.

INTRODUCTION

Different cell types of an organism contain different sets of proteins that regulate transcription. Cell-type-specific genes, in turn, are generally designed to respond to particular combinations of these regulatory proteins. These two ideas are commonly summarized by the term combinatorial control, instances of which have been documented in a wide variety of organisms (see Alberts et al. 1989).

Studies of cell-type specification in the yeast *Saccharomyces cerevisiae* have revealed a small-scale regulatory network of this type and have provided a number of insights into the design and behavior of the regulatory proteins that comprise the network. *S. cerevisiae* has three distinct types of cells termed $\mathbf{a}$, α, and $\mathbf{a}/\alpha$. The $\mathbf{a}$ and α cells are normally haploid in chromosome number and are specialized for mating. An $\mathbf{a}$ cell mates with an α cell in a process that involves cell fusion followed by nuclear fusion and culminates in the formation of the third cell type, the $\mathbf{a}/\alpha$ cell. Because it arises from the fusion of two haploid cells, the $\mathbf{a}/\alpha$ cell is normally diploid in chromosome number. The $\mathbf{a}/\alpha$ cell cannot mate; however, unlike the haploid cells types, it can be induced by the appropriate external signals to undergo meiosis. Each of the four meiotic products is packaged into a spore that contains a haploid number of

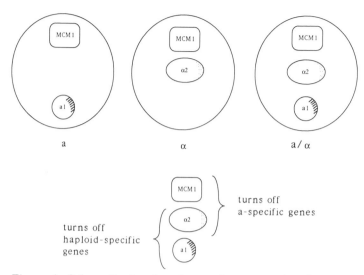

Figure 1 Schematic showing the regulatory proteins discussed in this paper, their distribution among the three yeast cell types, and their target genes. The diagram is based on work from many different laboratories and is discussed in recent review articles by Herskowitz (1989), Sprague (1990), and Dolan and Fields (1991).

chromosomes. Upon germination, a spore gives rise to either an **a** or an α cell type.

What regulatory proteins specify these different types of cells? A simplified view of the scheme discussed in this paper is shown in Figure 1. Only the regulatory proteins that *repress* transcription (MCM1, α2, and **a**1) will be considered in order to limit the scope and length of this chapter. A number of related issues have recently been reviewed by Herskowitz (1989), Sprague (1990), and Dolan and Fields (1991). As shown in Figure 1, the MCM1 protein is expressed in all three of the yeast cell types. This protein may thus be considered hardwired or ubiquitous; its presence does not signal a particular cell type. In contrast, the **a**1 and α2 regulators, the products of the *MATa1* and *MATα2* genes, respectively, are restricted to certain cell types. This restriction is the result of a DNA rearrangement that changes the expression of the structural genes for these proteins (see reviews cited above). These three regulatory proteins, MCM1, **a**1, and α2, act on two different sets of target genes. As shown in the figure, the **a**-specific genes are expressed in **a** cells, but are turned off by the combined action of α2 and MCM1 in the two other cell types. The haploid-specific genes are turned off by the combined action of **a**1 and α2, a situation found only in the **a**/α cell type.

Present in this simple regulatory scheme are the essential features of combinatorial control. In particular, the **a**- and haploid-specific genes exemplify the ability of target genes to respond only to the correct combination of regulatory proteins. For example, the α2/MCM1 combination, although strongly repressing **a**-specific genes, does not directly affect the expression of haploid-specific genes. Three additional features of the yeast regulatory network are reminiscent of situations observed in other eukaryotic cells. (1) Only specific combinations of regulatory proteins are functional. From a consideration of Figure 1, one might have predicted that **a**1 and MCM1 would cooperate in a manner analogous to the paired action of MCM1 and α2. This idea would provide a pleasing symmetry to the regulatory network and could in principle be used as an additional specifier of cell type. However, both genetic and biochemical observations have shown that these two proteins do not interact. Indeed, **a**1 appears to have no function at all in **a** cells (see Strathern et al. 1981). (2) An important component of the regulatory network, MCM1, is found in all three of the yeast cell types. Of the three regulators depicted in Figure 1, MCM1 is most abundant and consequently the easiest to detect biochemically. Without a knowledge of α2 (which derived from genetic studies) one would be faced with the familiar paradox that the control of a group of cell-type-specific genes would seem to be specified by a ubiquitous regulator. (3) A single protein (α2) participates in more than one regulatory pathway. Although not explicitly indicated in the scheme of Figure 1, the same is true for MCM1. In fact, MCM1 can act as either a positive or a negative regulator of transcription, depending on the context. As discussed in this review, the yeast studies have provided a molecular description of these context effects.

Not only do yeast and other eukaryotic cells share features of regulatory circuit design, they also employ highly related proteins to form such circuits. **a**1 and α2 are members of the homeodomain family, and MCM1 is a member of the serum response factor (SRF) family (for review, see Scott et al. 1989; Gehring et al. 1990; and Triesman, this volume).

The article is organized around several basic questions:

1. How is target specificity generated? As will become apparent, **a**1 and α2–like other homeodomain proteins–are DNA-binding proteins of modest specificity and affinity. On their own, **a**1 and α2 proteins lack the ability to efficiently recognize their regulatory sites on DNA over related sequences. In vivo, however, they act in a highly selective manner, turning off a small number of target genes with great efficiency. This apparent paradox can be resolved by the realization that

much of the target specificity arises from the nature of combinatorial control. α2 and **a**1 rely on both protein-DNA and protein-protein interactions to carry out their selective action.

2. How do these proteins interact? α2 and **a**1 engage in a series of protein-DNA and protein-protein interactions in order to recognize the appropriate target genes and to signal their repression. Studies are described that establish how these functions are dispersed along the proteins and the implications of the design of these two homeodomain proteins.

3. How does a single protein, such as MCM1, activate transcription in one setting, yet repress gene expression in another setting? This question raises another general issue of combinatorial control, namely, that the net effect (positive or negative) of the control event is not simply the sum of the intrinsic activities of the constituent proteins.

4. How do these proteins bring about transcriptional repression? As is described, these proteins repress by an active mechanism (as opposed to direct steric hindrance), and several models for repression are discussed.

GENERATION OF TARGET SPECIFICITY

Selective Recognition of the a-specific Genes

The example of α2 and MCM1 proteins working together to turn off **a**-specific genes (see Fig. 1) is considered first. A 34-bp operator (called the *asg* operator), controls the cell-type-specific expression of each of these genes (Fig. 2). When inserted upstream of the promoter of a test gene (otherwise unaffected by cell type), a synthetic copy of this operator converts the test gene into an **a**-specific gene (Fig. 3). That is, the modified test gene is expressed at its normal level in **a** cells but is repressed by a factor of approximately 100 in α and **a**/α cells.

The *asg* operator contains recognition sequences for both α2 and MCM1. The interaction of α2 with this operator is considered first. As shown in Figure 4, α2 consists primarily of two protease-resistant domains connected by a protease-sensitive flexible hinge (Sauer et al. 1988). Both nuclear magnetic resonance (NMR) and X-ray crystallographic studies (Phillips et al. 1991; Wolberger et al. 1991) have revealed that the carboxy-terminal domain of α2 is folded into the canonical three-helical structure of the homeodomain (see Wüthrich and Gehring, this volume). In fact, the backbone carbons of the α2 homeodomain are superimposable on those of the *Drosophila* engrailed homeodomain (Kissinger et al. 1990) and, by extension, Antennapedia (Quian et al. 1989), despite only a limited amino acid sequence similarity

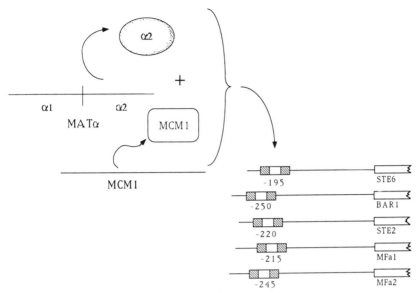

Figure 2 The **a**-specific genes and their associated operators. These genes encode a secreted protease (BAR1), a cell-surface receptor (STE2), the mating pheromone **a**-factor (MFa1 and MFa2), and a protein required for **a**-factor secretion (STE6). All of these gene products are involved in the specialized function of the **a** cell, which is to mate with an α cell. See reviews cited in Fig. 1.

(Laughon and Scott 1984; Shepherd et al. 1984). Moreover, the X-ray structures of α2 and engrailed complexed with DNA reveal that the two proteins interact with DNA in a fundamentally similar fashion despite the fact that they recognize different DNA sequences. Most of the amino acid residues conserved between α2 and engrailed (17/60 identities) participate either in the hydrophobic packing of the homeodomain core or in the interaction with DNA, particularly with the phosphodiester backbone. Thus, yeast and *Drosophila* homeodomains appear very similar, not only in the way they are folded, but also in the way they interact with DNA. A simplified view of a single α2 homeodomain complexed with a half-site of the *asg* operator is shown in Figure 5.

It is possible to obtain a rough idea of the specificity of the α2 homeodomain for its recognition site on DNA through the analysis of operator mutations. The α2 homeodomain recognizes a contiguous series of approximately 7 bp. Each *asg* operator contains two such sequences, arranged as inverted repeats. We refer to these 7-bp DNA sequences as α2 half-sites. The 10 examples of half-sites (from the 5 known *asg* operators) are nearly identical in sequence (Johnson and Herskowitz 1985; Miller et al. 1985). A number of mutations in the STE6 operator have

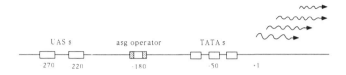

CELL TYPE	PROMOTER ACTIVITY
a	140
α	0.5
a/α	0.5

Figure 3 Cell-type control mediated by the **a**-specific gene operator. A synthetic 34-bp operator (that found upstream of the *STE6* gene) has been inserted in the *CYC1* promoter and introduced into yeast cells. Normally, *CYC1* is expressed in all cell types, but addition of the operator converts it to an **a**-specific gene. *CYC1* has been fused to the *E. coli lacZ* gene, and promoter activity is expressed as units of β-galactosidase (for details, see Guarente et al. 1984; Johnson and Herskowitz 1985; and Miller et al. 1985).

been isolated and examined both in vitro and in vivo (D. Smith and A. Johnson, in prep.). Although they differ in the severity of their effects, most single point mutations in the α2 half-sites reduce the affinity for the α2 homeodomain by a factor of only 3 to 10. In α cells, these mutations reduce the occupancy of the *asg* operator by α2 from approximately 99% (for a wild-type operator) to 70–90% for the mutants, a value consistent with the magnitude of the binding defect measured in vitro. One conclusion from these studies is that the α2 homeodomain binds to its recognition site with only modest specificity; the effect of operator mutations on α2 appears much less severe than that typically observed for the *lac* or λ repressors (see, e.g., Jobe et al. 1974; Johnson et al. 1979).

α2 differs from a typical bacterial repressor in another important respect. Whereas bacterial repressors typically dimerize in a way that sets the spacing of the two monomers exactly in phase with the two DNA half-sites, dimers of α2 display an unusual degree of flexibility, as evidenced by the following set of observations. As shown in the top line of Figure 6, the two half-sites of the naturally occurring *asg* operators are arrayed as inverted repeats, 2 1/2 turns apart center to center. Dimers of α2 are formed through contacts at the amino terminus of the protein, and each of the two homeodomains of the dimer makes a similar set of con-

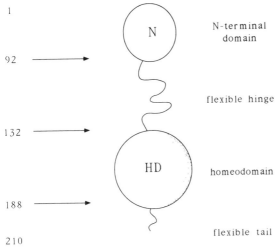

Figure 4 Domain structure of α2. Numbers on the left refer to amino acid positions; arrows mark the sites of attack by dilute chymotrypsin (Sauer et al. 1988). The three-dimensional structure of the homeodomain has been determined (Wolberger et al. 1991) and is depicted in Fig. 5.

tacts on each half-site; in vitro, however, a dimer of α2 binds with the same affinity to artificial operators where the spacing has been altered experimentally (Fig. 6). It seems that dimers of α2 must have considerable flexibility in order to recognize such diverse orientations of the half-sites. We have proposed that this flexibility is attributable to the hinge region of α2 that connects the amino-terminal domain to the homeodomain, and to the fact that the homeodomains do not interact with each other (Smith and Johnson 1992). It is tempting to speculate that because of this flexible region the orientation of one homeodomain in the dimer is relatively unconstrained with respect to the other. A prediction of this idea is that a dimer of α2 should be able to bind in vitro to an operator composed of a *direct* repeat of the two half-sites. Indeed, α2 dimers are also capable of recognizing not only a direct repeat configuration, but an everted (inside-out) configuration as well (see Smith and Johnson 1992). We conclude from these experiments that, although the α2 dimer is designed to recognize a pair of half-sites, it lacks the ability to discriminate the strictly conserved arrangement of the bona fide operators from other configurations. This organizational flexibility contrasts with the hardwired dimers of the typical bacterial repressor.

These two considerations—low intrinsic half-site specificity and flexibility with respect to half-site orientation—indicate that α2 does not

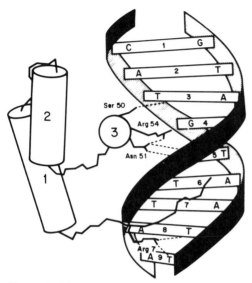

Figure 5 Diagram of the α2 homeodomain bound to a half-site of the *asg* operator. The three α helices form a compact structure stabilized by a network of hydrophobic interactions. Residues of both helix 3 and the amino-terminal arm contact bases in the major and minor groove, respectively. The numbering scheme was utilized to directly compare α2 with other homeodomains; position 1 corresponds to position 129 of the intact α2 protein depicted in Fig. 4 (see Wolberger et al. 1991).

possess the hallmarks of a DNA-binding protein designed to act on its own. In particular, the protein seems ill-suited to interpret the fixed spacing and orientation of the two half-sites of the *asg* operator. This problem, however, is resolved by the participation of the MCM1 protein. A model of the two proteins bound together on the *asg* operator is shown in Figure 7. MCM1 binds as a dimer to the central portion of the operator (Bender and Sprague 1987; Keleher et al. 1988; Passmore et al. 1989; Ammerer 1990) and contacts the flexible hinge of α2 that connects the two protease-resistant domains. (Evidence supportive of this latter point is discussed in the following section of this chapter.) The protein:protein contact mediated by the flexible hinge of α2 has two important consequences. First, it raises the apparent affinity of α2 for the operator by approximately 1000-fold. The simplest explanation is that attractive protein-protein interactions between α2 and MCM1 net 3–4 kcal/mole of binding energy. As discussed below, it is believed that MCM1 occupies the operator in vivo whether or not α2 is present in the cell; one could say (at least in a thermodynamic sense) that the operator for α2 is actual-

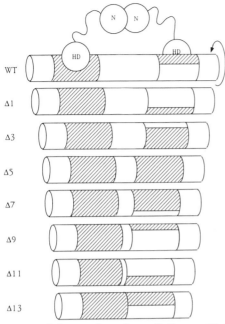

Figure 6 Interaction of an α2 dimer with the wild-type *asg* operator (WT) and a series of operators where the half-site spacing has been experimentally varied. As described in the text, the α2 dimer shows a similar affinity for all these operators. The wild-type *asg* operator has the half-sites spaced by 2 1/2 turns (see Smith and Johnson 1992).

ly an MCM1-DNA complex with important contributions to the energy of α2 binding coming from both α2-DNA interactions and α2-MCM1 interactions. Importantly, however, occupancy of the operator by MCM1

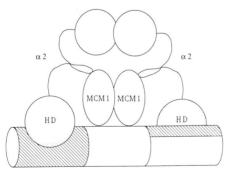

Figure 7 Model of α2 and MCM1 bound at the *asg* operator. As described in the text, the flexible hinge of α2 is believed to directly contact the 80-amino-acid domain of the MCM1 protein that is conserved in the human SRF protein.

alone does not lead to repression. Second, MCM1 guides α2 to recognize the correct spacing of its half-sites, raising its *specificity* as well as its affinity (Smith and Johnson 1992). This point is most easily illustrated by an experiment that utilized an artificial operator with 3-bp insertions placed between the α2 and MCM1 recognition sequences in a way that did not compromise the binding affinity of either protein for the operator. These insertions did, however, destroy the ability of the two proteins to bind cooperatively and, as a result, inactivated the operator when tested in vivo. One interpretation of this observation is that attractive protein-protein interactions with MCM1 freeze the flexible hinges of α2 in a configuration that sets the spacing and the orientation of the α2 homeodomains in register with those of the half-sites of the *asg* operator. What appeared at first as a puzzling feature of α2 and its DNA operator can be seen as an ingenious solution to the problem of recognizing an operator that is composed partly of DNA and partly of protein.

The cooperative binding of α2 and MCM1 to the a-specific gene operator was discovered in vitro, and the views summarized above were also developed largely from biochemical experiments. It is a legitimate concern whether or not this cooperative binding actually occurs in vivo. Although Keleher et al. (1989) presented results consistent with this view, the experiment described in Figure 8 demonstrates the point more convincingly (K. Komachi and A. Johnson, unpubl.). In vivo, an *asg* operator bearing an experimentally weakened MCM1 recognition sequence fails to bring about repression, presumably because the reduced affinity of the operator for MCM1 prevents its occupancy by MCM1 as well as by α2. However, when the intracellular level of α2 is elevated by an order of magnitude, repression by this operator is restored. Thus, a deficiency in the MCM1-operator interaction can be suppressed by the overexpression of α2. These results are most easily explained by the idea that the two proteins bind the operator cooperatively in vivo. An important control experiment shows that repression is not restored by α2 overproduction if the MCM1 binding site was deleted rather than weakened. Thus, assembly of a functional repressor complex, even under conditions of α2 overexpression, would appear to require MCM1.

Like α2, MCM1 is a member of a large class of eukaryotic regulatory proteins. As first pointed out by Norman et al. (1988), a 70-amino-acid section of the MCM1 protein is 55% identical with a corresponding section of the human SRF. Although structural information for these proteins is lacking, it is reasonable to assume that the two share a common structure in this related region (see Triesman, this volume).

The fact that MCM1 and SRF recognize similar DNA sequences (Passmore et al. 1989; Jarvis et al. 1989; Primig et al. 1991) prompted an

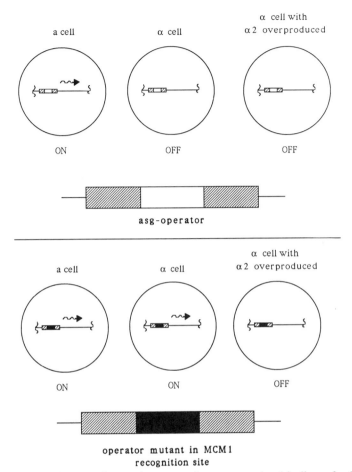

Figure 8 Experiment demonstrating cooperative binding of α2 and MCM1 in vivo. The top line of cells contains a *CYC1* promoter into which has been placed an *asg* operator, as in Fig. 3. The bottom line contains a similar construct in which the center of the operator (the MCM1 binding site) has been weakened by mutation; this change causes derepression of the promoter in α cells. As indicated, the defect in the MCM1-operator interaction can be suppressed by overproduction of the α2 protein. (Data from K. Komachi.)

examination of whether the human SRF could also interact with the flexible hinge of α2. Indeed, the fragment of SRF that contains only the region conserved with MCM1 binds cooperatively with α2 to the *asg* operator in vitro (A. Vershon and A. Johnson, in prep.). The simplest explanation is that the interaction between the flexible hinge of α2 and the conserved core of SRF/MCM1 has been conserved between yeast and humans. This idea predicts the existence of human proteins that have features similar to the α2 flexible hinge.

Selective Recognition of the Haploid-specific Genes

In addition to collaborating with MCM1 to repress the **a**-specific genes, α2 cooperates with **a**1 protein (another homeodomain protein) to repress transcription of the haploid-specific genes (Fig. 1). Although some underlying features of the α2/MCM1 combination are shared with **a**1/α2, the two forms of combinatorial control clearly differ in detail. The first obvious difference can be seen by comparing the *asg* operator with the operator that controls expression of the haploid-specific genes (the *hsg* operator; Fig. 9). The *hsg* operator is smaller and contains considerably less information than does the *asg* operator. The two operators, however, are related: The linear nucleotide sequence of the haploid-specific operator resembles that of an **a**-specific operator deleted for the MCM1 recognition sequence (Fig. 9) (Miller et al. 1985). Indeed, a 13-bp deletion of the center of the **a**-specific operator converts it into a haploid-specific gene operator, albeit a weak one (C. Goutte and A. Johnson, in prep.). The efficiency of this artificial *hsg* operator can, however, be raised to

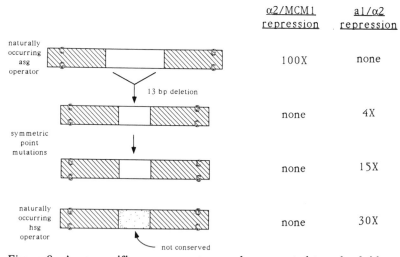

Figure 9   An **a**-specific gene operator can be converted to a haploid-specific gene operator by simple deletion. Both types of operator contain similar half-sites arrayed as inverted repeats (indicated by the hatched areas), although small differences in the half-site sequences also contribute to the difference between the operators. Numbers on the right refer to the extent of repression observed when the indicated operator was inserted into the *CYC1* promoter (Fig. 3) and introduced into **a**, α, and **a**/α cells. The factor of repression is the ratio of the unrepressed levels of expression (i.e., the level in **a** cells) divided by the repressed levels (the levels in α or **a**/α cells) (see Miller et al. 1985; Siliciano and Tatchell 1986; Goutte and Johnson 1988). (Data from C. Goutte.)

that of a naturally occurring *hsg* operator by a single base-pair change in sequence, as shown in Figure 9. From experiments such as these, it can be concluded that half-site spacing is the primary difference between *asg* and *hsg* operators and that slight nucleotide sequence differences in the half-sites serve to fine-tune the specificity.

How do **a**1 and α2 cooperate to recognize the *hsg* operator? α2, on its own, interacts weakly with this operator ($K_d \approx 10^{-7}$ M); **a**1 even at concentrations as high as 10^{-5} M fails to exhibit binding. However, when the two proteins are mixed at nanomolar concentrations, they efficiently occupy the operator (Goutte and Johnson 1988 and unpubl.; Dranginis 1990). A series of experiments performed in vitro has revealed that **a**1 and α2 form a weak heterodimer in solution and that this heterodimer then binds tightly to the operator (A. Mak and A. Johnson, unpubl.). UV-cross-linking experiments have demonstrated that in the **a**1/α2/DNA complex, the homeodomains of both proteins contact the operator. Finally, chemical probe experiments suggest that the **a**1 and α2 homeodomains of the heterodimer are bound to the operator in tandem, an arrangement that contrasts with the dyad symmetry of the operator (Model 2 of Fig. 10) (C. Goutte and A. Johnson, in prep.). This model implies that the two homeodomains "read" the two similar half-site sequences in opposite directions.

Given this model, it is puzzling that **a**1, on its own, binds very poorly, if at all, to the *hsg* operator. One possibility is that the **a**1 homeodomain normally exists in a conformation that is inappropriate to bind DNA. According to the model, **a**1 would be capable of adopting its DNA-binding conformation only upon contact with α2, and together the two proteins would efficiently occupy the *hsg* operators in the cell. It remains to be determined whether or not this model is correct.

PROTEIN-PROTEIN INTERACTIONS

As pointed out in the previous sections, α2 makes specific contact with DNA, MCM1, and **a**1. In addition, and as discussed in a subsequent section, α2 carries a determinant required to direct repression of the target genes. It has become clear that the α2 protein is constructed from individual modules, each of which is responsible for one of the functions listed above.

As described in Figure 5, the homeodomain of α2 (amino acids 132–188) folds into a compact DNA-binding structure consisting primarily of 3 α-helices and an amino-terminal arm. Extending from this structure toward the amino terminus of α2 is the flexible hinge (composed of approximately 40 amino acids) that links the homeodomain to the amino-terminal domain (Fig. 4). As indicated by the following two experimental results, this hinge provides most, if not all, of the interactions with MCM1 (A. Vershon and A. Johnson, in prep.). First, the amino acids of the hinge are necessary for the cooperative binding of α2 and MCM1 but not for the binding of α2 alone to the operator. Second, the flexible hinge of α2 was grafted onto the amino terminus of the *Drosophila* engrailed protein; the resulting hybrid protein displayed the DNA-binding specificity of engrailed and the ability to bind cooperatively with MCM1 to an artificial engrailed/MCM1 operator (Fig. 11). MCM1 and engrailed (without the α2 hinge) can co-occupy this same operator but bind without positive cooperativity. These results are most easily explained by the idea that the flexible hinge of α2 simply contacts MCM1 directly as illustrated in Figure 7, although we cannot rule out more complicated models where the hinge also makes contact with DNA.

This idea of a flexible polypeptide segment specifying a productive interaction with a second protein also applies to the a1/α2 combination. In this case, an unstructured tail that extends from the carboxyl terminus of the α2 homeodomain appears to contact the a1 homeodomain, as indicated by the following observations. The α2 homeodomain ends at amino acid 188, yet the protein extends another 22 amino acids before it terminates. In the X-ray structure of the α2 fragment complexed with DNA (Fig. 4), this carboxy-terminal tail is present but unstructured, contrasting markedly with the adjacent and highly ordered homeodomain (Wolberger et al. 1991). To determine the function of this unstructured tail, a mutant version of α2 was constructed that lacked the tail. In vivo, the mutant α2 still cooperates with MCM1 to turn off a-specific genes

Figure 10 Models for the a1/α2 heterodimer bound to the *hsg* operator. The homeodomains of a1 and α2 are indicated schematically with the a1 homeodomain shaded more darkly. The top line shows a dimer of α2 bound to the *hsg* operator, a condition obtained experimentally by using high concentrations of α2. From the disposition of backbone positions protected from attack by hydroxy radical (closed circles), it was deduced that this homodimer is bound symmetrically, a result expected from the fact that the *hsg* operator also shows dyad symmetry (see Fig. 9). The second and third lines show the hydroxy radical protection results observed when a1/α2 occupies the *hsg* operator. By analogy with the α2 homodimer, it was predicted that the two homeodomains should be arranged on the operator with dyad symmetry, as suggested in Model 1. However, Model 2, where the a1 and α2 homeodomains have been arranged in tandem, accounts much more satisfactorily for the protection data. Although we cannot definitively rule out either model, we favor the second. (Data from C. Goutte.)

(indicating that the protein is folded properly and retains a number of distinct functions) but fails to collaborate with **a**1 to turn off haploid-specific genes (A. Mak and A. Johnson, unpubl.; for a point mutation with this same phenotype, see Strathern et al. 1988). Biochemical studies have revealed the nature of this defect. Although competent to bind DNA on its own and with MCM1, the truncated α2 is deficient in binding the *hsg* operator cooperatively with **a**1. Evidence from NMR studies of α2

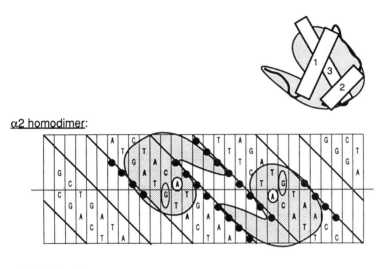

α2 homodimer:

a1α2 heterodimer:

Model 1

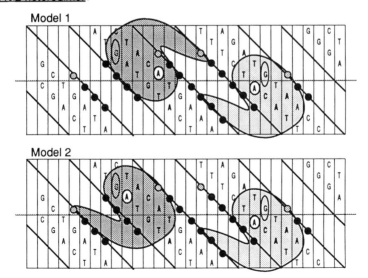

Model 2

Figure 10 (See facing page for legend.)

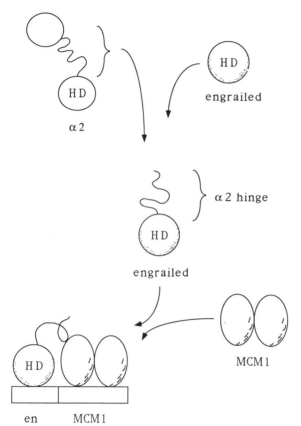

en   MCM1

Figure 11   A hinge graft experiment. The flexible hinge of α2 (amino acids 92–126; see Fig. 4) was fused to the *Drosophila* engrailed homeodomain. The hybrid protein exhibited the DNA-binding specificity of engrailed as well as the ability to bind cooperatively with MCM1, observable on an appropriately designed DNA site. (Data from A. Vershon.)

and **a**1 indicates that the carboxy-terminal tail of α2 directly contacts **a**1, even in the absence of DNA (C. Philips and F.W. Dalquist, unpubl.).

It thus appears that α2 interacts with its two accessory proteins using short, unstructured stretches of amino acids that extend immediately from its homeodomain. In both cases, these flexible stretches appear to contact a compact well-defined structure. In the case of **a**1, the recipient is the homeodomain of **a**1 itself (M. Stark and A. Johnson, unpubl.). For MCM1, the recipient is the 70-amino-acid DNA-binding domain common to both MCM1 and SRF (Primig et al. 1991; A. Vershon and A. Johnson, in prep.). Although structural information is currently unavailable for the MCM1/SRF DNA-binding domain, it seems reasonable to assume that it is also folded into a compact structure. The flexible extenders of α2 might be imagined to lie along these compact structures, making the estimated three or four attractive interactions necessary to account for the cooperative binding.

The idea that these extenders are unstructured derives from studies of the purified α2 protein. The clearest example is that of the carboxy-terminal tail, where the lack of defined structure was revealed by both X-ray crystallography (Wolberger et al. 1991) and NMR experiments (Phillips et al. 1991). For the amino-terminal extension, the evidence for the lack of a defined structure derives from protein-sensitivity experiments (Sauer et al. 1988) as well as NMR data (C. Phillips and F.W. Dalquist, unpubl.). It seems likely that, upon interaction with the appropriate partner protein (a1 or MCM1), these flexible extenders would assume an ordered configuration. The observation that MCM1 severely restricts the flexibility of the α2 dimer (see above) is consistent with this idea.

Is it possible that the flexible extender concept derived for α2 might also apply to the homeodomain proteins of higher eukaryotes? Comparisons of primary amino acid sequences of homeodomains have, in numerous cases, revealed additional sequence similarities that lie just outside the homeodomain. These sequences occupy the positions that correspond to the locations of the flexible extenders of α2. Although a detailed description of these comparisons is outside the scope of this review, two specific examples are given. First, a tetrapeptide (YPWM) occurs just upstream of the homeodomains of a number of *Drosophila* regulatory proteins including Ubx, Antp, abdA, and Dfd (Mavilio et al. 1986; Wilde and Akam 1987; Karch et al. 1990). Although this sequence is rather short and its position relative to the homeodomain differs from one protein to the next, it in principle carries sufficient information to specify an interaction with a partner protein. Second, when a given *Drosophila* homeodomain is compared with its vertebrate homolog, the amino acid similarity often extends outside the homeodomain to include the flanking regions. An example is found in the comparison of the *Drosophila* Deformed protein with the human Hox-4.2 gene (McGinnis et al. 1990). Not only are the homeodomains of the two proteins nearly identical in sequence, but the 24 amino acids immediately preceding the homeodomains are also very similar in sequence (11/24 identities including the YPWM discussed above). In addition, the sequences of the 5 amino acids directly downstream from the homeodomain are identical in the two proteins. Beyond these regions, the proteins largely diverge in sequence. It is tempting to speculate that the Deformed and Hox 4.2 proteins contact the same type of partner protein through these similar regions, an idea consistent with the observation that Hox 4.2 can provide at least some Deformed function when introduced into flies (McGinnis et al. 1990).

Finally, it may be useful to consider the problem of target specificity for the yeast homeodomain proteins from the perspective of several recent *Drosophila* studies. In some cases, the biological specificity (target gene specificity) of a given *Drosophila* homeodomain protein appears largely determined by the sequence of the homeodomain, a point established through the construction and study of chimeric proteins (Kuziora and McGinnis 1989, 1991; Gibson et al. 1990; Mann and Hogness 1990; for review, see Hayashi and Scott 1990). In other cases, target specificity, although dependent on the homeodomain, does not seem to reside solely in it. Although the directly comparable experiments have not been performed with the **a**1 and α2 homeodomain proteins from yeast, the same question can nevertheless be addressed. In the case of α2, correct target specificity requires not only the homeodomain but the amino- and carboxy-terminal flanking extenders as well. For **a**1, however, target specificity is determined largely, if not solely, by the homeodomain alone.

The mechanistic difference between these proteins can be highlighted by two points. First, α2 is able to *donate* regulatory specificity beyond the action of its homeodomain via its two flexible extenders. Second, the homeodomain of **a**1 acts as a *recipient* of one of these extenders (the carboxy-terminal). In fact, **a**1 requires the input of α2 in order to function as a competent DNA-binding domain. These studies provide a mechanistic explanation for the fact that whereas the homeodomain of one protein (**a**1) appears to determine the target specificity of that protein, the homeodomain of a second protein (α2) requires additional polypeptide determinants.

MOLECULAR EXPLANATION FOR SOME CONTEXT EFFECTS

Although the details of the α2-MCM1 interaction have already been described, it may be useful to view this example of combinatorial control from the vantage point of MCM1. As shown in Figure 12, there appear to be two context effects acting on MCM1. First, whether MCM1 acts as positive or negative regulator of transcription depends on neighboring DNA sequences that are not contacted directly by MCM1. Second, whether MCM1 acts in a positive or negative way also depends on the cell type.

The explanation for these effects is as follows. MCM1 bound to DNA *without* α2 activates transcription weakly. For example, the MCM1 recognition sequence, on its own, is capable of activating a UAS-less test

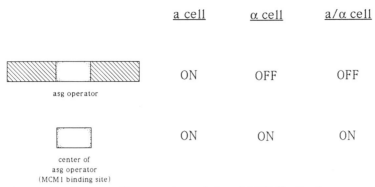

Figure 12 Context effects on the activity of MCM1. On the *asg* operator (*top* line) MCM1 formally acts as an activator in **a** cells, but a repressor in α and **a**/α cells. When the MCM1 recognition is removed from this sequence context, MCM1 acts as an activator in all three cell types (see Bender and Sprague 1987; Keleher et al. 1988).

promoter that otherwise lacks UAS activity (Bender and Sprague 1987; Keleher et al. 1988). Indeed, Kronstad et al. (1987), Elble and Tye (1991), and Hwang-Shum et al. (1991) have argued that this activation function of MCM1 is a crucial contributor to the expression of the **a**-specific genes in **a** cells. In the context of the complete *asg* operator in α cells, however, MCM1 formally becomes a repressor of transcription, because it helps recruit α2 to the operator (Fig. 13). Without MCM1, a situation that can be approximated by mutating the MCM1 binding site, α2 fails to occupy the operator because it lacks the additional 3–4 kcal/mole binding energy provided by MCM1. However, in the presence of the MCM1 recognition sequence, both proteins efficiently occupy the operator in vivo (Keleher et al. 1992).

Why does occupancy of the operator by both proteins signal repression of the linked gene? We know that α2 carries a determinant specifying repression (Fig. 13). This conclusion derives from the isolation of *negative control* (NC) mutants of α2 (Hall and Johnson 1987; K. Komachi, unpubl.). These are mutants of α2 that appear to bind normally to DNA and to MCM1 but are nevertheless defective for repression; that is, for negative control. These mutations lie at the extreme amino terminus of the α2 protein, distant from the homeodomain and the flexible hinge. Although it has not yet been rigorously established, we anticipate that these NC mutant proteins occupy the operator in vivo by binding cooperatively with MCM1, yet fail to signal repression. Consistent with this idea, overexpression of an NC mutant protein produces a dominant negative effect; that is, it causes derepression. These observa-

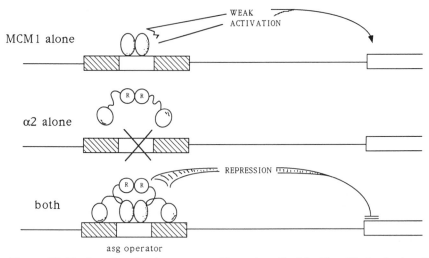

asg operator

Figure 13 Explanation for the context effects described in Fig. 12. As depicted in the top line, MCM1 on its own appears to be a weak transcriptional activator. Without MCM1 (a situation that can be approximated by mutation of the MCM1 recognition sequence), α2 does not occupy the operator, presumably because it lacks the helping effect of MCM1 (second line). With both proteins at the operator (third line), repression is signaled (at least in part) by a determinant at the amino terminus of α2 (see Johnson and Herskowitz 1985; Bender and Sprague 1987; Hall and Johnson 1987; Kronstad et al. 1987; Keleher et al. 1988; Passmore et al. 1989).

tions have led to the view that α2 carries at its amino terminus a determinant required to specify repression. This determinant is distinct from the polypeptide domains required for target site selection.

REPRESSION OF TRANSCRIPTION

Eukaryotic organisms probably employ a number of distinct mechanisms to bring about selective transcriptional repression. This interpretation was anticipated from prior studies on bacterial gene regulation which have shown that different repressors can specifically impede *different* steps in the transcription initiation pathway. For example, the cI repressor of bacteriophage λ appears to block the binding of RNA polymerase to the promoter (Hawley et al. 1985), whereas the arc repressor appears to block the transition between the closed and open complexes of RNA polymerase (W. McClure and R. Sauer, pers. comm.). Finally, the *Escherichia coli lac* repressor has been proposed to prevent release of polymerase from the open promoter complex (Straney and Crothers

1987). Examples of transcriptional repression mechanisms operative in eukaryotic organisms range from the competitive binding of repressor and activator proteins (for two of the many examples, see Barberis et al. 1987; Hoch et al. 1992) to the long-range silencing effects seen at the ends of yeast chromosomes (Gottschling et al. 1990). The repression directed by $\alpha 2$/MCM1 and $a1/\alpha 2$ seems to lie somewhere between these extremes: On the one hand, the $\alpha 2$/MCM1 operator complex does not competitively exclude the binding of activator proteins (see below). On the other hand, the complex does not appear capable of directing repression over extremely large distances along DNA. The final sections of this paper summarize the results of a number of experiments outlined to resolve the mechanistic basis of repression by the $\alpha 2$/MCM1 and $a1/\alpha 2$ complexes.

Involvement of SSN6 and TUP1

Evidence has already been presented showing that the $\alpha 2$/MCM1 and $a1/\alpha 2$ complexes are sufficient to recognize and occupy operators located upstream of, respectively, the **a**-specific genes and haploid-specific genes. However, operator occupancy is not sufficient to bring about repression. Rather, repression is effected only when two additional proteins, SSN6 and TUP1, are also present in the cell. These two proteins are present in all three cell types, and their effects on repression were first recognized from careful examination of the phenotypes produced by *ssn6* and *tup1* mutations (Schamhart et al. 1975; Lemontt et al. 1980; Rothstein and Sherman 1980; Stark et al. 1980; Carlson et al. 1984; Trumbly 1986; Schultz and Carlson 1987; Thrash-Bingham and Fangman 1989; Flick and Johnston 1990; Schultz et al. 1990; Mukai et al. 1991; Keleher et al. 1992). Mutant yeast strains lacking either SSN6 or TUP1 function show a number of different defects, including the inappropriate expression of **a**-specific genes in α and a/α cells and the inappropriate expression of haploid-specific genes in a/α cells. Such observations raised the possibility that SSN6 and TUP1 might form a corepressor complex that is recruited to various operators marked by regulatory proteins such as $\alpha 2$/MCM1 and $a1/\alpha 2$. Three additional observations are consistent with this view. First, $\alpha 2$ and MCM1 do occupy the **a**-specific gene operator in SSN6 mutants but fail to bring about repression (Keleher et al. 1992). Second, SSN6 and TUP1 physically interact, as they are components of a high-molecular-weight complex of proteins (Williams et al. 1991). Third, a LexA-SSN6 fusion protein will direct repression when bound to LexA operators, but only if TUP1 is also present (see Fig. 14 for summary) (Keleher et al. 1992). This example of

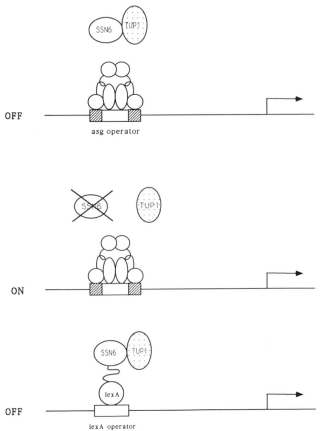

Figure 14 Summary of experiments suggesting that SSN6 and TUP1 carry out the repression directed by α2/MCM1. The top line depicts the situation in a normal α cell. α2 and MCM1 co-occupy the *asg* operator, and the target gene is repressed. The middle line summarizes the situation in an α cell that carries a null mutation in the *SSN6* gene; here, α2 and MCM1 occupy the *asg* operator, but repression is not effected. The third line indicates that SSN6, when brought to DNA by fusion with LexA, carries out repression in the absence of α2 (see Schultz and Carlson 1987; Mukai et al. 1991; Williams et al. 1991; Keleher et al. 1992).

repression does not require an *asg* operator, nor does it require α2 or, presumably, MCM1. This result suggests that the purpose of MCM1 and α2 is to recognize the *asg* operator and to recruit SSN6/TUP1. Hence, when SSN6/TUP1 is bound to DNA via fusion to LexA, α2, MCM1, and the *asg* operator become dispensable.

SSN6 and TUP1, like α2, **a**1, and MCM1, belong to extended protein families, members of which are found in many different eukaryotic organisms. SSN6 contains ten repeats of a 34-amino-acid sequence motif called the TPR (Sikorski et al. 1990; for review, see Goebl and Yanagida 1991). The function of the TPR is unknown, although it has been suggested to act as a module that facilitates specific protein-protein interactions (Hirano et al. 1990). TPR proteins in yeasts and *Drosophila* are involved in activities as diverse as chromosome separation during mitosis (CDC23, CDC16, nuc2, BimA, cut9), replication of double-stranded RNA (SKI3), neurogenesis (Crooked neck), transcriptional repression (SSN6), import of proteins into the mitochondria (MAS70), and RNA splicing (PRP6) (for review, see Goebl and Yanagida 1991 and references therein). Deletion studies have demonstrated that the TPRs are essential for SSN6 function (Schultz et al. 1990).

TUP1 contains six repeats of a 43-amino-acid domain originally identified in the β subunits of trimeric G proteins (e.g., bovine β-transducin; for review, see Simon et al. 1991). These repeats are also found in proteins involved in cell cycle regulation (CDC4), neurogenesis (Enhancer of split), and RNA splicing (PRP4) (for reviews, see Dalrymple et al. 1989; Goebl and Yanagida 1991 and references therein). The function of the β-transducin repeat is also not known; however, deletion of a single repeat eliminates TUP1 activity in vivo (Williams and Trumbly 1990). It seems remarkable that the TPR and β-transducin repeats are found in such a seemingly diverse group of proteins; it will be fascinating to learn their function.

Active Repression

The model that SSN6 and TUP1 constitute the actual repressor which is recruited to *asg* and *hsg* operators by $\alpha2$/MCM1 and **a**1/$\alpha2$ raises the question (largely semantic) as to which proteins should be called repressors. In the following sections, $\alpha2$/MCM1 and **a**1/$\alpha2$ will still be referred to as repressors with the underlying assumption that SSN6 and TUP1 act more proximal to the actual repression mechanism. Of initial concern is the question of whether this repressor complex works by excluding binding of the activator proteins to DNA. Two experimental results suggest that this is not the case. First, the *asg* operator can bring about repression when experimentally positioned in a variety of locations in a test promoter. The *asg* operator is active when located upstream of the UAS, between the UAS and TATA, or between the TATA and the start point of transcription (Johnson and Herskowitz 1985; M. Redd and A. Johnson, unpubl.). In each of these cases, the *asg* operator was inserted into nonessential parts of the promoter; that is, no effect of the inserted operator was observed in cells that lacked $\alpha2$ (i.e., **a** cells). A second experimental point relevant to the mechanism of repression is based on the behavior of the two artificial promoters shown in Figure 15. Each contains a single GAL4-binding site (Giniger et al. 1985) and a single *asg* operator, but the order of these elements has been reversed in the two cases. As indicated in Figure 15, both promoters are activated by GAL4. When the activator (GAL4) and the repressor (α2/MCM1) are both present in the cell, however, both promoters are strongly repressed. Dimethyl sulfate (DMS) protection experiments carried out in vivo (Church and Gilbert 1984; Giniger et al. 1985) revealed that GAL4 remains bound to its recognition sequences even when the two promoters are in the repressed state (M. Redd and A. Johnson, unpubl.). At least for these two cases, very strong repression is effected without displacing the activator GAL4.

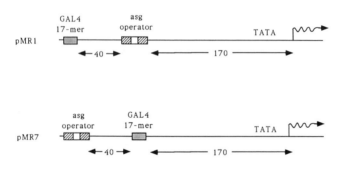

	pMR1	pMR7
MATα	2	88
matΔ	2500	3900
MATα gal4::LEU2	2	2
matΔ gal4::LEU2	220	30

Figure 15 Artificial promoters used to show that α2/MCM1 does not repress transcription by displacing the activator (GAL4) from DNA. Both promoters are fused to the *E. coli lacZ* gene, and the promoter activities listed at the bottom right are expressed as units of β-galactosidase. When both repressor and activator are present in the cell (the *MATα* cell, top line), the promoters are both repressed. DMS protection experiments performed in vivo (Church and Gilbert 1984) revealed that, under these conditions, GAL4 remains bound to its recognition site. (Data from M. Redd.)

Repression and RNA Polymerases I, II, and III

The known target genes for α2/MCM1- and a1/α2-directed repression are transcribed by RNA polymerase II. A set of artificial promoters was designed (B. Herschbach and A. Johnson, in prep.) to test whether repression by α2/MCM1 might also act on genes transcribed by the other two forms of polymerase in yeast; RNA polymerase I transcribes 35S ribosomal RNA genes, and RNA polymerase III transcribes tRNA and 5S RNA genes. Indeed, α2/MCM1 efficiently represses the 35S rRNA gene when the *asg* operator is placed approximately 200 bp upstream of the start point. (Insertion of the operator had no effect in cells that lack α2.) An indication that this repression reflects the authentic mechanism is the fact that it is dependent on SSN6 and TUP1. In contrast, α2/MCM1 did not repress a pol-III-transcribed gene (*SNR6*) when similar artificial promoters were constructed. Although this negative result is difficult to interpret, it was found that α2/MCM1 was bound to its operator in this experiment. It may be useful to point out that the long-range silencing mediated by the yeast *SIR* genes, which is thought to entail large-scale changes in chromatin structure, *does* turn off a pol-III-transcribed gene (Schnell and Rine 1986). Perhaps the inability of α2/MCM1 to repress this class of genes reflects an important difference in the mechanisms by which α2/MCM1- and SIR-mediated repression occur.

Models for Repression by α2/MCM1 and a1/α2

Many questions remain unresolved with regard to the roles of SSN6 and TUP1 in repression. It is useful, despite the uncertainties, to consider a few possible models for repression.

1. Nucleosome positioning. Roth et al. (1992) have shown that when α2/MCM1 is bound to the *asg* operator, nucleosomes around the operator become selectively positioned. On the basis of such observations, it has been proposed that a nucleosome positioned over the TATA sequence is responsible for repression. This model is consistent with many of the observations described herein. However, several results are, at least on the surface, difficult to reconcile with it. First, as described above, the *asg* operator can efficiently repress transcription when positioned upstream of a GAL4-binding site; under repressed conditions, GAL4 remains bound. According to the positioning model, GAL4 would be bound to DNA that is folded into a nucleosome. Although Taylor et al. (1991) have shown that this is possible (that is, GAL4 can occupy a binding site that is wrapped

around a nucleosome), the affinity of GAL4 for its site when incorporated into a nucleosome is substantially reduced from that in naked DNA. Second, Roth et al. (1992) have shown that mutations in the amino-terminal arm of histone H4 disrupt specific nucleosome positioning around the *asg* operator, yet produce only small effects on repression of **a**-specific genes. Although it is likely that nucleosome positioning contributes to the overall efficiency of repression, it would appear that at least one other mechanism is also involved.

2. Direct interaction with the transcription machinery. An economical way for short-range repressors like α2/MCM1 and **a**1/α2 to work would be to block the assembly of the transcription complex at one or more steps that must form at a promoter prior to the initiation of transcription (see Buratowski and Sharp, this volume). Although the nucleosome positioning model would in principle provide a block to the first step in this pathway (binding of TFIID to the TATA element), it is possible that SSN6/TUP1, once directed to the operator by α2/MCM1 or **a**1/α2, might interact directly with a component of the basic transcription machinery so as to effectively block later assembly steps. As described above, SSN6 and TUP1 both contain numerous repeated motifs that seem likely to mediate protein-protein interactions. Perhaps these repeats are capable of interacting with specific components of the transcription machinery, thus causing a specific clog in the transcription assembly process. According to this idea, MCM1/α2 and **a**1/α2 would direct SSN6/TUP1 to locations sufficiently near target promoters to allow such an interaction to occur.

3. Masking of the activator. As a third model, the DNA-bound repressor could interact with the activation surface of a DNA-bound activator, thereby masking its function. It is known that a single operator can bring about repression of a promoter activated by several UAS elements (Johnson and Herskowitz 1985; M. Redd and A. Johnson, unpubl.). Perhaps the multiple repeat motifs of SSN6 and TUP1 serve to simultaneously mask many activation surfaces.

It is emphasized that these three models are not mutually exclusive, and it is possible that more than one will turn out to be required for complete repression by α2/MCM1 and **a**1/α2.

SPECULATIONS ON THE ORIGINS OF THE YEAST MATING TYPE CIRCUITRY

Homeodomain proteins are often used in regulatory circuits that are involved in specifying cell identity (for review, see Gehring 1987). Striking examples of this specificational role have recently been described for the basidiomycetes *Ustilago maydis*, *Coprinus cinereus*, and *Schizophyllum commune* (for reviews, see Banuett 1992; Kues and Casselton 1992). For all three fungi, the mating of two haploids brings into the same cell a key pair of homeodomain proteins, one member of which is donated by each haploid cell. If the members of the homeodomain pair are compatible (one requirement for compatibility is that they be from nonidentical alleles), the dikaryon is able to differentiate. Although more complex, these circuits are reminiscent of that in *S. cerevisiae*, where the mating of an **a** cell with an α cell brings together the homeodomain proteins **a**1 and α2 (Fig. 1). An important distinction between *S. cerevisiae* and the basidiomycetes, however, lies in the number of pairwise combinations of homeodomain proteins that can signal the dikaryon to differentiate. For example, in *U. maydis*, the crucial homeodomain pair is composed of one member from the bE gene and one from the bW gene (Gillissen et al. 1992). At least 25 different bE-encoded and 25 different bW-encoded homeodomain proteins are known, resulting in over 600 pairwise combinations, most, but not all, of which are compatible and trigger further development. It remains to be seen how this remarkable phenomenon is accounted for mechanistically and how similar the situation is to that described for **a**1 and α2.

These results from the basidiomycetes do suggest that homeodomain proteins are particularly well-suited to act in specific pairwise combinations with other homeodomain proteins. On the basis of this idea, it is tempting to speculate that the **a**1/α2 combination is the most conserved feature of the yeast circuitry of Figure 1. Certainly the **a**/α diploid–which is specified by the **a**1/α2 combination–displays properties quite distinct from those of the two haploids, which in many respects resemble each other. The union of **a**1 and α2 by mating requires that **a**1 already be expressed in **a** cells and α2 in α cells. Perhaps this situation was exploited during evolution as a means of further distinguishing the phenotypic properties of the two types of haploids. In principle, either **a**1 or α2 could suffice for this purpose; according to this line of speculation, the role seems to have gone to α2. It is possible to further imagine that since α2 evolved to work in combination with **a**1, it could not act on its own but, instead, would require a second protein present in α cells. This protein need not have been specific to α cells, and MCM1, a protein involved in a number of regulatory circuits in yeast (see, e.g., Lydall et al. 1991), appears to have been utilized. As described in previous sections, the ability of α2 to interact with MCM1 requires only the α2 flexible extender; this design would presumably allow for relatively facile reshuffling of modules during evolution.

Although this hypothetical scenario is offered with the requisite severe disclaimers and caveats, it may be a useful way of imagining how a regulatory circuit specifying cell type makes use of both cell-type-specific and ubiquitous DNA-binding proteins. It may also be of use in attempting to rationalize the widespread occurrence of combinatorial regulatory networks that utilize homeodomain proteins.

ACKNOWLEDGMENTS

I thank the past and present members of the laboratory–Burk Braun, Caroline Goutte, Brenda Herschbach, Nancy Hollingsworth, Cindy Keleher, Kelly Komachi, Arkady Mak, Michael Redd, Dana Smith, Martha Stark, Drew Vershon, and Madhu Wahi–for generating many of the ideas and experimental results discussed in this article and for commenting critically on the manuscript. Ira Herskowitz and Flora Banuett gave valuable suggestions for improving the manuscript. I am especially grateful to Steve McKnight for his insightful criticisms and his many superb editorial suggestions. I also thank Mary Jo Kelley for timely help in preparing the text and Dana Smith and Kelly Komachi for drawing most of the figures. Work from the author's laboratory was supported by grants from the National Institutes of Health and the Pew Scholars Program.

REFERENCES

Alberts, B., D. Bray, J. Lewis, M. Raff, K. Roberts, and J.D. Watson. 1989. *Molecular biology of the cell*, 2nd edition. Garland, New York.

Ammerer, G. 1990. Identification, purification, and cloning of a polypeptide (PRTF/GRM) that binds to mating-specific promoter elements in yeast. *Genes Dev.* **4:** 299–312.

Banuett, F. 1992. *Ustilago maydis*, the delightful blight. *Trends Genet.* **8:** 174–180.

Barberis, A., G. Superti-Furga, and M. Busslinger. 1987. Mutually exclusive interaction of the CCAAT-binding factor and of a displacement protein with overlapping sequences of a histone gene promoter. *Cell* **50:** 347–359.

Bender, A. and G.F. Sprague, Jr. 1987. MATα1 protein, a yeast transcription factor, binds synergistically with a second protein to a set of cell-type specific genes. *Cell* **50:** 681–691.

Carlson, M., B.C. Osmond, L. Neigeborn, and D. Botstein. 1984. A suppressor of *SNF1* mutations causes constitutive high-level invertase synthesis in yeast. *Genetics* **107:** 19–32.

Church, G.M. and W. Gilbert. 1984. Genomic sequencing. *Proc. Natl. Acad. Sci.* **81:** 1991–1995.

Dalrymple, M.A., S. Petersen-Bjorn, J.D. Friesen, and J.D. Beggs. 1989. The product of the *PRP4* gene of *S. cerevisiae* shows homology to β subunits of G proteins. *Cell* **58:** 811–812.

Dolan, J.W. and S. Fields. 1991. Cell-type-specific transcription in yeast. *Biochim. Biophys. Acta* **1088:** 155–169.

Dranginis, A.M. 1990. Binding of yeast **a**1 and α2 as a heterodimer to the operator DNA of a haploid-specific gene. *Nature* **347:** 682–685.

Elble, R. and B.K. Tye. 1991. Both activation and repression of α-mating-type-specific genes in yeast require transcription factor MCM1. *Proc. Natl. Acad. Sci.* **88:** 10966–10970.

Flick, J.S. and M. Johnston. 1990. Two systems of glucose repression of the *GAL1* promoter in *Saccharomyces cerevisiae. Mol. Cell. Biol.* **10:** 4757–4769.

Gehring, W.J. 1987. Homeo boxes in the study of development. *Science* **236:** 1245–1252.

Gehring, W.J., M. Muller, M. Affolter, A. Percival-Smith, M. Billeter, Y.Q. Qian, G. Otting, and K. Wüthrich. 1990. The structure of the homeodomain and its functional implications. *Trends Genet.* **6:** 323–329.

Gibson, G., A. Schier, P. LeMotte, and W.J. Gehring. 1990. The specificities of sex combs reduced and Antennapedia are defined by a distinct portion of each protein that includes the homeodomain. *Cell* **62:** 1087–1103.

Gillissen, B., J. Bergemann, C. Sandmann, B. Schroeer, M. Bolker, and R. Kahmann. 1992. A two-component regulatory system for self/non-self recognition in *Ustilago maydis. Cell* **68:** 647–657.

Giniger, E., S. Varnum, and M. Ptashne. 1985. Specific DNA binding of GAL4, a positive regulatory protein of yeast. *Cell* **40:** 767–774.

Goebl, M. and M. Yanagida. 1991. The TPR snap helix: A novel protein repeat from mitosis to transcription. *Trends Biochem. Sci.* **16:** 173–177.

Gottschling, D.E., O.M. Aparicio, B.L. Billington, and V.A. Zakian. 1990. Position effect at *S. cerevisiae* telomeres: Reversible repression of Pol II transcription. *Cell* **63:** 751–762.

Goutte, C. and A.D. Johnson. 1988. **a**1 protein alters the DNA binding specificity of α2 repressor. *Cell* **52:** 875–882.

Guarente L., B. Lalonde, P. Gifford, and E. Alani. 1984. Distinctly regulated tandem upstream activation sites mediate catabolite repression of the *CYC1* gene of *S. cerevisiae. Cell* **36:** 503–511.

Hall, M.N. and A.D. Johnson. 1987. Homeodomain of the yeast repressor α2 is a sequence-specific DNA-binding domain but is not sufficient for repression. *Science* **237:** 1007–1012.

Hawley, D.K., A.D. Johnson, and W.R. McClure. 1985. Functional and physical characterization of transcription initiation complexes in the bacteriophage λ O_r region. *J. Biol. Chem.* **260:** 8618–8626.

Hayashi, S. and M.P. Scott. 1990. What determines the specificity of action of *Drosophila* homeodomain proteins? *Cell* **63:** 883–894.

Herskowitz, I. 1989. A regulatory hierarchy for cell specialization in yeast. *Nature* **342:** 749–757.

Hirano, T., N. Kinoshita, K. Morikawa, and M. Yanagida. 1990. Snap helix with knob and hole: Essential repeats in *S. pombe* nuclear protein nuc2⁺. *Cell* **60:** 319–328.

Hoch, M., N. Gerwin, H. Taubert, and H. Jackle. 1992. Competition for overlapping sites in the regulatory region of the *Drosophila* gene *Kruppel. Science* **256:** 94–97.

Hwang-Shum, J.J., D.C. Hagen, E.E. Jarvis, C.A. Westby, and G.F. Sprague, Jr. 1991. Relative contributions of MCM1 and STE12 to transcriptional activation of **a**- and α-specific genes from *S. cerevisiae. Mol. Gen. Genet.* **227:** 197–204.

Jarvis, E.E., K.L. Clark, and G.F. Sprague, Jr. 1989. The yeast transcription activator PRTF, a homolog of the mammalian serum response factor, is encoded by the *MCM1* gene. *Genes Dev.* **3:** 936–945.

Jobe, A., J.R. Sadler, and S. Bourgeois. 1974. *lac* Repressor–operator interaction. IX. The binding of *lac* repressor to operators containing O^c mutations. *J. Mol. Biol.* **85:** 231–248.

Johnson, A.D. and I. Herskowitz. 1985. A repressor (MATα2 product) and its operator control expression of a set of cell-type-specific genes in yeast. *Cell* **42:** 237–247.

Johnson, A.D., B.J. Meyer, and M. Ptashne. 1979. Interactions between DNA-bound repressors govern regulation by the λ phage repressor. *Proc. Natl. Acad. Sci.* **76:** 5061–5065.

Karch, F., W. Bender, and B. Weiffenbach. 1990. *abdA* expression in *Drosophila* embryos. *Genes Dev.* **4:** 1573–1587.

Keleher, C.A., C. Goutte, and A.D. Johnson. 1988. The yeast cell-type-specific repressor α2 acts cooperatively with a non-cell-type-specific protein. *Cell* **53:** 927–936.

Keleher, C.A., S. Passmore, and A.D. Johnson. 1989. Yeast repressor α2 binds to its operator cooperatively with yeast protein Mcm1. *Mol. Cell. Biol.* **9:** 5228–5230.

Keleher, C.A., M.J. Redd, J. Schultz, M. Carlson, and A.D. Johnson. 1992. SSN6-TUP1 is a general repressor of transcription in yeast. *Cell* **68:** 709–719.

Kissinger, C.R., B. Liu, E. Martin-Blonco, T.B. Kornberg, and C.O. Pabo. 1990. Crystal structure of an engrailed homeodomain-DNA complex at 2-8Å resolution: A framework for understanding homoeodomain-DNA interactions. *Cell* **63:** 579–590.

Kronstad, J.W., J.A. Holly, and V.L. MacKay. 1987. A yeast operator overlaps an upstream activation site. *Cell* **50:** 369–377.

Kues, U. and L.A. Casselton. 1992. Homeodomains and regulation of sexual development in basidiomycetes. *Trends Genet.* **8:** 154–155.

Kuziora, M.A. and W. McGinnis. 1989. A homeodomain substitution changes the regulatory specificity of the Deformed protein in *Drosophila* embryos. *Cell* **59:** 563–571.

———. 1991. Altering the target specificity of the Deformed protein in *Drosophila* embryos by substituting the abdominal-β homeodomain. *Mech. Dev.* **33:** 83–94.

Laughon, A. and M.P. Scott. 1984. The sequence of a *Drosophila* segmentation gene: Protein structure homology with DNA binding proteins. *Nature* **310:** 25–30.

Lemontt, J.F., D.R. Fugit, and V.L. MacKay. 1980. Pleiotropic mutations at the *TUP1* locus that affect the expression of mating-type-dependent functions in *Saccharomyces cerevisiae. Genetics* **94:** 899–920.

Lydall, D., G. Ammerer, and K. Nasmyth. 1991. A new role for MCM1 in yeast: Cell cycle regulation of SW15 transcription. *Genes Dev.* **5:** 2405–2419.

Mann, R.S. and D.S. Hogness. 1990. Functional dissection of Ultrabithorax proteins in *D. melanogaster. Cell* **60:** 597–610.

Mavilio, G., A. Simeone, A. Giampaolo, A. Faiella, V. Zappavigna, D. Acampora, G. Poiana, G. Russo, C. Peschle, and E. Boncinelli. 1986. Differential and stage-related expression in embryonic tissues of a new human homeobox gene. *Nature* **324:** 664–668.

McGinnis, N., M.A. Kuziora, and W. McGinnis. 1990. Human Hox-4.2 and *Drosophila* Deformed encode similar regulatory specificities in *Drosophila* embryos and larvae. *Cell* **63:** 969–976.

Miller, A.M., V.L. MacKay, and K.A. Nasmyth. 1985. Identification and comparison of two sequence elements that confer cell-type transcription in yeast. *Nature* **314:** 598–603.

Mukai, Y., S. Harashima, and Y. Oshima. 1991. AAR1/TUP1 protein, with a structure similar to that of the β subunit of G proteins, is required for **a**1/α2 and α2 repression in cell type control of *Saccharomyces cerevisiae. Mol. Cell. Biol.* 11: 3773–3779.

Norman, C., M. Runswick, R. Pollock, and R. Treisman. 1988. Isolation and properties of cDNA clones encoding *SRF*, a transcription factor that binds to the *c-fos* serum response element. *Cell* 55: 989–1003.

Passmore, S., R. Elble, and B.K. Tye. 1989. A protein involved in minichromosome maintenance in yeast binds a transcriptional enhancer conserved in eukaryotes. *Genes Dev.* 3: 921–935.

Phillips, C.L., A.K. Vershon, A.D. Johnson, and F.W. Dahlquist. 1991. Secondary structure of the homeodomain of yeast α2 repressor determined by NMR spectroscopy. *Genes Dev.* 5: 764–772.

Primig, M., H. Winkler, and G. Ammerer. 1991. The DNA binding and oligomerization domain of MCM1 is sufficient for its interaction with other regulatory proteins. *EMBO J.* 10: 4209–4218.

Quian, Y.Q., M. Billeter, G. Otting, M. Mueller, W.J. Gehring, and K. Wüthrich. 1989. The structure of antennapedia homeodomain determined by NMR spectroscopy in solution: Comparison with prokaryotic repressons. *Cell* 59: 573–580.

Roth, S.Y., M. Shimizu, L. Johnson, M. Grunstien, and R.T. Simpson. 1992. Stable nucleosome positioning and complete repression by the yeast α2 repressor are disrupted by amino-terminal mutations in histone H4. *Genes Dev.* 6: 411–425.

Rothstein, R.J. and F. Sherman. 1980. Genes affecting the expression of cytochrome *c* in yeast: Genetic mapping and genetic interactions. *Genetics* 94: 871–889.

Sauer, R.T., D.L. Smith, and A.D. Johnson. 1988. Flexibility of the yeast α2 repressor enables it to occupy the ends of its operator, leaving the center free. *Genes Dev.* 2: 807–816.

Schamhart, D.H.J., A.M.A. Ten Berge, and K.W. Van De Poll. 1975. Isolation of a catabolite repression mutant of yeast as a revertant of a strain that is maltose negative in the respiratory-deficient state. *J. Bacteriol.* 121: 747–752.

Schnell, R. and J. Rine. 1986. A position effect on the expression of a tRNA gene mediated by the SIR genes in *Saccharomyces cerevisiae. Mol. Cell. Biol.* 6: 494–501.

Schultz, J. and M. Carlson. 1987. Molecular analysis of *SSN6*, a gene functionally related to the *SNF1* protein kinase of *Saccharomyces cerevisiae. Mol. Cell. Biol.* 7: 3637–3645.

Schultz, J., L. Marshall-Carlson, and M. Carlson. 1990. The N-terminal TPR region is the functional domain of *SSN6*, a nuclear phosphoprotein of *Saccharomyces cerevisiae. Mol. Cell. Biol.* 10: 4744–4756.

Scott, M.P., J.W. Tamkun, and G.W. Hartzell. 1989. The structure and function of the homeodomain. *Biochim. Biophys. Acta* 989: 25–48.

Shepherd, J.C.W., W. McGinnis, A.E. Carrasco, E.M. DeRobertis, and W.J. Gehring. 1984. Fly and frog homeo domains show homologies with yeast mating type regulatory proteins. *Nature* 310: 70–71.

Sikorski, R.S., M.S. Boguski, M. Goebl, and P. Hieter. 1990. A repeating amino acid motif in CDC23 defines a family of proteins and a new relationship among genes required for mitosis and RNA synthesis. *Cell* 60: 307–317.

Siliciano, P.G. and K. Tatchell. 1986. Identification of the DNA sequences controlling the expression of the *MATα* locus of yeast. *Proc. Natl. Acad. Sci.* 83: 2320–2324.

Simon, M.I., M.P. Strathmann, and N. Gautam. 1991. Diversity of G proteins in signal transduction. *Science* 252: 802–808.

Smith, D.L. and A.D. Johnson. 1992. A molecular mechanism for combinatorial control in yeast; MCM1 protein sets the spacing and orientation of the homeodomains of an α2 dimer. *Cell* 68: 133–142.

Sprague, G.F., Jr. 1990. Combinatorial associations of regulatory proteins and the control of cell type in yeast. *Adv. Genet.* **27:** 33–62.

Stark, H.C., D. Fugit, and D.B. Mowshowitz. 1980. Pleiotropic properties of a yeast mutant insensitive to catabolite repression. *Genetics* **94:** 921–928.

Straney, S.B. and D.M. Crothers. 1987. Lac repressor is a transient gene-activating protein. *Cell* **51:** 699–707.

Strathern, J.N., J. Hicks, and I. Herskowitz. 1981. Control of cell type in yeast by the mating type locus: The α1-α2 hypothesis. *J. Mol. Biol.* **147:** 357–372.

Strathern, J.N., B. Shafer, J. Hicks, and C. McGill. 1988. a/α-specific repression by MATα2. *Genetics* **120:** 75–81.

Taylor, I.C.A., J.L. Workman, T.J. Schuetz, and R.E. Kingston. 1991. Facilitated binding of GAL4 and heat shock factor to nucleosomal templates: Differential function of DNA-binding domains. *Genes Dev.* **5:** 1285–1298.

Thrash-Bingham, C. and W.L. Fangman. 1989. A yeast mutation that stabilizes a plasmid bearing a mutated *ARS1* element. *Mol. Cell. Biol.* **9:** 809–816.

Trumbly, R.J. 1986. Isolation of *Saccharomyces cerevisiae* mutants constitutive for invertase synthesis. *J. Bacteriol.* **166:** 1123–1127.

Wilde, C.D. and M. Akam. 1987. Conserved sequence elements in the 5′ region of the *Ultrabithorax* transcription unit. *EMBO J.* **6:** 1393–1401.

Williams, F.E. and R.J. Trumbly. 1990. Characterization of TUP1, a mediator of glucose repression in *Saccharomyces cerevisiae. Mol. Cell. Biol.* **10:** 6500–6511.

Williams, F.E., U. Varanasi, and R.J. Trumbly. 1991. The CYC8 and TUP1 proteins involved in glucose repression in *Saccharomyces cerevisiae* are associated in a protein complex. *Mol. Cell. Biol.* **11:** 3307–3316.

Wolberger, C., A.K. Vershon, B. Liu, A.D. Johnson, and C.O. Pabo. 1991. Crystal structure of a MATα2 homeodomain-operator complex suggests a general model for homeodomain-DNA interactions. *Cell* **67:** 517–528.

38

Mechanism and Regulation of Transcriptional Activation in Eukaryotes: Conserved Features from Yeasts to Humans

Leonard Guarente
Department of Biology
Massachusetts Institute of Technology
Cambridge, Massachusetts 02139

OVERVIEW

The mechanism of transcriptional initiation of protein-coding genes is remarkably conserved in eukaryotic organisms ranging from yeast to humans. Yeast transcriptional activators can function in mammalian cells, and mammalian activators can work in yeast. This conservation is reflected in the common functional properties of *cis*-acting elements of eukaryotic promoters, the TATA box and upstream activation sites, and in the factors that bind to these sites (TFIID and transcriptional activators). Yeast TFIID, as well as certain yeast activators, has stringently conserved homologs in mammals. The major thrust of studies described in this chapter is to employ yeast genetics and biochemistry to address central questions relating to eukaryotic transcription. First, what is the mechanism by which transcriptional activators function at a distance? Recent experiments have prompted us to propose the existence of adapters that bridge the interaction between activators bound at UASs and TFIID (and the other general factors) bound at or near the TATA box. Second, how have the functional properties of a particular activator been altered over evolution? The HAP2/3/4 heteromeric complex that binds to the CCAAT box has been the focus of this study. Third, how do signal transduction pathways influence the activity of transcriptional activators? Regulation of HAP1 activity by heme and by its cognate DNA sequence provides a model to study aspects of gene control that may relate to other systems, including the steroid hormone receptors.

Transcriptional Regulation.
Copyright 1992 Cold Spring Harbor Laboratory Press 0-87969-410-6/92 $3 + 00

INTRODUCTION

A central and intriguing problem in eukaryotic biology is how gene transcription can be activated by regulatory DNA sequences that lie hundreds or thousands of base pairs from the promoter. These long-range regulatory elements, termed enhancers, were originally identified in the form of the 72-bp repeats that occur upstream of the early promoter region of the SV40 virus. The SV40 enhancer, when placed upstream or downstream from a heterologous promoter, was found to augment the accumulation of correctly initiated RNA (Banerji et al. 1981; Moreau and Chambon 1981). Whether enhancers exerted their effects on the promoter directly by increasing the rate of transcription initiation, or indirectly, for example, by altering the subcellular localization of DNA, was not evident from these early experiments.

In subsequent studies, it was found that other, well-characterized regulatory sites met the basic definition of the enhancer, i.e., distance and orientation-independent function, as well as ability to stimulate a heterologous promoter. These sites include the GAL4 regulatory region (termed the upstream activation site or UAS) located in the GAL1–10 cluster of *Saccharomyces cerevisiae* (Guarente et al. 1982), the glucocorticoid responsive element (GRE) of mouse mammary tumor virus, which responds to hormone-mediated transcriptional activation via the glucocorticoid receptor (Chandler et al. 1983), and the HIS4 UAS of *S. cerevisiae* which binds GCN4 (Hinnebusch et al. 1985; Hope and Struhl 1986). The novel aspect of the latter observations was that the activity of the enhancer or UAS sites was mediated by previously known transcriptional regulatory proteins. Thus, models for enhancer activity that proposed activation by transcriptional activator proteins became a primary focus of attention.

An important conceptual advance in our understanding of eukaryotic regulatory proteins came from the observation that they contain distinct domains for DNA binding and transcriptional activation. In particular, GAL4 could be separated into a domain that bound specifically to the UAS sequence element and a domain that could activate transcription when attached to a "neutral" DNA-binding domain, that of the bacterial repressor, LexA (Brent and Ptashne 1985). The transcriptional activation domains of both GAL4 and GCN4 were found to have a high content of acidic residues (Ma and Ptashne 1987a; Hope and Struhl 1986). Various experiments have indicated that some structural component is required in addition to net negative charge (Giniger and Ptashne 1987; Hope et al. 1988). In the cases of several mammalian transcriptional activators, identified by protein purification, nonacidic motifs predominate within activation domains. Sp1 bears a glutamine-rich activation domain (Courey and Tjian 1988; see also Courey and Tjian, this volume), whereas CTF/NF1 contains a region enriched in proline residues that is required for its role in transcriptional activation (Mermod et al. 1989).

Finally, the existence of a universal mechanism of transcriptional activation came from the observations that yeast activators function in mammalian cells (for review, see Guarente 1988; Kakidani and Ptashne et al. 1988; Webster et al. 1988), plant cells (Ma et al. 1988), and fruit flies (Fischer et al. 1988), and that certain mammalian activators function in yeast (Metzger et al. 1988; Schena and Yamamoto 1988).

How, then, do activators influence transcription at distantly located sites of transcription initiation? We must first consider that the transcription reaction requires a set of "general transcription factors" for both basal and activated transcription (Matsui et al. 1980; Samuels et al. 1982). The critical promoter element that governs the activity of these general factors is the TATA box, which lies close to the initiation site (Benoist and Chambon 1981). The TATA box is bound most immediately by one of the general factors termed TFIID (Sawadogo and Roeder 1985). Subsequent to the binding of TFIID, an ordered pathway of assembly occurs primarily through protein-protein and nonspecific protein-DNA interactions (Van Dyke et al. 1988; Buratowski et al. 1989; see also Buratowski and Sharp, this volume).

It has been proposed that the activation surface of a DNA-bound activator transmits a signal from the enhancer to the promoter via the general machinery. Various concepts have been outlined to describe this communication. Perhaps the most appealing is the suggestion that direct protein-protein contact is made between the activation surface of a DNA-bound activator and one of the general factors, thereby looping out intervening DNA (for review, see Ptashne 1986, 1988). This interaction has been postulated to facilitate a rate-limiting step in the assembly of the general factors at the TATA box. Alternatively, activators may serve as entry sites for the binding of one of the general factors to the DNA template. Finally, activators may act to prevent the promoter from being occluded by nucleosomes (Han and Grunstein 1989; Workman et al. 1991; see also Grunstein et al.; Winston; both this volume). Clearly, an identification of the direct target of activation surfaces would provide a key breakthrough in our understanding of the mechanism of enhancer function. Early studies from Roeder and colleagues showed that bound activators could alter the DNase footprint at the TATA box (Sawadogo and Roeder 1985; Horikoshi et al. 1988). It was suggested that this alteration was due to an interaction between the activator and TFIID, present in the crude mammalian fraction that was used in footprinting reactions. Recent experiments, to be discussed below, have provided evidence both for and against a direct interaction between an acidic activator and TFIID.

This chapter is organized into two broad sections. In the first section, I outline experiments conducted in our laboratory aimed at understanding the mechanism of transcriptional activation. In this section, I discuss molecular studies on TFIID from yeast and other eukaryotes. Recent studies on this topic provide evidence that the target for acidic activators is not one of the general factors, but an adapter that bridges the interaction with the general machinery. In the second section, I discuss our studies on a specific set of yeast activators which reveal three distinct ways in which cells regulate the activity of transcriptional regulatory proteins. These modes of regulation will be related to other, more complex systems of transcriptional regulation.

MECHANISM OF TRANSCRIPTIONAL ACTIVATION

The fact that yeast activators work in mammalian cells and mammalian activators work in yeast qualifies the microbe as an excellent system in which to dissect the general mechanisms of eukaryotic transcriptional activation. Although gene-specific activator proteins have been purified, cloned, sequenced, and are available in large quantities, the factors of the general machinery have remained more elusive. The exception was the multisubunit RNA polymerase II (RNA pol II), which has been purified from both yeast and mammalian cells (see Sentenac et al., this volume). In fact, the sequences of the large subunit of RNA polymerase from yeast and mammals reveal that the proteins are very similar to each other and to the β subunit of the *Escherichia coli* enzyme (Allison et al. 1985; Corden et al. 1985; Sweetser et al. 1987; Corden and Ingles; Greenleaf; Dahmus and Dynan; all this volume). The largest subunit of eukaryotic RNA pol II, unlike its bacterial counterpart, contains a repeated sequence at its carboxyl terminus consisting of $PTSPSYS_{26}$ in the yeast subunit (Allison et al. 1985, 1988) and $PTSPSYS_{52}$ in the human subunit (Corden et al. 1985). This carboxyl tail is not found in the large subunit of RNA pol III, which is otherwise similar in sequence (Sweetser et al. 1987). Although the role of the repeat sequence in RNA pol II transcription is not known, the tail is essential for cell viability, and it has been suggested that it may interact with gene-specific activator proteins (Allison and Ingles 1989; Scafe et al. 1990).

TFIID

To begin an analysis of the activation mechanism, we set out to identify the key general factor, TFIID, from *S. cerevisiae*. When the mammalian fraction containing TFIID is omitted from an in vitro transcription reaction, initiation is abolished (Matsui et al. 1980; Samuels et al. 1982). Our approach was to complement this TFIID-depleted reaction with yeast extracts in order to identify a possible yeast functional counterpart. Although the crude yeast extract was inhibitory to the complete in vitro reaction, fractionation of the yeast extract over heparin agarose removed the inhibitor and unmasked a TFIID-complementing activity (Buratowski et al. 1988; Cavallini et al. 1989). The yeast factor was purified using this assay and found to comprise a 25-kD polypeptide that bound specifically to the TATA box.

Partial amino acid sequence derived from the purified yeast TFIID protein facilitated the cloning of the gene (Cavallini et al. 1989; Eisenmann et al. 1989; Hahn et al. 1989a; Horikoshi et al. 1989; Schmidt et al. 1989). The sequence of TFIID is significant in that the carboxyl 180 residues of the 240-amino-acid protein comprise one large direct repeat of a 90-amino-acid sequence (Fig. 1). Interestingly, the sequences of the *TFIID* gene and another cloned gene, *SPT15*, were found to be identical (Eisenmann et al. 1989; Hahn et al. 1989a). Mutations in *SPT15* (*TFIID*) can alter the site of mRNA initiation and thereby suppress the effects of TY1 insertion mutations in yeast promoters (Winston et al. 1984). These findings provide the first evidence that TFIID, identified by an in vitro activity, plays a key role in initiation in vivo (see Winston, this volume).

The cloning of *TFIID* from *S. cerevisiae* provided a direct means of isolating the corresponding gene from other eukaryotes. Approaches based on nucleic acid homologies were used to isolate the gene from *Schizosaccharomyces pombe* (Hoffmann et al. 1990a), *Drosophila melanogaster* (Hoey et al. 1990), *Arabidopsis thaliana* (Gasch et al. 1990), and *Homo sapiens* (Hoffmann et al. 1990b; Kao et al. 1990; Peterson et al. 1990). We employed a functional complementation assay to

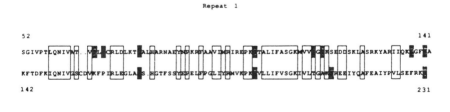

Figure 1 Direct repeats in TFIID. The two repeats of the *S. pombe* protein between residues 52 and 231 are aligned with identical or conserved positions boxed. Positions where the *S. cerevisiae* TFIID differs from *S. pombe* are shaded and are found outside the repeated residues.

isolate the gene from *S. pombe* (Fikes et al. 1990). In this approach, cDNA libraries were constructed in yeast expression vectors using RNA isolated either from *S. pombe* or HeLa cells. Clones that complemented the spt15 defect were obtained from *S. pombe* but not from the HeLa cell source. More recent studies indicate that the human TFIID does not function in *S. cerevisiae* (Cormack et al. 1991; Gill and Tjian 1991). The sequences of all the TFIID clones isolated by either approach reveal a very high degree of sequence similarity in the direct repeat segments of the respective proteins, yet divergence in the amino-terminal regions. The *S. cerevisiae* and *S. pombe* protein sequences, for example, are 93% identical across the repeats, yet are not recognizably related in the respective amino-terminal regions. Mutational studies have shown that the directly repeated portion is critical to both DNA-binding and transcriptional promoting activities of TFIID (Horikoshi et al. 1990), whereas the non-conserved amino terminus is not. It is noteworthy, however, that the human and *Drosophila* clones contain extended amino termini that are enriched in glutamines. It has been proposed that this extension is required for stimulation in vitro by the Sp1 glutamine-rich activation domain (Pugh and Tjian 1990) (see below).

Additional studies on TFIID have provided several important insights as to the function of this important general factor. First, TFIID initiates the assembly of the general factors in the ordered pathway of complex formation on promoters (Van Dyke et al. 1988; Buratowski et al. 1989). Second, TFIID binds to a surprisingly degenerate set of TATA box elements with an affinity of about 10^{-9} M (Hahn et al. 1989b). This degeneracy implies that TFIID should bind to the vast majority of promoters. Finally, no evidence for multiple TATA box factors has emerged from searches for structural or functional homologs of TFIID.

Target of Acidic Transcriptional Activators

To search for the target of transcriptional activation surfaces, we began a study of the potent mammalian activator, VP16, in the yeast in vitro system. VP16 is a virion protein from herpes simplex virus that attaches to particular cellular DNA-binding proteins and augments their activity because it provides a potent acidic activation domain (McKnight et al. 1987; Gerster and Roeder 1988; O'Hare et al. 1988; Preston et al. 1988; Triezenberg et al. 1988). We set out to analyze a fusion protein wherein the acidic activation domain of VP16 was fused to the DNA-binding domain of GAL4. We wanted to compare the activity of this fusion to that of similar fusions containing mutations in the VP16 domain. A better understanding of the VP16 activation surface, we reasoned, might provide a means to identify the target. The wild-type and mutant VP16 activation domains were constructed and purified by our collaborators on this project, D. Cress, A. Cress, and S. Triezenberg (Michigan State University).

The three DNA templates employed in the in vitro system include the TATA box-mRNA initiation region from the yeast *CYC1* gene (Hahn et al. 1985) and varying upstream sequences. The basal template lacks a UAS. The gal.3 template contains three GAL4-binding sites upstream of the TATA box, and thus can be stimulated by the GAL4-VP16 activator (Chasman et al. 1989). The dA:dT template contains a UAS for the dA:dT activator present in the yeast extract and can be stimulated 5- to 10-fold by this protein (Chasman et al. 1989). Transcription from gal.3 was stimulated about 100-fold by addition of the GAL4-VP16 fusion protein. Surprisingly, however, transcription from this same template was inhibited at slightly higher concentrations of the activator (Berger et al. 1990; Kelleher et al. 1990). The dA:dT and basal templates were not stimulated by GAL4-VP16, since they do not have specific binding sites for GAL4, but were very strongly inhibited by the protein (Berger et al. 1990; Kelleher et al. 1990). Inhibition was to a level far lower than that of the basal template in the absence of addition of GAL4-VP16. This inhibition is reminiscent of in vivo inhibition or "squelching" observed in mammalian cells (Triezenberg et al. 1988) and studied in greater detail in yeast (Gill and Ptashne 1988). In both of these in vivo studies, mutant versions of the activation domains were also examined. A close correlation was found between the ability of mutants to activate and their ability to inhibit.

As proposed in the yeast studies of Gill and Ptashne (1988), inhibition might reflect the sequestration of a limiting target from the promoter by VP16. This idea has been confirmed by the use of mutated variants of the VP16 acidic surface. We have tested three kinds of mutants in the acidic domain of VP16 that vary in their ability to activate transcription: a partial deletion of the acidic surface; single amino acid substitutions, F442–P, F442–A, and F442–Y; and clustered substitutions in the activation domain F6 (E429–Q, D443–N, D445–N, D449–N) and F7 (E429–Q, D440–N, D443–N, D449–N) (Cress and Triezenberg 1991). As in the in vivo studies mentioned above, there was a close correlation between the ability of GAL4-VP16 derivatives to activate gal.3 and their ability to inhibit dA:dT (Berger et al. 1990 and unpubl.). We concluded that both activation and inhibition utilize the same surface of VP16 and, therefore, reflect the interaction with target.

Although the dA:dT template does not contain any GAL4 sites near the CYC1 promoter, nonspecific DNA binding to the 12-kb plasmid template may conceivably play some role in inhibition by GAL4-VP16. We set out, therefore, to prevent such binding in order to specifically examine the interaction between VP16 and its target in solution (in *trans*). Two methods were used to prevent DNA binding by GAL4-VP16. In the first approach, we added an oligonucleotide encoding GAL4-binding sites to the transcription reaction. In the second approach, we added the DNA-binding domain of GAL4 free of VP16, so that it might occupy nonspecific sites on the plasmid template. In each case, the same effect was observed upon addition of GAL4-VP16. Transcription of the basal template was no longer inhibited by GAL4-VP16 (Berger et al. 1990). Transcription of the dA:dT template was inhibited by GAL4-VP16. However, unlike the very strong inhibition seen when GAL4-VP16 was allowed to bind to the plasmid DNA, inhibition of the dA:dT template under these conditions was only to the basal level. Thus, under these conditions, i.e., in *trans*, GAL4-VP16 specifically inhibited activated, but not basal, transcription. Our view of the putatively sequestered target therefore shifted from that of a general factor needed for all transcription to that of an adapter needed specifically for activation by the dA:dT activator (Berger et al. 1990). In this model, the adapter bridges the interaction between the dA:dT activator and the general machinery and is efficiently sequestered by the acidic activation surface of VP16 (Fig. 2). When nonspecific DNA binding of GAL4-VP16 is not prevented, we surmise that the general factors that interact with the adapter are also sequestered from the promoter (for more details, see Berger et al. 1990).

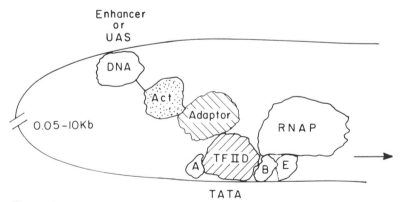

Figure 2 Mechanism of transcriptional activation at RNA pol II promoter. Depicted are a transcriptional activator bound at a UAS and the general transcription factors bound at the TATA box. The activator contains two domains, DNA-binding and activation (Act). The interaction between the activation domain of the activator and the general factors is bridged by the adapter. The line of reasoning that invokes the existence of adapters is discussed in the text.

In a separate study, Kelleher et al. (1990) noted similar inhibition by GAL4-VP16 in the in vitro transcription reaction. The provision of TFIID or RNA pol II did not relieve this inhibition, leading to the suggestion that the factor that was sequestered might not be a basal factor but a "mediator" of activation. A fraction containing this putative factor has been described by these workers (Flanagan et al. 1991).

Will all upstream activators be coupled to the general factors by adapters? Although the hypothetical role of adapters for acidic activators is not yet confirmed, recent in vivo experiments reveal the same pattern of inhibition by GAL4-VP16 and its mutant derivatives. GAL4-VP16 bearing a wild-type acidic surface is strongly inhibitory to cell growth, and mutations in this surface alleviate growth inhibition in proportion to the magnitude of their defects as activators (S. Berger et al., unpubl.). Moreover, the inhibition of cell growth by GAL4-VP16 is not reversed by a high copy clone that expresses TFIID. We are attempting to exploit the in vivo system to identify the gene encoding the putative adapter. It is not yet clear how our findings relate to those that demonstrated a direct interaction between VP16 and TFIID (Stringer et al. 1990) or VP16 and TFIIB (Lin and Green 1991) by affinity chromatographic methods. If TFIID were the direct target for VP16, one could reconcile the various findings by proposing that the *trans*-inhibition of activated transcription is due to blockage of a particular site on TFIID that responds to upstream activators. However, we believe that the adapter model is more easily reconciled with both the in vitro and in vivo observations that we have made.

The inference that there might be factors to bridge the interaction between activators bound at upstream sites and the general factors bound at the TATA box first came from the observation that the cloned TFIID could not fully substitute for the TFIID fraction (Hoey et al. 1990; Pugh and Tjian 1990; R. Tjian, pers. comm.). In these studies, the mammalian or *Drosophila* TFIID chromatographic fraction supported activation by Sp1, but the cloned *Drosophila*, yeast, or human TFIID, purified from overexpression in bacteria, did not. Furthermore, when bacterially produced TFIID was added to a mammalian extract in which endogenous TFIID had been heat-inactivated, both basal and Sp1-activated transcription was restored. Finally, bacterially produced variants of TFIID lacking the long amino-terminal extension restored basal, but not Sp1-activated, transcription. The model derived from these observations proposed that Sp1 requires a "coactivator" present in the mammalian TFIID fraction. This coactivator would appear to require the amino-terminal extension of TFIID in order to function. Recent findings indicate that the coactivator activity resides in one or more polypeptides tightly bound to the TATA-binding protein (Dynlacht et al. 1991). The coactivator described by Tjian and colleagues could be equivalent to the adapter identified in the yeast studies, or it could be a protein that works at some later step in initiation.

Although adapters or coactivators have not yet been isolated, they would make an appealing addition to the assortment of known transcription factors. Clearly, the levels of different adapters present could vary from one cell type to the next and thereby impose an additional level of regulation in which classes of activators would be coordinately modulated. This new level of control would provide an additional layer of diversity in the pattern of gene expression. The viral immediate-early proteins, such as the adenovirus E1A, activate transcription from a subset of cellular promoters and could function as adapters for host transcription factors (Martin et al. 1990).

Equally important, the isolation of an adapter would provide an important step in linking the function of enhancer-bound activator proteins and general factors bound at the TATA box. An elucidation of the role of adapters in transcription would provide an answer to the question raised 10 years ago as to how distantly located enhancers influence transcription at a promoter.

YEAST ACTIVATORS HAP1 and HAP2/3/4: REGULATION OF ACTIVITY

Whatever the mechanism of activation, it is the regulation of activation that differs from one gene to the next and from one cell type to the next. Numerous mechanisms have been identified that define the terminal step in signal transduction pathways and control the activity of transcriptional activators. In total, these mechanisms determine the patterns of gene expression, the potential for genetic responses, and the very identity of cell type. In the remaining section of this chapter, I describe our studies on two yeast activators and place these findings in the context of other systems that have been described.

We began studying expression of the *CYC1* gene of *S. cerevisiae*, which encodes the iso-1 cytochrome *c*. Like many functions dedicated to mitochondrial biogenesis, this gene is regulated by oxygen and carbon source. Expression is off under anaerobic conditions, on at a low level in oxygen (Guarente and Mason 1983) with a fermentable carbon source, and on at a high level in medium with a nonfermentable carbon source (Zitomer et al. 1979). We found that the oxygen signal was transduced by the cytochrome cofactor, heme, which cells synthesize in response to oxygen. Heme-deficient mutants of *S. cerevisiae* do not express *CYC1* (Guarente and Mason 1983). The ability of heme to induce *CYC1* transcription required the product of a regulatory gene, termed *HAP1* (or *CYP1*). Deleterious mutations in the *HAP1* gene abolish the activity of UAS1 of *CYC1* (Guarente et al. 1984; Verdiere et al. 1986). *hap1⁻* mutations also lower the expression of a second gene, *CYC7*, which encodes the iso-2-cytochrome *c*. The *CYC7* gene is expressed at a much lower level than *CYC1* in wild-type yeast strains. Subsequent analysis of *hap1* mutants revealed that the gene also controls CTT1 (catalase T) (Winkler et al. 1988), SOD1 (superoxide dismutase), and CYT1 (cytochrome *c*1) (Schneider and Guarente 1991). *hap1⁻* mutants still respire, however, indicating that a second activation system must exist for nuclear genes encoding important mitochondrial functions.

This second regulatory system was first identified by mutations in a gene, *HAP2*, which abolish activation at the second upstream activation site of *CYC1*, termed UAS2 (Guarente et al. 1984). Subsequently, mutations in two other genes, *HAP3* (Hahn et al. 1988) and *HAP4* (Forsburg et al. 1989), were identified which imparted the same effect as mutations in *HAP2*. Unlike *hap1⁻* mutants, strains defective in *HAP2, 3*, or *4* fail to grow on nonfermentable carbon sources, illustrating the central nature of the latter regulator in mitochondrial biogenesis. The primary regulatory signal affecting UAS2 is carbon source: Activity is low in glucose and high in lactate. This signal is transduced by the *HAP2/3/4* system as described below.

Heme Activates by Alleviating Repression of *HAP1* DNA Binding

The ability of *HAP1* to respond to heme in vivo is mirrored by its DNA-binding properties in vitro. Heme induces the binding of *HAP1* to UAS1 or CYC7 in yeast extracts (Pfeifer et al. 1987a). The concentration of heme required to induce binding is 1–10 μM. Heme also induces the binding of *HAP1* fragments produced by in vitro translation (Pfeifer et al. 1989). A fragment encoding residues 1–444 required heme to bind, whereas a 1–245 residue fragment binds DNA specifically in the absence or presence of heme. Internal deletions in *HAP1* that remove the region between residues 245 and 444 also render the protein as a constitutive activator in vivo. We therefore proposed that heme acted by counteracting an internal repression sequence in *HAP1* located between residues 245 and 444 (Fig. 3). This model is analogous to what had been observed in the case of the hormonal induction of the glucocorticoid receptor (Godowski et al. 1987). Interestingly, this internal repression region of *HAP1* contains seven repeats of a sequence containing cysteine and histi-

Figure 3 The domain structure of *HAP1*. The DNA-binding, heme regulatory, and transcriptional activation domains, as defined by mutational analysis, are indicated in the linear sequence of *HAP1*. The DNA-binding domain contains a zinc finger, and the activation domain is highly acidic. The heme regulatory domain in an internal repression sequence that blocks DNA binding in the absence of the inducer, heme, is shown. This block is probably not as simple as indicated, since it can be transferred to heterologous DNA-binding domains, as discussed in the text.

dine, which may be required for heme binding (Pfeifer et al. 1989). Direct evidence that heme binds to the protein does not yet exist.

In more recent experiments, we have found that heme induction of activation in vivo and DNA binding in vitro can be transferred to the bacterial protein LexA by fusing the DNA-binding domain of LexA to a carboxyl fragment encompassing the entirety of *HAP1* (J. Fikes and L. Guarente, unpubl.). Similar observations in studies of the glucocorticoid receptor have led to the suggestion that an associated protein may cause repression in the absence of inducer (Picard et al. 1988). Because the receptor can be regulated by steroid hormones in yeast (Metzger et al. 1988; Schena and Yamamoto 1988), this protein may be conserved in many eukaryotes. This external protein may be the heat-shock protein, HSP90, which is conserved in yeast (Borkovich et al. 1989) and has been implicated in glucocorticoid receptor regulation in yeast cells (Picard et al. 1990).

Influence of DNA Sequence in the Binding Site
on *HAP1* Activity

A striking feature of the UASs that bind and respond to *HAP1* is their sequence dissimilarity, originally noted as a difference between two *HAP1*-binding sites in UAS1 (UAS1B) and CYC7 (Pfeifer et al. 1987b) (Fig. 4). The two *HAP1* sites bind the protein with indistinguishable relative affinities. How does *HAP1* bind to two highly degenerate sequence elements? A single region of the protein, within residues 1–148 and containing a C-6 zinc finger motif, is sufficient to bind to both elements

```
UAS1A   TTCACCGATCTTTCCGGTCTCT
UAS1B   TTGGCCGGGGTTTACGGACGAT
CYT1    GCCGCCGGAAATACCGGCCGCC
CTT1    CGGAATGGAGATAACGGAGGTT
CYC7    ATTATCGCTATTATCGCTCCCG
```

Figure 4 HAP1 binding sites. Five sites that are bound by HAP1 in vitro and respond to HAP1 in vivo are shown. The similarity shared by all five sites is emboldened. The sites UAS1A, UAS1B (Pfeifer et al. 1987a,b), CYT1 (J. Schneider and L. Guarente, unpubl.), and CTT1 (Winkler et al. 1988) have considerably more similarity when compared pairwise.

(Pfeifer et al. 1989). Mutations of Cys-64 or Cys-81 to several other residues eliminates binding to both sites. Moreover, a Pro-79–Leu substitution created a requirement for higher concentrations of zinc for binding at both sites (Kim et al. 1990). Within this region of the protein, however, particular amino acids discriminate between the two elements. One key position for discrimination is Ser-63 (Pfeifer et al. 1989). Mutations at this position to arginine, isoleucine, or methionine resulted in partial or total specificity for the *CYC7* site. Changes to serine, threonine, and cysteine bound to both the *UAS1* and *CYC7* sites, and aspartic acid, asparagine, glutamic acid, glutamine, leucine, tyrosine, lysine, valine, or tryptophan substitutions blocked binding to both sites (Kim and Guarente 1989).

A more intriguing phenomenon is the differential response of UAS1 and CYC7 to *HAP1* in vivo. Synthetic oligonucleotides corresponding to each of the sites were inserted into a *CYC1-lacZ* reporter otherwise lacking any UAS activity, allowing a direct comparison of the two response elements. The construct containing the UAS1 oligonucleotide directed a high level of activity, comparable to the native UAS1, whereas the CYC7 construct directed very low activity (Kim and Guarente 1989). This difference was even greater than the normal disparity in expression between CYC1 and CYC7. Most telling was the effect of the *HAP1-18* (*CYP1-18*) mutation on the activity of the CYC7 sites. This allele of *HAP1* was originally selected according to its increased expression of the *CYC7* gene (Clavelier et al. 1976). The increase in activity of the CYC7 oligo construct caused by this mutation was greater than 100-fold (Kim and Guarente 1989). How does this allele cause such a dramatic increase in *CYC7* expression? The *HAP1-18* mutation is Ser-63–Arg, one of the changes mentioned above that binds specifically to *CYC7*. The fact that *HAP1-18* fails to bind to UAS1, however, does not explain the increase in *CYC7* activity. Other changes at Ser-63 that bound specifically to *CYC7* did not increase expression at that site. The obvious possibility that the *HAP1-18* change increases the affinity of the protein for *CYC7* was ruled out by direct measurements. HAP1 and HAP1-18 bound to *CYC7* with the same affinities (Kim and Guarente 1989).

We are left to speculate how the *HAP1-18* change increases expression at CYC7. Given that activity of HAP1 is abnormally low at CYC7, it is possible that some mechanism operates to lower HAP1 activity at that site which is abolished by the 1-18 change. We have considered two possible models to explain this puzzle (Kim and Guarente 1989). In the first, we imagine that the DNA-binding domain of HAP1 augments the activity of the acidic domain (which lies between residues 1308 and 1483) in activation. This augmentation could occur if both domains contacted components of the transcriptional machinery. Differential activity could result from different conformations in the DNA-binding domain of HAP1 when the protein is bound at the dissimilar sites, UAS1 and CYC7. By this model, the *HAP1-18* mutation would improve the interaction between HAP1 and its target in the machinery. Alternatively, the augmentation could occur if the DNA-binding domain recruited another protein to the HAP1-binding sites. In this case, the differential activity could result from the recruitment of two different proteins to the two sites. The *HAP1-18* mutation may strengthen an interaction with a protein recruited to the CYC7 site.

The second model involves a negative control mechanism. In it we suggest that the acidic activation domain of HAP1 is somehow masked when the protein is bound at CYC7. This masking could occur by a direct interaction between the acidic domain and the DNA-binding domain, which we again postulate is in a particular conformation when bound at CYC7. This *intra*molecular interaction would mimic the *inter*molecular interaction between GAL4 and GAL80 in which the acidic activation domain of GAL4 is masked by GAL80 (Ma and Ptashne 1987b; Johnston et al. 1987; see also Gann et al., this volume). Recent findings in the glucocorticoid receptor (GR) system may be relevant to this model. It was found that the GR receptor and the Jun-Fos heterodimer function antagonistically at a composite element that contains sites for both factors (Diamond et al. 1990; Schule et al. 1990; Yang-yen et al. 1990). The simultaneous binding of the GR and Jun-Fos is evidently stabilized by protein-protein interactions. By analogy, it is possible that HAP1 is inhibited by a second protein that also binds within the CYC7 site. To date, there is no evidence for this second protein, either from gel shift analysis of yeast extracts or from the appearance of mutant genetic loci with properties like *HAP1-18*.

Repression of Genes by HAP1

In addition to genes that are activated by oxygen in yeast, other genes are *repressed* by oxygen, an effect also mediated by heme. Among these loci is *ANB1*, which is expressed only in anaerobically grown or heme-deprived cells (Lowry and Zitomer 1984). A genetic locus, *ROX1*, is involved in this repression; loss-of-function mutations in *ROX1* render *ANB1* expression constitutive (Lowry and Lieber 1986; Lowry and Zitomer 1988). Because of the involvement of heme in the repression of *ANB1*, we were prompted to investigate whether HAP1 played a role in this process. Indeed, *ANB1* is expressed constitutively in strains lacking HAP1 function (E. Young and L. Guarente, unpubl.). Thus, both HAP1 and ROX1 are required to repress *ANB1* under aerobic conditions. It is possible that HAP1 is the transducer of the heme signal in repression, just as in activation. How repression might occur is not yet clear. We are currently investigating why there is a dual requirement for ROX1 and HAP1 in repression, considering the possibility of a repressor that is a heterodimer of these gene products.

The HAP2/3/4 CCAAT-binding Complex in *S. cerevisiae*: Distribution of Functions among Subunits

UAS2 of *CYC1* and UASs of many other genes encoding cytochromes contain CCAAT boxes and respond to HAP2/3/4 (Guarente et al. 1984; Keng and Guarente 1987). Methylation interference shows protein-DNA contacts that are restricted to the CCAAT box (Olesen et al. 1987), although linker scanning (Forsburg and Guarente 1988) as well as DNase footprinting (S. Hahn and L. Guarente, unpubl.) analysis indicates that the functional site is much larger (25 nucleotides). The normal UAS2 actually contains the sequence CCAAC. A base change to CCAAT was isolated in a screen of random mutations that increase the activity of the site (Guarente et al. 1984). These UASs are all regulated by carbon source/glucose repression. Why are three gene products necessary for the complex to bind to the CCAAT box and to activate transcription? Gel shift analysis using size variants of HAP2, HAP3, or HAP4 indicated that all three proteins bound simultaneously to UAS2 (Olesen et al. 1987; Hahn and Guarente 1988; Forsburg and Guarente 1989). Biochemical fractionation of the binding activity showed that the subunits of the complex are stably associated, even when not bound to DNA (Hahn and Guarente 1988). Experiments described in the paragraphs below summarize the arguments that lead to the schematic shown in Figure 5, which shows HAP2 and HAP3 bound to the DNA site and HAP4 providing the activation domain.

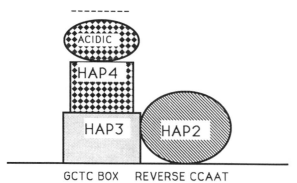

GCTC BOX   REVERSE CCAAT

Figure 5   The HAP2/3/4 transcriptional activation complex. The HAP2 and HAP3 subunits are primarily responsible for binding to the UAS2 site, which contains a CCAAT box. HAP4 provides an acidic activation domain required for the activation function of the complex. The logic leading to the distribution of functions as depicted in the figure is discussed in the text.

Deletional analysis of HAP2 revealed that a 60-amino-acid, highly basic region of the 265-residue protein, which we term the core, complemented a hap2-deficient strain of yeast (Olesen and Guarente 1990). Other interesting motifs in the protein, such as poly Gln, can be deleted without abolishing function. The core can be divided into two subdomains spaced by nonessential amino acids (Fig. 6). For reasons outlined below, we believe that the amino-terminal subdomain is required for the assembly of the complex, whereas the more carboxyl of the two subdomains specifically binds to the CCAAT DNA substrate.

Sequences in HAP2 required for assembly of the HAP2/3/4 complex were assayed by attaching the DNA-binding domain of LexA to the nonessential amino terminus of HAP2 and assaying the ability of the fusion to activate transcription from a gene containing the LexA operator (Olesen and Guarente 1990). The DNA-binding domain of LexA directs

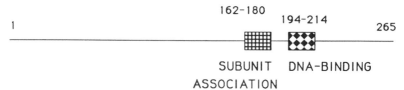

SUBUNIT   DNA-BINDING
ASSOCIATION

Figure 6   The domain structure of *HAP2*. The essential core of *HAP2* is encompassed between residues 162 and 214 of the 265-residue protein. Within this core are two subdomains. The subdomain between residues 162 and 180 is involved in complex assembly. It is likely that this region binds to *HAP3*, as discussed in the text. The subdomain between residues 194 and 214 is required for binding to UAS2 and recognizes the CCAAT sequence.

the LexA-HAP2 fusion to bind to its operator site adjacent to the TATA box of the reporter gene that was being assayed. Ability to activate via the LexA operator, however, required the HAP4 product, which contains an acidic activation domain (see below). Activation also required HAP3, indicating that this subunit might serve to connect HAP2 and HAP4. Although (in the context of the LexA-HAP2 fusion protein) the carboxyl subdomain of HAP2 was not required for activation at the LexA operator, the amino-terminal subdomain was absolutely required. This analysis demonstrated the discrete nature of the subunit assembly and DNA-binding subdomains of HAP2. In addition, consistent with earlier biochemical data, the study showed that the HAP complex assembles normally at the LexA operator, and, therefore, assembly does not require binding to UAS2.

The subunit association domain of HAP2 is unlike any other oligomerization motif described in DNA-binding proteins, such as the helix-loop-helix (Murre et al. 1989) or leucine zipper (Landschulz et al. 1988a). It is very short, consisting of 18 amino acids, and rich in arginine. The partner surface in HAP3 that interacts with this domain has not yet been delineated.

In contrast to LexA-HAP2 fusions, LexA-HAP4 fusions were strong constitutive activators at the LexA operator and did not require the other HAP subunits (Olesen and Guarente 1990). This finding is not surprising, because the acidic region of HAP4, although essential for activity, could be functionally replaced with the acidic activation domain II from GAL4 (Forsburg and Guarente 1989).

Although gel shift analysis of yeast extracts has indicated that all three HAP subunits are required for DNA binding (Forsburg and Guarente 1989), further genetic analysis showed that HAP2 and HAP3 were sufficient (and necessary) for at least some level of specific binding to UAS2. In particular, a fusion of the acidic activation domain II of GAL4 to *HAP2* (containing the entire HAP2 core) partially complemented a *hap4* deletion, indicating that HAP2 and HAP3 could bind to UAS2 without HAP4 (Olesen and Guarente 1990). The HAP2-GAL4 fusion did not, however, bypass a *hap3* deletion. This latter finding substantiates the interpretation that HAP3 is required, along with HAP2, for UAS2 binding and that HAP2 and HAP3 can associate without HAP4.

Unlike GAL4 (see Gann et al., this volume) and GCN4 (see Struhl, this volume), the two functions of DNA binding and transcriptional activation are separated among subunits in the HAP complex. DNA-binding function is provided by HAP2 and HAP3 and transcriptional activation function is provided by HAP4. The role of HAP4 is comparable to the herpes virion protein, VP16, which associates with DNA via host cell DNA-binding proteins (see Herr et al. this volume). We do not know whether the acidic region of HAP4 is sufficient for activation in the HAP2/3/4 complex. We have not been able to truncate the HAP3 protein substantially without losing all activity and, therefore, cannot rule out the possibility that HAP3 also contributes to the activation function of the complex.

Why are *both* HAP2 and HAP3 required for UAS2-binding? The model in Figure 4 indicates that HAP2 contacts the CCAAT box directly, and HAP3 contacts sequences adjacent to the CCAAT box. This aspect of the model is predicated on two findings. First, a mutant in the HAP complex has recently been isolated that has an altered specificity for the DNA site: an increased activity at CCAAC and a decreased activity at CCAAT (Y.Y. Xing and L. Guarente, unpubl.). This mutation lies in the DNA-binding subdomain of HAP2, implying that HAP2 recognizes the CCAAT sequence directly. Second, linker scanning mutagenesis of UAS2 has indicated that the functional site had *two* important elements, the CCAAT box and a region separated from CCAAT by about 10 bp (Forsburg and Guarente 1988). What subunit of the HAP complex might contact this second region in UAS2? We do not favor the idea that it is a second molecule of HAP2. HAP complexes assembled in the presence of two size variants of HAP2 yield two protein-DNA complexes by gel shift, suggesting that there is but one molecule of HAP2 bound per complex (J. Olesen and L. Guarente, unpubl.). Therefore, we suggest that this second region of UAS2 may be contacted by HAP3.

An alternate model that must be considered is that HAP2 and HAP3 *together* comprise a single DNA-binding unit which is not simply the sum of the parts. In this light, it is noteworthy that the DNA-binding domain of HAP2 contains a cluster of three histidine residues that are critically important for DNA binding (Y.Y. Xing and L. Guarente, unpubl.). HAP3 contains three cysteine residues of unknown function. A fascinating possibility is that a hybrid zinc finger between the two subunits may form to comprise the DNA-binding domain (see van Huijsduijnen et al. 1990). A hybrid zinc coordinated complex is formed at the dimer interface of aspartate transcarbamylase, which served as a basis to model the zinc finger (see Schmidt and Berg, this volume).

Regulation of Transcriptional Activation by HAP2/3/4

How is the carbon source signal transduced by the HAP complex? One obvious advantage in partitioning the DNA-binding and activation domains among different subunits is that separate control can be exerted on each. It has been argued that strong activation domains, such as that of HAP4, are toxic to cells unless their activity is masked when not needed (Ptashne 1988). Indeed, available evidence indicates that regulation of the HAP complex occurs through HAP4. The level of HAP4 RNA itself is somewhat repressed in glucose (Forsburg and Guarente 1989). Moreover, placing the HAP4 coding sequence under control of the constitutive ADH1 promoter renders UAS2 activity constitutively high in glucose (P. Sugiono and L. Guarente, unpubl.). Thus, HAP2 and HAP3 appear not to be rate-limiting, and HAP4 is the regulated subunit in the complex. In this regard, HAP4 would follow the example of another global yeast activator, GCN4, which is regulated at the level of synthesis (Hinnebusch 1984). It remains to be determined whether translational control, which is the central theme of GCN4 regulation, will play an important role in modulating synthesis of HAP4. The long 5′ untranslated leader of the HAP4 mRNA (280 nucleotides) contains two AUG codons that could be targets for such regulation (Forsburg and Guarente 1989). Regulation at the level of HAP4 synthesis contrasts to the HAP1 case, which involves a posttranslational masking of the DNA-binding potential by the internal repression sequence in the protein.

Our in vitro experiments with GAL4-VP16, described above, may also be relevant to the issue of masking of transcriptional activators. This potent activator is a general inhibitor of transcription because it apparently titrates a key component of the transcriptional machinery. Interestingly, when the fusion protein is severed at the GAL4-VP16 junction, neither the GAL4 nor VP16 halves can inhibit transcription in the in vitro system (S. Berger et al., unpubl.). Cross-linking experiments suggest that the VP16 moiety employed (residues 413–490) is monomeric unless fused to the GAL4 fragment encompassing residues 1–147 and containing the DNA-binding and dimerization domains of GAL4 (S. Berger and L. Guarente, unpubl.). A possible interpretation from these observations is that inhibition, and thus interaction with target, requires a dimeric acidic activation surface. We do not yet know whether a requirement for a dimeric activation surface is met in the HAP2/3/4 complex, for example, by inclusion of two molecules of HAP4 per complex, or by a concerted action of HAP3 and HAP4. In any case, limiting the synthesis of HAP4 obviously would prevent inhibition of the transcriptional machinery. In the case of HAP1, the internal repression sequence could prevent inhibition of the machinery if it functioned by preventing dimerization of the protein.

Conservation of the HAP2/3/4 Complex in Evolution

In vitro experiments have demonstrated an amazing degree of functional conservation between the subunits of the CCAAT-binding complex from yeast to HeLa cells (Chodosh et al. 1988b). The human counterpart of the HAP2/3/4 complex, CP1, is one of several different factors that bind to CCAAT-like elements (Graves et al. 1986; Johnson et al. 1987; Chodosh et al. 1988a; Dorn et al. 1988; Landschulz et al. 1988b; Santoro et al. 1988). The binding specificity of these CCAAT factors is distinct, evidently determined by sequences flanking the CCAAT box. CP1 could be fractionated into two components, neither of which could bind to the CCAAT box by itself (Chodosh et al. 1988a). The CP1A fraction could restore binding to a yeast extract lacking HAP3, and the CP1B fraction would do likewise to a yeast extract lacking HAP2 (Chodosh et al. 1988b). These findings indicate that the DNA recognition and protein-protein specificity in HAP2 and HAP3 have been conserved in their human counterparts, CP1B and CP1A. More recently, we exploited the functional conservation in the CCAAT complex to clone *HAP2* from *S. pombe* (Olesen et al. 1991) and humans (Becker et al. 1991).

The sequences of the *S. pombe* and human clones that complement HAP2 function indicate that they encode proteins of 334 and 257 amino acids, respectively. Sequence comparisons among all three show a striking conservation of the HAP2 core and no conservation of any other parts of the protein. The core lies at the amino terminus of the *S. pombe* HAP2 and, like the protein from *S. cerevisiae*, toward the carboxyl terminus of the human protein. The CCAAT complex has recently been purified from the rat (termed CBF) (Maity et al. 1990) and from the mouse (termed NFY) (van Huijsduijnen et al. 1990). Sequences derived from peptides were used to clone the HAP2 homologs from these two mammals. The sequences of these clones are very similar to the human HAP2-complementing clone, with strong similarity to the yeast proteins in the core. The sequences of all five cores are shown in Figure 7. The critical sequences that had been defined as the subunit association and DNA-binding domains are highly conserved. The spacer region has diverged in both size and primary amino acid sequence.

We were also able to isolate a HAP3 functional homolog from *S. pombe* (J. Fikes et al., unpubl.). The Mathis group described the sequence of the corresponding mouse clone, which, along with the HAP2-like subunit, comprises the CCAAT-binding complex, NFY, from mouse cells (van Huijsduijnen et al. 1990). The cDNAs from *S. pombe*, the mouse, and *S. cerevisiae* all bear extensive similarity. Unlike the case of HAP2, this similarity is not concentrated in one portion of the protein, but occurs along most of its length. Experiments to dissect functional domains of HAP3 are in progress. According to the model displayed in Figure 5, we anticipate three domains (HAP2 association, DNA-binding, and HAP4 association).

	SUBUNIT ASSOCIATION	*DNA-BINDING*
Sc	YVNAKQYYRILKRRYARAKLEEKLRISE	ERKPYLHESRHKHAMRRPRGEGGRF
Sp	YVNAKQYHRILKRREARAKLEERLRGVQTTKKP	YLHESRHKHAMRRPRGPGGRF
Hu	YVNAKQYHRILKRRQARAKLEAEGKIPK	ERRKYLHESRHRHAMARKRGEGGRF
Rat	YVNAKQYHRILKRRQARAKLEAEGKIPK	ERRKYLHESRHRHAMARKRGEGGRF
Mouse	YVNAKQYHRILKRRQARAKLEAEGKIPK	ERRKYLHESRHRHAMARKRGEGGRF

Figure 7 Sequence of *HAP2* subunits of CCAAT complexes. Clones of *HAP2* homologs from *S. pombe* (Sp) (Olesen et al. 1991), human (Hu) (Becker et al. 1991), rat (Maity et al. 1990), and mouse (van Huijsduijnen et al. 1990) all contain a region of similarity to the core of *HAP2* of *S. cerevisiae* (Sc). Identical residues are emboldened. The similarities fall into two regions, those defined as the subunit association and DNA-binding subdomains of *HAP2*, by functional analysis. Note that the sequence and the precise spacing *between* these two subdomains has been altered over evolution.

Regulatory Role of the HAP Complex in Different Eukaryotes

Many mammalian gene promoters contain CCAAT boxes, a substantial subset of which use CP1. There is no clear functional relationship among these genes that might dictate coordinate control (such as carbon source control in *Saccharomyces*). In an initial attempt to gain insight into the role of the HAP2/3/4 complex in an organism divergent from *S. cerevisiae*, we constructed a gene disruption of the *S. pombe HAP2* gene, which we termed php2. The Δphp2 strain of *S. pombe* exhibited a phenotype similar to the Δhap2 strain of *S. cerevisiae*—an inability to grow on nonfermentable carbon sources (Olesen et al. 1991). It would appear, therefore, that the CCAAT complex in *S. pombe*, as in *S. cerevisiae*, is dedicated to mitochondrial function. It will be of interest to see the outcome of similar gene disruption experiments in mammalian cells.

Gel shift analysis of *S. pombe* extracts displayed a prominent factor that binds to the UAS2 probe (Olesen et al. 1991). Because this complex was missing in the Δphp2 strain, it almost certainly corresponds to the HAP complex. A major difference from *S. cerevisiae*, however, was evident in the regulation of the *S. pombe* DNA-binding activity. Whereas in *S. cerevisiae* the activity was never observed in extracts from glucose-grown cells, in *S. pombe* it was constitutively present. The absence of the complex in *S. cerevisiae* is attributed to the lack of HAP4 synthesis in glucose. Although we are lacking direct evidence, we presume that HAP4 improves the binding affinity of the HAP2/3 complex (but is not absolutely required for binding, as discussed above). Our findings in *S. pombe* may be interpreted in one of two ways. Because the binding activity is constitutive, a HAP4 counterpart in *S. pombe* may be synthesized constitutively. Alternatively, there may be no HAP4 homolog in *S. pombe*. In either case, it is probable that carbon source does not strongly regulate mitochondrial functions in *S. pombe*. If there were such regulation, it would have to occur by a mechanism different from a restriction in synthesis of an activation component of the complex. Consistent with the notion that HAP4 may not exist in *S. pombe*, we have not succeeded in isolating a cDNA from the *S. pombe* library capable of complementing a HAP4-deficient strain of *S. cerevisiae*.

The mammalian CCAAT-binding complexes purified from the rat (Maity et al. 1990) and the mouse (van Huijsduijnen et al. 1990) both rely on two subunits, one homologous to HAP2 and the other to HAP3. The fractionation of the HeLa extract also suggested that the human factor had two subunits. Although it is possible that the mammalian complex can bind to the CCAAT box at high affinity without a HAP4 counterpart, it is less clear how the complex might activate transcription without this subunit. One possible answer may be provided by inspection of the sequence of the amino terminus of the human HAP2 (Becker et al. 1991). This region is rich in glutamine residues, much like the activation domain of Sp1.

If HAP4 were present in an ancestral eukaryote, it might have been lost during the evolution of mammals. The glutamine-rich domain might have been acquired by HAP2 to compensate for the loss of HAP4. Its acquisition would divorce the complex from regulation by carbon source and render it a constitutive activator. Alternatively, HAP4 might have been missing in the ancestor and acquired during the evolution of *S. cerevisiae* lineage to cause the complex to be regulated by carbon source.

In a teleological sense, it is surprising that an activator composed of multiple subunits only serves a constitutive function. Indeed, Northern blotting with the human HAP2 probe suggests that the situation may actually be more complex (Becker et al. 1991). A 1.67-kb mRNA, which corresponds to the size of the cDNA clone, appeared in all cell types examined but was greatly augmented in HeLa cells. A 4.0-kb mRNA was found in all cell types in comparable amounts to the 1.6-kb mRNA (with the exception of HeLa cells) and probably encodes the HAP2-like subunit of the constitutive CCAAT-binding factor. This size corresponds to the expanse of the HAP2 coding sequences isolated from the rat and the mouse. The 4.0-kb cDNA differs from the 1.6-kb clone in that it is capable of encoding an extra 90 amino acids at the amino terminus of the HAP2 polypeptide.

Interestingly, in addition to the 1.6-kb and 4.0-kb mRNA species, a 7.0-kb RNA was observed in a B-cell line termed RAJI (Becker et al.

1991). This finding raises the possibility that a larger protein related to HAP2 may play a role in B-cell transcription. In this regard, it is noteworthy that a factor is induced in B cells and macrophages which binds to CP1-like CCAAT boxes and is involved in activation of class II genes of the major histocompatibility locus (Finn et al. 1990). Whether the 7.0-kb clone encodes this "induced" form of CP1 is not known.

SUMMARY AND PERSPECTIVE

A major goal of biological research is to understand processes that govern the control of cell growth and mechanisms responsible for the determination and differentiation of specialized cell types. Ultimately, many of these processes involve signaling pathways that activate or repress gene expression. The critical molecules acting at this terminal step in many signal transduction pathways are transcriptional regulatory proteins. In recent years, a body of evidence has accumulated indicating that transcriptional activators in eukaryotes from yeast to mammals are similar in two important respects. First, they have the capacity of activating transcription at great distances from the promoter, and this capacity is due to a common mechanism of action. Second, the function of activators is regulated by a variety of mechanisms that also are similar in divergent eukaryotes. These observations place yeast in a unique position as an experimental system to analyze the mechanistics of transcriptional activation and regulation. The combination of classic genetics, molecular biology, and biochemistry in this organism provides powerful tools to fashion these investigations. The ability to study differentiation processes directly in yeast is limited by the biological simplicity of the organism. However, even in this area of study, it is likely that basic transcriptional mechanisms, which are amenable to study in yeast, will play an important role in modeling more complex systems.

Where is the field of eukaryotic transcription heading? Clearly, the study of transcription factors in the context of embryonic and cell type development will unfold in ever greater depth. One also hopes that analysis of these factors will lead away from the nucleus and toward the multitude of signal transduction pathways that determine the response of gene expression to genetic and environmental cues. In higher cells, the identification and purification of membrane receptors, GTP-binding proteins, and protein kinases have begun to map out the components of some of these pathways. In yeast, similar components have been isolated through mutations that alter patterns of gene expression. The next era of transcriptional studies may well merge with cell biology, as cytoplasmic enzymes continue to be tied to gene expression and connections are made that trace out continuous pathways of signal transduction. Yeast will assume a place in this field as a cell in which genetic dissection of these complex pathways is possible.

ACKNOWLEDGMENTS

I thank members of my laboratory for their many contributions over the past 10 years and my colleagues for their helpful input. The work from my laboratory was supported by grants from the National Institutes of Health and the American Cancer Society.

REFERENCES

Allison, L. and J. Ingles. 1989. Mutations in RNA polymerase II enhance or suppress mutation in GAL4. *Proc. Natl. Acad. Sci.* **86:** 2794–2798.

Allison, L., M. Moyle, M. Shales, and C.J. Ingles. 1985. Extensive homology among the largest subunits of eukaryotic and prokaryotic RNA polymerases. *Cell* **42:** 599–610.

Allison, L.A., J.K. Wong, V.D. Fitzpatrick, M. Moyle, and C.J. Ingles. 1988. The c-terminal domain of the largest subunit of RNA polymerase II of *Saccharomyces cerevisiae, Drosophila melanogaster,* and mammals: A conserved structure with an essential function. *Mol. Cell. Biol.* **8:** 321–329.

Banerji, J., S. Rusconi, and W. Schaffner. 1981. Expression of a β-globin gene is enhanced by remote SV40 DNA sequences. *Cell* **27:** 299–308.

Becker, D.M., J.D. Fikes, and L. Guarente. 1991. A cDNA encoding a human CCAAT-binding protein cloned by functional complementation in yeast. *Proc. Natl. Acad. Sci.* 88: 1968–1972.

Benoist, C. and P. Chambon. 1981. In vivo sequence requirements of the SV40 early promoter region. *Nature* **290:** 304–310.

Berger, S.L., W.D. Cress, A. Cress, S.J. Triezenberg, and L. Guarente. 1990. Selective inhibition of activated but not basal transcription by the acidic activation domain of VP16: Evidence for transcriptional adaptors. Cell 61: 1199–1208.

Borkovich, K.A., F.W. Farrelly, D.B. Finkelstein, J. Taulien, and S. Lindquist. 1989. hsp82 is an essential protein that is required in higher concentrations for growth of cells at higher temperatures. *Mol. Cell. Biol.* **9:** 3919–3930.

Brent, R. and M. Ptashne. 1985. A eukaryotic transcriptional activator bearing the DNA specificity of a prokaryotic repressor. *Cell* **43:** 729–736.

Buratowski, S., S. Hahn, L. Guarente, and P. Sharp. 1989. Five intermediate complexes in transcription initiation by RNA polymerase II. *Cell* **56:** 549–561.

Buratowski, S., S. Hahn, P. Sharp, and L. Guarente. 1988. Function of a yeast TATA element-binding protein in a mammalian transcription system. *Nature* **334:** 37–42.

Cavallini, B., I. Faus, H. Matthes, J. Chipoulet, B. Winsor, J. Egly, and P. Chambon. 1989. Cloning of the gene encoding the yeast protein BTF1Y, which can substitute for the human TATA box-binding factor. *Proc. Natl. Acad. Sci.* **86:** 9803–9807.

Chandler, V.L., B.A. Maler, and K.R. Yamamoto. 1983. DNA sequences bound specifically by glucocorticoid receptor in vitro render a heterologous promoter hormone responsive in vivo. *Cell* **33:** 489–499.

Chasman, D., J. Leatherwood, M. Ptashne, and R. Kornberg. 1989. Activation of yeast polymerase II transcription by herpesvirus VP16 and GAL4 derivative in vitro. *Mol. Cell Biol.* **9:** 4746–4749.

Chodosh, L., A. Baldwin, R. Carthew, and P. Sharp. 1988a. Human CCAAT-binding proteins have heterologous subunits. *Cell* **53:** 11–24.

Chodosh, L., J. Olesen, S. Hahn, A. Baldwin, L. Guarente, and P. Sharp. 1988b. A yeast and a human CCAAT-binding protein have heterologous subunits that are functionally interchangeable. *Cell* **53:** 25–35.

Clavelier, L., G.P. Auber, M. Somlo, and P.P. Slonimski. 1976. Reseau d'interactions entre des genes non lies: Regulation synergique ou antagoniste de la synthese de l'iso-l-cytochrome *c*, et du cytochrome b2. *Biochimie* **58:** 155–172.

Corden, J., D. Cadena, J. Ahearn, and M. Dahmus. 1985. A unique structure at the carboxyl terminus of the largest subunit of eukaryotic RNA poymerase II. *Proc. Natl. Acad. Sci.* **79:** 34–38.

Cormack, B., M. Strubin, F. Ponticelli, and K. Struhl. 1991. Functional differences between yeast and human TFIID are localized to the highly conserved region. *Cell* **65:** 341–348.

Courey, A. and R. Tjian. 1988. Analysis of SP1 *in vivo* reveals multiple transcriptional domains, including a novel glutamine rich activation motif. *Cell* **55:** 887–898.

Cress, W. and S. Triezenberg. 1991. Critical structural elements of the VP16 transcriptional activation domain. Science 251: 87–90.

Diamond, M.I., J.N. Miner, S.K. Yoshinaga, and K.R. Yamamoto. 1990. Transcription factor interactions: Selectors of positive or negative regulation from a single DNA element. *Science* **249:** 1266–1272.

Dorn, A., J. Bellekens, A. Stauls, C. Benoist, and D. Mathis. 1988. A multiplicity of CCAAT-binding proteins. *Cell* **50:** 863–872.

Dynlacht, B., T. Hoey, and R. Tjian. 1991. Isolation of coactivators associated with the TATA-binding protein that mediates transcriptional activation. *Cell* **66:** 563–576.

Eisenmann, D.M., C. Dollard, and F. Winston. 1989. *SPT15*, the gene encoding the yeast TATA binding factor TFIID, is required for normal transcription initiation in vivo. *Cell* **58:** 1183–1191.

Fikes, J.D., D.M. Becker, F. Winston, and L. Guarente. 1990. Striking conservation of TFIID in *Schizosaccharomyces pombe* and *Saccharomyces cerevisiae*. *Nature* **346:** 291–294.

Finn, P.W., C.J. Kara, J. Douhan III, T.T. Van, V. Folsom, and L.H. Glimcher. 1990. Interferon γ regulates binding of two nuclear protein complexes in a macrophage cell line. *Proc. Natl. Acad. Sci.* **87:** 914–918.

Fischer, J.A., E. Giniger, T. Maniatis, and M. Ptashne. 1988. GAL4 activates transcription in *Drosophila*. *Nature* **332:** 853–856.

Flanagan, P., R. Kelleher, M. Sayre, H. Tschochner, and R. Kornberg. 1991. A mediator required for activation of RNA polymerase II transcription in vitro. *Nature* **350:** 436–438.

Forsburg, S. and L. Guarente. 1988. Mutational analysis of the upstream activation sequence 2 of the *CYC1* gene of *Saccharomyces cerevisiae:* A *HAP2-HAP3*-responsive site. *Mol. Cell Biol.* **8:** 647–654.

———. 1989. Identification and characterization of HAP4, a third component of the CCAAT-bound HAP2/HAP3 heteromer. *Genes Dev.* **3:** 1166–1178.

Gasch, A., A. Hoffmann, M. Horikoshi, R.G. Roeder, and N.-H. Chua. 1990. *Arabidopsis thaliana* contains two genes for TFIID. *Nature* **346:** 390–394.

Gerster, R. and R.G. Roeder. 1988. A herpes virus *trans*-activating protein interacts with transcriptional factor OTF-1 and other cellular proteins. *Proc. Natl. Acad. Sci.* **85:** 6347-6351.

Gill, G. and M. Ptashne. 1988. Negative effect of the transcriptional activator GAL4. *Nature* **334:** 721-724.

Gill, G. and R. Tjian. 1991. A highly conserved domain of TFIID displays species specificity in vivo. *Cell* **65:** 333-340.

Giniger, E. and M. Ptashne. 1987. Transcription in yeast activated by a putative amphipathic a helix linked to a DNA binding unit. *Nature* **330:** 670-672.

Godowski, P., S. Rusconi, R. Miesfeld, and K. Yamamoto. 1987. Glucocorticoid receptor mutants that are consitutive activators of transcriptional enhancement. *Nature* **325:** 365-368.

Graves, B., P. Johnson, and S. McKnight. 1986. Homologous recognition of a promoter domain common to the MSV LTR and the HSV tk gene. *Cell* **44:** 565-576.

Guarente, L. 1988. UASs and enhancers: Common mechanism of transcriptional activation in yeast and mammals. *Cell* **52:** 302-305.

Guarente, L. and T. Mason. 1983. Heme regulates transcription of the *CYC1* gene of *Saccharomyces cerevisiae* via an upstream activation site. *Cell* **32:** 1279-1286.

Guarente, L., R. Yocum, and P. Gifford. 1982. A GAL10-CYC1 hybrid promoter identifies the GAL4 regulatory region as an upstream site. *Proc. Natl. Acad. Sci.* **79:** 7410-7414.

Guarente, L., B. Lalonde, P. Gifford, and E. Alani. 1984. Distinctly regulated tandem upstream activation sites mediate catabolite repression of the *CYC1* gene of *Saccharomyces cerevisiae. Cell* **36:** 503-511.

Hahn, S. and L. Guarente. 1988. Yeast *HAP2* and *HAP3*: Transcription activators in a heteromeric complex. *Science* **240:** 317-321.

Hahn, S., E. Hoar, and L. Guarente. 1985. Each of three TATA elements specifies a subset of the transcription initiation sites at the CYC1 promoter of *S. cerevisiae. Proc. Natl. Acad. Sci.* **82:** 8562-8566.

Hahn, S., S. Buratowski, P. Sharp, and L. Guarente. 1989a. Isolation of the gene encoding the yeast TATA-binding protein TFIID: A gene identical to the SPT15 suppressor of TY element insertions. *Cell* **58:** 1173-1181.

Hahn, S., J. Pinkham, R. Wei, R. Miller, and L. Guarente. 1988. The *HAP3* regulatory locus of *Saccharomyces cerevisiae* encodes divergent overlapping transcripts. *Mol. Cell. Biol.* **8:** 655-663.

————. 1989b. Yeast TATA binding protein TFIID binds to TATA elements with both consensus and nonconsensus DNA sequences. *Proc. Natl. Acad. Sci.* **86:** 5718-5722.

Han, M. and M. Grunstein. 1989. Nucleosome loss activates yeast downstream promoters *in vivo. Cell* **55:** 1137-1145.

Hinnebusch, A.G. 1984. Evidence for translational regulation of the activator of general amino acid control in yeast. *Proc. Natl. Acad. Sci.* **81:** 6442-6446.

Hinnebusch, A.G., G. Lucchini, and G.R. Fink. 1985. A synthetic *HIS4* regulatory element confers general amino acid control of the cytochrome *c* gene (*CYC1*) of yeast. *Proc. Natl. Acad. Sci.* **82:** 498-502.

Hoey, T., B.D. Dynlacht, M.G. Peterson, B.F. Pugh, and R. Tjian. 1990. Isolation and characterization of the *Drosophila* gene encoding the TATA box binding protein, TFIID. *Cell* **61:** 1179-1186.

Hoffmann, A., M. Horikoshi, C.K. Wang, S. Schroeder, P.A. Weil, and R.G. Roeder. 1990a. Cloning of the *Schizosaccharomyces pombe* TFIID gene reveals a strong conservation of functional domains present in *Saccharomyces cerevisiae* TFIID. *Genes Dev.* **4:** 1141-1148.

Hoffmann, A., E. Sinn, T. Yamamoto, J. Wang, A. Roy, M. Horikoshi, and R.G. Roeder. 1990b. Highly conserved core domain and unique N terminus with presumptive regulatory motifs in a human TATA factor (TFIID). *Nature* **346:** 387-390.

Hope, I.A. and K. Struhl. 1986. Functional dissection of a eukaryotic transcriptional activator protein, GCN4 of yeast. *Cell* **46:** 885-894.

Hope, I.A., S. Mahadevan, and K. Struhl. 1988. Structural and functional characterization of the short acidic transcriptional activation region of yeast GCN4 protein. *Nature* **333:** 635-640.

Horikoshi, T., T. Hai, Y. Lin, M. Green, and R. Roeder. 1988. Transcription factor ATF interacts with the TATA factor to facilitate establishment of a preinitiation complex. *Cell* **54:** 1033-1042.

Horikoshi, M., T. Yamamoto, Y. Ohkuma, P.A. Weil, and R.G. Roeder. 1990. Analysis of structure-function relationships of yeast TATA box binding factor TFIID. *Cell* **61:** 1171-1178.

Horikoshi, M., C. Wang, H. Fujii, J. Cromlish, P.Weil, and R. Roeder. 1989. Cloning and structure of a yeast gene encoding a general transcription initiation factor TFIID that binds to the TATA box. *Nature* **341:** 299-303.

Johnson, P., W. Landschulz, B. Graves, and S. McKnight. 1987. Identification of a rat liver nuclear protein that binds to the enhancer core element of three animal viruses. *Genes Dev.* **1:** 133-146.

Johnston, S.A., J.M. Salmeron, Jr., and S.S. Dincher. 1987. Interaction of positive and negative regulatory proteins in the galactose regulon of yeast. *Cell* **50:** 143-146.

Kakidani, H. and M. Ptashne. 1988. GAL4 activates gene expression in mammalian cells. *Cell* **52:** 161-167.

Kao, C.C., P.M. Lieberman, M.C. Schmidt, Q. Zhou, R. Pei, and A.J. Berk. 1990. Cloning of a transcriptionally active human TATA binding factor. *Science* **248:** 1646-1650.

Kelleher, R.J., III, P.M. Flanagan, and R.D. Kornberg. 1990. A novel mediator between activator proteins and the RNA polymerase II transcription apparatus. *Cell* **61:** 1209-1215.

Keng, T. and L. Guarente. 1987. Multiple regulatory systems result in constitutive expression of the yeast *HEM1* gene. *Proc. Natl. Acad. Sci.* **84:** 9113-9117.

Kim, K.S. and L. Guarente. 1989. Mutations that alter transcriptional activation but not DNA binding in the zinc finger of yeast activator HAP1. *Nature* **342:** 200-203.

Kim, K.S., K. Pfeifer, L. Powell, and L. Guarente. 1990. Internal deletions in the yeast transcriptional activator HAP1 have opposite effects at two sequence elements. *Proc. Natl. Acad. Sci.* **87:** 4524-4528.

Landschulz, W.H., P.F. Johnson, and S.L. McKnight. 1988a. The leucine zipper: A hypothetical structure common to a new class of DNA binding proteins. *Science* **240:** 1759-1764.

Landschulz, W.H., P. Johnson, E. Adashi, B. Graves, and S. McKnight. 1988b. Isolation of a recombinant copy of the gene encoding C/EBP. *Genes Dev.* **2:** 786-800.

Lin, Y.S. and M. Green. 1991. Mechanism of action of an acidic transcriptional activator in vitro. *Cell* **64:** 971-981.

Lowry, C.V. and R.H. Lieber. 1986. Negative regulation of the *Saccharomyces cerevisiae ANB1* gene by heme as mediated by *ROX1* gene product. *Mol. Cell. Biol.* **6:** 4145-4148.

Lowry, C.V. and R.S. Zitomer. 1984. Oxygen regulation of anaerobic and aerobic genes mediated by common factor in yeast. *Proc. Natl. Acad. Sci.* **81:** 6129-6133.

―――――. 1988. *ROX1* encodes a heme-induced repression factor regulating *ANB1* and *CYC7* of *Saccharomyces cerevisiae*. *Mol. Cell. Biol.* **8:** 4651-4658.

Ma, J. and M. Ptashne. 1987a. Deletion analysis of GAL4 defines two transcriptional activating segments. *Cell* **48:** 847–853.

———. 1987b. The carboxy-terminal 30 amino acids of GAL4 are recognized by GAL80. *Cell* **50:** 137–142.

Ma, J., E. Przibilla, J. Hu, L. Bogorad, and M. Ptashne. 1988. Yeast activators stimulate plant gene expression. *Nature* **334:** 631–633.

Maity, S.N., T. Vuorio, and B. de Crombrugghe. 1990. The B subunit of a rat heteromeric CCAAT-binding transcription factor shows a striking sequence identity with the yeast Hap2 transcription factor. *Proc. Natl. Acad. Sci.* **87:** 5378–5382.

Martin, K., J. Lillie, and M. Green. 1990. Evidence for interaction of different eukaryotic transcriptional activators with distinct cellular targets. *Nature* **346:** 147–152.

Matsui, T., J. Segall, P. Weil, and R. Roeder. 1980. Multiple factors required for accurate initiation of transcription by purified RNA polymerase II. *J. Biol. Chem.* **255:** 11992–11996.

McKnight, J.L.C., T.M. Kristie, and B. Roizman. 1987. Binding of the virion protein mediating a gene induction in herpes simplex virus-1 infected cells to its *cis* site requires cellular proteins. *Proc. Natl. Acad. Sci.* **84:** 7061–7065.

Mermod, N., E. O'Neill, T. Kelly, and R. Tjian. 1989. The proline-rich transcriptional activator of CTF/NF-1 is distinct from the replication and DNA binding domain. *Cell* **58:** 741–753.

Metzger, D., J.H. White, and P. Chambon. 1988. The human oestrogen receptor functions in yeast. *Nature* **334:** 31–36.

Moreau, P., R. Hen, B. Wasylyk, R. Everett, M.P. Gaub, and P. Chambon. 1981. The SV40 72 base pair repeat has a striking effect on gene expression both in SV40 and other chimeric recombinants. *Nucleic Acids Res.* **9:** 6047–6056.

Murre, C., P.S. McCaw, and D. Baltimore. 1989. A new DNA-binding and dimerization motif in immunoglobulin enhancer binding, daughterless, myo D and myc proteins. *Cell* **66:** 777–783.

O'Hare, P., C.R. Goding, and A. Haigh. 1988. Direct combinatorial interactions between a herpes simplex virus regulatory protein and a cellular octamer binding factor mediates virus immediate early gene expression. *EMBO J.* **7:** 4231–4238.

Olesen, J.T. and L. Guarente. 1990. The HAP2 subunit of yeast CCAAT transcriptional activator contains adjacent domains for subunit association and DNA recognition: A model for the HAP2/3/4 complex. *Genes Dev.* **4:** 1714–1729.

Olesen, J.T., J. Fikes, and L. Guarente. 1991. The fission yeast homolog of budding yeast HAP2 reveals selective and stringent conservation of the small "essential core" protein domain. *Mol. Cell. Biol.* **11:** 611–619.

Olesen, J., S. Hahn, and L. Guarente. 1987. Yeast *HAP2* and *HAP3* activators both bind to the *CYC1* activation site, UAS2, in an interdependent manner. *Cell* **51:** 953–961.

Peterson, M.G., N. Tanese, B.F. Pugh, and R. Tjian. 1990. Functional domains and upstream activation properties of cloned human TATA binding protein. *Science* **248:** 1625–1630.

Pfeifer, K., B. Arcangioloi, and L. Guarente. 1987a. Yeast *HAP1* activation competes with the factor RC2 for binding to the upstream activation site UAS1 of the CYC1 gene. *Cell* **49:** 9–18.

Pfeifer, K., T. Prezant, and L. Guarente. 1987b. Yeast *HAP1* activator binds to two upstream activation sites of different sequence. *Cell* **49:** 19–27.

Pfeifer, K., K.S. Kim, S. Kogan, and L. Guarente. 1989. Functional dissection and sequence of yeast transcriptional activator HAP1. *Cell* **56:** 291–301.

Picard, D., S.J. Salser, and K.R. Yamamoto. 1988. A movable and regulable inactivation function within the steroid binding domain of the glucocorticoid receptor. *Cell* **54:** 1073–1080.

Picard, D., B. Khursheed, M.J. Garabedian, M.G. Fortin, S. Lindquist, and K.R. Yamamoto. 1990. Reduced levels of hsp90 compromise steroid receptor action in vivo. *Nature* **348:** 166–168.

Preston, C.M., M.C. Frame, and M.E.M. Campbell. 1988. A complex formed between cell components and an HSV structural polypeptide binds to a viral immunoglobulin early gene regulatory sequence. *Cell* **52:** 425–434.

Ptashne, M. 1986. Gene regulation by proteins acting nearby and at a distance. *Nature* **322:** 697–701.

————. 1988. How eukaryotic transcriptional activators work. *Nature* **335:** 683–689.

Pugh, B.F. and R. Tjian. 1990. Mechanism of transcriptional activation by Sp1: Evidence for coactivators. *Cell* **61:** 1187–1197.

Samuels, M., A. Fire, and P. Sharp. 1982. Separation and characterization of factors mediating accurate transcription by RNA polymerase II. *J. Biol. Chem.* **257:** 14419–14427.

Santoro, C., M. Mermod, P.C. Andrews, and R. Tjian. 1988. A family of human CCAAT-box binding proteins active in transcription and DNA replication: Cloning and expression of multiple cDNAs. *Nature* **334:** 218–224.

Sawadogo, M. and R.G. Roeder. 1985. Interaction of a gene-specific transcription factor with the adenovirus major late promoter upstream of the TATA box region. *Cell* **43:** 165–175.

Scafe, C., D. Chao, J. Lopes, J.P. Hirsch, S. Henry, and R.A. Young. 1990. RNA polymerase II C-terminal repeat influences response to transcriptional enhancer signals. *Nature* **347:** 491–494.

Schena, M. and K.R. Yamamoto. 1988. Mammalian glucocorticoid receptor derivates enhance transcription in yeast. *Science* **241:** 965–968.

Schmidt, M., C. Kao, R. Pei, and A. Berk. 1989. Yeast TATA box transcription factor gene. *Proc. Natl. Acad. Sci.* **86:** 7785–7789.

Schneider, J.C. and L. Guarente. 1991. Regulation by HAP1 and HAP2/3/4 of the yeast gene encoding cytochrome C1. *Mol. Cell. Biol.* **11:** 4934–4942.

Schule, R., P. Rangarajan, S. Kliewer, L.J. Ransone, J. Bolado, N. Yang, I.M. Verma, and R.M. Evans. 1990. Functional antagonism between oncoprotein c-Jun and the glucocorticoid receptor. *Cell* **62:** 1217–1226.

Stringer, K.F., C.J. Ingles, and J. Greenblatt. 1990. Direct and selective binding of an acidic transcriptional activation domain to the TATA-box factor TFIID. *Nature* **345:** 783–786.

Sweetser, D., M. Nonet, and R.A. Young. 1987. Prokaryotic and eukaryotic RNA polymerases have homologous core subunits. *Proc. Natl. Acad. Sci.* **84:** 1192–1196.

Triezenberg, S.J., K.L. LaMarco, and S.L. McKnight. 1988. Evidence of a DNA:protein interaction that mediates HSV 1 immediate early gene activation by vp16. *Genes. Dev.* **2:** 730–742.

Van Dyke, M., R. Roeder, and M. Sawadogo. 1988. Physical analysis of transcription preinitiation complex assembly on a class II gene promoter. *Science* **241:** 1335–1338.

van Huijsduijnen, R.H., X.Y. Li, D. Black, H. Matthes, C. Benoist, and D. Mathis. 1990. Co-evolution from yeast to mouse: cDNA cloning of the two NF-Y (CP-1/CBF) subunits. *EMBO J.* **9:** 3119–3127.

Verdiere, J., F. Creusot, L. Guarente, and P. Slonimski. 1986. The overproducing CYP1 and underproducing HAP1 mutations are alleles of the same gene. *Curr. Genet.* **10:** 339–342.

Webster, N., J.R. Jin, S. Green, M. Hollis, and P. Chambon. 1988. The yeast UAS$_G$ is a transcriptional enhancer in human HeLa cells in the presence of the GAL4 *trans*activator. *Cell* **52:** 169–178.

Winkler, H., G. Adam, E. Mattes, M. Schanz, A. Hartig, and H. Ruis. 1988. Coordinate control of synthesis of mitochondria and non-mitochondria hemoproteins a binding site of the HAP1 (CYP1) protein in UAS region of the yeast catalase T (CTT) gene. *EMBO J.* **7:** 1799–1804.

Winston, F., D. Chaleff, B. Valent, and G. Fink. 1984. Mutations affecting Ty-mediated expression of the HIS4 gene of *S. cerevisiae*. *Genetics* **107:** 179–197.

Workman, J.L., I.C.A. Taylor, and R. Kingston. 1991. Activation domains of stably bound GAL4 derivatives alleviate repression of promoters by nucleosomes. *Cell* **64:** 533–544.

Yang-Yen, H.-F., J.-C. Chambard, Y.-L. Sun, T. Smeal, T.J. Schmidt, J. Drouin, and M. Karin. 1990. Transcriptional interference between c-*jun* and the glucocorticoid receptor: Mutual inhibition of DNA binding due to direct protein-protein interaction. *Cell* **62:** 1205–1215.

Zitomer, R.S., D.L. Montgomery, D.L. Nichols, and B.D. Hall. 1979. Transcriptional regulation of the yeast cytochrome c gene. *Proc. Natl. Acad. Sci.* **76:** 3627–3631.

39

The Myogenic Helix-Loop-Helix Family: Regulators of Skeletal Muscle Determination and Differentiation

Andrew B. Lassar[1] and Harold Weintraub
Department of Genetics
Fred Hutchinson Cancer Research Center
Seattle, Washington 98104

OVERVIEW

Pivotal in the control of skeletal muscle determination and differentiation are a family of regulatory proteins that can activate the myogenic differentiation program when expressed in a variety of cell types. Induction of both muscle-specific structural genes and other muscle-specific regulators in various cellular backgrounds indicates that the myogenic helix-loop-helix (HLH) genes are nodal points of regulation controlling muscle gene expression. This family of proteins has been evolutionarily conserved, and homologous proteins have been implicated in controlling skeletal muscle gene expression in nematodes, insects, amphibians, birds, and mammals. These proteins share a region of structural homology (basic helix-loop-helix motif) that serves as a DNA binding–protein oligomerization structure. In this chapter, we discuss the structure, function, and regulation of the myogenic HLH proteins and how interactions between these factors and other non-tissue-restricted HLH proteins control muscle gene expression.

INTRODUCTION

A key aspect of development is the specification of cell fate during embryogenesis. The phenotypic manifestation of cell fate (differentiation) is usually uncoupled, both temporally and spatially, from the initial cellular determination events. Therefore, in the absence of biochemical markers,

---

[1]Present address: Department of Biological Chemistry and Molecular Pharmacology, Harvard Medical School, 240 Longwood Avenue, Boston, Massachusetts 02115.

Transcriptional Regulation.
Copyright 1992 Cold Spring Harbor Laboratory Press 0-87969-410-6/92 $3 + 00

cell determination is functionally defined as the latent capacity of a cell or its progeny to elaborate a specific differentiation repertoire in a permissive environment. During the past several years, both genetic and biochemical approaches have shed considerable light on a family of factors that apparently control skeletal muscle cell determination and differentiation in both vertebrates and invertebrates.

The skeletal muscle lineage has been particularly amenable to analysis, due primarily to the availability of cell lines that can be manipulated experimentally to display characteristics of pluripotent mesodermal precursor cells, determined proliferating myoblasts, or differentiated nondividing myotubes. In established myoblast cell lines, deprivation of serum factors constitutes a permissive environment that triggers the differentiation of determined and proliferation-competent myoblasts into syncytial nondividing myotubes. The latter express a repertoire of muscle-specific gene products encoding, among other things, myosin light and heavy chains, desmin, muscle-specific cardiac and skeletal α-actin, muscle creatine kinase, and the subunits of the acetylcholine receptor. In this chapter, we discuss the identification and characterization of a family of nuclear proteins that determine commitment to the myogenic lineage and regulate differentiation of myoblasts into fused myotubes.

TRANSFECTION OF A SINGLE DNA LOCUS CONVERTS 10T1/2 FIBROBLASTS INTO MYOBLASTS

Jones and colleagues were the first to document that brief treatment of a mouse embryonic fibroblast cell line C3H10T1/2 (10T1/2) with the demethylating agent 5-azacytidine would convert these cells into one of three different mesenchymal lineages: myoblast, adipoblast, or chondroblast (Taylor and Jones 1979). The isolation of stable myogenic, adipogenic, and chondrogenic lines after drug treatment indicated that 5-azacytidine was inducing these new phenotypes by a heritable alteration, i.e., demethylation (Chapman et al. 1984; Konieczny and Emerson 1984; Lassar et al. 1986). The high frequency of conversion into the myogenic lineage (50%) led Konieczny and Emerson (1984) to speculate that demethylation of only a few genes was sufficient to establish this lineage. Moreover, transfection experiments employing parental 10T1/2 cells and 5-azacytidine-derived myogenic cell lines (aza-myoblasts) indicated that cloned muscle-specific genes (troponin I and cardiac α-actin) were inert when transfected into 10T1/2 cells but were expressed in aza-myoblasts when induced to differentiate in low serum (Konieczny and Emerson 1985; Lassar et al. 1986). These latter experiments firmly established that 5-azacytidine treatment was inducing the expression of one or more muscle-specific regulators in phenotypically converted cells. Heterokaryon experiments had previously demonstrated that such regulators, functional in *trans*, were present in muscle cells (Blau et al. 1983; Wright 1984).

To test whether demethylation of a single regulatory locus was sufficient to activate myogenesis in 10T1/2 cells, these cells were cotransfected with aza-myoblast genomic DNA and a selectable marker. Transfected colonies expressing several muscle markers were found to arise at a frequency consistent with the transfection of a single locus (or group of tightly linked loci separated by less than 100 kb). Transfection with genomic DNA from a non-azacytidine-derived muscle cell line or primary muscle DNA gave rise to similar frequencies of myogenic colonies, whereas transfection of 10T1/2 genomic DNA did not yield muscle colonies (Konieczny et al. 1986; Lassar et al. 1986). These transfection experiments suggested that a single gene could transform 10T1/2 cells into muscle.

ISOLATION OF A FAMILY OF MYOGENIC REGULATORS

One approach taken to identify the locus capable of activating the muscle program in 10T1/2 cells was focused on isolating cDNAs specifically expressed in proliferating myoblasts and absent from proliferating 10T1/2 cells (Davis et al. 1987; see also Pinney et al. 1988). This approach relied on the fact that most muscle structural genes are expressed upon terminal differentiation and are not present in proliferating myoblasts. Therefore, myoblast-specific RNAs were expected to encode differentiation-independent muscle cell lineage markers as well as regulatory factors necessary to both maintain expression of these markers and activate myogenic differentiation upon mitogen withdrawal. A subtractive hybridization approach identified 26 such myoblast-specific sequences. Subsequent attention was focused on three sequences, MyoD, MyoA, and MyoH, because their expression was not maintained in myoblast variant lines that had lost the capacity to differentiate. Furthermore, these genes could be considered molecular markers of myoblast determination, since their pattern of expression in proliferating cells mirrored the capacity of these cells to differentiate into muscle (under conditions of mitogen deprivation).

To assay what role these sequences might play in activating muscle-specific gene expression, each cDNA was cloned into a long terminal repeat (LTR)-driven expression vehicle and cotransfected with a selectable marker ($G418^R$) into 10T1/2 cells. Forced expression of one of these cDNAs, MyoD, had two apparent phenotypes: The number of $G418^R$ colonies to emerge was reduced by 90% relative to control transfections, and 50% of the colonies that grew could be induced to express myosin heavy chain. Cell lines established from differentiation-competent colonies transfected with LTR-MyoD expressed MyoD, MyoA, and MyoH during proliferation and a repertoire of muscle differentiation markers upon mitogen withdrawal (Davis et al. 1987). Transfection of the MyoH and MyoA constructs (the latter representing only a partial cDNA) neither decreased colony number nor showed any phenotypic conversion. Thus, forced expression of a single myoblast-specific cDNA, MyoD, was sufficient to convert 10T1/2 cells into apparently determined myoblasts, capable of expressing a repertoire of muscle structural genes when challenged to differentiate. A variety of approaches taken by several laboratories has led to the identification of three additional proteins, structurally similar to MyoD, which are also capable of myogenic conversion of 10T1/2 cells: myogenin, isolated both by a subtractive hybridization strategy (Wright et al. 1989) and by homology with MyoD (Edmondson and Olson 1989); Myf-5 (Braun et al. 1989a); and herculin/MRF4/Myf-6 (Rhodes and Konieczny 1989; Braun et al. 1990b; Miner and Wold 1990). MyoD, myogenin, and Myf-5 have each been demonstrated to be nuclear proteins, and in the cases of MyoD and myogenin, to be phosphorylated in the cell (Tapscott et al. 1988; Braun et al. 1990a; Brennan and Olson 1990).

In addition to the MyoD-related genes, two other potential myogenic regulatory loci have been identified. In the first case, Stavnezer and colleagues have documented that muscle differentiation markers (and endogenous MyoD synthesis; E. Stavnezer, pers. comm.) can be activated in primary quail fibroblasts after infection with a retrovirus containing the *ski* oncogene (Colmenares and Stavnezer 1989); *ski* has not been shown to activate muscle genes in established fibroblast lines. In the second case, an as yet uncloned locus, *myd*, present in a human genomic cosmid library, is capable of activating both muscle differentiation and MyoD synthesis in transfected 10T1/2 cells; this finding suggested that a pathway exists in which *myd* regulates MyoD expression (Pinney et al. 1988). However, recent findings indicate that all cloned skeletal myogenic regulators can cross-activate one another (see below); therefore, defining epistatic relationships between various muscle regulators, in transfected 10T1/2 cells, are complicated by the potential for myogenic regulator cross-activation in this cellular background. In addition, cosmids containing genomic MyoD can independently initiate myogenesis in 10T1/2 cells (S. Tapscott et al. unpubl.), suggesting that MyoD may be regulated by factors other than *myd* (see below).

MYOD ACTIVATES MUSCLE-SPECIFIC GENE EXPRESSION IN MANY BUT NOT ALL CELL TYPES

Activation of muscle genes induced by MyoD expression was not unique to 10T1/2 cells. Transfection of MyoD into a number of other murine fibroblast cell lines (Swiss 3T3, NIH-3T3, and L cells) similarly activated muscle differentiation markers (Davis et al. 1987). Because the ancestry of established cell lines is uncertain, it was possible that all these lines represented dedifferentiated myoblasts; if this were the case, MyoD would be complementing a tissue-culture-induced deficiency rather than rerouting a developmental program. However, infection of primary dermal fibroblasts with a MyoD-encoding retrovirus led to the activation of myosin heavy chain and desmin, establishing that MyoD-induced myogenic conversion was not limited to established cell lines (Weintraub et al. 1989).

We also examined the capacity of MyoD to activate muscle-specific gene expression both in nonmesodermal cells and in cell lines already displaying a lineage-specific differentiation program. LTR-driven expression of MyoD was shown to activate both myosin heavy chain and desmin expression (as assayed by immunofluorescence) in a line of liver-derived cells (BNL), melanoma cells (B16), neuroblastoma cells (B50 clone 5), and several adipocyte cell lines (F442A, 3T3L1, and TA1). Northern analysis revealed that myoblast determination markers, MyoA and MyoH, were induced in proliferating melanoma, neuroblastoma, and adipocyte cells by MyoD expression; in addition, myosin heavy chain and myosin light chain 2 were also expressed in each of these MyoD-expressing cell types following serum withdrawal (Weintraub et al. 1989). In MyoD-expressing neuroblastoma and melanoma cells, the extant differentiation program was coexpressed with muscle structural genes, whereas the endogenous program was apparently suppressed in adipocytes converted into muscle.

Other workers later observed MyoD-induced activation of muscle-specific genes in other differentiated cell types, including osteosarcoma cells (P. Jones, pers. comm.), baby hamster kidney (S. Hauschka and R. Palmiter, pers. comm.), and primary chicken gizzard smooth muscle, chondrocyte, and pigmented retinal epithelial cells (Choi et al. 1990). In the last two cell types, the resident differentiation program was extinguished in parallel with MyoD expression. In all chicken primary cell types examined, MyoD induced expression of desmin, α-actins, myosin heavy and light chains, titin, nebulin, α-actinin, troponin I, tropomyosin, and myomesin, as well as the assembly of a highly organized myofibrillar apparatus, indicating the coordinated expression of a cohort of muscle structural genes (Choi et al. 1990).

The capacity of MyoD to activate muscle gene expression in various cellular contexts implies that no tissue-specific factors other than MyoD are needed to *initiate* muscle differentiation in the mesodermal and non-mesodermal cells tested. Furthermore, if additional muscle-specific factors are necessary to execute this program, such factors are themselves activated by MyoD in these responding cells. In fact, it is now clear that MyoD recruits the expression of other muscle-specific regulators, including myogenin (see below) and at least two additional factors that bind to muscle-specific regulatory regions (MEF2 and MCAT; Lassar et al. 1991).

In contrast to the above results, MyoD has been reported not to activate muscle-specific gene expression in primary hepatocytes (Schafer et al. 1990) and in some established cell lines: CV1, HeLa, and HepG2 (Weintraub et al. 1989; Schafer et al. 1990). In these three cell lines, not only are the resident muscle structural genes refractory to MyoD-induced activation, but also cloned muscle genes cotransfected with LTR-MyoD are transcriptionally inert (Weintraub et al. 1989). These negative results may reflect the presence of transforming HPV sequences in HeLa cells, an activated n-RAS in HepG2 (Richards et al. 1990), or other genetic alterations associated with establishment of cell lines. Many oncogenes are known to interfere with differentiation and, in the case of myogenesis, to inhibit directly both expression of MyoD RNA and the activity of the MyoD protein (Lassar et al. 1989a). Heterokaryon analysis indicated that fusion of CV1 cells or HepG2 cells stably expressing MyoD with 10T1/2 cells resulted in activation of muscle genes in heterokaryons (Weintraub et al. 1989; Schafer et al. 1990), suggesting that factors in 10T1/2 cells can complement these two cell lines for muscle-specific gene expression. Thus, CV1 and HepG2 cells either lack components necessary for the activity of MyoD or contain inhibitors of MyoD (as suggested by the work of Schafer et al. 1990) that are titrated or inactivated in 10T1/2 heterokaryons. In CV1 cells stably expressing LTR-MyoD, a complex containing MyoD and other HLH proteins (E proteins, see below) is apparent in nuclear extracts, although these cells do not activate myogenin, MCAT-binding activity, or muscle-specific gene expression. Thus, the block to muscle differentiation in CV1 cells lies distal to complex formation of MyoD and E proteins.

Studies by Gurdon and colleagues indicate that injection of *Xenopus laevis* MyoD RNA into the early frog embryo can activate cardiac α-actin expression in "animal cap" ectoderm that would otherwise not express this gene (Hopwood and Gurdon 1990). Interestingly, another muscle differentiation marker failed to be induced in these animal caps, and the cardiac α-actin expression disappeared as the injected MyoD RNA was degraded. Both the incompleteness and the transience of muscle gene activation could reflect either the transience of MyoD expression from the injected RNA or the absence of other factors required for proper MyoD function. Alternatively, other gene products (e.g., other basic-HLH proteins that are activated during development) may have inhibited MyoD activity (see below). Nevertheless, these experiments clearly indicate that transient expression of MyoD is not adequate to commit these developing tissues to myogenesis.

MYOGENIC REGULATORS ARE MEMBERS OF THE HLH FAMILY

A region of extreme sequence similarity consisting of about 65 amino acids is shared by the myogenic regulators MyoD, myogenin, Myf-5, and herculin. This motif (termed basic-HLH) is also present in a number of other regulatory proteins and has been proposed to encode a stretch of basic amino acids just amino-terminal to two amphipathic α-helices separated by an intervening loop (Murre et al. 1989a; see Murre and Baltimore, this volume). Proteins that share this basic-HLH motif (for review, see Benezra et al. 1990) include proteins that affect cell growth (the *myc* protein family, Lyl-1, and SCL), that play important roles in *Drosophila* sex determination and/or early development (twist, hairy, extramacrochaetae [emc], enhancer of split, achaete-scute, and daughterless), that are specific DNA-binding proteins (the E2A gene products: E12 and E47; E2-2, TFE3, AP4, and USF), that interact with the yeast centromere (CBF), that inhibit other HLH interactions (ID, inhibitor of DNA binding), and the skeletal muscle-specific proteins that have high homology with MyoD over the basic-HLH domains (MyoD, myogenin, Myf-5, and herculin/MRF4/Myf-6). The basic-HLH domain was shown to be both necessary and sufficient for myogenic conversion of 10T1/2 cells by MyoD (Tapscott et al. 1988) and/or site-specific DNA binding by both MyoD and E2A proteins (Lassar et al. 1989b; Murre et al. 1989a; Davis et al. 1990; Voronova and Baltimore 1990), suggesting that this structural motif plays a crucial role in the biology of all basic-HLH family members. The DNA-binding sequence recognized by several different basic-HLH proteins includes the core sequence CANNTG (see Blackwell and Weintraub 1990), indicating that aspects of this shared protein structure confer potentially overlapping DNA binding site specificities.

MYOGENIC REGULATORS ARE SKELETAL-MUSCLE-SPECIFIC

MyoD, myogenin, Myf-5, and herculin are expressed only in skeletal muscle throughout development (Davis et al. 1987; Braun et al. 1989b,

1990b; Edmondson and Olson 1989; Rhodes and Konieczny 1989; Wright et al. 1989; Miner and Wold 1990), and each has a unique pattern of expression. For example, in mouse somites, Myf-5 RNA accumulation precedes that of myogenin, which in turn precedes MyoD expression; in contrast, Myf-5 expression in limb bud precedes the coordinate activation of MyoD and myogenin, and herculin expression is restricted to adult skeletal muscle (Rhodes and Konieczny 1989; Sassoon et al. 1989; Braun et al. 1990b; Miner and Wold 1990; M. Buckingham, pers. comm.).

The distinct expression patterns of these proteins may reflect regulatory differences in the lineages constituting somitic, limb bud, and adult skeletal muscle, and their temporal expression pattern raises the possibility that these genes induce (and potentially repress) one another via a regulatory cascade. Although cardiac and skeletal muscle share many muscle-specific structural proteins, none of these skeletal-muscle-specific HLH proteins has been detected in cardiac muscle.

Each of these proteins has been demonstrated to activate muscle-specific gene expression in transfected 10T1/2 cells, consistent with their strong sequence similarity across the basic-HLH domain and with the ability of the 65-amino-acid basic-HLH domain of MyoD alone to activate myogenesis in 10T1/2 cells (Tapscott et al. 1988). Because these factors cross-activate one another in stably transfected 10T1/2 cells (see below), it has been difficult to assay the role of any of these factors individually; however, transient cotransfection of muscle reporter constructs with different myogenic HLH constructs indicates that these regulators have different transcriptional activation properties (Yutzey et al. 1990). Established murine myogenic cell lines, without exception, express more than one of these regulators (Davis et al. 1987; Braun et al. 1989b; Edmonson and Olson 1989; Montarras et al. 1989; Wright et al. 1989; Peterson et al. 1990). In comparing these lines, a pattern emerges that MyoD and/or Myf-5 is expressed in proliferating myoblasts and that upon differentiation, all lines induce myogenin expression. The importance of myogenin in the activation of at least some differentiation markers has been demonstrated in BC3H1 and L6 myogenic cell lines, in which antisense myogenin oligonucleotides have been reported to inhibit acetylcholine receptor formation and muscle creatine kinase activation (Brunetti and Goldfine 1990; Florini and Ewton 1990). Although their individual roles have not yet been elucidated, the expression of MyoD or Myf-5 in proliferating myoblasts may indicate that these two gene products are in a signal transduction pathway that senses extracellular cues and, given the correct stimuli, initiate myogenesis by recruiting expression of myogenin, MCAT, and MEF2.

SKELETAL MUSCLE HLH PROTEINS ARE EVOLUTIONARILY
CONSERVED MYOGENIC REGULATORS

Proteins sharing homology with the mammalian myogenic HLH family have been identified in chicken (Lin et al. 1989), quail (Charles de la Brousse and Emerson 1990), *X. laevis* (Hopwood et al. 1989; Harvey 1990; Scales et al. 1990), *Drosophila* (Michelson et al. 1990; B. Paterson, pers. comm.), and *Caenorhabditis elegans* (Krause et al. 1990). In each case examined, the expression of these homologs has been shown to be a very early step in myogenesis and to be limited either to skeletal muscle or to the anlage which gives rise to this lineage. For example, in *C. elegans*, an organism in which embryonic cell fate can be predicted by cell lineage, a protein homologous to MyoD is expressed only in cells clonally restricted to give rise to body wall muscle and is detected several cell divisions prior to terminal differentiation (Krause et al. 1990). Similarly, in *X. laevis*, MyoD is expressed in gastrula mesoderm 2 hours prior to the accumulation of cardiac α-actin, and as noted above, ectopic expression of *Xenopus* MyoD in embryonic ectodermal tissue has been demonstrated to induce the expression of this skeletal muscle marker (Hopwood and Gurdon 1990). In vertebrates, regions outside the basic-HLH are also conserved among MyoD homologs, suggesting an important role for regions of the molecule outside the DNA-binding domain. One such conserved region in vertebrate MyoD homologs is the acidic amino terminus of MyoD, which contains a powerful transcriptional activation domain as assayed in vivo (Weintraub et al. 1991) and has been shown to mediate cooperative DNA binding to a target site in vitro (Weintraub et al. 1990). Apparently, the function of these structurally related proteins has been conserved during evolution, probably reflecting the ancient phylogenetic origin of both target sites and the regulatory molecules that coordinate skeletal muscle gene expression.

AUTOGENOUS ACTIVATION AND CROSS-TALK BETWEEN
MYOGENIC REGULATORS

Because signals that induce new cell fates are likely to be transiently expressed during embryogenesis, a stable epigenetic "memory" of these events must be maintained in the induced cell type. One plausible mechanism for generating memory of a transient inductive signal is the activation of a regulator that maintains its own synthesis (i.e., a positive feedback loop). In fact, several *Drosophila* and *C. elegans* proteins that control or affect cell fate have been demonstrated to maintain their own synthesis once activated (Hiromi and Gehring 1987; Bienz and Tremml 1988; Kuziora and McGinnis 1988; Way and Chalfie 1989). MyoD appears to display this capacity in some but not all cellular contexts (Thayer et al. 1989). Expression of exogenous MyoD in 10T1/2 cells activates the endogenous locus (Thayer et al. 1989), and this activation is maintained even after segregation of the exogenous MyoD from the cell (Thayer and Weintraub 1990). However, maintenance of the activity of the MyoD locus may not depend solely on the continued expression of MyoD (see below); myoblasts exposed to agents that severely depress or extinguish MyoD synthesis (bromodeoxyuridine [BrdU], activated *ras*) reexpress the myogenic phenotype once these inhibitors are removed (see, e.g., Gossett et al. 1988; A.B. Lassar; S. Tapscott; both unpubl.). Similarly, transient treatment of myoblasts with protein synthesis inhibitors does not "deprogram" these cells upon removal of the inhibitor (H. Weintraub, unpubl.).

In addition to MyoD, other members of the myogenic HLH family have been shown both to activate their own synthesis and to cross-activate one another (Braun et al. 1989; Rhodes and Konieczny 1989; Thayer et al. 1989; Miner and Wold 1990). These positive loops may contribute to the maintenance of cell determination as well as ensure that a sufficient amount and number of myogenic regulators are recruited to support muscle differentiation.

MYOD EXPRESSION IS REGULATED IN BOTH *CIS* AND *TRANS*

MyoD is located on human chromosome 11. Introduction of this chromosome from primary human fibroblasts (in which the MyoD locus is inactive) into 10T1/2 cells results in efficient activation of both the human and mouse MyoD (Thayer and Weintraub 1990). This experiment indicates that factors preexist in 10T1/2 cells that can activate MyoD synthesis from the human chromosome, but that the endogenous mouse locus is silenced in *cis*, perhaps due to methylation. Both the hypermethylation of MyoD in 10T1/2 cells (Jones et al. 1990) and its activation by 5-azacytidine are of course consistent with this model. Because the human fibroblast MyoD locus is available to respond to such activators in the context of the 10T1/2 cell, whereas 10T1/2 x human skin fibroblast hybrids do not activate MyoD, the MyoD locus must be silenced in primary human fibroblasts in *trans*, perhaps due to repressive loci on human fibroblast chromosomes 4 and/or 8 (Thayer and Weintraub 1990). In this scenario, the human MyoD locus, free from the repressive human fibroblast environment, responds to activators in 10T1/2 cells and, in turn, activates synthesis of mouse MyoD.

Data of Jones et al. (1990) indicate that the MyoD locus is significantly undermethylated in aza-myoblasts relative to 10T1/2 cells, suggesting that methylation may in fact directly regulate expression of this gene in 10T1/2 cells. On the other hand, hypermethylation of the MyoD locus, which is a CpG island, may occur only in established cell lines (Jones et al. 1990) and therefore may not be relevant to developmental regulation of the gene. Thus, although positive regulatory loops, *cis* control, and *trans* factors have been documented to control expression of the myogenic HLH family in established cell lines, it is unclear what events lead to activation of these genes during normal development. A challenge for future research will entail extending the observations made in tissue culture systems to include an exploration of the events that lead to induction of these genes during embryogenesis.

ACTIVATED *RAS* AND *FOS* PREVENT MYOGENESIS BOTH BY INHIBITING EXPRESSION OF MYOD AND BY ALTERING MYOD PROTEIN ACTIVITY

Oncogenic transformation of myoblasts by various oncogenes (*src, fps, erbA, ras, fos, myc,* and E1A) and constitutive expression or administration of various growth factors (proliferin, FGF, TGF-β) have been shown to inhibit myogenic differentiation (for review, see Lassar et al. 1989a). Both activated *ras* and *fos* inhibit terminal muscle differentiation via suppression of both MyoD and myogenin expression (Konieczny et al. 1989; Lassar et al. 1989a). LTR-driven expression of MyoD in either activated *ras*- or *fos*-transformed myoblasts results in reactivation of both the endogenous MyoD and myogenin loci and allows these cells to express terminal differentiation markers. Thus, the repressive activity of activated *ras* or *fos* can be reversed by constitutive expression of LTR-MyoD. It is possible that these oncogenes act to somehow attenuate the autoactivation of the MyoD locus such that MyoD expression falls below a threshold required to maintain the activity of the gene. Forced expression of LTR-MyoD may relieve this repression by supplying a sufficient amount of gene product to both reactivate the endogenous gene and initiate differentiation.

Whereas forced expression of MyoD can reactivate muscle gene expression in *ras*- or *fos*-transformed myoblasts, high-level expression of either activated *ras* or *fos* can inhibit the activity of LTR-MyoD to *trans*-activate muscle-specific enhancers in a transient cotransfection, indicating that these agents can suppress the activity of the MyoD protein (Lassar et al. 1989a). We have proposed that these different phenotypes reflect relatively higher amounts of oncogene products in the transient assay than occur in stably transformed cell lines and thus that the activity of MyoD is modulated by the ratio of MyoD to oncogene product, rather than by the absolute amount. The mechanism by which oncogene products inhibit MyoD activity is not understood; however, recent data that *fos* and *jun* gene products can directly interact with other transcription factors (the glucocorticoid receptor; Diamond et al. 1990; Jonat et al. 1990; Schüle et al. 1990; Yang-Yen et al. 1990) raise the possibility that similar interactions may modulate the activity of the myogenic HLH family. Data of Peterson et al. (1990) suggest that a mutagenized myoblast cell line that fails to differentiate may also contain a negative regulator of myogenic HLH function.

Interestingly, substitution of DNA with BrdU, an agent that inhibits differentiation of several cell lineages, also extinguishes MyoD expression and muscle differentiation. Expression of LTR-MyoD in these cells reactivates muscle differentiation but not the endogenous MyoD locus in BrdU-substituted cells (Tapscott et al. 1989). Perhaps the pleiotropic effects of BrdU on so many different differentiation programs reflect the repression of similar positive regulatory loops in other lineages.

MYOGENIC HLH PROTEINS BIND TO MUSCLE-SPECIFIC REGULATORY REGIONS

The regulatory regions necessary for tissue-specific expression of various muscle differentiation markers have been defined in several laboratories (for review, see Lassar et al. 1989b). Buskin and Hauschka (1989) were the first to demonstrate that a muscle-specific nuclear factor could interact with a sequence (MEF1 site), containing the core sequence CANNTG, within the muscle creatine kinase (MCK) enhancer. It was subsequently established that bacterially produced or in-vitro-translated myogenic HLH proteins could directly bind the MEF1 site in vitro (Lassar et al. 1989b; Braun et al. 1990a; Brennan and Olson 1990) and that this site in the MCK enhancer in vivo was occupied by factors specifically in differentiated myotubes (Mueller and Wold 1989). Mutational analysis has revealed that one or more CANNTG sequence motifs, which are bound by MyoD in vitro, are necessary for high-level tissue-specific expression of MCK (Lassar et al. 1989b), myosin light chain 1,3 (Wentworth et al. 1991), the α subunit of the acetylcholine receptor (Piette et al. 1990), and the cardiac α-actin gene (Sartorelli et al. 1990). Concatamers of MEF1 sites placed upstream of basal promoters are sufficient for muscle-specific expression and for MyoD-mediated *trans*-activation in transient assay (Piette et al. 1990; Weintraub et al. 1990).

Interestingly, the MEF1 sites are often duplicated in muscle-specific regulatory regions, and at least two such elements are necessary for maximal MyoD *trans*-activation either in their native configuration (Lassar et al. 1989b; Piette et al. 1990; N. Rosenthal, pers. comm.) or upstream of a minimal promoter (Weintraub et al. 1990); a single MEF1 site upstream of a minimal promoter can apparently bind MyoD in vivo (as assayed by competition) but does not confer *trans*-activation by MyoD (Weintraub et al. 1990). MyoD binds cooperatively to two nearby sites (Weintraub et al. 1990). Simultaneous occupancy of at least two MyoD-binding sites is necessary for efficient stimulation of a basal promoter unless a second site is filled by a second type of transcriptional activator, as in the human cardiac α-actin promoter, in which simultaneous occupancy of a MyoD-binding site and flanking SRF and Sp1 sites by their cognate factors is necessary for transcriptional activation (Sartorelli et al. 1990). Because all myogenic HLH proteins bind to the MEF1 site in vitro, it is not clear in cells expressing more than one such regulator which one of these factors occupies these sites in vivo.

THE HLH OLIGOMERIZATION MOTIF MEDIATES ASSOCIATION BETWEEN THE MYOGENIC HLH PROTEINS AND THE E2A GENE PRODUCTS

It was initially shown by Murre et al. (1989b) that two HLH proteins, E12 and E47 (encoded by the E2A gene), which are expressed in many cell types (including muscle), can form heterodimers with the cell-type-specific HLH gene products, MyoD and *Drosophila* T3 achaete-scute (Murre et al. 1989b). Moreover, in vitro DNA-binding assays indicated that hetero-oligomers between E12 and MyoD bind tightly to the MEF1 site in the MCK enhancer, whereas E12 or MyoD homo-oligomers bind weakly to this site.

In muscle, three lines of evidence support the notion that the non-tissue-restricted E2A gene products, E12 and E47, interact with the myogenic HLH proteins in vivo: (1) 10T1/2 cells expressing antisense E2A transcripts contain low levels of E2A gene products and display less terminal muscle differentiation when infected with retroviral MyoD; (2) cotransfection of MyoD and E2A gene products into COS cells indicates that these factors synergistically enhance transcription of a reporter gene containing multiple MyoD-binding sites; and (3) mobility shift assays of muscle cell nuclear extracts, double-shifted with specific antisera, have identified complexes (with the MEF1 site) containing either MyoD or myogenin in association with E2A gene products. (Homo-oligomeric complexes of these proteins bound to the MEF1 site were not detected [Lassar et al. 1991], implying that homotypic complexes of either muscle-specific [MyoD or myogenin] or general [E2A] HLH proteins do not interact with this site in the cell.) It should be noted that inhibition of myogenesis by antisense E2A transcripts as well as "super shift" of MyoD or myogenin complexes with anti-E12/E47 antisera do not rule out the possibility that other E proteins (that are cross-reactive with anti-E12/E47 antisera and whose transcripts hybridize to antisense E12 RNA) rather than the E2A gene products per se are required for myogenesis. Because there are at least four different mammalian "E proteins," containing a high degree of homology with the basic HLH domain of E12/E47, that are detectable in skeletal muscle (E12, E47, E-2-2, and HEB; Henthorn et al. 1990; R. Kingston; V. Mahdavi; both pers. comm.), it is unclear whether all E proteins or only a subset of this protein family is necessary for skeletal myogenesis. Studies that investigate the association of the myogenic HLH proteins with *specific* members of the E protein family are necessary to further clarify this issue.

The HLH domains of MyoD and the E2A gene product, E47, are alone sufficient to mediate hetero-oligomerization, whereas the upstream basic region is needed, in addition, for specific DNA interaction (Davis et al. 1990; Voronova and Baltimore 1990). Mutations in the basic region yield molecules capable of hetero-oligomerization but not DNA binding; such mutants extinguish wild-type MyoD activity in vivo, indicating that functional MyoD is in an oligomeric state in the cell (Davis et al. 1990). By promoting hetero-oligomerization, the HLH domain juxtaposes heterotypic basic regions to generate a different DNA-binding specificity than either homo-oligomeric species (Blackwell and Weintraub 1990]. Thus, HLH-mediated hetero-oligomerization promotes increased DNA binding affinity, alters the site specificity of the individual components, and combines the transcriptional activation domains of both MyoD and the E2A gene products into a single complex (Henthorn et al. 1990; Weintraub et al. 1991).

Alterations of conserved hydrophobic residues or insertions of prolines into the putative amphipathic helices disrupt oligomerization and DNA binding (Davis et al. 1990; Voronova and Baltimore 1990). Although the sequence of the intervening loop region is highly conserved in the myogenic HLH family, extensive substitutions can be made in this region without loss of function. However, the necessity of helix breakers in this segment (as indicated by mutational analysis) suggests that the loop region may serve both to properly space and to structurally uncouple the two helices from one another (Davis et al. 1990).

Helix swap experiments indicate that helices from some HLH family members (T4 achaete-scute), when substituted into MyoD, can support hetero-oligomerization, DNA binding, and myogenesis, whereas substitution of the helices of c-*myc* into MyoD yields inert molecules in these same assays (Davis et al. 1990). The apparent functional equivalence of MyoD and T4 achaete-scute HLH domains is consistent with previous genetic and biochemical arguments that the achaete-scute gene products functionally interact with daughterless, an apparent E2A gene product homolog in *Drosophila* (Murre et al. 1989b). Moreover, these results confirm genetically and biochemically that the HLH sequence motif is functionally similar in some HLH family members (T4 achaete-scute and MyoD) and functionally dissimilar in others (*myc* and MyoD).

THE MYOD BASIC REGION CONTAINS A RECOGNITION CODE FOR MUSCLE-SPECIFIC GENE ACTIVATION

Swapping the basic regions from E12 or T4 achaete-scute into MyoD yielded molecules (termed MyoD-E12 basic and MyoD-T4 basic, respectively) capable of binding the MEF1 site in vitro, yet incapable of either myogenic conversion or *trans*-activation of muscle reporter genes in vivo (Davis et al. 1990). Employing a reporter gene containing MyoD-binding sites located downstream from the transcription start site, it has been shown that MyoD-E12 basic can bind the MEF1 site in vivo and inhibit transcription elongation (Weintraub et al. 1991). Back mutations of the E12 basic region in MyoD-E12 basic to the corresponding residues in MyoD indicate that a specific alanine and threonine conserved in the basic regions of all myogenic HLH proteins are necessary for the functional activity of this chimeric protein. Thus, these residues in the basic region of the myogenic HLH proteins have been operationally defined to be a recognition code for muscle-specific gene activation and indicate that the capacity for specific DNA binding is insufficient to activate the muscle program.

Interestingly, transcriptional activation by the MyoD-E12 basic chimera is cell-type-specific. Whereas this fusion is inactive in 10T1/2 cells, it is able to activate transcription of a promoter containing a multimerized MyoD-binding site in CV1 cells (Weintraub et al. 1991). This finding suggests that transcriptional activation by HLH regulators requires cell-type-specific recognition factors that interact with the basic region of HLH proteins. It is presently unclear how these putative cell-type-specific recognition factors work; however, it is possible that they either augment the activity of the MyoD activation domain or alter the conformation of HLH proteins to unmask a cryptic activation domain in the MyoD/E protein hetero-oligomer (see below). Addition of the VP16 activation domain into MyoD-E12 basic restores the ability of this fusion to *trans*-activate a promoter containing a multimerized MyoD-binding site in 10T1/2 cells, indicating that the requirement for the cell-type-specific recognition element can be abrogated by the presence of a strong activation domain.

Fusion proteins made between the GAL4 DNA-binding domain and either E2A proteins or MyoD and Myf-5 indicate that the transcriptional activation domains of these HLH proteins lie outside the basic-HLH motif (Braun et al. 1990a; Henthorn et al. 1990; Weintraub et al. 1991) and that this region of MyoD (contained in the amino-terminal 56 amino acids) can be functionally replaced by the transcriptional activation domain of VP16 (H. Weintraub et al., in prep.). That the activation domains of MyoD, Myf-5, and the E proteins may be cryptic and require an event that unmasks them is suggested by deletion analysis of GAL4-HLH chimeras, which indicate that deletion of regions outside the activation domain greatly potentiates the activity of the GAL4-HLH fusions (Braun et al. 1990a; Henthorn et al. 1990; Weintraub et al. 1991). The inability of MyoD mutants containing either the E12 or T4 achaete-scute basic regions to activate transcription implies that these activation domains, in the context of MyoD, are not sufficient to activate transcription in the absence of a MyoD basic domain. These observations have led us to propose that joint recognition, direct or indirect, of both the DNA sequence bound by MyoD and specific residues of the MyoD basic region is required for myogenic activation. This finding helps resolve the paradox that the E2A gene products are present in nonmuscle cells and can, in principle, bind to muscle-specific enhancers sharing the CANNTG core, yet myogenesis is not activated. (On the other hand, E2A-MyoD hetero-oligomers show a binding site preference distinct from either homo-oligomeric species [Blackwell and Weintraub 1990]; thus, homo-oligomeric E2A gene products may fail to bind muscle-specific regulatory regions in vivo [also see above].) Why are the E2A and MyoD activation domains nonfunctional when the complex binds to the wrong DNA sequence or when the wrong amino acids are present in the basic region of MyoD? It would seem that either the activation region of MyoD is buried only to be released when the "correct" interactions occur at the DNA-binding site or that another factor (a coactivator) interacts specifically with the MyoD basic region and is necessary to augment the activity of MyoD.

THE HLH DOMAIN OF MYOD CAN MEDIATE CELL CYCLE WITHDRAWAL INDEPENDENT OF MUSCLE DIFFERENTIATION

The initial transfection experiments of MyoD into 10T1/2 cells indicated that high-level expression of MyoD inhibited colony formation (Davis et al. 1987); this was originally interpreted to reflect cell cycle withdrawal of MyoD-transfected cells due to promiscuous differentiation. Subsequent work has established that MyoD-induced cell cycle withdrawal can also occur in transiently transfected or microinjected transformed cell lines that fail to differentiate into muscle (Crescenzi et al. 1990; Sorrentino et al. 1990). Moreover, cell cycle withdrawal can be divorced from muscle differentiation, since mutations of the MyoD basic region that render the molecule incapable of initiating muscle differentiation still effect cell cycle withdrawal (Crescenzi et al. 1990; Sorrentino et al. 1990). Because the HLH domain of MyoD is necessary for cell cycle withdrawal, it is possible that this phenomenon may be mediated by hetero-oligomerization with another HLH protein(s) necessary for progression through the cell cycle. It is an attractive possibility that a similar type of HLH interaction is responsible for terminal cell cycle withdrawal during muscle differentiation. A tempting speculation would be an interaction with Myc, an HLH protein known to be required for cell cycle progression; however, all attempts to detect such an interaction in vitro have failed. It should be noted that MyoD expression does not result in obligate withdrawal from the cell cycle, since this protein is expressed in proliferating myoblasts. It is possible that cell cycle withdrawal requires very high levels of MyoD expression. Indeed, the instances when MyoD-induced cell cycle withdrawal have been observed have all employed transient expression of MyoD, which may result in a higher level of MyoD than occurs in proliferating myoblasts.

HLH PROTEINS INTERACT WITH ONE ANOTHER TO ENHANCE OR EXTINGUISH DNA BINDING

Genetic experiments indicate that a network of hetero-oligomer HLH interactions control several developmental events in *Drosophila*. Both the ubiquitously expressed HLH protein, daughterless, and members of the neural-specific achaete-scute gene cluster are required for peripheral neurogenesis. In contrast, other HLH proteins (hairy, extramacrochaetae, and members of the enhancer of split cluster) are repressors of peripheral and/or central neurogenesis; their mutation or deletion affects additional neural tissue. Neurogenesis in *Drosophila* is apparently controlled by a balance between positively acting HLH proteins and negative HLH regulators (for review, see Campos-Ortega and Knust 1990). In addition to regulating neurogenesis, both daughterless (an autosomal locus) and the X-linked achaete-scute T4 gene play a central role in transducing the X chromosome to autosome ratio (Gaudy et al. 1988; Cline 1988; Cronmiller et al. 1988; Torres and Sanchez 1989), probably by titrating either one another or other HLH proteins, to initiate a cascade of events regulating both sex determination and dosage compensation. Thus, complex developmental pathways are regulated by an interplay of apparently positively and negatively acting HLH proteins.

Similarly, mammalian skeletal myogenesis is controlled by interactions between both tissue-specific (MyoD, myogenin, Myf-5, herculin) and more widely expressed HLH proteins (E2A gene products) and, like *Drosophila* neurogenesis, may also be regulated by HLH repressors. A putative negative regulator of mammalian HLH protein interactions was initially identified in Friend erythroleukemia cells but is expressed in many cell types, including muscle. This protein, termed ID for inhibitor of DNA binding, has an HLH domain without an adjacent basic region and is analogous to dominant negative MyoD mutants with deletions in the basic region (Benezra et al. 1990). ID associates efficiently with the E2A gene products, E12 and E47, and less well with MyoD; heterooligomers between these proteins and ID extinguishes their DNA binding in vitro. In transient transfections, ID expression inhibits the ability of MyoD to *trans*-activate a muscle reporter gene. Similarly, muscle differentiation is delayed in a muscle cell line stably transfected with an ID expression vector (R. Benezra and H. Weintraub, in prep.). Interestingly, ID RNA and protein levels decrease upon myogenic differentiation (Benezra et al. 1990; R. Benezra, unpubl.). This raises the possibility that aspects of muscle differentiation are controlled by titration of transcription factors (MyoD, myogenin, and the E2A gene products) with negative regulators of DNA binding. The *Drosophila* HLH protein extramacrochaetae also lacks a basic region adjacent to the HLH motif and may act to inhibit peripheral neurogenesis by similarly titrating positive HLH regulators of neurogenesis (Ellis et al. 1990; Garrell and Modolell 1990).

MyoD protein is present in proliferating myoblasts, which do not express differentiation markers, implying that MyoD activity is somehow masked during proliferation. On the other hand, because LTR-MyoD expression activates endogenous MyoD, MyoA, and MyoH in proliferating 10T1/2 cells, MyoD has apparent biological effects during proliferation. The differential control of these two patterns of gene expression is presently unclear. The identification of a negative competitor of MyoD-E2A interaction (ID) has provided one plausible mechanism for cryptic MyoD activity in proliferating myoblasts. However, gel shift experiments suggest that factors independent of ID also serve to silence the transcriptional activation properties of the MyoD-E2A complex in proliferating cells (A.B. Lassar et al., in prep.) or in myoblasts exposed to the differentiation inhibitor TGF-β (Brennan et al. 1991). In this manner, multiple mechanisms of regulation may generate a failsafe to ensure that only under the appropriate environmental conditions will terminal differentiation markers be activated in the determined myoblast.

CONCLUSIONS AND PERSPECTIVES: A NODAL POINT
FOR REGULATION

The capacity of MyoD to activate both its own synthesis and a battery of muscle-specific genes in several different mesodermal and non-mesodermal cell types suggests that stable activation of this gene (or the other myogenic HLH regulators) is a nodal decision point that commits responsive cells to the skeletal muscle lineage. This type of hierarchical genetic circuitry in which a cell-type-specific "master controlling gene" induces a cascade of intermediate regulators, which together coordinate and activate a battery of downstream genes, is to be contrasted with a completely combinatorial means of regulation in which various combinations of non-tissue-specific regulators determine cell type. In the former case, phenotype is determined by decree, in the latter by consensus. Of course, the initial activation of a "master controlling gene" sitting at a regulatory nodal point may itself be controlled by a combination of multiple upstream regulators. However, the continued expression of these upstream factors may be unnecessary due to the capacity of the myogenic HLH genes to activate themselves.

In the case of skeletal myogenesis, it is clear that an interplay of tissue-specific regulators (MyoD, myogenin, Myf-5, herculin) and non-tissue-restricted factors (E12, E47, and ID) specifies activation of muscle-specific genes. Although MyoD may be the only tissue-specific factor necessary to initiate myogenesis in different cell types, activity of this molecule can clearly be negatively modulated by both environmental conditions (serum factors) and cellular context (CV1, HepG2, and HeLa). Thus, skeletal myogenesis is coordinated both by tissue-specific factors that sit at a nodal point in a regulatory hierarchy and by other factors that permit or restrict activity of these regulators.

Nodal points of regulation that control cell lineage serve as integrators of diverse inputs of upstream information, allowing multiple signals to converge into a simple on or off decision and thus to coordinate the regulation of downstream genes. For example, certain muscle-precursor cells, born in the somites, migrate to the limb bud, proliferate, and differentiate into muscle masses surrounding condensing bone. Because all terminal differentiation products are controlled directly or indirectly by a nodal point of upstream regulation, in the "off state" (during migration into the limb bud and proliferation), there is not leaky expression of aberrantly expressed differentiation markers, and in the "on state" (during differentiation), the entire differentiation program is coordinately expressed. Cooperative binding of MyoD to reiterated target sites is another aspect of MyoD biology that may ensure all-or-none activation of muscle differentiation markers, and the cessation of cell growth upon differentiation may reinforce the stable activation of these genes.

Another apparent example of a nodal point of cell-type regulation is seen in *Drosophila* neurogenesis. Like mammalian myogenesis, *Drosophila* neurogenesis entails a multiplicity of interacting HLH regulators encoding both tissue-restricted specificity factors (achaete-scute genes), non-tissue-restricted activators (daughterless), and genetically established negative regulators (emc, enhancer of split, and hairy). The achaete-scute genes positively regulate peripheral neurogenesis in *Drosophila* (Ghysen and Dambly-Chaudiere 1988; Campos-Ortega and Knust 1990). Achaete-scute RNA is initially expressed in a large domain of the neuroectoderm, whereas protein accumulates only in a subset of these cells, the definitive neuroblast precursors (Cabrera 1990). The definitive neuroblast precursors give rise to neural, glial, and supporting cells of both microchaetae and macrochaetae sensory organ structures. Achaete-scute expression is lost in the mature sensory organ, thus achaete-scute gene products may act to directly coordinate the division pattern and cell fate of the neuroblast progeny in addition to directly activating a battery of neural-specific genes. A regulatory nodal point in this system may ensure that each sensory organ contains the appropriate number and type of neurons, glia, and support cells.

Mutations in the neurogenic loci, *Notch* and *delta*, effect a widening in the expression of *achaete-scute* protein and a subsequent recruitment of more neuroblast precursor cells (Cabrera 1990). The neurogenic genes are thought to mediate lateral inhibition, in which the definitive neuroblast precursor inhibits the neural fate in the surrounding neuroectodermal cells. In *Notch* mutants, the *Drosophila* MyoD homolog is expressed in a larger patch of mesodermal precursor cells than in wild type (T. Maniatis, pers. comm.), suggesting that myogenesis in *Drosophila* may also may be controlled by a lateral inhibitory mechanism.

Although a complete understanding of the events leading to muscle cell commitment and differentiation in the embryo is not yet at hand, the identification of the myogenic HLH family and interacting HLH regulators has shed considerable light on some of the key players involved in these processes. Future studies will no doubt address how the myogenic HLH proteins are themselves activated during development as well as probe the intricacies of their transcriptional activation properties.

ACKNOWLEDGMENTS

We thank the following individuals for sharing information prior to publication that helped to increase the scope of this review: S. Aaronson, S. Abmayr, H. Arnold, M. Buckingham, M. Crescenzi, V.J. Dwarki, J. Gurdon, S. Hauschka, H. Holtzer, N. Hopwood, P. Jones, L. Kedes, S. Konieczny, T. Maniatis, J. Mar, A. Michelson, E. Olson, C. Ordahl, R. Palmiter, B. Paterson, L. Philipson, N. Rosenthal, E. Stavnezer, I. Verma, and B. Wold. In addition, we thank our colleagues in the Genetics Department for thoughtfully reading this chapter and for their many helpful suggestions.

REFERENCES

Benezra, R., R.L. Davis, D. Lockshon, D.L. Turner, and H. Weintraub. 1990. The protein Id: A negative regulator of helix-loop-helix DNA binding proteins. *Cell* **61:** 49–59.

Bienz, M. and G. Tremml. 1988. Domain of ultrabithorax expression in *Drosophila* visceral mesoderm from autoregulation and exclusion. *Nature* **333:** 576–578.

Blackwell, T.K. and H. Weintraub. 1990. Differences and similarities in DNA-binding preferences of MyoD and E2A protein complexes revealed by binding site selection. *Science* **250:** 1104–1110.

Blau, H.M., C.-P. Chiu, and C. Webster. 1983. Cytoplasmic activation of human nuclear genes in stable heterokaryons. *Cell* **32:** 1171–1180.

Braun, T., B. Winter, E. Bober, and H.H. Arnold. 1990a. Transcriptional activation domain of the muscle-specific gene-regulatory protein myf5. *Nature* **346:** 663–665.

Braun, T., E. Bober, B. Winter, N. Rosenthal, and H.H. Arnold. 1990b. *myf-6*, a new member of the human gene family of myogenic determination factors: Evidence for a gene cluster on chromosome 12. *EMBO J.* **9:** 821–831.

Braun, T., G. Buschhausen-Denker, E. Bober, E. Tannich, and H.H. Arnold. 1989a. A novel human muscle factor related to but distinct from MyoD1 induces myogenic conversion in 10T1/2 fibroblasts. *EMBO J.* **8:** 701–709.

Braun, T., E. Bober, G. Buschhausen-Denker, S. Kotz, K. Grzeschik, and H.H. Arnold. 1989b. Differential expression of myogenic determination genes in muscle cells: Possible autoactivation by the Myf gene products. *EMBO J.* **8:** 3617–3625.

Brennan, T.J. and E.N. Olson. 1990. Myogenin resides in the nucleus and acquires high affinity for a conserved enhancer element on heterodimerization. *Genes Dev.* **4:** 582–595.

Brennan, T.J., D.G. Edmondson, and E.N. Olson. 1991. TGF-β represses the actions of myogenin through a mechanism independent of DNA binding. *Proc. Natl. Acad. Sci.* **88:** 3822–3826.

Brunetti, A. and I.D. Goldfine. 1990. Role of myogenin in myoblast differentiation and its regulation by fibroblast growth factor. *J. Biol. Chem.* **265:** 5906–5963.

Buskin, J.N. and S.D. Hauschka. 1989. Identification of a myocyte nuclear factor which binds to the muscle-specific enhancer of the muscle creatine kinase gene. *Mol. Cell. Biol.* **9:** 2627–2640.

Cabrera, C. 1990. Lateral inhibition and cell fate during neurogenesis in *Drosophila*: The interactions between *acute, Notch*, and *Delta. Development* **109:** 733–742.

Campos-Ortega, J.A. and E. Knust. 1990. Molecular analysis of a cellular decision during embryonic development of *Drosophila melanogaster*: Epidermogenesis or neurogenesis. *FEBS Lett.* **190:** 1–10.

Caudy, M., H. Vässin, M. Brand, R. Tuma, L.Y. Jan, and Y.N. Jan. 1988. *daughterless*, a *Drosophila* gene essential for both neurogenesis and sex determination, has sequence similarities to *myc* and the *achaete-scute* complex. *Cell* **55:** 1061–1067.

Chapman, A.B., D.M. Knight, B.S. Dieckmann, and G.M. Ringold. 1984. Analysis of gene expression during differentiation of adipogenic cells in culture and hormonal control of the developmental program. *J. Biol. Chem.* **259:** 15548–15555.

Charles de la Brousse, F. and C.P. Emerson, Jr. 1990. Localized expression of a myogenic regulatory gene, qmf1, in the somite dermatome of avian embryos. *Genes Dev.* **4:** 567–581.

Choi, J., M.L. Costa, C.S. Mermelstein, C. Chagas, S. Holtzer, and H. Holtzer. 1990. MyoD converts primary dermal fibroblasts, chondroblasts, smooth muscle and retinal pigmented epithelial cells into striated, mononucleated myoblasts and multinucleated myotubes. *Proc. Natl. Acad. Sci.* **87:** 7988–7992.

Cline, T.W. 1988. Evidence that *sisterless-a* and *sisterless-b* are two of several discrete, "numerator elements" of the X/A sex determination signal in *Drosophila* that switch *Sxl* between two alternative stable expression states. *Genetics* **119:** 829–862.

Colmenares, C. and E. Stavnezer. 1989. The *ski* oncogene induces muscle differentiation in quail embryo cells. *Cell* **59:** 293–303.

Crescenzi, M., T.P. Fleming, A.B. Lassar, H. Weintraub, and S.A. Aaronson. 1990. MyoD induces growth arrest independent of differentiation in normal and transformed cells. *Proc. Natl. Acad. Sci.* **87:** 8442–8446.

Cronmiller, C., P. Schedl, and T.W. Cline. 1988. Molecular characterization of *daughterless*, a *Drosophila* sex determination gene with multiple roles in development. *Genes Dev.* **2:** 1666–1676.

Davis, R.L., H. Weintraub, and A.B. Lassar. 1987. Expression of a single transfected cDNA converts fibroblasts to myoblasts. *Cell* **51:** 987–1000.

Davis, R.L., P.-F. Cheng, A.B. Lassar, and H. Weintraub. 1990. The MyoD DNA binding domain contains a recognition code for muscle-specific gene activation. *Cell* **60:** 733–746.

Diamond, M.I., J.N. Miner, S.K. Yoshinaga, and K.R. Yamamoto. 1990. Transcription factor interactions: Selectors of positive or negative regulation from a single DNA element. *Science* **249:** 1266–1272.

Edmondson, D.G. and E.N. Olson. 1989. A gene with homology to the *myc* similarity region of MyoD1 is expressed during myogenesis and is sufficient to activate the muscle differentiation program. *Genes Dev.* **3:** 628–640.

Ellis, H.M., D.R. Spann, and J.W. Posakony. 1990. Extramacrochaetae, a negative regulator of sensory organ development in *Drosophila*, defines a new class of helix-loop-helix proteins. *Cell* **61:** 27–38.

Florini, J.R. and D.Z. Ewton. 1990. Highly specific inhibition of IGF-I-stimulated differentiation by an antisense oligodeoxyribonucleotide to myogenin mRNA. *J. Biol. Chem.* **265:** 13435–13437.

Garrell, J. and J. Modelell. 1990. The *Drosophila* extramacrochaetae locus, an antagonist of proneural genes that, like these genes, encodes a helix-loop-helix protein. *Cell* **61:** 39–48.

Ghysen, A. and C. Dambly-Chaudiere. 1988. From DNA to form: The *achaete-scute* complex. *Genes Dev.* **2:** 495–501.

Gossett, L.A., W. Zhang, and E.N. Olson. 1988. Dexamethasone-dependent inhibition of differentiation of C2 myoblasts bearing steroid-induced N-*ras* oncogenes. *J. Cell Biol.* **106:** 2127–2137.

Harvey, R.P. 1990. The *Xenopus* MyoD gene; an unlocalised maternal mRNA predates lineage-restricted expression in the early embryo. *Development* **108:** 669–680.

Henthorn, P., M. Kiledjian, and T. Kadesch. 1990. Two distinct transcription factors that bind the immunoglobulin enhancer μE5/κE2 motif. *Science* **247:** 467–470.

Hiromi, Y. and W.J. Gehring. 1987. Regulation and function of the *Drosophila* segmentation gene *fushi tarazu*. *Cell* **50:** 963–974.

Hopwood, N.D. and J.B. Gurdon. 1990. Activation of muscle genes without myogenesis by ectopic expression of MyoD in frog embryo cells. *Nature* **347:** 197–200.

Hopwood, N.D., A. Pluck, and J.B. Gurdon. 1989. MyoD expression in the forming somites is an early response to mesoderm induction in *Xenopus* embryos. *EMBO J.* **8:** 3409–3417.

Jonat, C., H.J. Rahmsdorf, K.-K. Park, A.C.B. Cato, S. Gebel, H. Ponta, and P. Herrlich. 1990. Antitumor promotion and antiinflammation: Down-modulation of AP1 (fos/jun) activity by glucocorticoid hormone. *Cell* **62:** 1189–1204.

Jones, P.A., M. Wolkowicz, W.M. Rideout III, F.A. Gonzales, C.M. Marziasz, G.A. Coetzee, and S.J. Tapscott. 1990. De novo methylation of the MyoD1 CpG island during the establishment of immortal cell lines. *Proc. Natl. Acad. Sci.* **87:** 6117–6121.

Konieczny, S.F. and C.P. Emerson, Jr. 1984. 5-Azacytidine induction of stable mesodermal stem cell lineages from 10T1/2 cell; evidence for regulatory genes controlling determination. *Cell* **38:** 791–800.

———. 1985. Differentiation, not determination regulates muscle gene activation: Transfection of troponin I genes into multipotential and muscle lineages of 10T1/2 cells. *Mol. Cell. Biol.* **5:** 2423–2432.

Konieczny, S.F., A.S. Baldwin, and C.P. Emerson, Jr. 1986. Myogenic determination and differentiation in 10T1/2 cell lineages: Evidence for a simple genetic regulatory system. *UCLA Symp. Mol. Cell. Biol. New Ser.* **29:** 21–34.

Konieczny, S.F., B.L. Drobes, S.L. Menke, and E.J. Taparowsky. 1989. Inhibition of myogenic differentiation by the H-*ras* oncogene is associated with the down regulation of the MyoD1 gene. *Oncogene* **4:** 473–481.

Krause, M., A. Fire, S.W. Harrison, J. Priess, and H. Weintraub. 1990. CeMyoD accumulation defines the body wall muscle cell fate during *C. elegans* embryogenesis. *Cell* **63:** 907–919.

Kuziora, M.A. and W. McGinnis. 1988. Autoregulation of a *Drosophila* homeotic selector gene. *Cell* **55:** 477–485.

Lassar, A.B., B.M. Paterson, and H. Weintraub. 1986. Transfection of a DNA locus that mediates the conversion of 10T1/2 fibroblasts to myoblasts. *Cell* **47:** 649–656.

Lassar, A.B., M.J. Thayer, R.W. Overell, and H. Weintraub. 1989a. Transformation by activated *ras* or *fos* prevents myogenesis by inhibiting expression of MyoD1. *Cell* **58:** 659–667.

Lassar, A.B., J.N. Buskin, D. Lockshon, R.L. Davis, S. Apone, S.D. Hauschka, and H. Weintraub. 1989b. MyoD is a sequence-specific DNA binding protein requiring a region of *myc* homology, to bind to the muscle creatine kinase enhancer. *Cell* **58:** 823–831.

Lassar, A.B., R.L. Davis, W.E. Wright, T. Kadesch, C. Murre, A. Voronova, D. Baltimore, and H. Weintraub. 1991. Functional activity of myogenic HLH proteins requires hetero-oligomerization with E12/E47-like proteins in vivo. *Cell* **66:** 305–315.

Lin, A.-Y., C.A. Dechesne, J. Eldridge, and B.M. Paterson. 1989. An avian muscle factor related to MyoD1 activates muscle-specific promoters in nonmuscle cells of different germ-layer origin and in BrdU-treated myoblasts. *Genes Dev.* **3:** 986–996.

Michelson, A.M., S.M. Abmayr, M. Bate, A. Martinez-Arias, and T. Maniatis. 1990. Expression of a MyoD family member prefigures muscle pattern in *Drosophila* embryos. *Genes Dev.* **4:** 2086–2097.

Miner, J.H. and B. Wold. 1990. Herculin, a fourth member of the MyoD family of myogenic regulatory genes. *Proc. Natl. Acad. Sci.* **87:** 1089–1093.

Montarras, D., C. Pinset, J. Chelly, A. Kahn, and F. Gros. 1989. Expression of MyoD1 coincides with terminal differentiation in determined but inducible muscle cells. *EMBO J.* **8:** 2203–2207.

Mueller, P.R. and B. Wold. 1989. In vivo footprinting of a muscle specific enhancer by ligation mediated PCR. *Science* **246:** 780–786.

Murre, C., P.S. McCaw, and D. Baltimore. 1989a. A new DNA binding and dimerization motif in immunoglobulin enhancer binding, daughterless, MyoD, and myc proteins. *Cell* **56:** 777–783.

Murre, C., P.S. McCaw, H. Vässin, M. Caudy, L.Y. Jan, Y.N. Jan, C.V. Cabrera, J.N. Buskin, S.D. Hauschka, A.B. Lassar, H. Weintraub, and D. Baltimore. 1989b. Interactions between heterologous helix-loop-helix proteins generate complexes that bind specifically to a common DNA sequence. *Cell* **58:** 537–544.

Peterson, C.A., H. Gordon, Z.W. Hall, B.M. Paterson, and H.M. Blau. 1990. Negative control of the helix-loop-helix family of myogenic regulators in the NFB mutant. *Cell* **62:** 493–502.

Piette, J., J.-L. Bessereau, M. Huchet, and J.-P. Changeux. 1990. Two adjacent MyoD1-binding sites regulate expression of acetyl choline receptor α-subunit. *Nature* **345:** 353–355.

Pinney, D.F., S.H. Pearson-White, S.F. Konieczny, K.E. Lathan, and C.P. Emerson, Jr. 1988. Myogenic lineage determination and differentiation evidence for a regulatory gene pathway. *Cell* **53:** 781–793.

Rhodes, S.J. and S.F. Konieczny. 1989. Identification of MRF4: A new member of the muscle regulatory factor gene family. *Genes Dev.* **3:** 2050–2061.

Richards, C.A., S.A. Short, S.S. Thorgeisson, and B.E. Huber. 1990. Characterization of a transforming N-*ras* gene in the human hepatoma cell line HepG2; additional evidence for the importance of c-*myc* and *ras* cooperation in hepatocarcinogenesis. *Cancer Res.* **50:** 1521–1527.

Sartorelli, W., K.A. Webster, and L. Kedes. 1990. Muscle-specific expression of the cardiac α-actin gene requires MyoD1, CarG-box binding factor, and Sp1. *Genes Dev.* **4:** 1811–1822.

Sassoon, D., G. Lyons, W.E. Wright, V. Lin, A. Lassar, H. Weintraub, and M. Buckingham. 1989. Expression of two myogenic regulatory factors, myogenin, and MyoD1, during mouse embryogenesis. *Nature* **341:** 303–307.

Scales, J.B., E.N. Olson, and M. Perry. 1990. Two distinct *Xenopus* genes with homology to MyoD1 are expressed before somite formation in early embryogenesis. *Mol. Cell. Biol.* **10:** 1516–1524.

Schafer, B.W., B.T. Blakely, G.J. Darlington, and H.M. Blau. 1990. Effect of cell history on response to helix-loop-helix family of myogenic regulators. *Nature* **344:** 454–458.

Schüle, R., P. Rangarajan, S. Kliewer, L.J. Ransone, J. Bolado, N. Yang, I.M. Verma, and R.M. Evans. 1990. Functional antagonism between oncoprotein c-*jun* and the glucocorticoid receptor. *Cell* **62:** 1217–1226.

Sorrentino, V., R. Pepperkok, R.L. Davis, W. Ansorge, and L. Philipson. 1990. Cell proliferation inhibited by MyoD1 independently of myogenic differentiation. *Nature* **345:** 813–815.

Tapscott, S.J., A.B. Lassar, and H. Weintraub. 1989. 5-Bromo-2′-deoxyuridine blocks myogenesis by extinguishing expression of MyoD1. *Science* **245:** 532–536.

Tapscott, S.J., R.L. Davis, M.J. Thayer, P.-F. Cheng, H. Weintraub, and A.B. Lassar. 1988. MyoD: A nuclear phosphoprotein requiring a *myc* homology region to convert fibroblasts to myoblasts. *Science* **242:** 405–411.

Taylor, S.M. and P.A. Jones. 1979. Multiple new phenotypes induced in 10T1/2 and 3T3 cells treated with 5-azacytidine. *Cell* **17:** 771–779.

Thayer, M. and H. Weintraub. 1990. Activation and repression of myogenesis in somatic cell hybrids: Evidence for *trans*-negative regulation of MyoD in primary fibroblasts. *Cell* **63:** 23–32.

Thayer, M.J., S.J. Tapscott, R.L. Davis, W.E. Wright, A.B. Lassar, and H. Weintraub. 1989. Positive autoregulation of the myogenic determination gene MyoD1. *Cell* **58:** 241–248.

Torres, M. and L. Sanchez. 1989. The *scute* (T4) gene acts as a numerator element of the X:A signal that determines the state of activity of *sex-lethal* in *Drosophila. EMBO J.* **8:** 3079–3086.

Voronova, A. and D. Baltimore. 1990. Mutations that disrupt DNA binding and dimer formation in the E47 helix-loop-helix protein map to distinct domains. *Proc. Natl. Acad. Sci.* **87:** 4722–4726.

Way, J.C. and M. Chalfie. 1989. The *mec-3* gene of *Caenorhabditis elegans* requires its own product for maintained expression and is expressed in three neuronal cell types. *Genes Dev.* **3:** 1823–1833.

Weintraub, H., R. Davis, D. Lockshon, and A. Lassar. 1990. MyoD binds cooperatively to two sites in a target enhancer sequence: Occupancy of two sites is required for activation. *Proc. Natl. Acad. Sci.* **87:** 5623–5627.

Weintraub, H., S.J. Tapscott, R.L. Davis, M.J. Thayer, M.K. Adam, A.B. Lassar, and A.D. Miller. 1989. Activation of muscle specific genes in pigment, nerve, fat, liver, and fibroblast cell lines by forced expression of MyoD. *Proc. Natl. Acad. Sci.* **86:** 5434–5438.

Weintraub, H., V.J. Dwarki, I. Verma, R. Davis, S. Hollenberg, L. Snider, A. Lassar, and S.J. Tapscott. 1991. Muscle-specific transcriptional activation by MyoD. *Genes Dev.* **5:** 1377–1386.

Wentworth, B.M., M. Donoghue, J.C. Engert, E.B. Berglund, and N. Rosenthal. 1991. Paired MyoD-binding sites regulate myosin light chain gene expression. *Proc. Natl. Acad. Sci.* **88:** 1242–1246.

Wright, W.E. 1984. Induction of muscle genes in neural cells. *J. Cell Biol.* **98:** 427–435.

Wright, W.E., D.A. Sassoon, and V.K. Lin. 1989. Myogenin, a factor regulating myogenesis, has a domain homologous to MyoD. *Cell* **56:** 607–617.

Yang-Yen, H.-F., J.-C. Chambard, Y.-L. Sun, T. Smeal, T.J. Schmidt, J. Drouin, and M. Karin. 1990. Transcriptional interference between *c-jun* and the glucocorticoid receptor: Mutual inhibition of DNA binding due to direct protein-protein interaction. *Cell* **62:** 1205–1215.

Yutzey, K.E., S.J. Rhodes, and S.F. Konieczny. 1990. Differential *trans* activation associated with the muscle regulatory factors MyoD1, myogenin, and MRF4. *Mol. Cell. Biol.* **10:** 3934–3944.

40

Transcriptional Regulatory Mechanisms in Liver and Midgut Morphogenesis of Vertebrates and Invertebrates

Gerald R. Crabtree
Stanford University School of Medicine
Howard Hughes Medical Institute, Stanford, California 94305

Ueli Schibler
Department of Biochemistry
University of Geneva, Switzerland

Matthew P. Scott
Department of Developmental Biology
Stanford University School of Medicine
Stanford, California 94305

OVERVIEW

Transcription factors play key roles in controlling animal morphogenesis. In an increasing number of cases, regulatory steps have been identified that carry information between the nucleus, where transcription is affected, and the cell surface, where communication events involved in induction and morphogenesis occur. Parallels between the genetic hierarchies worked out in genetically accessible organisms such as *Drosophila* and the regulatory events being dissected with molecular methods in mammals are increasingly apparent. The purpose of this chapter is to describe current views of regulatory pathways in the formation of internal organs in animals as diverse as flies and mice.

ROLES OF HOMEOTIC GENES AND GROWTH FACTORS IN THE DEVELOPMENT OF THE *DROSOPHILA* MIDGUT

Early Development of the *Drosophila* Embryo

In less than a day, a complete *Drosophila* larva develops from the fertilized egg (for detailed description, see Campos-Ortega and Hartenstein

Transcriptional Regulation.
Copyright 1992 Cold Spring Harbor Laboratory Press 0-87969-410-6/92 $3 + 00

1985). The cellular blastoderm stage *Drosophila* embryo consists of a monolayer of about 6000 cells overlying a yolk-filled interior. A fate map painted on the surface of the embryo would show the primordia for the ectoderm covering much of the surface. Bands about 4 cells wide in the anterior-posterior axis and about 100 cells wide around the circumference form the primordia for each body segment; there are about 14 such bands. A strip of about 1000 cells along the ventral midline forms the primordial mesoderm; the first event in gastrulation is the movement of those cells to the interior through a ventral furrow. The invagination of the cells creates two cell layers and sets in motion the developmental events that will build the larval body wall muscles and the visceral muscles that surround the gut and move food through it.

The origin of the gut endoderm is entirely different from the origin of the mesoderm. The cells that make up the endoderm originate from positions near the anterior and posterior ends of the blastoderm embryo. After the mesoderm precursors have moved to the interior of the embryo, at about 3 hours after fertilization, the endoderm precursors at both ends of the embryo move into the interior through holes called the anterior and posterior midgut invaginations. The invaginating cells form a tube that grows toward the tube at the opposite end of the embryo. The first endoderm cells to invaginate form the most central part of the gut, the midgut, whereas the cells that invaginate later at the anterior end form the foregut and the cells that invaginate later at the posterior end form the hindgut.

The midgut tubes are initially open along their dorsal sides, with the yolk protruding dorsally. The endoderm cells spread dorsally over the yolk and gradually enclose it. At the same time, some of the mesoderm cells that have lined the ectoderm separate from the somatic mesoderm and form a layer of cells over the endoderm. These visceral mesoderm cells then move dorsally along with the gut cells until the yolk is enclosed. At about 8–9 hours after fertilization, the two tubes join and form a continuous canal through the embryo. Within the tube is all the remaining yolk, which is gradually digested as organogenesis proceeds.

Morphogenesis of the gut continues by the formation of partially separate chambers of the midgut. The chambers are separated by drawstring-like constrictions that form in three places. It is not known whether these constrictions are imposed on the endoderm by forces in the mesoderm, or whether both germ layers participate. There is also formation of a complex structure of tubules at the anterior of the midgut. Four outpocketings of the anterior midgut form the tentacle-like gastric caeca which sprawl around the foregut. After the constrictions and caeca form, the final stages of embryonic gut development involve a lengthening of the tube, which throws the gut into convoluted spirals. The constrictions disappear as the diameter of the wide part of the gut decreases.

Roles of Homeotic Genes in Gut Morphogenesis

The relatively simple events that create the midgut are an attractive subject for investigations of the genetic control of morphology. Homeotic genes, known from mutations that transform the morphological fate of one part of the fly into another, also control the development of internal structures in the nervous system and gut. The midgut has proven useful for learning about the control of target genes by homeotic genes. The studies reveal the dramatic specificity with which the products of homeotic genes, transcription factors, control their targets and how tissue-specific cofactors and competition among homeotic proteins lead to the final patterns of target gene expression. Because very few of the target genes regulated by the homeotic genes are known, the identification of the targets and their functions are of central importance for learning how homeotic genes control morphogenesis.

Many of the homeotic genes are located in two clusters known as the Antennapedia complex (ANT-C) and the bithorax complex (BX-C) (Lewis 1978; Kaufman et al. 1980, 1990; Duncan 1987; Mahaffey and Kaufman 1988). There are five homeotic genes in the ANT-C and three in the BX-C. Each gene was first identified by means of its specific effects on the epidermis of the fly. However, all eight genes are expressed in internal tissues as well. Each gene encodes a protein that contains a homeodomain, and several of the proteins have been shown to bind to DNA and/or to activate transcription. The order of the genes in the ANT-C is *labial (lab), proboscipedia (pb), Deformed (Dfd), Sex combs reduced (Scr)*, and *Antennapedia (Antp)*. The order of the genes in the BX-C is *Ultrabithorax (Ubx), abdominal-A (abd-A)*, and *Abdominal-B (Abd-B)*. In the cuticle, the order of the genes along the chromosome, which is the order in which they are listed here, is the same as the order of the body parts that they affect. Thus, the *Abd-B* gene affects structures in the posterior segments of the abdomen, *abd-A* affects the central abdomen, *Ubx* affects the anterior abdomen and posterior thorax, *Antp* affects all the thoracic segments, *Scr* affects the anterior thorax and posterior head, and so on. The only exception is that structures affected by *pb* are anterior to parts affected by *lab*. In internal tissues, for the most part, the same spatial organization of expression prevails.

In the midgut, the tissue most relevant to the focus of this chapter, the homeotic gene expressed in the most anterior cells is *Scr*, which is active in a patch of the visceral mesoderm near the base of the gastric caeca

(Mahaffey and Kaufman 1987; LeMotte et al. 1989; Tremml and Bienz 1989; Reuter and Scott 1990). Just posterior to *Scr*, the *Antp* gene is active, again only in the visceral mesoderm and not in the endoderm. *Ubx* comes next, and then *abd-A*. All four genes are expressed in the visceral mesoderm, and no cell contains more than one of the homeotic gene products (Fig. 1). There is one additional homeotic gene, *lab*, expressed in the midgut. However, unlike the other genes, it is active in the endoderm, in a position appropriately aligned with the *Ubx* protein in the overlying mesoderm cells (Diederich et al. 1989). In terms of the anterior-posterior axis and the order of homeotic gene expression, *lab* is completely out of order. One simple rationalization is that cells expressing *lab* may control the secretion of, for example, digestive enzymes in both locations, but no genes transcriptionally regulated by *lab* are known at present.

The homeotic genes are required to specify segmental fate. Fortunately, transformations of segmental identity that occur in homeotic mutants do not drastically disrupt the basic structure of the embryo. Early effects, such as changes in epidermal structures, do not preclude the later development of the midgut. It is easy, therefore, to examine the midgut in homeotic mutants.

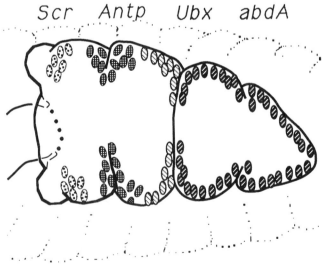

Figure 1 Expression of the homeotic genes along the embryonic midgut. The nuclei containing the *Sex combs reduced (Scr)*, *Antennapedia (Antp)*, *Ultrabithorax (Ubx)*, and *abdominal-A (abdA)* proteins in a *Drosophila* embryo are diagrammed. Anterior is to the left. The genes indicated are expressed exclusively in visceral mesoderm cells and not in the underlying endoderm cells. The dotted outline shows the positions of the segments of the overlying epidermis.

If the *Antp* gene is nonfunctional, the first gut constriction that normally forms under the visceral mesoderm where *Antp* would be expressed does not form (Tremml and Bienz 1989; Reuter and Scott 1990). Similarly, the second constriction where *Ubx* protein is normally found is absent in *Ubx* mutants. The posterior limit of *Ubx* expression is at about the position where the third constriction forms, and *abd-A* expression abuts *Ubx* expression and extends posterior to it (Tremml and Bienz 1989). The third constriction requires both gene activities; it is missing in embryos lacking *abd-A* or *Ubx* function. For all three constrictions there is a good correspondence between where the homeotic gene is expressed and where it exerts its effect. The same does not hold for the effects of *Scr* mutations. *Scr* mutants lack the gastric caeca (Reuter and Scott 1990). This is surprising because *Scr* is not expressed in the mesoderm that overlies the caeca; rather, *Scr* protein is found in mesoderm cells just posterior to the caeca. It appears that *Scr* controls caeca formation from a short distance. A factor controlled by *Scr* may induce caeca formation in nearby cells or may be permissive for caeca formation.

A second example of this "action at a distance" is the effect of the loss of *Antp* function on *Scr* expression. Although there is no detectable overlap in the expression of the two genes in wild-type embryos, *Scr* expression in the midgut is greatly reduced in mutants that lack *Antp* function (Reuter and Scott 1990). *Antp* is expressed in cells just posterior to the cells where *Scr* is expressed. Again there appears to be a communication process among cells located near each other.

The homeotic genes are also known to interact in more readily understandable ways. In the epidermis and nervous system, homeotic genes expressed in the abdomen negatively regulate homeotic genes that are expressed more anteriorly, keeping the products of the anterior genes at low levels in the abdomen (Hafen et al. 1984; Struhl and White 1985; Carroll et al. 1986). *Antp*, for example, is negatively regulated in posterior regions by *Ubx* and the abdominal region genes *abd-A* and *Abd-B*. In *Ubx* mutants, *Antp* expression in the midgut expands a short distance to the posterior, filling the cells where *Ubx* would have been, but if the abdominal genes are removed as well, there is no further expansion of *Antp* to the posterior (Tremml and Bienz 1989). Thus, the cross-regulation among the homeotics in the midgut is different from the cross-regulation in neural and epidermal cells. The interactions among the homeotic genes complicate the interpretation of the loss of the second constriction. Is its disappearance due to the loss of *Ubx*, the presence of *Antp*, or to both changes? An experiment that may resolve this ambiguity will require the analysis of a double mutant defective in both *Antp* and *Ubx* function. *Ubx* is also negatively regulated in the gut by *abd-A*; in the absence of *abd-A* function, *Ubx* products are detected from their normal anterior boundary all the way back through the entire midgut (Bienz and Tremml 1988).

Regulation of Growth Factors by Homeotic Genes

Homeotic genes must control more than just other homeotic genes. Unfortunately, the identities of directly regulated, downstream "target genes" are mostly unknown. Recently, two genes that encode proteins related to vertebrate growth factors were found to be regulated by homeotic genes in the midgut of *Drosophila* embryos (Immerglück et al. 1990; Panganiban et al. 1990; Reuter et al. 1990). It is not known whether such regulation is direct or indirect. One of the targets is the *decapentaplegic (dpp)* gene, originally identified because certain mutant alleles remove all the appendages of the fly (Spencer et al. 1982). *dpp* controls several different processes, including dorsal-ventral differentiation of the embryo, development of imaginal discs, and, now, midgut morphogenesis. The product of *dpp* is a protein related to the TGF-β family of growth factors, secreted proteins that play multiple roles in development (Padgett et al. 1987).

The second target of homeotic gene regulation is the *wingless (wg)* gene, which encodes a protein highly related to the *int-1* proto-oncogene (Rijsewijk et al. 1987). *int-1* was found because its expression is frequently altered by retroviral integration of mouse mammary tumor virus. Since deregulated expression of *int-1* has been implicated in the formation of mammary tumors, the protein is believed to be involved in growth control. From a genetic standpoint, the function of the *wg* gene is much better understood. It is a segmentation gene and also is required for the proper development of the wings (Morata and Lawrence 1977). Embryos that lack *wg* function have the posterior part of each segment transformed into a mirror image of the anterior part (Nusslein-Volhard and Wieschaus 1980). The *wg* protein, like the *dpp* protein, is secreted but only appears to move short distances in the embryo (van den Heuvel et al. 1989). As expected from the ability of the protein to move between cells, in a mosaic, cells that lack *wg* function can be phenotypically rescued by nearby cells that have a functional gene (Morata and Lawrence 1977).

In the midgut, *dpp* is expressed in the visceral mesoderm in three places: in the anterior where the gastric caeca will form, in the center where *Ubx* is expressed, and weakly in a more posterior region (Panganiban et al. 1990). The early function of *dpp* in an embryo is to promote dorsal differentiation; correspondingly, *dpp* mRNA is found along the dorsal side of the embryo (Irish and Gelbart 1987). In the absence of *dpp* function at this stage, a highly deformed, ventralized embryo develops. Thus, meaningful analysis of *dpp* function at later stages is impossible. Fortunately, alleles exist that preferentially affect *dpp* expression in the gut, leaving the early embryonic function largely unaffected. In such embryos, it is possible to assess the effects of loss of *dpp* function on midgut morphogenesis. In the appropriate *dpp* mutants, the gastric caeca do not form, and the middle of the three midgut constrictions does not form (Panganiban et al. 1990). *Scr* and *Ubx* expression is affected by the loss of *dpp*. *Scr* spreads anteriorly into the region where *dpp* would normally occur, and *Ubx* expression is reduced.

Regulatory intersections between *dpp* and *Ubx* are reciprocal. That is, *Ubx* function is needed to activate *dpp* transcription in the central region of the visceral mesoderm (Immerglück et al. 1990; Panganiban et al. 1990; Reuter et al. 1990). In embryos that lack *Ubx* function, *dpp* protein is expressed normally in most tissues but is largely or completely absent from the central midgut. The regulation of *dpp* by *Ubx* is revealing of the rules that govern transcription factor function during development. In the simplest case, wherever *Ubx* protein is expressed, *dpp* may also be expected to be found. Simple inspection of wild-type embryos reveals that there is no such correlation. *Ubx* is expressed in places where there is no *dpp*. Likewise, *dpp* is expressed in places where there is no *Ubx*. Rule 1 holds, therefore, that cellular context governs whether a transcription factor is able to activate a particular target.

Ectopic expression of *Ubx* was examined to define additional rules regarding the specificity of homeotic gene function. By using embryos mutant for *abd-A*, high levels of *Ubx* expression could be attained in the posterior visceral mesoderm. *Ubx* is also derepressed in the posterior epidermis and nervous system in such embryos. Strikingly, ectopic *dpp* expression in *abd-A* deficient flies follows *Ubx* to the posterior, *but only in the visceral mesoderm* (Immerglück et al. 1990; Reuter et al. 1990). There is no *dpp* expression in the midgut of embryos lacking both *Ubx* and *abd-A*. One can conclude that a tissue-specific factor facilitates the activation of *dpp* by *Ubx* in visceral mesoderm, or prevents *Ubx* from activating *dpp* in other tissues. Rule 2 posits, therefore, that the effects of cellular context extend to many cells where neither the regulator nor the target is normally expressed. This was further demonstrated by producing *Ubx* protein at high levels in all the cells of the embryo using a heat-shock-inducible promoter driving *Ubx* mRNA expression (Reuter et al. 1990). In this situation, ectopic *dpp* expression followed *Ubx* throughout the anterior region of the visceral mesoderm but nowhere else. Presumably, the same tissue-specific regulation is at work, but now the surprise is that *Ubx* is unable to activate *dpp* in the posterior region of the midgut. The simplest explanation is that with *abd-A* protein still present in the posterior midgut, *Ubx* is prevented from activating *dpp*. This was tested by producing *Ubx* protein with a heat shock promoter in embryos that lacked all *abd-A* function. Now *dpp* protein is found throughout the visceral mesoderm (Reuter et al. 1990).

Rule 3 predicts, therefore, that the presence of one transcription factor can preclude the action of another. *abd-A* could have controlled *dpp* indirectly in the posterior midgut. By turning off *Ubx*, *abd-A* would directly prevent *dpp* expression. However, when *Ubx* and *abd-A* protein are present in the same cells, *dpp* is off. Thus, in some way, perhaps by competing for binding sites on the *dpp* gene, *abd-A* prevents *Ubx* from activating *dpp*. Nothing is known at present about the degree to which *Ubx* and *abd-A* proteins bind to the same sequences in vivo. This is a specific example of a gene interaction that agrees with the observation that ectopic *Ubx* expression has no consequences for development of posterior embryonic segments if *abd-A* is present (Gonzales-Reyes et al. 1990; Mann and Hogness 1990).

The other putative target gene of the homeotic genes, *wg*, is activated in a region of the midgut just posterior to the *Ubx/dpp* region. In *abd-A* mutants, there is no *wg* activation in the midgut, but other *wg* expression in the epidermis is unaffected (Immerglück et al. 1990; Reuter et al. 1990). This, together with the *dpp* results, defines Rule 4: A target gene can be activated by completely separate sets of regulators in different cells. The expression of *wg* is limited to only part of the region where *abd-A* can activate *wg*. The *wg* case is akin to the tissue-specific factors that affect *dpp*, but would be position-specific rather than tissue-specific. This is reminiscent of the activation of the P_{RM} promoter of bacteriophage λ by repressor protein in the same cell where it represses P_R (for review, see Ptashne 1986). Finally, *abd-A* has opposite effects on *dpp* and *wg*. Thus, Rule 5 holds that a transcription factor can negatively regulate one target gene in the same cell where it activates another.

Communication between Germ Layers

The activation of *dpp* by *Ubx* in the central midgut mesoderm is the first step of a signaling pathway that carries differentiation information to the underlying endoderm. Using an antibody against *dpp* protein, it was possible to conclude that the protein moves from the mesoderm to the endoderm; in fact, to the side of the endoderm cells against the yolk and away from the mesoderm (Panganiban et al. 1990). No *dpp* RNA is ever seen in the endoderm (although it is readily detectable in the mesoderm).

The *dpp* protein is secreted and moves to the other germ layer. This may have many effects on the endoderm, but one that has been detected is the localized activation of the homeotic gene *lab*. In embryos lacking *Ubx* function, or lacking *dpp* function in the midgut, *lab* expression is absent in the endoderm (Immergück et al. 1990; Panganiban et al. 1990; Reuter et al. 1990). In addition, if *Ubx* is ectopically expressed, both *dpp* and *lab* follow along according to the restrictions described above.

What does *lab* do? The answer is not known, but because *lab* encodes a homeodomain protein (presumably a transcription factor), it may regulate genes that encode digestive enzymes whose secretion is needed in only the central part of the gut. Perhaps *lab* controls production of some of the same enzymes in the head epidermis. In any case, the interactions show a clear cascade of effects in which a transcription factor in one tissue controls a secreted product that moves to a nearby tissue and controls the activation of a second transcription factor. It is notable that the effects of *dpp* are very local; the protein does not seem free to move very far. In addition, the movement is only observed in the central part of the midgut; the *dpp* protein in the anterior part of the midgut does not appear to move (Panganiban et al. 1990).

Many Missing Pieces

The interactions among genes that are known to function in the development of the midgut are summarized in Figure 2. There may be parallels between the induction of endoderm gene expression by signals from the mesoderm in flies and the induction of endoderm structures by mesoderm in mammals. In many instances in vertebrates and invertebrates, inducing factors such as secreted TGF-β molecules may be activated locally by transcription factors such as those encoded by homeotic genes, thus leading to localized induction. There are also parallels in the effects of growth factors on homeotic gene expression. Just as *dpp* affects the expression of *Scr* and of *Ubx*, peptide growth factors have been shown to affect homeobox gene expression in manipulated frog embryos (Ruiz i Altaba and Melton 1989). We expect that in *Drosophila* the interactions characterized to date represent only a small fraction of the interactions that occur, even if our attention is limited to the midgut. The target genes regulated by *Antp* and *Scr* in the midgut are completely unknown, and there are almost certainly many more targets for *Ubx* and *abd-A*. It is curious that both of the target genes identified in studies of the gut are growth-factor-related; both are genes that are themselves viewed as regulators. If these two genes are representative of other homeotic gene targets, at least one more layer of regulators must be in-

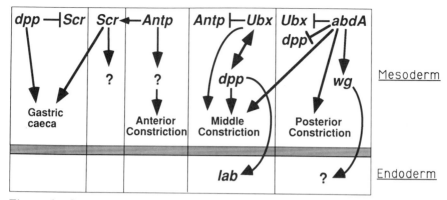

Figure 2 Summary of gene functions in the visceral mesoderm; homeotic growth factor gene interactions in the midgut. The diagram is a schematic representation of the visceral mesoderm and endoderm of an embryo, not to scale, with anterior to the left. Results are incorporated from Tremml and Bienz (1989), Bienz and Tremml (1988), Reuter and Scott (1990), Immerglück et al. (1990), Panganiban et al. (1990), and Reuter et al. (1990). In the visceral mesoderm, *Scr* and *dpp* are required for formation of the gastric caeca. *Scr* is expressed in cells posterior to the cells that form the caeca and therefore appears to act at a distance to affect caeca formation. *Scr* expression here is activated, apparently at a distance, by *Antp* function. The target genes acted on by *Scr* are unknown. *dpp* is active in visceral mesoderm cells that overlie the developing caeca, but *dpp* protein has not been observed to move into the endoderm in this part of the embryo. *dpp* prevents *Scr* expression from spreading to the anterior. *Antp* is expressed in the visceral mesoderm, acts on unknown targets, and is required for the formation of the anterior midgut constriction. Both *Ubx* and *abd-A* functions are required for the formation of the posterior midgut constriction. In the central part of the midgut, *Ubx* prevents *Antp* transcription and activates *dpp*, setting the anterior border of *dpp* expression. *dpp* protein moves across to the endoderm and activates *lab*. *abd-A* represses the expression of both *Ubx* and *dpp* and sets the posterior border of *dpp* and *Ubx* expression. *abd-A* is essential for the expression of *wg*, and the *wg* protein moves to the endoderm. The factors controlling the posterior limit of *wg* expression are not known. (Reprinted, with permission, from Reuter et al. 1990.)

terposed between the homeotic proteins and differentiation markers, such as digestive enzymes or other specialized products.

DEVELOPMENTAL ORIGINS OF THE LIVER FROM MIDGUT AND FOREGUT ENDODERM

Mammalian organogenesis is believed to result from inductive influences arising from the developmental apposition of tissues generally derived from two germ layers (for review, see Smith 1989). Although the molecular details of induction are not known for any mammalian system, there is little reason to doubt that the general features will parallel those described for the formation of midgut structures in *Drosophila* (see above) or the sequential inductive influences involved in the formation of the invertebrate eye (for review, see Rubin 1989). Since developmental induction is the result of extracellular influences that almost certainly include cell-cell interactions, cell-matrix interactions, and cytokines, the question arises as to how precursor cells are conditioned to receive these influences and, as a result, to activate the proteins essential for the expression of genes characteristic of terminally differentiated cells. In the absence of genetic approaches that have been largely inaccessible to mammalian developmental studies, in vitro systems have provided alternative approaches to these questions.

The Inductive Influence for the Liver Is Provided by Cardiac Mesenchyme

Early morphological observations of embryos indicated that the liver forms at the point of contact between a loosely defined mesodermal structure, the cardiac mesenchyme, and the anterior aspect of the developing endoderm. The inductive influence appears to be provided by the mesoderm, since it can be placed next to endoderm from a variety of locations and give rise to a liver or at least hepatocytes (Le Douarin 1975). These relationships point to developmental cross-talk. The mesoderm is first formed as a result of interactions between endoderm and ectoderm. Later in development, regional specialization of the mesoderm occurs so that different parts are able to induce different structures following contact with endoderm and ectoderm. In its undifferentiated state, the endoderm has the option of developing into one of several structures, including intestine, lung, pancreas, or liver. The choice of these cell fates is in some way determined by the proximity of specialized mesoderm. This particular aspect of mammalian endodermal differentiation and organogenesis is reminiscent of midgut development in *Drosophila*, where mesodermal regions expressing specific homeodomain protein induce the formation of specialized endodermally derived structures.

An In Vitro Model of a Developmental Influence

The potential to dissect molecular events involved in these cell fate decisions arises from the studies of Le Douarin, who found that foregut endodermal cells removed from the 4–6-somite embryo would differentiate into hepatocytes if placed into culture with lateral plate mesoderm but not with mesoderm derived from other parts of the organism (Le Douarin 1964a,b). Presumably, mesoderm from other locations might be expected to induce other endoderm-derived cell types. The induction of hepatocyte-specific traits in the endoderm-derived cells occurred even if the cells were separated by a filter. This observation was judged to rule out cell-cell interaction; however, upon close inspection of the filters by electron microscopy, it was found that cell processes actually penetrated the filter and made contact with the endodermal cells (Le Douarin 1975). The interaction of the two cell types was also necessary for the formation of certain hematopoeitic cells, since these cell types did not appear without the influence of the cardiac mesenchyme. Nevertheless, this in vitro system and the identification of a group of transcription factors likely to be under the control of this inductive influence (described below) have set the stage for a molecular analysis of the processes involved in embryonic induction.

TRANSCRIPTION FACTORS IN THE ORIGINS OF HEPATOCYTE-SPECIFIC GENE REGULATION

A Plethora of Liver Factors

In contrast to the strategy used in invertebrates, where genetic approaches have allowed the implication of specific transcription factors in morphogenesis, most studies in vertebrates have proceeded from target genes characteristic of a specific cell type to the transcription factors that control these genes. In general, the mammalian transcription factors have been found by first identifying *cis*-acting control regions in the promoters or enhancers of selectively expressed genes using transfection techniques. These functional sequences can be used to characterize the protein(s) interacting with them using the DNase I protection or by examining complexes formed with the functional sequence on nondenaturing gels, the so-called gel mobility shift (GMS) technique. These techniques allow one to devise a purification scheme based on the observed binding characteristics of a given protein. This approach suffers from the uncertainty that the protein purified is the one responsible for the biological activity associated with site, and from the difficulty in understanding the developmental significance of the proteins purified by this approach.

   The simple virtues of size and accessibility led many investigators interested in the biochemistry of transcription factors to study genes expressed in the liver. This attention has resulted in a wealth of information, and the liver may be the most thoroughly characterized vertebrate tissue in terms of the number of transcription factors known to be expressed in the adult differentiated tissue. Despite the accumulation of considerable information, insight into their roles in establishing or maintaining the hepatic phenotype is just emerging. We attempt to review what is known about some of the members of this group. A summary of the factors and their characteristics is given in Table 1.

HNF-1α and -β, a New Family of Dimerizing Homeodomain Proteins

HNF-1α, also termed APF, LFB1, and HP, was identified as a result of a search for proteins that coordinate the expression of liver-specific genes during development by binding to *cis*-acting transcriptional control regions. When the protein was first purified, it was found to bind to a dyad symmetrical sequence in the promoters of several liver-specific genes (Courtois et al. 1987, 1988). A list of the functional binding sites is shown in Table 2. The symmetry of the HNF-1α site suggested that the protein might interact with its cognate sequence as a dimer. Indeed, when the gene encoding the protein was cloned, allowing overexpression and detailed analysis of the HNF-1α protein, this proved to be the case (Frain et al. 1989). Furthermore, the protein appears to form a stable dimer in solution, since its size estimated from its migration on glycerol gradients and sizing columns is double that of the predicted sequence and that found on denaturing gels (Mendel et al. 1991a). The sequences responsible for the dimerization have been localized to a short sequence at the amino terminus of the protein that is required for both dimerization and binding. This sequence forms an α-helix in solution, as is indicated by the circular dichroism of the peptide (Nicosia et al. 1990).

The structural features of the HNF-1α molecule indicate that it is distantly related to the homeodomain family of transcriptional activators. Several features of the protein suggest that it may be a member of a special class distinct from those previously identified (Scott et al. 1990). First, it contains a 21-amino-acid loop between helix II and helix III of the homeodomain that is not present in the other homeodomain proteins (Baumhueter et al. 1990). Second, the dimerization domain does not appear in other homeodomain-containing proteins even though some of them bind to their cognate sequences as dimers. Finally, two short motifs similar to those of the POU proteins are present in HNF-1α (Baumhueter et al. 1990). These motifs are sufficiently different from those in the POU family to indicate that HNF is not homologous, in the evolutionary sense, to the POU group. Nevertheless, these short motifs correspond to functionally important sequences of the POU proteins (see Herr, this volume).

Table 1 Transcription factors selectively expressed in the liver and endoderm-derived tissues

Name	Other names	Recognition sequence	M.W.	Class	References
CEBP	none	GCAAT	45	LZ	Landschulz et al. (1988); Vinson et al. (1989)
DEBP	none	ATGATTTTGTAATGG	43	LZ	Mueller et al. (1990)
LAP	AGP/EBP, IL6DBP	GCAAT	32	LZ	Descombes et al. (1990)
HNF-1α	LF-B2, HP, APF	GTTAATNATTAAC	88	HD	Courtois et al. (1987)
HNF-1β	vHNF-1, vAPF	same as HNF-1α?	70	HD	Baumhueter et al (1988); Cereghini et al. (1988)
HNF-2	HNF-4?, LF-A1?	GGCTAAGTCCAC	68	?	Rangan and Das (1990); Hardon et al. (1988)
HNF-3α	none	CTAAGTCAATAATCAG	48	*fkh*	Costa et al. (1989)
HNF-3β	none	CTAAGTCAATAATCAG	50	*fkh*	Lai et al. (1991)
HNF-3γ	none	CTAAGTCAATAATCAG	35	*fkh*	Lai et al. (1991)
HNF-4	LF-A1?	$G/_TGC^A/_T^A/_G^G/_T^T/_CCAT$	54	ZF	Costa et al. (1989); Sladek et al. (1990)

Abbreviations include: (HD) homeodomain, (*fkh*) *fork head*, (ZF) zinc finger, (LZ) leucine zipper.

Table 2 Regulatory sequences interacting with HNF-1α or β

Promoter	Species	Sequence	Position	References
Fibrinogen α	rat	GGTGATGATTAAC	−47	Courtois et al. (1987, 1988)
Fibrinogen β	rat	GTCAAATATTAAC	−84	Courtois et al. (1987, 1988); Huber et al. (1990)
Fibrinogen β	human	ATTAAATATTAAC	−77	G. Courtois (unpubl.)
Albumin	mouse	GTTAATGATCTAC	−52	Lichtsteiner et al. (1987); Lichtsteiner and Schibler (1989); Maire et al. (1989)
Albumin	rat	GTTAATGATCTAC	−53	Crowley et al. (1983); Courtois et al. (1988); Jose-Estanyol et al. (1989); Maire et al. (1989)
Albumin	human	GTTAATAATCTAC	−51	Sawadaishi et al. (1988)
Albumin	Xenopus	GTTAATAATTTTC	−53	Schorpp et al. (1988)
α-Fetoprotein	mouse	GTTACTAGTTAAC	−50	Courtois et al. (1988)
α-Fetoprotein	mouse	GTTAATTATTGGC	−116	Godbout et al. (1986); Feuerman et al. (1989)
α-Fetoprotein	rat	GTTACTAGTTAAC	−49	Jose-Estanyol et al. (1989); Poliard et al. (1990)
α-Fetoprotein	rat	GTTAATTATTGGC	−115	Jose-Estanyol et al. (1989); Poliard et al. (1990)
α-Fetoprotein	human	GTTACTAGTTAAC	−47	Sawadaishi et al. (1988)
α-Fetoprotein	human	GATTAATAATTAC	−3400	Sawadaishi et al. (1988)
α-Fetoprotein	human	GTTAATTATTGGC	−118	Sawadaishi et al. (1988)
Transthyretin	mouse	GTTACTTATTCTC	−116	Costa et al. (1986)
Transthyretin	rat	GTTACTTATTCTC	−116	Costa et al. (1986)
Transthyretin	human	GTTACTTATTCTC	−116	(by inference)
α1-Antitrypsin	mouse	GTTAAT−ATTCAT	−63	Courtois et al. (1987)
α1-Antitrypsin	human	GTTAAT−ATTCAC	−63	Monaci et al. (1988)
Aldolase B	human	GTGTTGAATAAAC	−74	Izzo et al. (1989)
Aldolase B	chicken	AGGGAGAATAAAC	−71	(by inference)
L-Pyruvate kinase	rat	GTTATACTTTAAC	−79	Vaulont et al. (1989a,b)
HBV pre-S	human	GTTAATCATTACT	−75	Courtois et al. (1988)
PEPCK	rat	AACATTCATTAAC	−182	Roesler et al. (1989); Trus et al. (1990)
Vitellogenin A2	Xenopus	GGTAATTGTTTAC	−98	Kaling et al. (1991)
α2-6 Transferase	rat	GTTAATGTTTAAC	−66	Svensson et al. (1992)
CYP2E1	rat	GCTAATAATAAAC	−95	Ueno and Gonzalez (1990)
CRPβ	human	GAAAATTATTTAC	−74	Toniatti et al. (1990)
CRPγ	human	GGTTATTTATTAC	−151	Toniatti et al. (1990)

HNF-1 consensus (29 sequences) G26T21T24A24A21T23N A23T27T23A11A20C27.

The observation that HNF-1α can dimerize suggested that the functions of HNF-1α might be diversified by pairing with a second protein. A protein with identical binding characteristics (vHNF-1) had been described in somatic cell hybrids in which the extinguishing locus was active and dedifferentiated hepatomas (Baumhueter et al. 1988; Cereghini et al. 1988). This protein, now called HNF-1β, was cloned and found quite similar to HNF-1α with conserved dimerization and homeodomains (Kuo et al. 1990; Mendel et al. 1991a). The homeodomain includes the 21-amino-acid loop between helix II and helix III as shown in Figure 3. The distribution of these two proteins in various tissues suggests that they have a very broad function in several cell types and have a complex relationship to the activation of genes that they regulate.

DCoH: A *trans*-Acting Regulator of Homeodomain Protein Function

Genetic observations in *Drosophila*, mentioned above, suggest that other proteins might modulate the function of homeodomain-containing proteins. Recently, HNF-1α was found to copurify with an 11-kD protein that appears to be required for its transcriptional activity (Mendel et al. 1991b). The recombinant protein interacts with the dimerization domain of HNF-1α and HNF-1β and stabilizes their dimers. The stoichiometry of the complex was found to be two DCoH molecules to each HNF-1 dimer, as illustrated in Figure 3C. Transfection experiments indicated that transcription by HNF-1α is almost entirely dependent on DCoH (Mendel et al. 1991b). DCoH does not appear to have an activation domain that can be discerned using GAL4 fusions, and as yet, the mechanism of its transcriptional coactivation remains a mystery.

HNF-2: Possibly Identical to HNF-4

One of the proteins that binds to an essential *cis*-regulatory element of the α_1-antitrypsin promoter was recently purified and found to exhibit a monomeric molecular mass of 68 kD. It protects the sequence 5'-ATCCCAGCCAGTGGACTTAGCCCCTGTTTGCTCCTCC   located 125 bp upstream of the mRNA start site of the α_1-antitrypsin gene. This protein also appears to bind to sequences within the human apolipoprotein A-I promoter and the A-II enhancer, as well as the haptoglobin and pyruvate kinase promoters (Rangan and Das 1990). Recently, recombinant HNF-4 protein was found to bind the same *cis*-regulatory sequence shown above. However, when examined on SDS-reducing gels, HNF-4 is only 54 kD compared with 68 kD for the puri-

A   *Functional Domains within HNF-1α and β*

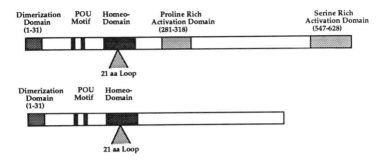

B   *Dimerization Domain*

C   *A Model of the HNF-1/DCoH Tetramer*

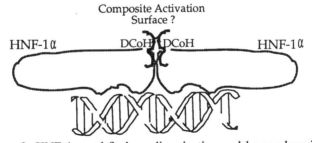

Figure 3 HNF-1α and β share dimerization and homeodomains but have different activation domains. (*A*) Schematic of functional sequences within HNF-1 (Baumhueter et al. 1990; Nicosia et al. 1990). Note the lack of conservation of the transcriptional activation domains of HNF-1β. (*B*) The dimerization domain in HNF-1α and β. Identical residues are shaded. Note the conservation of hydrophobic residues. (Modified from Mendel et al. 1991a.) (*C*) A model for the structure of the HNF-1/DCoH tetramer. A composite activation surface is suggested by the ability of DCoH to confer transcription competence on HNF-1 without interacting directly with the activation domains (Mendel et al. 1991b).

fied HNF-2. Cloning of the cDNA encoding the 68-kD protein will be necessary to resolve this paradox.

HNF-3α: A Liver-specific Transcription Factor with a Novel DNA-binding Domain Homologous to *fork head*

Analysis of the promoters of the genes for transthyretin and α_1-antitrypsin led to the identification of HNF-3, which binds to a sequence required for the expression of these two genes in transfection studies (Costa et al. 1989). The HNF-3 protein was purified and found to consist of at least three distinct polypeptide chains which are not the degradation products of the full-length product. A cDNA for the A form was cloned and found to predict a novel DNA-binding domain. However, shortly after the publication of the sequence of HNF-3, it was found to bear substantial similarity to *fork head* (*fkh*), which had been cloned, sequenced, but not published (Weigel and Jackle 1990; Lai et al. 1991). This relationship almost certainly reflects true evolutionary homology, since two other similarity regions were noted in sequences distinct from the DNA-binding domain (Fig. 4). The *fork head* protein is found in the nucleus of cells positioned at the anterior and posterior of the embryo and is necessary for terminal rather than segmental development (Weigel et al. 1989). One small deletion mutation of *fkh* that eliminates the gene's function (amorphic mutant in Fig. 4) occurs at a point corresponding to the DNA-binding domain identified by Darnell's group (Lai et al. 1990). Two other proteins related to HNF-3α have been purified and shown to be related to the *fork head* group. These proteins have been termed HNF-3β and γ (Lai et al. 1991). The underlying functional similarity between a gene necessary for expression of the adult hepatic phenotype and a gene

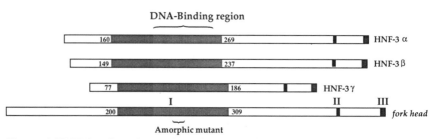

Figure 4 HNF-3α, β, and γ are homologous to *fork head*. Similar sequences are shaded in *fork head* and HNF-3α. The position of the DNA-binding domain in HNF-3α is indicated; as yet the DNA-binding region of HNF-3β and γ or *fork head* has not been mapped. The position of the mutation in *fork head* associated with a failure of head development is indicated. (Modified from Lai et al. 1991.)

required for terminal morphogenesis in insects remains an enticing mystery; however, the pattern of expression of this group of proteins in mammalian and *Drosophila* embryos is remarkably similar: Both are confined to endoderm and its precursors (J. Darnell, pers. comm.).

HNF-4: A New Member of the Steroid Receptor Family of DNA-binding Proteins

HNF-4 was first identified by virtue of its affinity for *cis*-regulatory sequences within the promoters for the genes encoding transthyretin and apolipoprotein CIII (Costa et al. 1989). The protein was purified using its binding site in the transthyretin promoter, and cDNA clones were isolated. The predicted sequence contains a DNA-binding motif similar to the zinc fingers of the steroid receptors (Sladek et al. 1990). The HNF-4 cDNA predicts a substantial region on the carboxy-terminal side of the zinc-finger motif. In the case of the steroid receptors, the analogous component is responsible for hormone binding, implying that a natural ligand remains to be discovered. Since HNF-4 is an extremely powerful activator of its target genes in normal cells, the putative natural ligand must be present in adult cells in culture. HNF-4 is found in the liver, kidney, and intestine, a distribution that is similar to its target genes. Recently, a *Drosophila* homolog of this protein was identified and found to be expressed in the gut cells of the developing embryo (J.E. Darnell, pers. comm.).

A Family of Transcription Factors Selectively Expressed in the Liver with Similar DNA-binding Specificity: C/EBP, LAP, and DBP

Multiple transcription factors exhibiting affinity for the same or similar DNA sequences have emerged from a variety of biological systems. For example, several albumin promoter elements can be occupied by more than one distinct DNA-binding protein (Lichtsteiner et al. 1987; Mueller et al. 1990; Wuarin et al. 1990). This observation is particularly striking for site D, a *cis*-acting element of the albumin promoter important for both the amplitude and liver-specificity of albumin expression. cDNAs and the genes for three distinct proteins with high affinity to this site have been isolated by molecular cloning techniques (Landschulz et al. 1988; Descombes et al. 1990; Mueller et al. 1990). The three proteins are compared in Figure 5. Two of them, C/EBP (Johnson and McKnight 1989) and LAP (also termed AGP/EBP by Chang et al. [1990] and IL-6DBP by Poli et al. [1990]), dimerize via a carboxy-terminal leucine zipper structure and bind DNA as dimers via an adjacent basic peptide

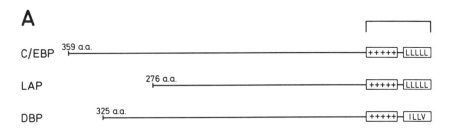

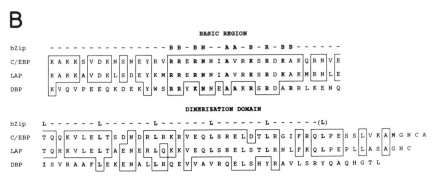

Figure 5 Comparison of three distinct proteins recognizing site D of the albumin promoter. The general structures of C/EBP, LAP, and DBP are compared in *A*. The amino acid domains required for DNA binding and dimerization (indicated by a bracket) are compared in *B*. All three proteins recognize their cognate DNA sequences via a basic peptide region (+++++). Within this segment, C/EBP and LAP share extensive sequence homology. The sequence similarity also extends into the leucine zipper structures (LLLLL), required for homodimer and heterodimer formation of these two proteins. Within the basic region and the dimerization region, DBP also shares limited sequence similarity with C/EBP and LAP, although it contains a rather degenerate leucine zipper (ILLV). The positions of the amino acids that are generally conserved in basic leucine zipper proteins (bZip) are given above the amino acid sequences of C/EBP, LAP, and DBP. Residues that conform to this consensus sequence are shown in bold letters.

region (for details, see McKnight, this volume). The basic regions and the leucine zippers of LAP and C/EBP show an extraordinary sequence similarity (see Fig. 5B). However, the amino termini of the two proteins exhibit no notable similarity in primary amino acid sequence. The two proteins bind the same DNA sequences in vitro and can readily form homodimers and heterodimers (Descombes et al. 1990). Surprisingly, these proteins show affinity to quite dissimilar DNA elements. For example, site D in the albumin promoter (Fig. 6), which shows the highest affinity for CEBP and LAP, is recognized only about three times more avidly than the lower affinity sites A and F (Descombes et al. 1990; Mueller et al. 1990). Transient cotransfection experiments have shown that C/EBP and LAP only *trans*-activate transcription efficiently from promoters carrying an intact site D (Friedman et al. 1989; Maire et al. 1989; Descombes et al. 1990).

DBP, the third well-characterized protein binding to the D site of the albumin promoter, is only distantly related to LAP and C/EBP (Mueller et al. 1990). The most extensive sequence conservation between DBP and either LAP or C/EBP lies in the basic region (see Fig. 5B). In contrast to C/EBP and LAP, DBP contains a very degenerate leucine zipper structure of the type ILLV (see Fig. 5). Furthermore, DBP has a much more restricted binding specificity than LAP and C/EBP. Within the albumin promoter, only site D has significant affinity for this factor (Mueller et al. 1990).

In transient cotransfection experiments, C/EBP, LAP, and DBP, when expressed at high levels, greatly enhance the expression of reporter genes carrying an appropriate binding site within their promoter. However, at

A Transcriptional Hierarchy is the Common Target of Somatic Mutation and Extinguishing Loci

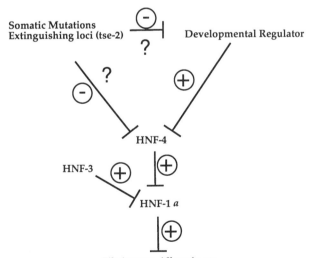

Figure 6   A regulatory hierarchy for the actions of HNF-4 and HNF-1α. Somatic mutations and the extinguishing loci are proposed to act either by directly inhibiting HNF-4 or by acting on a developmental locus controlling HNF-4. HNF-3 is inserted as controlling HNF-1 since it binds to the HNF-1 promoter and is capable of activating it in cotransfection studies. (Modified from Kuo et al. 1992.)

lower concentrations, combinations of either LAP and DBP, or C/EBP and DBP, *trans*-activate severalfold more efficiently than any of the individual factors (P. Descombes et al., in prep.). This synergistic action has been observed in cell lines of hepatic origin (Hep G2 hepatoma cells) and nonhepatic origin (mouse LTK cell) but is much more dramatic in the latter. Further work is required to elucidate the precise mechanism of the synergistic action of LAP, C/EBP, and DBP. In particular, it will be important to determine whether the proteins can bind simultaneously and cooperatively to their common recognition sequence. If so, this would explain why sequences binding only LAP or C/EBP but not DBP, such as the albumin promoter elements A and F, cannot mediate efficient transcriptional activation.

As mentioned above, LAP and C/EBP exhibit similar properties in in vitro binding and transient transfection assays. However, this does not necessarily imply the functional redundancy of these two proteins. Indeed, in these simplified experimental systems, many important parameters, such as the organization of transfected genes into particular chromatin structures, the nuclear concentration of transcription factors, and the ratio of factor to recognition sites, are not faithfully reproduced. It is possible that LAP and C/EBP execute different functions. Conceivably, the divergent amino-terminal sequences establish distinct protein:protein contacts with other proteins participating in transcriptional preinitiation complexes, thereby guiding LAP and C/EBP homodimers, and perhaps even LAP:C/EBP heterodimers, to *cis*-acting elements of different promoters. If correct, this model would have an interesting corollary. The change in promoter binding in only one of the two proteins, LAP or C/EBP, might differentially affect the expression of genes controlled by either LAP homodimers, C/EBP homodimers, or LAP:C/EBP heterodimers. For example, an increase in LAP alone would augment the concentration of LAP homodimers and, to a lower extent, also that of LAP:C/EBP heterodimers. In contrast, this same increase of LAP would result in a significant reduction of the C/EBP homodimer concentration. As a consequence, the transcription of the genes positively regulated by LAP homodimers and LAP:C/EBP heterodimers would be strongly and moderately stimulated, respectively, whereas the transcription of the genes positively regulated by C/EBP would actually decrease (Falvey and Schibler 1990).

The three transcriptional activator proteins, C/EBP, LAP, and DBP, although not strictly liver-specific, are nevertheless restricted to a limited number of cell types. In adult rats, these proteins accumulate to much higher levels in liver than in brain, kidney, lung, and spleen and are completely absent in testis (Birkenmeier et al. 1989; Descombes et al. 1990;

Mueller et al. 1990; J. Wuarin and U. Schibler, unpubl.). Within the liver, they are exclusively found in the nuclei of parenchymal hepatocytes (Birkenmeier et al. 1989; M. Chojkier et al., unpubl.). The tissue distribution of LAP and DBP is most certainly regulated by a translational or posttranslational mechanism, since significant levels of mRNA for both LAP and DBP can be observed in most of the analyzed tissues (Descombes et al. 1990; Mueller et al. 1990; Wuarin and Schibler 1990). In contrast, C/EBP expression may be mainly transcriptionally regulated in the different tissues (Birkenmeier et al. 1989; Xanthopoulos et al. 1991).

In liver, the accumulation of DBP follows a stringently controlled cir cadian rhythm (Wuarin and Schibler 1990). The level of this protein and its mRNA is insignificant in the morning, increases by three orders of magnitude during the afternoon, and then decreases again during the night. Maximal and minimal expression are observed at 8 A.M. and 8 P.M., respectively. This diurnal oscillation is governed by systemic cues and does not involve a feedback regulatory mechanism by DBP itself, since the accumulation of DBP mRNA also oscillates in spleen, which does not express the DBP protein. The transcription efficiency of the albumin gene, a putative target gene of DBP, also fluctuates during the day, presumably as a consequence of the DBP oscillation. Despite the rhythmicity of albumin transcription, the albumin mRNA levels do not change significantly during the day, probably as a consequence of the long half-life of albumin mRNA. Conceivably, the major role of DBP is to modulate the transcription of genes whose products are short-lived and only required during a certain period of the day. It will therefore be interesting to search for additional DBP target genes and to identify their products.

C/EBP, LAP, and DBP are maximally expressed in nondividing terminally differentiated hepatocytes and do not accumulate to high levels in proliferating cells of young animals or regenerating liver. Thus, these transcription factors may also be involved in the growth control of hepatocytes (Mueller et al. 1990). Transfection experiments support this notion. Cells grown in culture and transfected with C/EBP expression vectors cease to divide (Umek et al. 1991). Both a functional DNA-binding and an activation domain are required for growth arrest of cells. A negative correlation between differentiation and proliferation has been observed in many cellular systems, including differentiating adipocytes (Christy et al. 1989) and myoblasts/myotubes (Sorrentino et al. 1990). The dual properties of C/EBP and other regulatory proteins as transcriptional activators and proliferation inhibitors suggest a pivotal role of these regulatory molecules in the coordination of gene expression and cell division during terminal cell differentiation.

Strategies for Cell-type Specification: The HNF-4→1α Hierarchy

The order of action of the known regulatory proteins expressed in the adult liver was suggested from observing the patterns of expression of these proteins in cell lines. HNF-4 and HNF-1α correlated very well with the expression of liver-specific proteins, whereas little correlation with the differentiated phenotype was observed for HNF-3α, β, γ, or c/EBP or DBP or LAP (Kuo et al. 1992). Furthermore, rare cells selected for growth in glucose-free media (and hence expression of the hepatic gluconeogenic enzymes) coordinately reexpress both HNF-1α and HNF-4, raising the possibility that HNF-4 may regulate HNF-1α or vice versa. The HNF-1α promoter was found to have a functional HNF-4 site, but the HNF-4 promoter does not have an HNF-1α site. These observations suggested that HNF-4 might regulate HNF-1α. This possibility was tested by transfecting dedifferentiated cells with HNF-1α and HNF-4. HNF-4 transfected cells expressed both HNF-1α and albumin and fibrinogen (Kuo et al. 1992), suggesting the operation of the regulatory hierarchy shown in Figure 6.

TRANSCRIPTION FROM THE ALBUMIN PROMOTER: A PARADIGM FOR COOPERATIVE INTERACTIONS BETWEEN TRANSCRIPTION FACTORS IN THE GENERATION OF TISSUE SPECIFICITY

Organization of the Albumin Promoter

The albumin gene is one of the most actively transcribed genes. A number of *cis*-acting regulatory elements are required for this potent hepatocyte-specific transcription. These include an enhancer situated between 8 and 10 kb upstream of the transcription initiation site (Pinkert et al. 1987), promoter elements contained within the immediate 5´-flanking sequences, and a large enhancer region, located downstream from the albumin polyadenylation site and upstream of the α-fetoprotein (AFP) gene (Camper and Tilghman 1989). The downstream enhancer may be required for the correct temporal and spatial expression of both the albumin and the AFP genes. Although all these *cis*-regulatory elements may be indispensable for the establishment and maintenance of albumin transcription in the intact animal, only 150 nucleotides of albumin promoter sequences are required for hepatocyte-specific transcription in transient transfection (Heard et al. 1987) and cell-free transcription experiments (Gorski et al. 1986). This promoter region contains a TATA box and six individual *cis*-regulatory motifs (A–F) for sequence-specific DNA-binding proteins (Cereghini et al. 1987, 1988; Lichtsteiner et al. 1987; Friedman et al. 1989; Descombes et al. 1990; Mueller et al. 1990; Wuarin and Schibler 1990).

Figure 7 displays the inventory of DNA-binding proteins that exhibit specific affinity for these six sites. Despite its complexity, this inventory may yet be incomplete. With the exception of NF-Y and some members of the NF-1 family, the DNA-binding proteins listed in Figure 7 are enriched in liver as compared to nonhepatic tissues. The relative importance of the six binding sites for both the amplitude and the cell-type specificity of transcription has been examined in cell-free transcription experiments by two complementary approaches (Maire et al. 1989). In one approach, each of the elements has been substituted with unrelated DNA. In a second approach, artificial promoters have been constructed by the insertion of multimeric elements of each motif (A–F) upstream of a minimal albumin promoter (consisting only of the TATA motif and the mRNA CAP site). The resulting promoters, carrying either mutated or multimerized binding sites, were tested for transcriptional capacity in either liver or spleen nuclear extracts. The results obtained in these assays

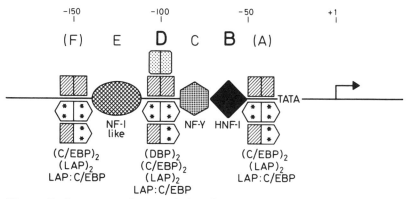

Figure 7 Inventory of transcription factors with affinity to mouse albumin promoter elements. The mouse albumin promoter sequences required for cell-type-specific transcription in transient transfection and in vitro transcription assays contain six binding sites (A–F) for nuclear factors present in rat liver nuclear extracts. With the exception of the CCAAT-binding factor NF-Y, which is present at very similar concentrations in nuclei from all examined tissues, all the proteins listed in this scheme are enriched in liver. Sites B and D are indicated by bold letters because these two elements are particularly important for liver-specific transcription. In contrast, the two elements A and F contribute only marginally to the transcription efficiency of the albumin promoter and are therefore indicated by letters in parentheses. Although all the transcription factors depicted in the scheme probably bind their cognate elements in dimeric forms, this is explicitly shown only for the proteins compared in Fig. 1, since at least two of these proteins, LAP and C/EBP, can bind the same DNA sequences as homodimers and heterodimers.

suggest the following hierarchy of importance of the six *cis*-acting albumin promoter elements for hepatocyte-specific transcription: B, D>C>E>A,F. Interestingly, none of the promoters composed of oligomeric binding sites was transcribed as efficiently as the wild-type albumin promoter. This appears puzzling, since one might have expected a higher efficiency from promoters composed exclusively of strong activator elements, such as B or D, than from promoters containing a mixture of strong and weak activator elements, such as the albumin promoter. The simplest explanation for this apparent enigma invokes cooperative interactions between different transcription factors binding to the various albumin promoter elements.

Synergism and Cooperativity

The participation of *cis*-acting elements and their cognate factors in synergistic transcriptional activation has been verified for elements B and C, the cognate sites for HNF-1 and NF-Y, respectively (Lichtsteiner and Schibler 1989; Tronche et al. 1989; Wuarin et al. 1990). For example, a linker scanning mutation within element B reduces transcription from the albumin promoter by a factor of 10. However, more subtle modification of the B element, which reduces the affinity for HNF-1 by roughly 30-fold, has little effect on transcription, as long as other albumin promoter elements remain intact. This same subtle modification of element B in a truncated promoter that also lacks the upstream elements C–F decreases the transcriptional efficiency to the same extent as the deletion of element B. Therefore, the affinity of HNF-1 for element B must be greatly enhanced by cooperative interactions with other factors bound to nearby elements. A similar conclusion has been reached for element C. In the latter case, cell-free transcription assays, in which the binding of the ubiquitous CCAAT-factor, NF-Y, was challenged by the addition of excess of its cognate binding site (site C), it was found that much larger amounts of competitor binding sites were required to decrease transcription from the albumin promoter in liver nuclear extracts than in spleen nuclear extracts. In spleen extracts, the transcription factors binding to adjacent sites (e.g., B and D) are underrepresented as compared to liver nuclear extract. The cooperative interplay of ubiquitous and tissue-enriched transcription factors, as exemplified by the albumin promoter, presents a mechanistic rationalization of how even generic factors can enhance gene expression in a cell-type-specific manner.

We envision three ways that transcription factors may interact cooperatively (Fig. 8). The first involves direct protein:protein contacts between factors bound to the same DNA molecule (Fig. 8A). The coop-

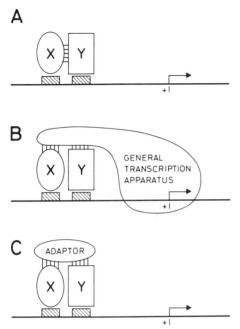

Figure 8 Cooperative interactions between transcription factors. Transcription factors can act synergistically in three different ways, shown schematically for the hypothetical factors X and Y in panels *A, B,* and *C*. (*A*) Direct cooperative binding requires special peptide surfaces that can interact with each other. Also, the binding sites when separated by short distances have to be located on the same surface of the DNA (see Ptashne 1986). (*B*) Indirect cooperativity is the result of simultaneous interactions of multiple factors with one or multiple components of the general transcription apparatus. (*C*) This mechanism is mechanistically related to the one shown in panel *B*, but involves a specially designed bridging protein, called adapter or coactivator. The net result of all the interactions shown in the three panels is a prolongation of the occupancy time of a given transcription factor. The three mechanisms shown are by no means mutually exclusive but, on the contrary, can act in concert. In particular, the mechanism shown in *B* is likely to contribute to the activity of most promoters that are regulated by multiple factors.

perative binding of the CI repressor of bacteriophage λ to its adjacent operator sites is a paradigm for such interactions (for review, see Ptashne 1986 and references therein). Second, indirect or nonspecific cooperativity (Fig. 8B) is an additional way to generate synergistic activation (Ptashne 1988; Muller and Schaffner 1990 and references therein). In this case, two or more transcriptional activators occupy adjacent sites that do not touch each other directly, but simultaneously contact a component of the general transcriptional apparatus. A third type of cooperative binding, related to the second one, is depicted in Figure 8C. It involves the postulated transcriptional adapter or coactivator proteins (Berger et al. 1990; Kelleher et al. 1990; Liu and Green 1990; Pugh and Tjian 1990; for review, see Lewin 1990). These hypothetical proteins are probably unable to bind DNA on their own but have affinity for multiple DNA-binding proteins occupying sites within the same DNA molecule. An example falling in this category is a protein postulated to bridge the transcription factor Sp1 with TFIID, the TATA-binding factor (Pugh and Tjian 1990). At present we do not know which, if any, of these mechanisms account for the synergistic activation observed for the factors binding to the albumin promoter.

TRANSCRIPTIONAL CONTROL IN CELL LINES AND GENETIC MODELS
USED TO STUDY ENDODERMAL DIFFERENTIATION AND EMBRYOGENESIS
Retinoic Acid Induction of F9 Cell Differentiation

Teratomas and teratocarcinoma are unusual tumors that maintain the potential to differentiate into tissues of all germ layers including endoderm and to express genes such as AFP normally expressed in the developing liver. The F9 cell line was derived from a murine teratocarcinoma and, if treated with retinoic acid (RA), it undergoes sequential activation of a group of genes characteristic of early developmental stages of embryos (Strickland and Mahdavi 1978). The activation of these genes is accompanied by the development of characteristic morphological structures called embryoid bodies that resemble a developing blastocyst (Strickland and Mahdavi 1978; Martin 1980; Hogan and Taylor 1981).

The appearance of very low levels of mRNA for a few liver-specific genes other than AFP has been taken to indicate that RA-induced changes are characteristic of the early developmental stages of the liver. A more common view is that these changes are characteristic of the preimplantation embryo up to about days 3–5. Several homeodomain proteins are induced during this process of differentiation, one of which is HNF-1β. The protein is induced 24 hours after addition of RA and correlates with the development of embryoid bodies and the activation of the AFP gene, which contains two functional binding sites for the protein. In contrast to HNF-1β, the mRNA for HNF-1α is present at a near-constant level during F9 differentiation, but protein cannot be detected until 3–5 days post-RA treatment, implying either that the mRNA is initially translationally blocked or that the protein is unstable (Kuo et al. 1991).

Cell Lines Used to Study Hepatocyte and Endodermal Differentiation

A wide variety of hepatocyte cell lines have been described, and several have proved quite useful for studying the transcriptional regulatory events that may be involved in specifying the full hepatic phenotype. However, most of these cell lines do not transcribe liver-specific genes at rates as high as the adult liver. Hence, the fully developed phenotype is somehow compromised (Jefferson et al. 1984). An inventory and extensive description of these cell lines has been reviewed by Darlington (1987).

The rat Reuber hepatoma cell line and its derivatives have given rise to a wide variety of cell lines that are useful for studying liver-specific transcription. Perhaps the most useful cell lines for studying liver-specific gene expression arose from the work of Deschatrette and Weiss (Deschatrette and Weiss 1974; Deschatrette et al. 1980). Using morphological criteria and single-cell manipulation, Weiss and colleagues were able to select individual clones of dedifferentiated cells, which arose spontaneously at a frequency of about 10^{-6} from the well-differentiated FAO cell line that expresses most liver-specific genes. These morphologically dedifferentiated cells lacked expression of nearly all liver-specific proteins, with the exception of tyrosine aminotransferase and phosphoenolpyruvate kinase (PEPCK). They are probably bona fide somatic cell mutants, since they arise at very low frequency and have had a stable phenotype for 13 years. The lack of expression of most of the gluconeogenic enzymes in these dedifferentiated cell lines allowed the selection of revertants (to cells that express liver markers) by growth in glucose-free media. Since this method selects for expression of two or more proteins, it has proved to be very effective for deriving both morphological and functional revertants. It is also quite powerful, since the revertants can be selected at the spontaneous frequency of 10^{-9}. Recent investigation of these three cell lines has shown that whereas HNF-1α is expressed in the differentiated FAO cell line, the dedifferentiated cells contain only the HNF-1β (also called vHNF-1) and neither HNF-1α mRNA nor protein. Selection of rare revertants among the C2 dedifferentiated cells results in the reappearance of HNF-1α. Since the revertants also show changes in phenotype involving other traits, including RNA stability (Clayton et al. 1985; Baumhueter et al. 1988), these studies suggest that the switch from the expression of HNF-1α to HNF-1β is controlled by a locus acting on several genes in addition to HNF-1α and β (Kuo et al. 1992; D.B. Mendel et al., unpubl.).

TRANS-ACTING GENETIC LOCI REGULATING TISSUE-SPECIFIC GENE EXPRESSION

Naturally Occurring Mutations in Mice and Man

Genetic diseases of mice and humans have been useful in studying gene regulation and offer a certain level of the acuity typical of genetic approaches used in invertebrates. Unfortunately, these approaches in mammals tend to be incomplete and lack the ability to discern epistasis or to saturate genetic pathways. However, since there are some 5 billion humans on earth, it is probable that at this moment there is at least one individual alive with a mutation in any gene that one cares to study. In the following section, we attempt to inventory mutations and genetic loci associated with altered regulation of genes expressed in the liver and endodermally derived tissues.

An autosomal dominant human disease has been described in which AFP production persists into adulthood at levels about 20- to 30-fold higher than normal (Ferguson-Smith 1983; Ferguson-Smith et al. 1985). Normally, AFP levels fall quickly after birth (Tilghman and Belayew 1982). The persistence may be related to a change in the HNF-1 site, since all people with this disease bear a G to A transition in the distal HNF-1 site (GTTAATTATTGGC to GTTAATTATTGAC). This change brings the sequence closer to the consensus shown in Table 2. Moreover, in transfection studies, promoters containing this mutation give a much higher level of expression in adult hepatoma cells than does the native promoter. Apparently, this change is sufficient to give continued transcription of the gene past the normal time that it is repressed at birth (J.H. McVey et al., in prep.). This explanation is consistent with the recent demonstration that the region of the gene responsible for developmental repression in transgenic mice includes the region containing the two HNF-1 sites but does not involve the enhancer (Camper and Tilghman 1989).

A patient with a form of hemophilia characterized by reduced levels of Factor IX has been found to have a mutation in the C/EBP binding site and underexpression of Factor IX (Crossley and Brownlee 1990). Here the mutation A to G at 13 results in a site with reduced affinity for C/EBP in gel mobility shift assays compared to the native protein. Furthermore, the mutant promoter is less active when transfected into HEPG2 cells than is the native promoter.

Several mutant mouse strains have been used to study the expression of liver-specific genes. The lethal albino mutation results from a deletion on chromosome 7 and hence is distinct from the genes encoding proteins that are underexpressed in mice bearing the lethal albino mutation (for review, see Glueksohn-Waelsch 1987). Mice homozygous for this deficiency are born with greatly reduced production of several proteins that are synthesized primarily in the liver and kidney. Morphologically, these organs are relatively normal prior to birth. The defect in this disease is associated with defective regulation of a set of genes that overlaps those regulated by *tse-1* and *tse-2* (see below) but is nevertheless distinct from these groups, indicating that these three loci operate independently (Ruppert et al. 1990). The mRNA for the transcription factors HNF-1, HNF-4, and to a lesser degree, CEBP, is reduced in the liver, but not in the lung (McKnight et al. 1989), whereas HNF-1 is normal (Ruppert et al. 1990; Tonjes et al. 1991) in tissues from animals bearing this mutation. Since CEBP is encoded by a locus on chromosome 7, about 30 cM away from the lethal albino locus, it is likely that the lethal albino defect is not a deletion of the CEBP structural gene but rather a mutation in a regulatory gene termed *hsdr* (Tonjes et al. 1991).

Two other genetic loci that regulate liver-specific gene expression, *rif* and *raf*, were defined by their ability to control AFP synthesis (Olsson et al. 1977; Belayew and Tilghman 1982). BALB/c/J mice have an unusually high level of AFP in their plasma after birth, about 10–20 times normal. By means of genetic crosses, this effect can be mapped to a single locus termed Raf (regulation of alpha-fetoprotein) (Olsson et al. 1977). The *raf^b* allele is recessive to the *raf^a* allele and is responsible for the hereditary persistence of elevated levels of AFP mRNA in adult BALB/c/J mice. Although it is not known how *raf* works, a simple explanation such as a change in the rate of catabolism of AFP in these mice has been eliminated.

A second unlinked locus termed *Rif* controls the levels of AFP produced during liver regeneration. The *Rif^b* allele, identified in C57BL/6 mice, is dominant over wild-type *Rif^a* and results in a 10- to 15-fold lower magnitude of induction of AFP mRNA in C57BL/6 mice during liver regeneration. The *rif^b* and *rif^a* loci act in a cell-autonomous manner as shown by the production of chimeric mice in which the liver was composed of cells of both the mutant strain and the normal strain (Vogt et al. 1987).

The Tissue-specific Extinguishing Loci: *tse-1* and *tse-2*

When two types of differentiated cells are fused in a homokaryon, the resultant hybrid generally loses expression of both sets of differentiated genes. This phenomenon is referred to as extinction (Schneider and Weiss 1971; Thompson and Gelehrter 1971) and has been used to genetically map loci associated with repression of tissue-specific genes. In contrast, in transient heterokaryons, fusion of a muscle cell to other cell types leads to the activation of muscle genes in most cells except the liver (Blau et al. 1985; Chiu and Blau 1985). Recently, two different tissue-specific extinction loci (*tse*) for hepatocyte-specific genes have been mapped. *tse-1*, which extinguishes expression of PEPCK and several other genes, is located on chromosome 11; *tse-2*, which extinguishes a nonoverlapping set of genes including albumin, fibrinogen, and α_1-antitrypsin, is located on chromosome 1 (Lem et al. 1988). Recently, the effects of *tse-1* have been shown to be reversed by treating the extinguished hybrids with cAMP and glucocorticoids, suggesting that the *tse-1* locus operates by interfering with hormonal activation. Consistent with this possibility is the fact that all the genes that are repressed by *tse-1* are cAMP-regulated and are first expressed at birth. Recently, *tse-1* was shown to be the regulatory subunit of cAMP-dependent kinase. This subunit is somehow expressed at higher levels in the hybrid cell lines giving rise to an apparent extinction of liver-specific genes. At present, it is not clear if this mechanism plays a role in tissue-specific gene expression.

The second extinguishing locus shows more promise for revealing physiological mechanisms of cell type specification. The *tse-2* locus regulates a different set of genes that are not cAMP inducible. The target genes for *tse-2* appear embryonically at the time of endodermal differentiation; most bear an HNF-1 site as a prominent regulatory element. Thus, the *tse-2* locus may be more fundamentally involved with establishment or maintenance of tissue-specific gene expression. Since somatic hybrids that have active *tse-2* cease production of HNF-1α and express HNF-1β (which is not expressed in either parent cell line), one action of *tse-2* is to repress HNF-1α and activate HNF-1β (Mendel et al. 1991a). Since activation of HNF-1β expression is associated with repression of hepatocyte-specific genes in several situations (Mendel et al. 1991a), *tse-2* could function by activating HNF-1β.

Recently, both HNF-1α and HNF-4, but not other regulatory proteins, were found to be repressed in the extinguished hybrids containing a mix of both fibroblast and hepatocyte chromosomes, suggesting that these two proteins are either coregulated or that one regulates the other (Kuo et al. 1992). The finding that HNF-4 can rescue the repression of HNF-1α expression as well as the liver-specific proteins, fibrinogen and albumin, supports the regulatory hierarchy illustrated in Figure 6 (Kuo et al. 1992).

SUMMARY AND PERSPECTIVE

Several important parallels exist in both generalities and details between the events that give rise to the structure of endodermally derived tissues in *Drosophila* and vertebrates. Clearly, the major generality is that morphological structures such as the gastric caeca arise as a result of the action of specialized mesoderm on nonspecialized endoderm. Several details of the process of morphogenesis are also used in both insects and mammals, as indicated by the remarkably similar pattern of embryologi cal expression of the homologs of HNF-3 (*fork head*) and HNF-4. In *Drosophila*, genetic approaches have shown that homeodomain proteins such as Antennapedia and Ultrabithorax, which are essential to the early development of the organism, are expressed in the specialized mesoderm and play a second role in inducing structure in the midgut. Furthermore, such studies provide evidence for at least one specific mechanism leading to morphological structure, i.e., the production of growth factors with restricted diffusion allowing localized cell growth.

The events that cause the induction of organs such as the liver and lung from a specific part of the endoderm are also likely to require spatially and temporally controlled transcriptional regulators, such as the homeodomain and zinc finger proteins, and cell-cell communication factors akin to *dpp* and *wg*. The crucial components in this pathway leading to morphogenesis may be identified by following the trail of transcription factors from regulating genes such as the AFP or albumin back to the earliest origins of the liver precursors. Alternatively, it may only be possible to identify the important components at the time and place when key inductive events occur. Morphogenesis requires more than the production of tissue types; the tissues must be shaped and positioned. The impressive progress in identifying mammalian regulatory factors, and the recent development of cell culture systems in which the role of these factors can be studied, should soon begin to reveal how their interactions shape multicellular organization and cell differentiation.

ACKNOWLEDGMENTS

G.R.C. thanks Jean Oberlindacher for preparation of the manuscript; Robb Krumlauf, John McVey, Keith Fornier, and James Darnell for sharing unpublished data; and Dirk Mendel, Linda Hansen, Calvin Kuo, and Pam Conley for many helpful discussions. M.P.S. thanks Rolf Reuter, Grace Panganiban, and F. Michael Hoffmann for many fruitful discussions about midgut development; and Rolf Reuter for an earlier version of Figure 2. In addition, he acknowledges the National Institutes of Health (grant 18163) for support of the research discussed here. M.P.S. was an investigator of the Howard Hughes Medical Institute during part of the time when the research was done. Additional support was provided by the Howard Hughes Medical Institute and National Institutes of

Health grants CA-39612 and HL-33942 to G.R.C. U.S. acknowledges support from the Swiss National Science Foundation and from the state of Geneva.

REFERENCES

Baumhueter, S., G. Courtois, and G.R. Crabtree. 1988. A variant nuclear protein in dedifferentiated hepatoma cells binds to the same functional sequences in the β fibrinogen gene promoter as HNF-1. *EMBO J.* **7:** 2485–2493.

Baumhueter, S., D.B. Mendel, P.B. Conley, C.J. Kuo, C. Turk, M.K. Graves, C.A. Edwards, G. Courtois, and G.R. Crabtree. 1990. HNF-1 shares three sequence motifs with the POU domain proteins and is identical to LF-B1 and APF. *Genes Dev.* **4:** 372–379.

Belayew, A. and S.M. Tilghman. 1982. Genetic analysis of α-fetoprotein synthesis in mice. *Mol. Cell Biol.* **2:** 1427–1435.

Berger, S.L., W.D. Cress, A. Cress, S.J. Triezenberg, and L. Guarente. 1990. Selective inhibition of activated but not basal transcription by the acidic activation domain of VP16: Evidence for transcriptional adaptors. *Cell* **61:** 1199–1208.

Bienz, M. and G. Tremml. 1988. Domain of *Ultrabithorax* expression in *Drosophila* visceral mesoderm from autoregulation and exclusion. *Nature* **333:** 576–578.

Birkenmeier, E.H., B. Gwynn, S. Howard, J. Jerry, J.I. Gordon, W.H. Landschulz, and S.L. McKnight. 1989. Tissue-specific expression, developmental regulation, and genetic mapping of the gene encoding CCAAT/enhancer binding protein. *Genes Dev.* **3:** 1146–1156.

Blau, H.M., G.K. Pavlath, E.C. Hardeman, C.P. Chiu, L. Silberstein, S.G. Webster, S.C. Miller, and C. Webster. 1985. Plasticity of the differentiated state. *Science* **230:** 758–766.

Camper, S.A. and S.M. Tilghman. 1989. Postnatal repression of the α-fetoprotein gene is enhancer independent. *Genes Dev.* **3:** 537–546.

Campos-Ortega, J.A. and V. Hartenstein. 1985. *The embryonic development of* Drosophila melanogaster. Springer-Verlag, New York.

Carroll, S.B., R.A. Laymon, M.A. McCutcheon, P.D. Riley, and M.P. Scott. 1986. The localization and regulation of *Antennapedia* protein expression in *Drosophila* embryos. *Cell* **47:** 113–122.

Cereghini, S., M. Blumenfeld, and M. Yaniv. 1988. A liver-specific factor essential for albumin transcription differs between differentiated and dedifferentiated rat hepatoma cells. *Genes Dev.* **2:** 957–974.

Cereghini, S., M. Raymondjean, A.G. Carranca, P. Herbomel, and M. Yaniv. 1987. Factors involved in control of tissue-specific expression of albumin gene. *Cell* **50:** 627–638.

Chang, C.J., T.T. Chen, H.Y. Lei, D.S. Chen, and S.C. Lee. 1990. Molecular cloning of a transcription factor, AGP/EBP that belongs to members of the C/EBP family. *Mol. Cell. Biol.* **10:** 6642–6653.

Chiu, C.P. and H.M. Blau. 1985. 5-Azacytidine permits gene activation in a previously noninducible cell type. *Cell* **40:** 417–424.

Christy, R.J., V.W. Yang, J.M. Ntambi, D.E. Geiman, W.H. Landschulz, A.D. Friedman, Y. Nakabeppu, T.J. Kelley, and M.D. Lane. 1989. Differentiation-induced gene expression in 3T3-L1 preadipocytes: CCAAT/enhancer binding protein interacts with adipocyte-specific genes. *Genes Dev.* **3:** 1323–1335.

Clayton, D.F., M. Weiss, and J.E. Darnell, Jr. 1985. Liver-specific RNA metabolism in hepatoma cells: Variations in transcription rates and mRNA levels. *Mol. Cell Biol.* **5:** 2633–2641.

Costa, R.H., D.R. Grayson, and J.E. Darnell, Jr. 1989. Multiple hepatocyte-enriched nuclear factors function in the regulation of transthyretin and α1-antitrypsin genes. *Mol. Cell. Biol.* **9:** 1415–1425.

Costa, R.H., E. Lai, and J.E. Darnell, Jr. 1986. Transcriptional control of the mouse prealbumin gene: Both promoter and enhancer are cell specific. *Mol. Cell. Biol.* **6:** 4697–4708.

Courtois, G., S. Baumhueter, and G.R. Crabtree. 1988. Purified hepatocyte nuclear factor 1 interacts with a family of hepatocyte-specific promoters. *Proc. Natl. Acad. Sci.* **85:** 7937–7941.

Courtois, G., J.G. Morgan, L.A. Campbell, G. Fourel, and G.R. Crabtree. 1987. Interaction of a liver-specific nuclear factor with the fibrinogen and α1-antitrypsin promoters. *Science* **238:** 688–692.

Crossley, M. and G. Brownlee. 1990. Disruption of a C/EBP binding site in the factor IX promoter is associated with hemophilin B. *Nature* **345:** 444–446.

Crowley, C., C.C. Liu, and A.D. Levinson. 1983. Plasmid directed synthesis of hepatitis B surface antigen in monkey cells. *Mol. Cell. Biol.* **3:** 44–55.

Darlington, G.J. 1987. Liver cell lines. *Methods Enzymol.* **151:** 19–38.

Deschatrette, J. and M.C. Weiss. 1974. Characterization of differentiated and dedifferentiated clones of a rat hepatoma. *Biochimie* **56:** 1603–1611.

Deschatrette, J., E.E. Moore, M. Dubois, and M. Weiss. 1980. Dedifferentiated variants of a rat hepatoma: Reversion analysis. *Cell* **19:** 1043–1051.

Descombes, P., M. Chojkier, S. Lichsteiner, E. Falvey, and U. Schibler. 1990. LAP, a novel member of the C/EBP gene family, encodes a liver-enriched transcriptional activator protein. *Genes Dev.* **4:** 1541–1551.

Diederich, R.J., V.K.L. Merrill, M.A. Pultz, and T.C. Kaufman. 1989. Isolation, structure, and expression of *labial*, a homeotic gene of the *Antennapedia* complex involved in Drosophila head development. *Genes Dev.* **3:** 399–414.

Duncan, I.M. 1987. The bithorax complex. *Annu. Rev. Genet.* **21:** 285–319.

Falvey, E. and U. Schibler. 1990. How are the regulators required. *FASEB J.* **5:** 309–314.

Ferguson-Smith, M.A. 1983. The reduction in anencephalic and spina bifida births by maternal alpha fetoprotein screening. *Br. Med. Bull.* **4:** 368–372.

Ferguson-Smith, N.M., J.R.W. Yates, D. Kelly, D.A. Aitken, H.M. May, R. Krumlauf, and S.M. Tilghman. 1985. Hereditary persistence of alphafetoprotein maps to the long arm of chromosome 4. *Cytogenet. Cell Genet.* **40:** 628.

Feuerman, M.H., R. Godbout, R.S. Ingram, and S.M. Tilghman. 1989. Tissue-specific transcription of the mouse α-fetoprotein gene promoter is dependent on HNF-1. *Mol. Cell. Biol.* **9:** 4204–4212.

Frain, M., G. Swart, P. Monaci, A. Nicosia, S. Stämpfli, R. Frank, and R. Cortese. 1989. The liver-specific transcription factor LF-B1 contains a highly diverged homeobox DNA binding domain. *Cell* **59:** 145–157.

Friedman, A.D., W.H. Landschulz, and S.L. McKnight. 1989. C/EBP activates the promoter of the serum albumin gene in cultured hepatoma cells. *Genes Dev.* **3:**9 1314–1322.

Gluecksohn-Waelsch, S. 1987. Regulatory genes in development. *Trends Genet.* **3:** 123–127.

Godbout, R., R. Ingram, and S.M. Tilghman. 1986. Multiple regulatory elements in the intergenic region between the α-fetoprotein and albumin genes. *Mol. Cell. Biol.* **6:** 477–487.

Gonzales-Reyes, A., N. Urquia, W.J. Gehring, G. Struhl, and G. Morata. 1990. Are cross-regulatory interactions between homeotic genes functionally significant? *Nature* **344:** 78–80.

Gorski, K., M. Carneiro, and U. Schibler. 1986. Tissue-specific in vitro transcription from the mouse albumin promoter. *Cell* **47:** 767–776.

Hafen, E., M. Levine, and W.H. Gehring. 1984. Regulation of *Antennapedia* transcript distribution by the bithorax complex in *Drosophila. Nature* **307:** 287–289.

Hardon, E.M., M. Frain, G. Paonessa, and R. Cortese. 1988. Two distinct factors interact with the promoter regions of several liver-specific genes. *EMBO J.* **7:** 1711–1719.

Heard, J.M., P. Herbomel, M.-O. Ott, A. Mottura-Rollier, M. Weiss, and M. Yaniv. 1987. Determinants of rat albumin promoter tissue-specificity analyzed by an improved transient expression system. *Mol. Cell. Biol.* **7:** 2425–2434.

Hogan, B.L.M. and A. Taylor. 1981. Cell interactions modulate embryonal carcinoma cell differentiation into parietal or visceral endoderm. *Nature* **291:** 235–237.

Huber, P., M. Laurent, and J. Dalmon. 1990. Human β-fibrinogen gene expression. Upstream sequences involved in its tissue specific expression and its dexamethasone and interleukin 6 stimulation. *J. Biol. Chem.* **265:** 5695–5701.

Immergtück, K., P.A. Lawrence, and M. Bienz. 1990. Induction across germ layers in *Drosophila* mediated by a genetic cascade. *Cell* **62:** 261–268.

Irish, V.F. and W.M. Gelbart. 1987. The decapentaplegic gene is required for dorsal-ventral patterning of the *Drosophila* embryo. *Genes Dev.* **1:** 868–879.

Izzo, P., P. Costanzo, A. Lupo, E. Rippa, and F. Salvatore. 1989. *In vivo* activity of the most proximal promoter of the human aldolase A gene and analysis of transcriptional control elements. *FEBS Lett.* **257:** 75–80.

Jefferson, D.M., D.F. Clayton, J.E. Darnell, Jr., and L.M. Reid. 1984. Posttranscriptional modulation of gene expression in cultured rat hepatocytes. *Mol. Cell. Biol.* **4:** 1929–1934.

Johnson, P.F. and S.L. McKnight. 1989. Eucaryotic transcriptional activator proteins. *Annu. Rev. Biochem.* **58:** 799–839.

Jose-Estanyol, M., A. Poliard, D. Foiret, and J.-L. Danan. 1989. A common liver-specific factor binds to the rat albumin and α-foetoprotein promoters *in vitro* and acts as a positive *trans*-acting factor *in vivo. Eur. J. Biochem.* **181:** 761–766.

Kaling, M., W. Kugler, K. Ross, C. Zoidl, and G.U. Ryffel. 1991. Liver-specific gene expression: A-activator-binding site, a promoter module present in viellogenin and acute-phase genes. *Mol. Cell. Biol.* **11:** 93–101.

Kaufman, T.C., R. Lewis, and B. Wakimoto. 1980. Cytogenetic analysis of chromosome 3 in *Drosophila melanogaster*: The homeotic gene complex in polytene chromosomal interval 84A, B. *Genetics* **94:** 115–133.

Kaufman, T.C., A. Seeger, and G. Olsen. 1990. Molecular and genetic organization of the *Antennapedia* gene complex of *Drosophila melanogaster. Adv. Genet.* **27:** 309–362.

Kelleher, R.J., III, P.M. Flanagan, and R.D. Kornberg. 1990. A novel mediator between activator proteins and the RNA polymerase II transcription apparatus. *Cell* **61:** 1209–1215.

Kuo, C.J., D.M. Mendel, L.P. Hansen, and G.R. Crabtree. 1991. Independent regulation of HNF-1α and HNF-1β by retinoic acid in F9 teratocarcinoma cells. *EMBO J.* **10:** 2231–2236.

Kuo, C.J., P.B. Conley, C.-L. Hsieh, U. Francke, and G.R. Crabtree. 1990. Molecular cloning, functional expression, and chromosomal localization of mouse hepatocyte nuclear factor 1. *Proc. Natl. Acad. Sci.* **87:** 9838–9842.

Kuo, C.J., P.B. Conley, L. Chen, F.M. Sladek, J.E. Darnell, Jr., and G.R. Crabtree. 1992. A transcriptional hierarchy involved in cell-type specification is selectively inhibited by extinguishing loci. *Nature* **335:** 457–461.

Lai, E., V.R. Prezioso, W. Tao, W.S. Chen, and J.E. Darnell, Jr. 1991. Hepatocyte nuclear factor 3α belongs to a family of genes in mammals that is homologous to the *Drosophila* homeotic gene *fork head. Genes Dev.* **5:** 416–427.

Lai, E., V.R. Prezioso, E. Smith, O. Litvin, R.H. Costa, and J.E. Darnell, Jr. 1990. HNF-3A, a hepatocyte-enriched transcription factor of novel structure is regulated transcriptionally. *Genes Dev.* **4:** 1427–1436.

Landschulz, W.H., P.F. Johnson, E.Y. Adashi, B.J. Graves, and S.L. McKnight. 1988. Isolation of a recombinant copy of the gene encoding C/EBP. *Genes Dev.* **2:** 786–800.

Le Douarin, N. 1964a. Isolement experimental du mesenchyme propre du foie et role morphogene de la composante mesodermique dans l'organogenese hepatique. *J. Embryol. Exp. Morphol.* **12:** 141–160.

————. 1964b. Induction de l'endoderme pre-hepateque par le mesoderme de laire cardiaque chex l'embryon de Poulet. *J. Embryol. Exp. Morphol.* **12:** 651–664.

————. 1975. An experimental analysis of liver development. *Med. Biol.* **53:** 427–455.

Lem, J., A.C. Chin, M.J. Thayer, R.J. Leach, and R.E.K. Fournier. 1988. Coordinate regulation of two genes encoding gluconeogenic enzymes by the *trans*-dominant locus *Tse-1. Proc. Natl. Acad. Sci.* **85:** 7302–7306.

LeMotte, P.K., A. Kuroiwa, L.I. Fessler, and W.H. Gehring. 1989. The homeotic gene *Sex combs reduced* of *Drosophila*: Gene structure and embryonic expression. *EMBO J.* **8:** 219–227.

Lewin, B. 1990. Commitment and activation at Pol II promoters: A tale of protein-protein interactions. *Cell* **61:** 1161–1164.

Lewis, E.B. 1978. A gene complex controlling segmentation in *Drosophila. Nature* **276:** 565–570.

Lichsteiner, S. and U. Schibler. 1989. A glycosylated liver-specific transcription factor stimulates transcription of the albumin gene. *Cell* **57:** 1179–1187.

Lichsteiner, S., J. Wuarin, and U. Schibler. 1987. The interplay of DNA-binding proteins on the promoter of the mouse albumin gene. *Cell* **51:** 963–973.

Liu, F. and M.R. Green. 1990. A specific member of the ATF transcription factor family can mediate transcription activation by the adenovirus E1a protein. *Cell* **61:** 1217–1224.

Mahaffey, J.W. and T.C. Kaufman. 1987. Distribution of the *sex combs reduced* gene products in *Drosophila melanogaster. Genetics* **117:** 51–60.

————. 1988. The homeotic genes of the *Antennapedia* complex and the *bithorax* complex of *Drosophila*. In *Developmental genetics of higher organisms: A primer in developmental biology* (ed. G.M. Malacinsiki), pp. 329–360. Macmillan, New York.

Maire, P., J. Wuarin, and U. Schibler. 1989. The role of *cis*-acting promoter elements in tissue-specific albumin gene expression. *Science* **244:** 343–346.

Mann, R.S. and D.S. Hogness. 1990. Functional dissection of Ultrabithorax proteins in *D. melanogaster. Cell* **60:** 597–610.

Martin, G.R. 1980. Teratocarcinomas and mammalian embryogenesis. *Science* **209:** 768–776.

McKnight, S.L., M.D. Lane, and S. Gluecksohn-Waelsch. 1989. Is CCAAT/enhancer-binding protein a central regulator of energy metabolism? *Genes Dev.* **3:** 2021–2024.

Mendel, D.B., L.P. Hansen, M.K. Graves, P.B. Conley, and G.R. Crabtree. 1991a. HNF-1α and HNF-1β (vHNF-1) share dimerization and homeo domains, but not activation domains, and form heterodimers *in vitro. Genes Dev.* **5:** 1042–1056.

Mendel, D.B., P.A. Khavari, P.B. Conley, M.K. Graves, L.P. Hansen, A. Admon, and G.R. Crabtree. 1991b. Regulated dimerization by DCoH determines the transcriptional activity of a mammalian homeodomain protein. *Science* (in press).

Monaci, P., A. Nicosia, and R. Cortese. 1988. Two different liver-specific factors stimulate *in vitro* transcription from the human α1-antitrypsin promoter. *EMBO J.* **7:** 2075–2087.

Morata, G. and P.A. Lawrence. 1977. The development of *wingless,* a homeotic mutation of *Drosophila. Dev. Biol.* **56:** 227–240.

Mueller, C.R., P. Maire, and U. Schibler. 1990. DBP, a liver-enriched transcriptional activator, is expressed late in ontogeny and its tissue specificity is determined posttranscriptionally. *Cell* **61:** 279–291.

Muller, H.-P. and W. Schaffner. 1990. DBP, a liver-enriched transcriptional activator is expressed late in ontogeny and its tissue-specificity is determined posttranslationally. *Trends Genet.* **6:** 300–304.

Nicosia, A., P. Monaci, L. Tomei, R. De Francesco, M. Nuzzo, H. Stunnenberg, and R. Cortese. 1990. A myosin-like dimerization helix and an extra-large homeodomain are essential elements of the tripartite DNA binding structure of LFB1. *Cell* **61:** 1225–1236.

Nusslein-Volhard, C. and E. Wieschaus. 1980. Mutations affecting segment number and polarity in *Drosophila. Nature* **287:** 795–801.

Olsson, M., G. Lindahl, and E. Ruoslahti. 1977. Genetic control of α-fetoprotein synthesis in the mouse. *J. Exp. Med.* **145:** 819–827.

Padgett, R.W., R.D. St. Johnston, and W.M. Gelbart. 1987. A transcript from a *Drosophila* pattern gene predicts a protein homologous to the transforming growth factor-β family. *Nature* **325:** 81–84.

Panganiban, G.E.F., R. Reuter, M.P. Scott, and F.M. Hoffman. 1990. A *Drosophila* growth factor homolog, decapentaplegic, regulates homeotic gene expression within and across germ layers during midgut morphogenesis. *Development* **110:** 1041–1050.

Pinkert, C.A., D.M. Ornitz, R.L. Brinster, and R.D. Palmiter. 1987. An albumin enhancer located 10 kb upstream functions along with its promoter to direct efficient, liver-specific expression in transgenic mice. *Genes Dev.* **1:** 268–276.

Poliard, A., L. Bakkali, M. Poiret, D. Foiret, and J.-L. Danan. 1990. Regulation of the rat α-fetoprotein gene expression in liver. Both the promoter region and an enhancer element are liver-specific and negatively modulated by dexamethasone. *J. Biol. Chem.* **265:** 2137–2141.

Poli, V., F.P. Mancini, and R. Cortese. 1990. IL-6DBP, a nuclear protein involved in IL-6 signal transduction defines a new family of leucine zipper proteins related to C/EBP. *Cell* **63:** 643–653.

Ptashne, M. 1986. *A genetic switch.* Cell, Cambridge, Massachusetts and Blackwell Scientific, Palo Alto, California.

———. 1988. How eukaryotic transcriptional activators work. *Nature* **335:** 683–689.

Pugh, B.F. and R. Tjian. 1990. Mechanism of transcriptional activation by Sp1: Evidence for coactivators. *Cell* **61:** 1187–1197.

Rangan, V.S. and G.C. Das. 1990. Purification and biochemical characterization of hepatocyte nuclear factor 2 involved in liver-specific transcription of the human α-1-antitrypsin gene. *J. Biol. Chem.* **265:** 8874–8879.

Reuter, R. and M.P. Scott. 1990. Expression and functions of the homeotic genes *Antennapedia* and *sex combs reduced* in the embryonic midgut of *Drosophila. Development* **109:** 289–303.

Reuter, R., G.E.F. Panganiban, F.M. Hoffman, and M.P. Scott. 1990. Homeotic genes regulate the spatial expression of putative growth factors in the visceral mesoderm of *Drosophila* embryos. *Development* 110: 1031–1040.

Rijsewijk, F., M. Schuermann, E. Wagenaar, P. Parren, D. Weigel, and R. Nusse. 1987. The *Drosophila* homolog of the mouse mammary oncogene *int-1* is identical to the segment polarity gene *wingless*. *Cell* 50: 649–657.

Roesler, W.J., G.R. Vandenbark, and R.W. Hanson. 1989. Identification of multiple protein binding domains in the promoter-regulatory region of the phosphoenolpyruvate carboxykinase gene. *J. Biol. Chem.* 264: 9657–9664.

Rubin, G.M. 1989. Development of the *Drosophila* retina: Inductive events studied at single cell resolution. *Cell* 57: 519–520.

Ruiz i Altaba, A. and D.A. Melton. 1989. Interaction between peptide growth factors and homeobox genes in the establishment of antero-posterior polarity in frog embryos. *Nature* 341: 33–38.

Ruppert, S., M. Boshart, F.X. Bosch, W. Schmid, R.E.K. Fournier, and G. Schutz. 1990. Two genetically defined *trans*-acting loci coordinately regulate overlapping sets of liver-specific genes. *Cell* 61: 895–904.

Sawadaishi, K., T. Morinaga, and T. Tamaoki. 1988. Interaction of a hepatoma-specific nuclear factor with transcription-regulatory sequences of the human α-fetoprotein and albumin genes. *Mol. Cell. Biol.* 8: 5179–5187.

Schneider, J.A. and M.C. Weiss. 1971. Expression of differentiated functions in hepatoma cell hybrids: Tyrosine aminotransferase in hepatoma-fibroblast hybrids. *Proc. Natl. Acad. Sci.* 68: 127–131.

Schorpp, M., W. Kugler, U. Wagner, and G.U. Ryffel. 1988. Hepatocyte-specific promoter element HP1 of the *Xenopus* albumin gene interacts with transcriptional factors of mammalian hepatocytes. *J. Mol. Biol.* 202: 307–320.

Scott, M.P., J.W. Tamkun, and G.W. Hartzell. 1990. The structure and function of the homeodomain. *Biochim. Biophys. Acta* 989: 25–48.

Sladek, F.M., W. Zhong, E. Lai, and J.E. Darnell. 1990. Liver-enriched transcription factor HNF-4 is a novel member of the steroid hormone receptor superfamily. *Genes Dev.* 4: 2353–2365.

Smith, J.C. 1989. Mesodermal induction and mesoderm-inducing factors in early amphibian development. *Development* 105: 665–677.

Sorrentino, V, R. Pepperkok, R.L. Davis, W. Ansorge, and L. Philipson. 1990. Cell proliferation inhibited by MyoD1 independently of myogenic differentiation. *Nature* 345: 813–815.

Spencer, F.A., F.M. Hoffman, and W.M. Gelbart. 1982. *Decapentaplegic*: A gene complex affecting morphogenesis in *Drosophila melanogaster*. *Cell* 28: 451–461.

Strickland, S. and V. Mahdavi. 1978. The induction of differentiation in teratocarcinoma stem cells by retinoic acid. *Cell* 15: 393–403.

Struhl, G. and R.A. White. 1985. Regulation of the *Ultrabithorax* gene of *Drosophila* by other bithorax complex genes. *Cell* 43: 507–519.

Svensson, E.C., P.B. Conley, and J.C. Paulson. 1992. Activation of the α 2.6 dialyltransferase gene promoter by the liver-enriched transcription factors HNF-1, PBP and LAP. *Mol. Cell. Biol.* (in press).

Thompson, E.B. and T.D. Gelehrter. 1971. Expression of tyrosine aminotransferase activity in somatic cell heterokaryons. Evidence for negative control of enzyme expression. *Proc. Natl. Acad. Sci.* 68: 2589–2593.

Tilghman, S.M. and A. Belayew. 1982. Transcriptional control of the murine albumin/α-fetoprotein locus during development. *Proc. Natl. Acad. Sci.* 79: 5254–5257.

Toniatti, C., A. Demartis, P. Monaci, A. Nicosia, and G. Ciliberto. 1990. Synergistic *trans*-activation of the human C-reactive protein promoter by HNF-1 binding at two distinct sites. *EMBO J.* **9:** 4467–4475.

Tonjes, R.R., K.G. Xanthopoulos, and J.E. Darnell. 1991. Transcriptional control in hepatocytes of normal and c^{14CoF} albino deletion mice. *EMBO J.* (in press).

Tremml, G. and M. Bienz. 1989. Homeotic gene expression in the visceral mesoderm of *Drosophila* embryos. *EMBO J.* **8:** 2677–2685.

Tronche, F., A. Rollier, I. Bach, M.C. Weiss, and M. Yaniv. 1989. The rat albumin promoter: Cooperation with upstream elements is required when binding of APF/HNF-1 to the proximal element is impaired by mutation or bacterial methylation. *Mol. Cell. Biol.* **9:** 4759–4766.

Trus, M., N. Benvenisty, H. Cohen, and L. Reshef. 1990. Developmentally regulated interactions of liver nuclear factors with the rat phosphoenolpyruvate carboxykinase promoter. *Mol. Cell. Biol.* **10:** 2418–2422.

Ueno, T. and F.J. Gonzalez. 1990. Transcriptional control of the rat hepatic CYP2E1 gene. *Mol. Cell. Biol.* **9:** 4495–4505.

Umek, R.M., A.L. Friedman, and S.L. McKnight. 1991. CCAAT-enhancer binding protein: A component of a differentiation switch. *Science* **251:** 288–292.

van den Heuvel, M., R. Nusse, P. Johnston, and P. Lawrence. 1989. Distribution of the *wingless* gene product in *Drosophila* embryos: A protein involved in cell-cell communication. *Cell* **59:** 739–749.

Vaulont, S., N. Puzenat, A. Kahn, and M. Raymondjean. 1989a. Analysis by cell-free transcription of the liver-specific pyruvate kinase gene promoter. *Mol. Cell. Biol.* **9:** 4409–4415.

Vaulont, S., N. Puzenat, F. Levrat, M. Cognet, A. Kahn, and M. Raymondjean. 1989b. Proteins binding to the liver-specific pyruvate kinase gene promoter. A unique combination of known factors. *J. Mol. Biol.* **209:** 205–219.

Vinson, C.R., P.B. Sigler, and S.L. McKnight. 1989. Scissors-grip model for DNA recognition by a family of leucine zipper proteins. *Science* **246:** 911–916.

Vogt, T.F., D. Solter, and S.M. Tilghman. 1987. *Raf*, a *trans*-acting locus, regulates the α-fetoprotein gene in a cell autonomous manner. *Science* **236:** 301–303.

Weigel, D. and H. Jackle. 1990. The *fork head* domain: A novel DNA binding motif of eukaryotic transcription factors. *Cell* **63:** 455–456.

Weigel, D., G. Jurgens, F. Kuttner, E. Seifert, and H. Jackle. 1989. The homeotic gene *fork head* encodes a nuclear protein and is expressed in the terminal regions of the *Drosophila* embryo. *Cell* **57:** 645–658.

Wuarin, J. and U. Schibler. 1990. Expression of the liver-enriched transcriptional activator protein DBP follows a stringent circadian rhythm. *Cell* **63:** 1257–1266.

Wuarin, J., C.R. Mueller, and U. Schibler. 1990. A ubiquitous CCAAT-factor is required for efficient in vitro transcription from the mouse albumin promoter. *J. Mol. Biol.* **214:** 865–874.

Xanthopoulos, K.G., V.R. Prezioso, W.S. Chen, F.M. Sladek, R. Cortese, and J.E. Darnell. 1991. The different transcriptional patterns of genes for HNF-1, C/EBP, HNF-3 and HNF-4, protein factors that govern liver-specific transcription. *Proc. Natl. Acad. Sci.* **88:** 3807–3811.

41

Oct-1 and Oct-2: Differential Transcriptional Regulation by Proteins That Bind to the Same DNA Sequence

Winship Herr
Cold Spring Harbor Laboratory
Cold Spring Harbor, New York 11724

OVERVIEW

The human POU-homeodomain proteins Oct-1 and Oct-2 can activate transcription from different promoters even though they recognize the same *cis*-regulatory element, the octamer motif ATGCAAAT. Studies reveal two mechanisms by which this differential transcriptional regulation is achieved. In one case, Oct-1 and Oct-2 possess promoter-selective activation domains that result in preferential activation of RNA polymerase II transcription from a small nuclear RNA promoter by Oct-1 and an mRNA promoter by Oct-2. In the other case, selective association of Oct-1 with the herpes simplex virus activator VP16 results in recruitment of Oct-1, but not Oct-2, to a new *cis*-regulatory site that, in the absence of VP16, is not recognized effectively by either Oct-1 or Oct-2.

INTRODUCTION

One of the surprises arising from the study of transcriptional regulation in multicellular organisms has been the frequent occurrence of multiple regulatory proteins recognizing the same *cis*-acting DNA element. Little is known about how proteins that display the same DNA-binding activity can selectively modulate the levels of transcription from different promoters. In this chapter, I describe two modes by which such differential transcriptional regulation is achieved, as illustrated by studies of the homeodomain proteins Oct-1 and Oct-2, two proteins that bind to an 8-bp ATGCAAAT octamer sequence found in a variety of promoters. First, particular activation domains can selectively activate different promoters

Transcriptional Regulation.
Copyright 1992 Cold Spring Harbor Laboratory Press 0-87969-410-6/92 $3 + 00   **1103**

even when attached to an identical DNA-binding domain. Second, through selective interaction with an auxiliary protein, one of the two proteins can be recruited to a new *cis*-regulatory binding site. The second mode is exemplified by the selective interaction of the herpes simplex virus (HSV) activator VP16 with Oct-1, in which VP16 distinguishes among the seven amino acid differences between the Oct-1 and Oct-2 homeodomains—differences that themselves do not apparently affect the DNA-binding specificity of Oct-1 and Oct-2.

Homeodomain proteins were first discovered as regulators of *Drosophila* development (McGinnis et al. 1984; Scott and Weiner 1984). Subsequently, the 60-amino-acid homeodomain was shown to be related to the helix-turn-helix motif found in prokaryotic transcriptional regulators both in primary amino acid sequence (Laughon and Scott 1984; Shepherd et al. 1984) and in structure (Qian et al. 1989; Otting et al. 1990; Kissinger et al. 1990; Wolberger et al. 1991). Proteins containing homeodomains have been identified in regulatory proteins from organisms as diverse as yeast, maize, *Caenorhabditis elegans, Drosophila melanogaster*, and vertebrates (see Scott et al. 1989; Wüthrich and Gehring, this volume). In *D. melanogaster*, homeodomain proteins that elicit very different developmental programs can share very similar DNA-binding properties (see Levine and Hoey 1988; Hayashi and Scott 1990). Although in some instances subtle differences in DNA-binding specificity may be responsible for the different developmental programs observed in vivo, it is likely that in other instances it is differential protein-protein interactions that lead to different patterns of transcriptional regulation. Such interactions are illustrated by the mechanisms of differential transcriptional regulation used by the homeodomain proteins Oct-1 and Oct-2.

In this chapter, I first describe the components of the regulatory system my colleagues and I have studied: the octamer-motif-binding proteins Oct-1 and Oct-2, the octamer motif itself, and the HSV activator VP16. I then review a series of experiments by Tanaka et al. (1988) in which the activity of the octamer motif was assayed in the context of two different promoters. Such studies led to the suggestion that different types of activation domains can stimulate different promoters and that VP16 serves as a transcriptional activation domain adapter. In the remainder of the discussion, I describe the elucidation of different promoter-selective activation domains in Oct-1 and Oct-2 from structure:function studies of the Oct factors and how VP16 serves not only as a transcriptional activation domain adapter, but also as a recruiter of Oct-1 to a new *cis*-regulatory target that is not responsive to Oct-1 or Oct-2 in the absence of VP16.

THE COMPONENTS

Oct-1 and Oct-2

Oct-1 is a ubiquitously expressed protein with an apparent molecular mass of 95 kD to 100 kD (Fletcher et al. 1987; Sturm et al. 1987; O'Neill and Kelly 1988). It was originally called NF-A1 (Singh et al. 1986; Staudt et al. 1986) and has since also been referred to as OTF-1 (Fletcher et al. 1987), NFIII (Pruijn et al. 1986; O'Neill and Kelly 1988), and OBP100 (Sturm et al. 1987). Oct-2 (OTF-2) is a 60-kD protein (Scheidereit et al. 1987) whose expression is restricted to certain cell types, primarily B cells and cells from various regions of the brain (Landolfi et al. 1986; Staudt et al. 1986; He et al. 1989; Stoykova et al. 1992). Oct-1 and Oct-2 bind DNA with very similar, if not identical, sequence specificity (Staudt et al. 1986; Aurora and Herr 1992). Additional octamer-motif-binding proteins (Schöler et al. 1989; Lenardo et al. 1989), which are related to Oct-1 and Oct-2 (e.g., Oct-3/4 [Okamoto et al. 1990; Rosner et al. 1990; Schöler et al. 1990] and SCIP/Oct-6 [Monuki et al. 1989; Suzuki et al. 1990]), may not share precisely the same DNA-binding specificity as Oct-1 and Oct-2 (see Aurora and Herr 1992).

Figure 1 is a schematic diagram of the structures of the Oct-1 and Oct-2 proteins as revealed by molecular cloning and sequencing of their encoding cDNAs (Clerc et al. 1988; Müller et al. 1988; Scheidereit et al. 1988; Sturm et al. 1988). The first *oct-1* cDNA isolated (Sturm et al. 1988) encoded a protein of 743 amino acids; analysis of other *oct-1* cDNAs suggests that the major Oct-1 species contains extra amino-terminal residues and is about 800 amino acids long. There is also apparently at least one minor Oct-1 species that is smaller and results from differential *oct-1* mRNA processing (G. Das, unpubl.). The *oct-2* gene also encodes multiple protein forms (Clerc et al. 1988; Müller et al. 1988; Scheidereit et al. 1988; Hatzopoulos et al. 1990; Stoykova et al. 1992). The major Oct-2 species illustrated in Figure 1 (and referred to as Oct-2 throughout this chapter) consists of 479 amino acids. An Oct-2 variant, called Oct-2B (Schreiber et al. 1988), is also expressed in B cells but contains a carboxy-terminal extension of 135 amino acids in place of the carboxy-terminal 12 residues of Oct-2 and results from alternative splicing of the primary *oct-2* transcript (Hatzopoulos et al. 1990; Tanaka et al. 1992). This Oct-2B carboxy-terminal extension displays considerable sequence similarity to the carboxyl terminus of Oct-1, as indicated by the shading in Figure 1 (Hatzopoulos et al. 1990).

Centrally located within Oct-1 and Oct-2 are their respective DNA-binding domains (Clerc et al. 1988; Sturm et al. 1988; Sturm and Herr 1988), which, as might be expected for two proteins that display the

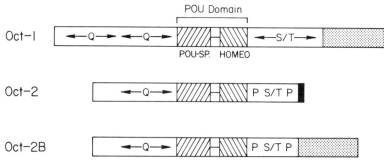

Figure 1 Schematic representations of Oct-1, Oct-2, and Oct-2B proteins are shown illustrating properties described in the text. The proteins are aligned with respect to the centrally located POU domain, which consists of POU-specific (POU-SP.) and POU-homeo (HOMEO) subsegments. The glutamine (Q)-rich amino-terminal regions and serine and threonine (S/T) and proline (P)-rich carboxy-terminal regions are identified. The unique 12-amino-acid Oct-2 car- boxyl terminus is the solid portion, and the carboxy-terminal region of similarity between Oct-1 and Oct-2B is stippled. (Reprinted, with permission, from Tanaka et al. 1992 [copyright held by Cell Press].)

same DNA-binding specificity, are very closely related. The Oct-1 and Oct-2 proteins exhibit 87% identity over the approximately 160 amino acids that encompass their respective DNA-binding domains. The 60-amino-acid Oct-1 and Oct-2 homeodomains are located on the carboxy-terminal side of the DNA-binding domain and are identical at 53 of 60 positions (Clerc et al. 1988; Ko et al. 1988; Müller et al. 1988; Scheidereit et al. 1988; Sturm et al. 1988). The amino-terminal 75 residues of the respective DNA-binding domains are even more highly conserved. Oct-1 and Oct-2 differ at only one position within this region (Clerc et al. 1988; Müller et al. 1988; Scheidereit et al. 1988; Sturm et al. 1988). These two highly conserved regions are separated by segments of 24 (in Oct-1) or 27 (in Oct-2) amino acids that display only 50% se- quence identity.

The bipartite pattern of Oct-1 and Oct-2 sequence conservation within the DNA-binding domain is also shared with the pituitary-specific tran- scription factor called Pit-1 or GHF-1 (Bodner et al. 1988; Ingraham et al. 1988) and the nematode cell lineage gene product unc-86 (Finney et al. 1988). This finding led to the identification of a new DNA-binding motif called the POU domain, which consists of both conserved regions (Herr et al. 1988). The homeodomains found among the POU domains of these four proteins, as well as other POU domains that have since been described (see Rosenfeld 1991), are more similar in sequence to one an- other than to any other homeodomain (Herr et al. 1988; Scott et al.

1989). This POU-type homeodomain has also always been found associated with the unusual amino-terminal POU-specific region. These observations suggest that the POU domain, even though it displays bipartite sequence conservation, has been conserved as a functional unit. Consistent with this hypothesis, the POU domain represents a bipartite DNA-binding structure in which both the POU-specific and POU homeodomains contribute to sequence-specific DNA binding (Sturm and Herr 1988; Ingraham et al. 1990; Kristie and Sharp 1990; Verrijzer et al. 1990b; Aurora and Herr 1992).

Outside of the very similar POU domains, Oct-1 and Oct-2 also display sequence similarity within the amino-terminal region where the shorter amino terminus of Oct-2 displays about 50% identity with amino-terminal Oct-1 sequences (Clerc et al. 1988; Sturm et al. 1988). Both amino-terminal regions are rich in glutamine residues, a feature shared with the ubiquitous activator Sp1, where such regions constitute transcriptional activation domains (Courey and Tjian 1988). The carboxy-terminal regions of Oct-1 and Oct-2 display little sequence identity, although both regions are rich in serines and threonines. Within this region, Oct-2 is also rich in prolines, a feature that has also been associated with transcriptional activation domains (Mermod et al. 1989).

The Octamer Motif

The *cis*-regulatory target of Oct-1 and Oct-2, the octamer motif, is unusual in that it is found in a large variety of promoters, including ubiquitously and cell specifically active promoters recognized by either RNA polymerase II or RNA polymerase III. It is also found in the promoters of viral genes. The octamer motif (Parslow et al. 1984), also referred to as a decamer motif because of a conserved adenine residue in the tenth position (ATGCAAATNA; Falkner and Zachau 1984), has been found both near the start site of transcription and in more distally located enhancer sequences. Among ubiquitously expressed genes, the octamer motif is found positioned near the transcriptional start site in the human and chicken histone H2B genes (Heintz et al. 1981; Harvey et al. 1982), where it has been implicated in cell cycle regulation of these promoters (LaBella et al. 1988), and in enhancers of small nuclear RNA (snRNA) gene promoters (Mattaj et al. 1985; Mangin et al. 1986). snRNAs are short, nonpolyadenylated RNAs involved in RNA processing, which are synthesized either by RNA polymerase II (e.g., U2 snRNA) or RNA polymerase III (i.e., U6 snRNA; see Hernandez, this volume). The snRNA promoter element responsible for discriminating between RNA polymerase II and RNA polymerase III transcription is a TATA box that, paradoxically, directs RNA polymerase III transcription (Mattaj et al. 1988; Lobo and Hernandez 1989). In both RNA polymerase II and RNA polymerase III snRNA promoters, the octamer motif can stimulate transcription (see Hernandez, this volume).

Among octamer-motif-containing genes whose expression is cell-specific, the B-cell-specific immunoglobulin genes are the best characterized. Octamer motifs occur in both heavy- (IgH) and light-chain immunoglobulin genes and are positioned near the transcriptional start site (Falkner and Zachau 1984; Parslow et al. 1984), as well as in the distal enhancers (Falkner and Zachau 1984; Currie and Roeder 1989; Meyer and Neuberger 1989; Pettersson et al. 1990). In viral genomes, the octamer motif can regulate DNA replication as well as transcription. It constitutes a functional part of the adenovirus origin of DNA replication where binding of either Oct-1 (NFIII) or Oct-2 can stimulate DNA replication in vitro (O'Neill et al. 1988; Verrijzer et al. 1990a). Among viral promoters, there is an octamer motif in the SV40 enhancer that directs B-cell-specific transcription (Davidson et al. 1986), and the octamer motif is also found in promoters of the immediate-early (IE) genes of herpes simplex virus (HSV) (Pruijn et al. 1986), where it is associated with the TAATGARAT (R = purine) motif (Mackem and Roizman 1982), the target of *trans*-activation by the viral protein VP16 (Kristie and Roizman 1984; Preston et al. 1984).

VP16

Virion protein 16 or VP16, also referred to as Vmw65, α-TIF, VF65, and ICP25, is a multifunctional protein consisting of 490 amino acids that serves as both a structural component of the HSV virion (Batterson and Roizman 1983; Campbell et al. 1984; Ace et al. 1988) and an activator of HSV IE transcription (for review, see Goding and O'Hare 1989). VP16 is expressed late during HSV infection, is encapsulated within the tegument of the virion and, upon infection, is released into the cell, where it forms a multiprotein-DNA complex on sequence elements matching or related to the sequence TAATGARAT (McKnight et al. 1987; O'Hare and Goding 1988; Preston et al. 1988); this multiprotein-DNA complex contains two cellular proteins, Oct-1 (Gerster and Roeder 1988; apRhys et al. 1989; Kristie et al. 1989; Stern et al. 1989) and a second, less well characterized, host cell factor(s) herein termed HCF (Stern and Herr 1991) but also referred to as C1, VCAF, and CFF (Gerster and Roeder 1988; Kristie et al. 1989; Katan et al. 1990; Xiao and Capone 1990). Although VP16 binds DNA poorly on its own (Marsden et al. 1987; Kristie and Sharp 1990; Stern and Herr 1991), when associated with Oct-1 and HCF, VP16 is able to bind to DNA avidly. Once bound to the enhancer of HSV IE genes, VP16 activates transcription through a potent carboxy-terminal 80-amino-acid acidic domain (Sadowski et al. 1988; Triezenberg et al. 1988; Cousens et al. 1989; Greaves and O'Hare 1989).

DIFFERENTIAL TRANSCRIPTIONAL REGULATION BY THE OCTAMER MOTIF

The presence of the octamer motif in promoters displaying either ubiquitous or cell-specific activities suggested that the ubiquitous Oct-1 and cell-specific Oct-2 proteins might direct transcription of different octamer-motif-containing promoters. It was difficult, however, to ascertain from early mutagenesis studies of different promoters whether the different activities of the octamer motif are due to intrinsic differences in Oct-1 and Oct-2 activation potentials or, rather, to interactions with different neighboring *cis*-acting elements that themselves confer the ubiquitous and cell-specific activation properties. For example, the ubiquitous activity of the octamer motif in the context of the human U2 snRNA enhancer could reflect interaction with Sp1, which binds cooperatively with Oct-1 to a site neighboring the octamer motif, which is also critical for U2 snRNA enhancer function (Ares et al. 1987; Janson and Pettersson 1990). To compare directly the intrinsic activity of an octamer motif in the context of promoters directing expression of either mRNA or snRNA transcripts, Tanaka et al. (1988) assayed the activity of the SV40 enhancer octamer motif as a multimerized synthetic enhancer in two model promoter constructs. These studies led to the suggestion that activators such as Oct-1 and Oct-2 can possess different types of activation surfaces that allow transcriptional stimulation by different kinds of RNA polymerase II initiation complexes.

The model mRNA and snRNA promoters used in these studies were the human β-globin promoter as a representative mRNA promoter and the human U2 promoter as a representative snRNA promoter directing transcription by RNA polymerase II. These two transcription units have a number of discriminating features, as illustrated in Figure 2A. The β-globin promoter, in common with many other mRNA promoters, has a TATA box, which serves as a binding site for the general transcription factor TFIID (Nakajima et al. 1988), as well as a number of proximal promoter elements (e.g., CCAAT box) that permit an effective response to a distal enhancer (Banerji et al. 1981; Dierks et al. 1983; Myers et al. 1986). Once transcription is initiated, the engaged polymerase proceeds

A

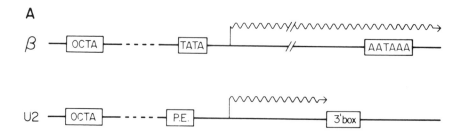

B

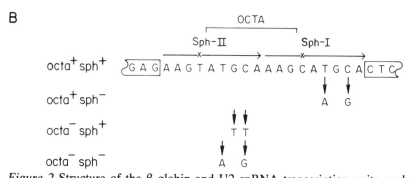

Figure 2 Structure of the β-globin and U2 snRNA transcription units, and the SV40 B proto-enhancer used to study the activity of the octamer motif in different promoter contexts. (*A*) The β-globin transcription unit, which possesses features typical of mRNA transcription units, is contrasted with the U2 snRNA RNA polymerase II transcription unit (see text). The β-globin promoter does not normally contain an octamer motif, but the promoter-proximal TATA box (TATA) can respond to an octamer motif inserted into the plasmid construct. Transcription of the β-globin gene terminates downstream from the polyadenylation signal (AATAAA) that encodes 3′ end formation. The U2 snRNA promoter possesses an octamer motif within the enhancer region and an snRNA-specific proximal element (P.E.) rather than a TATA box. The 3′ end of the U2 snRNA is specified by a signal at the 3′ end of the gene (3′ box), which probably induces termination of transcription. (*B*) The 18-bp SV40 B proto-enhancer is shown flanked by *Xho*I recognition site sequences (boxed) that separate the individual proto-enhancer sequences in the multimerized enhancer constructs. The two sets of overlapping motifs (octamer [OCTA], and Sph-I and Sph-II motifs) are identified above the sequence. Base changes in each of the three mutant B proto-enhancers are indicated below the sequence. Note that the two 5′ flanking residues of the *Xho*I recognition site (AG) match the wild-type SV40 enhancer sequence, but these are not essential for B proto-enhancer activity (Tanaka et al. 1988).

for about 2 kb before synthesis of a polyadenylation signal directs cleavage and polyadenylation of the transcript. Transcription of the β-globin gene terminates at one or more ill-defined positions downstream from the polyadenylation signal (see Proudfoot 1989).

Like other snRNA genes transcribed by RNA polymerase II, the U2 snRNA transcription unit differs in many respects from mRNA transcription units as described in detail by N. Hernandez (this volume). Briefly, promoters for these genes lack a TATA box and instead carry a conserved snRNA-specific proximal promoter element positioned 60 bp to 40 bp upstream of the transcriptional start site. Another unusual feature of these transcription units is that the 3′ end of the primary transcript is probably formed as the result of recognition of a termination signal in the DNA called the 3′ box (Ciliberto et al. 1985; Hernandez 1985; Yuo et al. 1985; Neuman de Vegvar et al. 1986; Ach and Weiner 1987). This 3′ box is recognized only if transcription is directed by an RNA polymerase II snRNA promoter (Hernandez and Weiner 1986; Neuman de Vegvar et al. 1986). These different initiation and termination properties suggest that the compositions of the transcribing β-globin and U2 RNA polymerase II complexes differ.

Figure 2B shows the 18-bp SV40 enhancer sequence flanked by *Xho*I recognition sites that was used to assay octamer motif function in these two different promoter contexts. This sequence represents the SV40 B element or proto-enhancer (Herr and Clarke 1986; Ondek et al. 1988) and contains two sets of functional overlapping motifs (Davidson et al. 1986). An imperfect 9-bp direct repeat represents two "sph enhansons" that together form the SV40 B proto-enhancer (Fromental et al. 1988; Ondek et al. 1988). The junction formed by the two sph enhansons represents a seven out of eight match to a perfect octamer motif. To assay the activity of these *cis*-regulatory motifs together and separately, three sets of double point mutations were used. One such double point mutation inactivates the sph enhansons (octa$^+$/sph$^-$), another inactivates the octamer motif (octa$^-$/sph$^+$), and the third inactivates both elements (octa$^-$/sph$^-$). By combining these different sets of mutations into otherwise identical multimerized enhancers, it was possible to contrast the activities of the sph and octamer motifs in the different promoter contexts. Furthermore, by positioning the multimerized enhancers at sites distal to the transcriptional start site, the activities of the octamer and sph motifs were segregated from the influence of other neighboring *cis*-acting elements. Therefore, the activities displayed by the two regulatory elements in these constructs probably reflect long-range interactions, either direct or indirect, between transcription factors bound to these reiterated proto-enhancers and general factors positioned near the transcriptional start site.

Assay of the native and mutant enhancer elements in the context of the β-globin promoter revealed that the octamer motif is active in B cells but not HeLa cells. Because HeLa cells are derived from a cervical carcinoma, they represent a non-B-cell line. Thus, consistent with previous results (Davidson et al. 1986; Dreyfus et al. 1987; Gerster et al. 1987; Lenardo et al. 1987; Wirth et al. 1987), the activity pattern of the multimerized octamer motif paralleled the expression pattern of Oct-2, which is expressed in B cells but not HeLa cells (Landolfi et al. 1986; Staudt et al. 1986). In the context of the U2 snRNA promoter, however, the octamer motif was active in both HeLa cells and B cells, correlating with the expression pattern of Oct-1. The ability of the octamer motif to activate the U2 snRNA promoter is unique to that element: Neither the sph enhansons nor other SV40 proto-enhancer elements (A and C), which activate the β-globin promoter in HeLa cells (Ondek et al. 1987), activate the U2 snRNA promoter in the same cell line (Tanaka et al. 1988). Moreover, even the combination of the "universal" yeast acidic activator GAL4 and GAL4-binding sites in the U2 snRNA reporter construct failed to activate U2 transcription in HeLa cells (Tanaka et al. 1988). Although the SV40 octamer motif failed to activate transcription of the β-globin gene in HeLa cells, it could be induced to do so by coexpression of the HSV *trans*-activator VP16, which associates with Oct-1 and provides an acidic mRNA promoter activation domain.

The multiple activities of the octamer and sph motifs in the context of the β-globin and U2 promoters led to the model for Oct-1 and Oct-2 function illustrated in Figure 3, which has been adapted from Tanaka et al. (1988). The first two panels of this model illustrate the cell-specific activities of the sph motifs in HeLa cells (panel A) and the octamer motif in B cells (panel B) in the context of the β-globin promoter. Both activities are the result of cell-specific expression of transcription factors: the sph enhanson-binding protein TEF-1, which is expressed in HeLa cells but not B cells (Davidson et al. 1988), and Oct-2, which is expressed in B cells but not HeLa cells (Landolfi et al. 1986; Staudt et al. 1986). These two transcription factors may activate transcription through mechanisms similar to GAL4, because all three transcription factors are capable of activating the same promoter. This is not to argue, however, that all three proteins make use of the same type of activation surfaces, because they may operate via one or more different intermediaries.

As shown in panel C of Figure 3, Oct-1 is postulated to activate transcription in the context of the U2 snRNA promoter by interacting directly or indirectly with an snRNA-specific transcription initiation complex. The Oct-1 activation surface responsible for stimulating transcription of the U2 gene is likely to be different from the GAL4 or TEF-1 activation

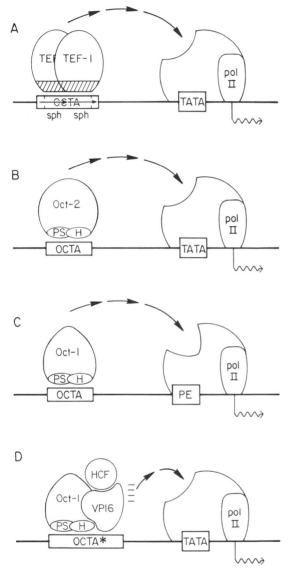

Figure 3 Selective stimulation of β-globin and U2 snRNA transcriptional initiation complexes by promoter-selective activation domains. Panels *A-D* illustrate possible interactions between SV40 B proto-enhancer-bound transcription factors and different transcriptional initiation complexes assembled on mRNA (*A,* *B,* and *D*) and snRNA (*C*) promoters. Each panel is described in detail in the text. (*A*) TEF-1 and sph motif activation of the β-globin promoter. (*B*) Oct-2 and octamer motif activation of the β-globin promoter. (*C*) Oct-1 and octamer motif activation of the U2 snRNA promoter. (*D*) Oct-1, VP16, and HCF complex assembly leading to activation of the β-globin promoter through octamer-related elements (OCTA*; see text). (P.S.) POU-specific region; (H) homeodomain.

surface, because these latter two transcription factors fail to stimulate the snRNA promoter. These results suggested the existence of different types of promoter-selective activation domains. Whether Oct-2 might stimulate snRNA transcription could not be addressed in the above experiments because Oct-2 activity could not be assayed in the absence of the ubiquitous Oct-1 protein. Oct-1, however, probably lacks activation surfaces carried by Oct-2, TEF-1, and GAL4 because it does not readily activate the β-globin promoter. VP16 can supply such an activation surface by associating with Oct-1 on particular octamer elements (including the SV40 octamer motif) with its potent acidic activation domain, effectively serving as an adapter for activation of mRNA-type transcription, as illustrated in panel D.

All four of the panels in Figure 3 emphasize long-range activation mechanisms that involve direct or indirect interactions with proximal promoter transcription complexes. The specificity of transcriptional activation by promoter elements is normally thought to result from selective interactions of transcription factors with different *cis*-acting elements (see, e.g., Maniatis et al. 1987; Ptashne 1988). The different activities of the same octamer element in the context of different proximal promoter elements, however, emphasize that promoter-proximal elements can also direct selective and cell-specific transcriptional regulation.

TRANSCRIPTIONAL REGULATION OF AN MRNA PROMOTER BY OCT-1 AND OCT-2

Oct-2 Is A More Potent Activator of β-Globin Gene Transcription Than Oct-1

The promoter-selective activation domain model shown in Figure 3 was deduced from the observed activation properties of the octamer motif in the context of different promoters and in different cell lines. The availability of cloned cDNAs for Oct-1 (Sturm et al. 1988) and Oct-2 (Clerc et al. 1988) allowed us to test this model directly by assaying the relative transcriptional regulatory activities of Oct-1 and Oct-2 in transient expression assays (Tanaka and Herr 1990; Tanaka et al. 1992). Müller et al. (1988) demonstrated that Oct-2 expressed in HeLa cells can activate a β-globin promoter containing an octamer motif, thus providing an assay to compare the activities of Oct-1 and Oct-2 on an mRNA promoter. In our assay, we cotransfected Oct-1 and Oct-2 expression vectors with reporter constructs containing the same aforementioned multimerized enhancers (see Fig. 2). By using multimerized binding sites separated from other promoter elements, these experiments focused on potential interactions between the different Oct factors and proximal promoter complexes, rather than between the Oct factors and proteins bound to neighboring *cis*-acting elements.

As predicted by the model in Figure 3, high-level expression of Oct-2, but not Oct-1, resulted in octamer-motif-dependent activation of the β-globin promoter (Tanaka and Herr 1990). This result argues that Oct-1 and Oct-2 possess different intrinsic abilities to activate β-globin transcription in vivo and that different levels of Oct-1 and Oct-2 expression are not responsible for the cell-specific β-globin promoter activation properties of the octamer motif. In these experiments, an "sph-enhanson repression" assay (see below) was used to show that both Oct-1 and Oct-2 were expressed effectively and were able to bind to the multimerized target sequences during the transient assay. To identify the region(s) of Oct-1 and Oct-2 responsible for their respective failure and success in activating the β-globin promoter, the activities of Oct-1/Oct-2 chimeras were assayed. Exchange of the amino-terminal or POU domain sequences had little or no effect on Oct-1 or Oct-2 activity, but exchange of the carboxy-terminal region resulted in a transfer of β-globin activation properties. Thus, Oct-1 carrying the carboxyl terminus of Oct-2 could now readily activate the β-globin promoter, whereas Oct-2 carrying the Oct-1 carboxyl terminus displayed little activity (Tanaka and Herr 1990). These results show that the different β-globin promoter activation properties of Oct-1 and Oct-2 are the result of sequences that are separable from the DNA-binding domain.

Deletion analysis of Oct-2 revealed that, in addition to the carboxy-terminal region, the glutamine-rich (Q) region amino-terminal of the POU domain (see Fig. 1) is also required to activate the β-globin promoter in this assay (Tanaka and Herr 1990). A similar requirement for amino- and carboxy-terminal components of Oct-2 was observed by Gerster et al. (1990). The ability of the Oct-1 amino-terminal region to replace its counterpart in Oct-2 in the Oct-1/Oct-2 chimeric protein shows that the Oct-1 amino-terminal sequences, which are also glutamine-rich, can participate in activation of the β-globin promoter by cooperating with the Oct-2 carboxyl terminus. Thus, in the β-globin promoter assay we used, Oct-2 employs two interdependent activation domains to activate transcription. Oct-1 apparently fails to activate transcription in this assay because it only possesses the equivalent of one of the two Oct-2 mRNA promoter activation domains. These results suggest that differential activation of mRNA promoters by Oct-1 and Oct-2 reflects quantitative differences in the ability of these two factors to activate this type of promoter.

Oct Factors Can Activate or Repress β-Globin Transcription

In the aforementioned studies, Oct-2 activated transcription when bound to the octamer motif. However, by subtly changing the sequences flanking the octamer motif, it is possible to convert Oct-2 into a repressor of β-globin transcription (Tanaka and Herr 1990). Recall that the octamer motif overlaps tandem sph enhansons in the SV40 B proto-enhancer (see Fig. 2B). For the activation assay described above, the octa$^+$/sph$^-$ enhancer was used to assay the activity of Oct-1 and Oct-2 in the absence of sph enhanson function. However, if the sph enhansons are left intact, then β-globin transcription is very active in HeLa cells in the absence of exogenously provided Oct-1 or Oct-2 protein. This activity probably reflects the activity of the HeLa cell factor TEF-1 (Davidson et al. 1988; Xiao et al. 1991). In the presence of the overlapping octamer motif, however, TEF-1 activation is sensitive to overexpression of either Oct-1 or Oct-2, resulting in repression of β-globin transcription. Because this repression is relieved by either the octamer-specific mutation octa$^-$/sph$^+$ (see Fig. 2B) or a mutation in the Oct-1 homeodomain that prevents DNA binding (Tanaka and Herr 1990), repression probably results from binding to the octamer motif of Oct molecules, which displace or inactivate TEF-1 molecules bound to the sph enhansons. The apparent repression by the activator Oct-2 probably results from the relatively weak ability of Oct-2 to activate transcription in transfected HeLa cells compared to the activity of TEF-1. Thus, using this β-globin promoter activation assay, Oct-2 is able to either activate or repress transcription, depending on the immediate context of the octamer motif, whereas Oct-1 only represses transcription.

TRANSCRIPTIONAL REGULATION OF THE U2 SNRNA PROMOTER BY OCT FACTORS

Oct-1 Is A More Potent Activator of U2 snRNA Gene Transcription Than Oct-2

The endogenous Oct-1 activity in mammalian cells made it more difficult to assay activation by transiently expressed Oct-1 than to assay activation by Oct-2. Because of the high level of activation by endogenous Oct-1, overexpression of Oct-1 yields less than a twofold stimulation of the U2 snRNA promoter containing the multimerized octamer motifs (Tanaka et al. 1992). To circumvent the endogenous activity, we used the strategy illustrated in Figure 4, in which the DNA-binding specificities of Oct-1 and Oct-2 were reprogrammed without changing the gross structure of either protein. This was accomplished by replacing the majority of the

A

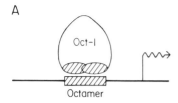

B

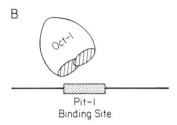

C

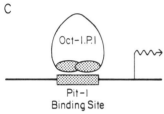

Figure 4 Alteration of the DNA-binding specificity of Oct-1 (and of Oct-2) by replacement of the Oct-1 POU domain with the Pit-1 POU domain. (*A*) Endogenous Oct-1 is shown bound to the octamer motif and activating snRNA transcription. (*B*) Endogenous Oct-1 does not recognize the Pit-1-binding site effectively and therefore fails to activate transcription of a U2 snRNA promoter containing Pit-1-binding sites in place of the octamer motif. (*C*) By replacing Oct-1 POU domain sequences with the corresponding Pit-1 POU domain sequences, to create Oct-1.P.1, the chimeric protein is now able to recognize the Pit-1-binding site and activate snRNA transcription from the promoter containing Pit-1-binding sites.

POU domain sequences of Oct-1 and Oct-2 with the corresponding Pit-1 POU domain sequences. As expected from the results of Ingraham et al. (1990) and Aurora and Herr (1992), the resulting chimeric POU domain displays a different DNA-binding specificity from that of Oct-1 and Oct-2. Thus, by using six tandem Pit-1-binding sites from the prolactin gene promoter (Nelson et al. 1988) upstream of the β-globin and U2 promoters, we could circumvent the activity of the endogenous Oct-1 and assay the ability of Oct-1 and Oct-2 Pit-1 POU domain chimeras to activate U2 and β-globin transcription (Tanaka et al. 1992).

We refer to the Oct-1 and Oct-2 chimeras carrying the Pit-1 POU domain as Oct-1.P.1 and Oct-2.P.2, respectively. Figure 5 shows the relative abilities of Oct-1.P.1 and Oct-2.P.2, and amino- and carboxy-terminal chimeras of the two proteins, to activate the U2 snRNA and β-globin mRNA promoters. In the context of the β-globin promoter, the Oct-1.P.1 and Oct-2.P.2 chimeras display the same activation properties on the Pit-1-binding site as do Oct-1 and Oct-2 on the octamer motif. Thus, Oct-2.P.2 effectively activates β-globin gene transcription (lane 12), whereas Oct-1.P.1 does not (lane 9). This result further establishes that, in the HeLa cell assay, the different abilities of Oct-1 and Oct-2 to activate the β-globin promoter are independent of the precise POU DNA-binding domain sequences. In the context of the U2 snRNA promoter, however, the activities of Oct-1.P.1 and Oct-2.P.2 are reversed. Now, the Oct-1.P.1 protein can activate transcription by more than tenfold (cf. lanes 2 and 3), whereas the Oct-2.P.2 protein displays little, if any, activity (lane 6). Thus, Oct-1 possesses a unique snRNA promoter activation potential that is either lacking or inactive in Oct-2 in this assay. Because the Oct-1.P.1 and Oct-2.P.2 molecules possess identical DNA-binding domains, the different promoter-selective activation potentials of these two proteins on the β-globin mRNA and U2 snRNA promoters demonstrate that activation domains, in addition to DNA-binding domains, can confer specificity of promoter activation. The assay of chimeras between Oct-1.P.1 and Oct-2.P.2 (lanes 4, 5, 10, and 11) and of Oct-1.P.1 deletion mutants (Tanaka et al. 1992) revealed that the major determinants for Oct-1 activation of the U2 promoter lie within the carboxy-terminal region, although the Oct-1 amino-terminal region can also independently activate transcription of the U2 promoter.

The Oct-2 Variant Oct-2B Can Activate the U2 snRNA Promoter

Although in our transient transfection assay using HeLa cells and Pit-1 POU domain chimeras Oct-2 fails to stimulate transcription of the U2 snRNA promoter, the *oct-2* gene can encode activators of U2 transcription through alternative splicing of the primary *oct-2* transcript. Recall that, as illustrated in Figure 1, the Oct-2 variant Oct-2B contains a carboxy-terminal extension that is similar to the carboxyl terminus of Oct-1 as a result of alternative splicing. Given the different activation properties of Oct-1 and Oct-2, the similarity in the carboxy-terminal sequences of Oct-1 and Oct-2B suggested that the Oct-2B splice might impart on Oct-2 the ability to activate the U2 snRNA promoter. Indeed, unlike its Oct-2.P.2 counterpart, a Pit-1 POU domain chimera carrying the

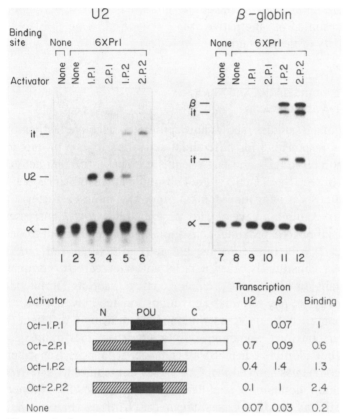

Figure 5 Oct-1 and Oct-2 possess distinct promoter-selective activation domains. An assay of transcriptional activation by Oct-1.P.1, Oct-2.P.1, Oct-1.P.2, and Oct-2.P.2 is shown. The U2 and β-globin reporter plasmids with (lanes *2–6* and *8–12*) or without (lanes *1* and *7*) the 6xPrl Pit-1-binding sites were transfected together into HeLa cells along with the appropriate effector plasmid expressing the activator listed above each lane. After transfection and RNA preparation, the samples were split into two and probed separately for U2 (lanes *1–6*) and β-globin (lanes *7–12*) transcripts. The correctly initiated internal reference α-globin transcripts (α) and experimental U2 (U2) and β-globin (β) transcripts are indicated along with incorrectly initiated readthrough transcripts (it). The structure of the effector proteins is illustrated at the bottom alongside quantitation of transcriptional activation and DNA binding by the transiently expressed effector proteins. U2 activation was normalized to the Oct-1.P.1 transfection, and the β-globin activation was normalized to the Oct-2.P.2 transfection. DNA binding is relative to the Oct-1.P.1 protein. (Reprinted, with permission, from Tanaka et al. 1992 [copyright held by Cell Press].)

Oct-2B flanking sequences can activate the U2 promoter effectively, while retaining some but not all of the Oct-2.P.2 potential to activate the β-globin promoter (Tanaka et al. 1992). Thus, the specificity of promoter activation can be modified by changes in promoter-selective activation domains as a result of an alternative splice without altering the DNA-binding specificity of the activator.

OCT-1 AND OCT-2 SHARE SNRNA AND MRNA PROMOTER ACTIVATION DOMAINS

The aforementioned studies show how promoter-selective activation domains can be responsible for differential activation of two promoters by proteins that bind to the same DNA sequence. These different activation properties of Oct-1 and Oct-2 are not absolute, however, since Oct-1 and Oct-2 both possess activation domain properties more characteristic of the other. For example, I have already described how Oct-1 possesses an amino-terminal mRNA promoter activation domain, equivalent to one of the two Oct-2 activation domains, but fails to activate our model mRNA promoter construct because it lacks an active carboxy-terminal activation domain. In a different promoter context, such as the histone H2B promoter, a carboxy-terminal activation domain may not be required to activate mRNA-type transcription. Indeed, using a different β-globin promoter construct containing only a single octamer motif near the TATA box but additional distal SV40 enhancer sequences, Schaffner, Matthias, and colleagues showed that Oct-2 does not require its carboxy-terminal activation domain to stimulate transcription (Müller-Immergluck et al. 1990) and that Oct-1 can activate mRNA transcription, albeit to a lesser extent than Oct-2 (Kemler et al. 1991). In vitro, Oct-1 is also able to activate transcription from mRNA promoters (LeBowitz et al. 1988; Johnson et al. 1990; Pierani et al. 1990), but the regions within Oct-1 responsible for the activation in vitro have not been mapped. The in vivo studies show that the different abilities of Oct-1 and Oct-2 to activate mRNA promoters reflect quantitative differences in their abilities to activate mRNA transcription, making Oct-1 the "weak" mRNA promoter activator and Oct-2 the "strong" activator. This type of quantitative difference in activation potential was first proposed by Schaffner (1989) to explain differential activation of transcription by Oct-1 and Oct-2.

In addition to its potent mRNA promoter activation properties, Oct-2 also possesses snRNA-type activation properties. For example, a modified Oct-2 protein carrying the GAL4 DNA-binding domain in place of the Oct-2 homeodomain is able to activate a U2 snRNA promoter containing GAL4-binding sites (Yang et al. 1991). Furthermore, in Oct-2B, the amino-terminal region, which is shared by Oct-2 and Oct-2B, is required for maximal U2 snRNA promoter activation by Oct-2B (K. Visvanathan, unpubl.), suggesting that these amino-terminal sequences cooperate with the unique carboxy-terminal Oct-2B extension to activate snRNA transcription.

The shared activation properties of Oct-1 and Oct-2 are consistent with the fact that the *oct-1* and *oct-2* genes are probably descendants of a single gene. Chromosomal mapping of the two genes suggests that they arose by chromosomal duplication, because they are both surrounded by other genes that are also related to one another (Ko et al. 1988; Hsieh et al. 1990). The common Oct-1 and Oct-2 mRNA and snRNA promoter activation properties suggest that the ancestral Oct factor could activate both mRNA promoters and snRNA promoters. Since their duplication, however, Oct-1 and Oct-2 may have diverged to activate more effectively snRNA and mRNA promoters, respectively.

DIVERSE DNA SEQUENCE RECOGNITION BY THE OCT FACTORS

The binding sites for Oct-1 and Oct-2 described thus far represent close matches to the consensus sequence ATGCAAAT. In contrast, in the immediate-early promoters of herpesvirus, Oct-1 can recognize VP16-responsive binding sites that exhibit poor matches to the octamer motif (Baumruker et al. 1988; apRhys et al. 1989). The poor match to the consensus sequence can be tolerated because, given the appropriate sequence context, Oct-1 (and Oct-2) can bind to degenerate octamer sequences. This flexibility in sequence recognition was first revealed in studies of Oct-1 binding to the SV40 enhancer, which showed that Oct-1 readily binds to a degenerate octamer sequence (five out of eight match) located in the SV40 enhancer adjacent to the prototypic SV40 octamer motif shown in Figure 2B (Sturm et al. 1987; Baumruker et al. 1988). An analysis of the nucleotide sequences required to bind to the degenerate SV40 octamer site, called Site II, showed that the sequences extending three base pairs both 5' and 3' of the divergent octamer motif are critical for Oct-1 to bind to this site (Baumruker et al. 1988). If the degenerate octamer site is converted to a perfect octamer motif, the critical dependence on the flanking sequences is relieved. Thus, the ability of Oct-1 to recognize a variant octamer site is governed by the context of the site.

Previous studies had noted nucleotide sequence similarity between the region of the SV40 enhancer containing the Site II octamer sequence and the HSV target for VP16 activation, the TAATGARAT motif

(Kristie and Roizman 1987). TAATGARAT motifs can be classified in two groups: (OCTA$^+$)TAATGARAT motifs, in which the TAAT-GARAT motif is overlapped by an octamer motif shown in bold, **ATGCTAATGARAT** (R = purine) (Pruijn et al. 1986), and (OCTA$^-$)TAATGARAT motifs, which lack an associated octamer motif (see apRhys et al. 1989). The divergent SV40 Site II octamer sequence displays considerable similarity to the (OCTA$^-$)TAATGARAT motif and, in fact, can be matched at every position if the insertion of a single base pair is permitted. Chemical modification interference and mutational analyses revealed that Oct-1 alone can bind directly to the (OCTA$^-$)TAATGARAT motif, albeit considerably more weakly than to an authentic octamer motif, by making DNA contacts with the full extent of the (OCTA$^-$)TAATGARAT motif (Baumruker et al. 1988; apRhys et al. 1989). The (OCTA$^+$)TAATGARAT site, in contrast, contains two Oct-1-binding sites, a higher affinity octamer site and the lower affinity TAATGARAT site. Because the two sites overlap, however, they cannot be simultaneously occupied by Oct-1 (apRhys et al. 1989; R. Aurora, unpubl.).

As shown in Figure 6B, when the SV40 Site I octamer motif used in the multimerized enhancers described above (see Fig. 2B) is aligned with an (OCTA$^-$)TAATGARAT motif from the HSV ICP4 (IE175K) promoter, there is no more than a 3 out of 8 match over the octamer motif or a 4 out of 14 match when flanking sequences are included. However, by comparing the different Oct-1-binding sites shown in Figure 6A, it was possible to establish a progression of binding site sequences by which the two very different SV40 Site I and (OCTA$^-$)TAATGARAT sites could be linked by a series of a few changes between each successive sequence in the progression (Baumruker et al. 1988). These patterns of DNA binding suggest that there are few if any base contacts that are absolutely necessary for Oct-1 to bind to DNA. It instead appears that the sum of numerous individual interactions leads to specific and effective binding.

Another instance of Oct-1 and Oct-2 recognition of a very degenerate octamer element is the heptamer motif found adjacent to the perfect octamer motif in immunoglobulin heavy-chain promoters (Kemler et al. 1989; LeBowitz et al. 1989; Poellinger and Roeder 1989). The ability of transcriptional regulators to recognize a diverse set of sequences permits added flexibility in promoter structure and transcriptional regulation. For example, as in the case of the SV40 B proto-enhancer, flexibility in sequence recognition permits two *cis*-acting elements, the octamer and sph motifs, to overlap one another and thus influence each other's activity, as in the ability of the octamer motif to inhibit sph enhanson function when

A

```
SV40        ┌───────────────┐
Site I      AGTATGCAAAGCAT
            :::::::::  :      9/14
H2B         CTTATGCAAATGAG
            :::::::: :        9/14
IgH         GAAATGCAAATTAC
            :  :::::::::     10/14
U2          GGCATGCAAATTCG
            :::::::::::: :   12/14
Perf.       TGCATGCAAATTAG
Site II     :::::  ::::::    11/14
SV40        TGCATCTCAATTAG
Site II     :::::::::: ::    11/14
Clone 12    TGCATCTCATTTCT
            :::::::::::  :   11/14
TAAT        GGCATCTCATTACC
            └───────────────┘
```

B

```
SV40        ┌──────────────x┐
Site I      AGTATGCAAAGCAT
            TCATACGTTTCGTA
            :  ::    :        4/14
TAAT        GGCATCTCATTACC
            CCGTAGAGTAATGG
            └──x x x──x──┘
```

Figure 6 A sequence progression among Oct-1-binding sites identifies the sequence relationship between two very different Oct-1-binding sites. (*A*) The sequences of eight different Oct-1-binding sites are aligned to give the greatest sequence similarity between adjacent sequences. The match between sequences is indicated to the right. A 14-bp sequence is compared in each case because the SV40 Site II Oct-1-binding site extends over 14 bp. The origin of the different sequences is described by Baumruker et al. (1988). Note that these sites differ in their affinity for Oct-1 (see Baumruker et al. 1988). (*B*) Direct sequence comparison of the two sequences, SV40 Site I octamer motif and ICP4 (OCTA⁻)TAATGARAT motif, shown at the extremities of the sequence progression in *A*. (Reprinted, with permission, from Baumruker et al. 1988.)

Oct-1 or Oct-2 is overexpressed. Degenerate sequence elements can also possess unique activities of their own, as in the case described below in which the (OCTA⁻)TAATGARAT motif fails to respond to either Oct-1 or Oct-2 alone but does respond to Oct-1 in association with VP16.

DIFFERENTIAL TRANSCRIPTIONAL REGULATION THROUGH SELECTIVE RECRUITMENT TO A NEW *CIS*-REGULATORY TARGET

VP16 Distinguishes between the Oct-1 and Oct-2 Homeodomains

VP16 can activate transcription of mRNA promoters by associating with Oct-1 and the second host cell factor termed HCF and thus serves as a transcriptional adapter (see Fig. 3). Association of VP16 with Oct-1 and HCF can be assayed by formation of a VP16-induced complex in an electrophoretic mobility retardation assay with DNA fragments containing the TAATGARAT motif (McKnight et al. 1987; Gerster and Roeder 1988; O'Hare and Goding 1988; Preston et al. 1988; apRhys et al. 1989; Kristie et al. 1989; Stern et al. 1989). Although Oct-1 can readily form such a complex, Oct-2 associates only very weakly if at all with VP16 (Gerster and Roeder 1988; Kristie et al. 1989; Stern et al. 1989). The HCF component of the VP16-induced complex is not essential for complex formation between Oct-1 and VP16 (Kristie and Sharp 1990) nor for discrimination between Oct-1 and Oct-2 by VP16 (Stern and Herr 1991). Thus, HCF serves as a stimulatory factor, not a discriminatory factor, in VP16-induced complex formation. By using cloned cDNAs encoding Oct-1 and Oct-2, we mapped the region of Oct-1 responsible for association with VP16 (Stern et al. 1989).

Surprisingly, it is the region of highest similarity between Oct-1 and Oct-2, the POU domain, which is responsible for directing complex formation with VP16. If the Oct-1 POU domain is replaced by the Oct-2 POU domain, the hybrid protein fails to associate with VP16 effectively, but if the Oct-2 POU domain is replaced by the Oct-1 POU domain, then the Oct-2 hybrid protein can readily associate with VP16. Thus, VP16 discriminates between two related proteins that bind to the same DNA sequence and alters patterns of transcriptional regulation by one of the two proteins by distinguishing between the DNA-binding domains of the two proteins. Further dissection of the Oct-1 and Oct-2 POU domains pinpointed the Oct-1 and Oct-2 residues responsible for differential VP16-induced complex formation to the seven residues that differ between the Oct-1 and Oct-2 homeodomains; if the Oct-2 homeodomain is replaced by the Oct-1 homeodomain, this Oct-2/Oct-1 chimera can complex with VP16 (Stern et al. 1989).

The molecular structure of the Oct-1 or Oct-2 homeodomain is not known, but the structures of three other homeodomains, Antennapedia (Qian et al. 1989), engrailed (Kissinger et al. 1990), and MATα2 (Wolberger et al. 1991), indicate that the homeodomain is a highly conserved tri-α-helical structure related to the helix-turn-helix motif found in prokaryotic transcriptional regulators such as λ repressor (for review, see Harrison and Aggarwal 1990). Figure 7 is a cartoon of the engrailed homeodomain bound to DNA that has been adapted from the study of Kissinger et al. (1990). The position and sequence of the seven Oct-1 residues that differ between the Oct-1 and Oct-2 homeodomains are shown superimposed on the engrailed homeodomain structure. The three homeodomain α-helices form a hydrophobic core and, when bound to

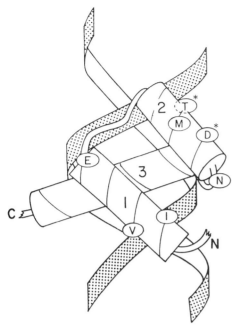

Figure 7 Positions of sequence differences between the Oct-1 and Oct-2 homeodomains superimposed on a cartoon of the *Drosophila* engrailed homeodomain. The diagram of the engrailed homeodomain was adapted from the study by Kissinger et al. (1990). The homeodomain is shown facing the viewer with the DNA double helix positioned behind the bound protein. The three α-helices (1–3) are shown as cylinders and the amino (N) and carboxyl (C) termini are indicated. The identity of the Oct-1 residues that differ from Oct-2 is shown circled over the position of their counterparts in the engrailed homeodomain. In order from the amino to the carboxyl terminus, the differences between Oct-1 and Oct-2 (listed Oct-1→Oct-2) are I→V; V→F; E→A; T→L; M→L; D→E; and N→H. The asterisks identify the analogous positions of two positive control mutations in λ repressor (λ*pc-2* and λ*pc-3*; Hochschild et al. 1983).

DNA, helices 1 and 2 face away from the DNA, whereas helix 3 faces the DNA and makes most of the sequence-specific contacts. Helix 3 is, therefore, referred to as the "DNA-recognition helix." As might be expected for two proteins that bind to the same DNA sequence, helix 3 in Oct-1 and in Oct-2 are identical. Instead, the differences between the Oct-1 and Oct-2 homeodomains all face away from the DNA and lie mainly in helices 1 and 2: positions that could be expected to make contact with a protein such as VP16.

In λ repressor, positions analogous to two of the positions that differ between Oct-1 and Oct-2 in helix 2 are responsible for positive control of transcription by λ repressor (Guarente et al. 1982; Hochschild et al. 1983). Mutations at these positions do not affect the ability of λ repressor to bind to DNA (Hawley and McClure 1983) but do affect its ability to stimulate transcription, probably by interfering with contacts with RNA polymerase (Hochschild et al. 1983). Thus, in λ repressor, positions in helix 2 are apparently critical for activation of transcription through protein-protein contacts but not protein-DNA contacts. The analogous residues in the Oct-1 homeodomain are also critical for protein-protein contacts involved in activation of transcription, because if the three helix-2 residues in Oct-1 that differ between Oct-1 and Oct-2 are re-placed by their Oct-2 counterparts, VP16 complex formation with Oct-1 is disrupted with little, if any, effect on DNA binding (Stern et al. 1989). These results provide an example of similarities in protein structure and function between prokaryotes and man.

VP16 Selectively Recruits Oct-1 to an (OCTA⁻)TAATGARAT Motif

Comparison of the abilities of Oct-1 and Oct-2 to stimulate the U2 snRNA promoter and the β-globin mRNA promoter showed that differential transcriptional regulation by two proteins that bind to the same DNA sequence can be achieved through the use of promoter-selective activation domains. The selective interaction of VP16 with Oct-1 reveals a second mechanism by which such differential transcriptional regulation can be achieved. In this case, through selective interaction with VP16, Oct-1, but not Oct-2, is recruited to a new *cis*-regulatory target that in the absence of VP16 is not responsive to either Oct-1 or Oct-2.

The new *cis*-regulatory target we have analyzed is the octamerless (OCTA⁻)TAATGARAT motif, which is a poor Oct-1-binding site (Baumruker et al. 1988; apRhys et al. 1989) but can form a VP16-induced complex (Preston et al. 1988; apRhys et al. 1989). In a DNase I footprinting assay, association of Oct-1 with VP16 results in higher occupancy of an (OCTA⁻)TAATGARAT site by Oct-1, whereas the affinity of Oct-2 for this site is unaffected by VP16 (Cleary et al. 1993). Thus, VP16 selectively recruits Oct-1 to an (OCTA⁻)TAATGARAT site. In the absence of VP16, multiple copies of the (OCTA⁻)TAATGARAT site fail to activate effectively either the U2 snRNA promoter or the β-globin mRNA promoter in the presence of Oct-1 or Oct-2 (Cleary et al. 1993), probably because of the low affinity of Oct-1 and Oct-2 for the (OCTA⁻)TAATGARAT site. Oct-1 and VP16 together, however, can activate a β-globin promoter containing multiple (OCTA⁻)TAATGARAT

sites (Cleary et al. 1993), probably because VP16 induces Oct-1 to associate with the (OCTA$^-$)TAATGARAT site and also provides an mRNA
promoter activation domain. In this manner, by associating with VP16,
Oct-1, a ubiquitously expressed protein, acquires cell-specific mRNA
promoter activation properties distinct from the octamer-dependent
mRNA promoter activation properties of Oct-2. Thus, in addition to
promoter-selective activation domains, selective recruitment to a new
cis-regulatory target can result in differential transcriptional regulation
by proteins that bind to the same DNA sequence.

CONCLUSIONS AND PERSPECTIVES

By studying the mechanisms of differential function and utilization of
Oct-1 and Oct-2, two principal molecular strategies have been uncovered
by which activators that recognize the same DNA sequence can activate
different promoters. On the one hand, Oct-1 and Oct-2 can selectively
regulate transcription of snRNA and mRNA genes by appending
promoter-selective transcriptional activation domains to very similar
DNA-binding domains. On the other hand, the activity of Oct-1 can be
selectively altered by association with the herpesvirus VP16 protein. This
viral protein endows Oct-1 with mRNA promoter activation properties
similar to those of Oct-2, but also with new DNA-binding properties distinct from those of Oct-2. In each case, differential transcriptional regulation is probably achieved through selective protein-protein interactions:
long-range interactions with proximal promoter complexes in the case of
promoter-selective activation domains and short-range interactions with
VP16 in the case of the Oct-1 homeodomain.

These two strategies serve as paradigms for how homeodomain
proteins that share the same DNA-binding specificity may elicit very different developmental programs. The different promoter-selective activation properties of Oct-1 and Oct-2 demonstrate that the specificity of
promoter activation can be conferred by activation domain specificity, as
well as by DNA-binding specificity. To achieve more complex
regulatory patterns, the activity of promoter-selective activation domains
may be differentially regulated either by protein modification or by
modulation of their regulatory target in the transcriptional apparatus. The
promoter-selective activation domains identified in Oct-1 and Oct-2 discriminate between an snRNA and an mRNA promoter, two very different types of promoters. A current challenge is to determine whether
promoter-selective activation domains can discriminate among different
mRNA promoters, the natural targets of differential transcriptional
regulation by homeodomain proteins that control development.

The second strategy, in which VP16 recruits Oct-1 to a new *cis*-

regulatory target and also provides Oct-1 with new activation domain properties, can already explain differential transcriptional regulation by homeodomain proteins that control development because it involves activation of two different mRNA promoters: an octamer-motif-containing mRNA promoter by Oct-2 and an (OCTA⁻)TAATGARAT-motif-containing mRNA promoter by Oct-1 in association with VP16. The restricted activation of the (OCTA⁻)TAATGARAT-motif-containing promoter to cells containing both Oct-1 and VP16 shows how a broadly expressed homeodomain protein such as Oct-1 can display cell-specific activity. The selective association of the acidic activator VP16 with the Oct-1 homeodomain also demonstrates that homeodomains are not only responsible for determining the DNA-binding specificity of homeodomain proteins, but are also important determinants of their activation specificity.

ACKNOWLEDGMENTS

Many of the ideas described here were formulated as a result of a collaboration with Nouria Hernandez and Masafumi Tanaka; I am indebted to them for many fruitful discussions and for critically reading this review. I thank the following former and present members of my laboratory: Rajeev Aurora, Gokul Das, and Kanna Visvanathan for contributing unpublished results referred to in the text. I also thank Angus Wilson for comments and Michele Cleary for editing the manuscript; Masafumi Tanaka for help with designing the figures; Jane Reader for help in preparing the manuscript; and Jim Duffy for art work.

REFERENCES

Ace, C.I., M.A. Dalrymple, F.H. Ramsay, V.G. Preston, and C.M. Preston. 1988. Mutational analysis of the herpes simplex virus type 1 *trans*-inducing factor Vmw65. *J. Gen. Virol.* **69:** 2595–2605.

Ach, R.A. and A.M. Weiner. 1987. The highly conserved U small nuclear RNA 3′-end formation signal is quite tolerant to mutation. *Mol. Cell. Biol.* **7:** 2070–2079.

aprhys, C.M.J., D.M. Ciufo, E.A. O'Neill, T.J. Kelly, and G.S. Hayward. 1989. Overlapping octamer and TAATGARAT motifs in the VF65-response elements in herpes simplex virus immediate-early promoters represent independent binding sites for cellular nuclear factor III. *J. Virol.* **63:** 2798–2812.

Ares, M., Jr., J.-S. Chung, L. Giglio, and A.M. Weiner. 1987. Distinct factors with Sp1 and NF-A specificities bind to adjacent functional elements of the human U2 snRNA gene enhancer. *Genes Dev.* **1:** 808–817.

Aurora, R. and W. Herr. 1992. Segments of the POU domain influence one another's DNA-binding specificity. *Mol. Cell. Biol.* **12:** 455–467.

Banerji, J., S. Rusconi, and W. Schaffner. 1981. Expression of a β-globin gene is enhanced by remote SV40 DNA sequences. *Cell* **27**: 299–308.

Batterson, W. and B. Roizman. 1983. Characterization of the herpes simplex virion-associated factor responsible for the induction of α genes. *J. Virol.* **46**: 371–377.

Baumruker, T., R. Sturm, and W. Herr. 1988. OBP100 binds remarkably degenerate octamer motifs through specific interactions with flanking sequences. *Genes Dev.* **2**: 1400–1413.

Bodner, M., J.-L. Castrillo, L.E. Theill, T. Deerinck, M. Ellisman, and M. Karin. 1988. The pituitary-specific transcription factor GHF-1 is a homeobox-containing protein. *Cell* **55**: 505–518.

Campbell, M.E.M., J.W. Palfreyman, and C.M. Preston. 1984. Identification of herpes simplex virus DNA sequences which encode a *trans*-acting polypeptide responsible for stimulation of immediate early transcription. *J. Mol. Biol.* **180**: 1–19.

Ciliberto, G., R. Buckland, R. Cortese, and L. Philipson. 1985. Transcription signals in embryonic *Xenopus laevis* U1 RNA genes. *EMBO J.* **4**: 1537–1543.

Cleary, M.A., S. Stern, M. Tanaka, and W. Herr. 1993. Differential positive control by Oct-1 and Oct-2: Activation of a transcriptionally silent motif through Oct-1 and VP16 corecruitment. *Genes Dev.* **7**: 72–83.

Clerc, R.G., L.M. Corcoran, J.H. LeBowitz, D. Baltimore, and P. A. Sharp. 1988. The B-cell-specific Oct-2 protein contains POU box- and homeo box-type domains. *Genes Dev.* **2**: 1570–1581.

Courey, A.J. and R. Tjian. 1988. Analysis of Sp1 in vivo reveals multiple transcriptional domains, including a novel glutamine-rich activation motif. *Cell* **55**: 887–898.

Cousens, D.J., R. Greaves, C.R. Goding, and P. O'Hare. 1989. The C-terminal 79 amino acids of the herpes simplex virus regulatory protein, Vmw65, efficiently activate transcription in yeast and mammalian cells in chimeric DNA-binding proteins. *EMBO J.* **8**: 2337–2342.

Currie, R.A. and R.G. Roeder. 1989. Identification of an octamer-binding site in the mouse kappa light-chain immunoglobulin enhancer. *Mol. Cell. Biol.* **9**: 4239–4247.

Davidson, I., J.H. Xiao, R. Rosales, A. Staub, and P. Chambon. 1988. The HeLa cell protein TEF-1 binds specifically and cooperatively to two SV40 enhancer motifs of unrelated sequence. *Cell* **54**: 931–942.

Davidson, I., C. Fromental, P. Augereau, A. Wildeman, M. Zenke, and P. Chambon. 1986. Cell-type specific protein binding to the enhancer of simian virus 40 in nuclear extracts. *Nature* **323**: 544–548.

Dierks, P., A. van Ooyen, M.D. Cochran, C. Dobkin, J. Reiser, and C. Weissmann. 1983. Three regions upstream from the cap site are required for efficient and accurate transcription of the rabbit β-globin gene in mouse 3T6 cells. *Cell* **32**: 695–706.

Dreyfus, M., N. Doyen, and F. Rougeon. 1987. The conserved decanucleotide from the immunoglobulin heavy chain promoter induces a very high transcriptional activity in B-cells when introduced into an heterologous promoter. *EMBO J.* **6**: 1685–1690.

Falkner, F.G. and H.G. Zachau. 1984. Correct transcription of an immunoglobulin κ gene requires an upstream fragment containing conserved sequence elements. *Nature* **310**: 71–74.

Finney, M., G. Ruvkun, and H.R. Horvitz. 1988. The *C. elegans* cell lineage and differentiation gene *unc-86* encodes a protein with a homeodomain and extended similarity to transcription factors. *Cell* **55**: 757–769.

Fletcher, C., N. Heintz, and R.G. Roeder. 1987. Purification and characterization of OTF-1, a transcription factor regulating cell cycle expression of a human histone H2b gene. *Cell* **51**: 773–781.

Fromental, C., M. Kanno, H. Nomiyama, and P. Chambon. 1988. Cooperativity and hierarchical levels of functional organization in the SV40 enhancer. *Cell* **54**: 943–953.

Gerster, T. and R.G. Roeder. 1988. A herpesvirus *trans*-activating protein interacts with transcription factor OTF-1 and other cellular proteins. *Proc. Natl. Acad. Sci.* **85**: 6347–6351.

Gerster, T., C.-G. Balmaceda, and R.G. Roeder. 1990. The cell type-specific octamer transcription factor OTF-2 has two domains required for the activation of transcription. *EMBO J.* **9**: 1635–1643.

Gerster, T., P. Matthias, M. Thali, J. Jiricny, and W. Schaffner. 1987. Cell type-specificity elements of the immunoglobulin heavy chain gene enhancer. *EMBO J.* **6**: 1323–1330.

Goding, C.R. and P. O'Hare. 1989. Herpes simplex virus Vmw65–octamer binding protein interaction: A paradigm for combinatorial control of transcription. *Virology* **173**: 363–367.

Greaves, R. and P. O'Hare. 1989. Separation of requirements for protein-DNA complex assembly from those for functional activity in the herpes simplex virus regulatory protein Vmw65. *J. Virol.* **63**: 1641–1650.

Guarente, L., J.S. Nye, A. Hochschild, and M. Ptashne. 1982. Mutant λ phage repressor with a specific defect in its positive control function. *Proc. Natl. Acad. Sci.* **79**: 2236–2239.

Harrison, S.C. and A.K. Aggarwal. 1990. DNA recognition by proteins with the helix-turn-helix motif. *Annu. Rev. Biochem.* **59**: 933–969.

Harvey, R.P., A.J. Robins, and J.R.E. Wells. 1982. Independently evolving chicken histone H2B genes: Identification of a ubiquitous H2B-specific 5′ element. *Nucleic Acids Res.* **10**: 7851–7863.

Hatzopoulos, A.K., A.S. Stoykova, J.R. Erselius, M. Goulding, T. Neuman, and P. Gruss. 1990. Structure and expression of the mouse Oct2a and Oct2b, two differentially spliced products of the same gene. *Development* **109**: 349–362.

Hawley, D.K. and W.R. McClure. 1983. The effect of a lambda repressor mutation on the activation of transcription initiation from the lambda P_{RM} promoter. *Cell* **32**: 327–333.

Hayashi, S. and M.P. Scott. 1990. What determines the specificity of action of *Drosophila* homeodomain proteins? *Cell* **63**: 883–894.

He, X., M.N. Treacy, D.M. Simmons, H.A. Ingraham, L.W. Swanson, and M.G. Rosenfeld. 1989. Expression of a large family of POU-domain regulatory genes in mammalian brain development. *Nature* **340**: 35–42.

Heintz, N., M. Zernik, and R.G. Roeder. 1981. The structure of the human histone genes: Clustered but not tandemly repeated. *Cell* **24**: 661–668.

Hernandez, N. 1985. Formation of the 3′ end of U1 snRNA is directed by a conserved sequence located downstream of the coding region. *EMBO J.* **4**: 1827–1837.

Hernandez, N. and A.M. Weiner. 1986. Formation of the 3′ end of U1 snRNA requires compatible snRNA promoter elements. *Cell* **47**: 249–258.

Herr, W. and J. Clarke. 1986. The SV40 enhancer is composed of multiple functional elements that can compensate for one another. *Cell* **45**: 461–470.

Herr, W., R.A. Sturm, R.G. Clerc, L.M. Corcoran, D. Baltimore, P.A. Sharp, H.A. Ingraham, M.G. Rosenfeld, M. Finney, G. Ruvkun, and H.R. Horvitz. 1988. The POU domain: A large conserved region in the mammalian *pit-1*, *oct-1*, *oct-2*, and *Caenorhabditis elegans unc-86* gene products. *Genes Dev.* **2**: 1513–1516.

Hochschild, A., N. Irwin, and M. Ptashne. 1983. Repressor structure and the mechanism of positive control. *Cell* **32**: 319–325.

Hsieh, C.-L., R. Sturm, W. Herr, and U. Francke. 1990. The gene for the ubiquitous octamer-binding protein Oct-1 is on human chromosome 1, region cen-q32, and near *Ly-22* and *Ltw-4* on mouse chromosome 1. *Genomics* **6**: 666–672.

Ingraham, H.A., S.E. Flynn, J.W. Voss, V.R. Albert, M.S. Kapiloff, L. Wilson, and M.G. Rosenfeld. 1990. The POU-specific domain of Pit-1 is essential for sequence-specific, high affinity DNA binding and DNA-dependent Pit-1–Pit-1 interactions. *Cell* **61**: 1021–1033.

Ingraham, H.A., R. Chen, H.J. Mangalam, H.P. Elsholtz, S.E. Flynn, C.R. Lin, D.M. Simmons, L. Swanson, and M.G. Rosenfeld. 1988. A tissue-specific transcription factor containing a homeodomain specifies a pituitary phenotype. *Cell* **55**: 519–529.

Janson, L. and U. Pettersson. 1990. Cooperative interactions between transcription factors Sp1 and OTF-1. *Proc. Natl. Acad. Sci.* **87**: 4732–4736.

Johnson, D.G., L. Carayannopoulos, J.D. Capra, P.W. Tucker, and J.H. Hanke. 1990. The ubiquitous octamer-binding protein(s) is sufficient for transcription of immunoglobulin genes. *Mol. Cell. Biol.* **10**: 982–990.

Katan, M., A. Haigh, C.P. Verrijzer, P.C. van der Vliet, and P. O'Hare. 1990. Characterization of a cellular factor which interacts functionally with Oct-1 in the assembly of a multicomponent transcription complex. *Nucleic Acids Res.* **18**: 6871–6880.

Kemler, I., E. Bucher, K. Seipel, M.M. Müller-Immerglück, and W. Schaffner. 1991. Promoters with the octamer DNA motif (ATGCAAAT) can be ubiquitous or cell type-specific depending on binding affinity of the octamer site and Oct-factor concentration. *Nucleic Acids Res.* **19**: 237–242.

Kemler, I., E. Schreiber, M.M. Müller, P. Matthias, and W. Schaffner. 1989. Octamer transcription factors bind to two different sequence motifs of the immunoglobulin heavy chain promoter. *EMBO J.* **8**: 2001–2008.

Kissinger, C.R., B. Liu, E. Martin-Blanco, T.B. Kornberg, and C.O. Pabo. 1990. Crystal structure of an engrailed homeodomain-DNA complex at 2.8 Å resolution: A framework for understanding homeodomain-DNA interactions. *Cell* **63**: 579–590.

Ko, H.-S., P. Fast, W. McBride, and L.M. Staudt. 1988. A human protein specific for the immunoglobulin octamer DNA motif contains a functional homeobox domain. *Cell* **55**: 135–144.

Kristie, T.M. and B. Roizman. 1984. Separation of sequences defining basal expression from those conferring α gene recognition within the regulatory domains of herpes simplex virus 1 α genes. *Proc. Natl. Acad. Sci.* **81**: 4065–4069.

———. 1987. Host cell proteins bind to the *cis*-acting site required for virion-mediated induction of herpes simplex virus 1 α genes. *Proc. Natl. Acad. Sci.* **84**: 71–75.

Kristie, T.M. and P.A. Sharp. 1990. Interactions of the Oct-1 POU subdomains with specific DNA sequences and with the HSV α-*trans*-activator protein. *Genes Dev.* **4**: 2383–2396.

Kristie, T.M., J.H. LeBowitz, and P.A. Sharp. 1989. The octamer-binding proteins form multi-protein–DNA complexes with the HSV αTIF regulatory protein. *EMBO J.* **8**: 4229–4238.

LaBella, F., H.L. Sive, R.G. Roeder, and N. Heintz. 1988. Cell-cycle regulation of a human histone H2b gene is mediated by the H2b subtype-specific consensus element. *Genes Dev.* **2**: 32–39.

Landolfi, N.F., J.D. Capra, and P.W. Tucker. 1986. Interaction of cell-type-specific nuclear proteins with immunoglobulin V_H promoter region sequences. *Nature* **323**: 548–551.

Laughon, A. and M.P. Scott. 1984. Sequence of a *Drosophila* segmentation gene: Protein structure homology with DNA-binding proteins. *Nature* **310**: 25–31.

LeBowitz, J.H., R.G. Clerc, M. Brenowitz, and P.A. Sharp. 1989. The Oct-2 protein binds cooperatively to adjacent octamer sites. *Genes Dev.* **3:** 1625–1638.

LeBowitz, J.H., T. Kobayashi, L. Staudt, D. Baltimore, and P.A. Sharp. 1988. Octamer-binding proteins from B or HeLa cells stimulate transcription of the immunoglobulin heavy-chain promoter in vitro. *Genes Dev.* **2:** 1227–1237.

Lenardo, M., J.W. Pierce, and D. Baltimore. 1987. Protein-binding sites in Ig gene enhancers determine transcriptional activity and inducibility. *Science* **236:** 1573-1577.

Lenardo, M., L. Staudt, P. Robbins, A. Kuang, R.C. Mulligan, and D. Baltimore. 1989. Repression of the IgH enhancer in teratocarcinoma cells associated with a novel octamer factor. *Science* **243:** 544–546.

Levine, M. and T. Hoey. 1988. Homeobox proteins as sequence-specific transcription factors. *Cell* **55:** 537–540.

Lobo, S.M. and N. Hernandez. 1989. A 7 bp mutation converts a human RNA polymerase II snRNA promoter into an RNA polymerase III promoter. *Cell* **58:** 55–67.

Mackem, S. and B. Roizman. 1982. Structural features of the herpes simplex virus α gene 4, 0 and 27 promoter-regulatory sequences which confer α regulation on chimeric thymidine kinase genes. *J. Virol.* **44:** 939–949.

Mangin, M., M. Ares, Jr., and A.M. Weiner. 1986. Human U2 small nuclear RNA genes contain an upstream enhancer. *EMBO J.* **5:** 987–995.

Maniatis, T., S. Goodbourn, and J.A. Fischer. 1987. Regulation of inducible and tissue-specific gene expression. *Science* **236:** 1237–1245.

Marsden, H.S., M.E.M. Campbell, L. Haarr, M.C. Frame, D.S. Parris, M. Murphy, R.G. Hope, M.T. Muller, and C.M. Preston. 1987. The 65,000-M_r DNA-binding and virion *trans*-inducing proteins of herpes simplex virus type 1. *J. Virol.* **61:** 2428–2437.

Mattaj, I.W., S. Lienhard, J. Jiricny, and E.M. De Robertis. 1985. An enhancer-like sequence within the *Xenopus* U2 gene promoter facilitates the formation of stable transcription complexes. *Nature* **316:** 163–167.

Mattaj, I.W., N.A. Dathan, H.D. Parry, P. Carbon, and A. Krol. 1988. Changing the RNA polymerase specificity of U snRNA gene promoters. *Cell* **55:** 435–442.

McGinnis, W., M.S. Levine, E. Hafen, A. Kuroiwa, and W.J. Gehring. 1984. A conserved DNA sequence in homoeotic genes of the *Drosophila* Antennapedia and bithorax complexes. *Nature* **308:** 428–433.

McKnight, J.L.C., T.M. Kristie, and B. Roizman. 1987. Binding of the virion protein mediating α gene induction in herpes simplex virus 1-infected cells to its *cis* site requires cellular proteins. *Proc. Natl. Acad. Sci.* **84:** 7061–7065.

Mermod, N., E.A. O'Neill, T.J. Kelly, and R. Tjian. 1989. The proline-rich transcriptional activator of CTF/NF-I is distinct from the replication and DNA binding domain. *Cell* **58:** 741–753.

Meyer, K.B. and M.S. Neuberger. 1989. The immunoglobulin κ locus contains a second, stronger B-cell-specific enhancer which is located downstream of the constant region. *EMBO J.* **8:** 1959–1964.

Monuki, E.S., G. Weinmaster, R. Kuhn, and G. Lemke. 1989. SCIP: A glial POU domain gene regulated by cyclic AMP. *Neuron* **3:** 783–793.

Müller, M.M., S. Ruppert, W. Schaffner, and P. Matthias. 1988. A cloned octamer transcription factor stimulates transcription from lymphoid-specific promoters in non-B cells. *Nature* **336:** 544–551.

Müller-Immerglück, M.M., W. Schaffner, and P. Matthias. 1990. Transcription factor Oct-2A contains functionally redundant activating domains and works selectively from a promoter but not from a remote enhancer position in non-lymphoid (HeLa) cells. *EMBO J.* **9:** 1625–1634.

Myers, R.M., K. Tilly, and T. Maniatis. 1986. Fine structure genetic analysis of a β-globin promoter. *Science* **232**: 613–618.

Nakajima, N., M. Horikoshi, and R.G. Roeder. 1988. Factors involved in specific transcription by mammalian RNA polymerase II: Purification, genetic specificity, and TATA box-promoter interactions of TFIID. *Mol. Cell. Biol.* **8**: 4028–4040.

Nelson, C., V.R. Albert, H.P. Elsholtz, L.I.-W. Lu, and M.G. Rosenfeld. 1988. Activation of cell-specific expression of rat growth hormone and prolactin genes by a common transcription factor. *Science* **239**: 1400–1405.

Neuman de Vegvar, H.E., E. Lund, and J.E. Dahlberg. 1986. 3′ end formation of U1 snRNA precursors is coupled to transcription from snRNA promoters. *Cell* **47**: 259–266.

O'Hare, P. and C.R. Goding. 1988. Herpes simplex virus regulatory elements and the immunoglobulin octamer domain bind a common factor and are both targets for virion transactivation. *Cell* **52**: 435–445.

Okamoto, K., H. Okazawa, A. Okuda, M. Sakai, M. Muramatsu, and H. Hamada. 1990. A novel octamer binding transcription factor is differentially expressed in mouse embryonic cells. *Cell* **60**: 461–472.

Ondek, B., L. Gloss, and W. Herr. 1988. The SV40 enhancer contains two distinct levels of organization. *Nature* **333**: 40–45.

Ondek, B., A. Shepard, and W. Herr. 1987. Discrete elements within the SV40 enhancer region display different cell-specific enhancer activities. *EMBO J.* **6**: 1017–1025.

O'Neill, E.A. and T.J. Kelly. 1988. Purification and characterization of nuclear factor III (origin recognition protein C), a sequence-specific DNA binding protein required for efficient initiation of adenovirus DNA replication. *J. Biol. Chem.* **263**: 931–937.

O'Neill, E.A., C. Fletcher, C.R. Burrow, N. Heintz, R.G. Roeder, and T.J. Kelly. 1988. Transcription factor OTF-1 is functionally identical to the DNA replication factor NFIII. *Science* **241**: 1210–1213.

Otting, G., Y.Q. Qian, M. Billeter, M. Müller, M. Affolter, W.J. Gehring, and K. Wüthrich. 1990. Protein–DNA contacts in the structure of a homeodomain–DNA complex determined by nuclear magnetic resonance spectroscopy in solution. *EMBO J.* **9**: 3085–3092.

Parslow, T.G., D.L. Blair, W.J. Murphy, and D.K. Granner. 1984. Structure of the 5′ ends of immunoglobulin genes: A novel conserved sequence. *Proc. Natl. Acad. Sci.* **81**: 2650–2654.

Pettersson, S., G.P. Cook, M. Brüggemann, G.T. Williams, and M.S. Neuberger. 1990. A second B cell-specific enhancer 3′ of the immunoglobulin heavy-chain locus. *Nature* **344**: 165–168.

Pierani, A., A. Heguy, H. Fujii, and R.G. Roeder. 1990. Activation of octamer-containing promoters by either octamer-binding transcription factor 1 (OTF-1) or OTF-2 and requirement of an additional B-cell-specific component for optimal transcription of immunoglobulin promoters. *Mol. Cell. Biol.* **10**: 6204–6215.

Poellinger, L. and R.G. Roeder. 1989. Octamer transcription factors 1 and 2 each bind to two different functional elements in the immunoglobulin heavy-chain promoter. *Mol. Cell. Biol.* **9**: 747–756.

Preston, C.M., M.G. Cordingley, and N.D. Stow. 1984. Analysis of DNA sequences which regulate the transcription of a herpes simplex virus immediate early gene. *J. Virol.* **50**: 708–716.

Preston, C.M., M.C. Frame, and M.E.M. Campbell. 1988. A complex formed between cell components and an HSV structural polypeptide binds to a viral immediate early gene regulatory DNA sequence. *Cell* **52**: 425–434.

Proudfoot, N.J. 1989. How RNA polymerase II terminates transcription in higher eukaryotes. *Trends Biochem. Sci.* **14:** 105–110.

Pruijn, G.J.M., W. van Driel, and P.C. van der Vliet. 1986. Nuclear factor III, a novel sequence-specific DNA-binding protein from HeLa cells stimulating adenovirus DNA replication. *Nature* **322:** 656–659.

Ptashne, M. 1988. How eukaryotic transcriptional activators work. *Nature* **335:** 683–689.

Qian, Y.Q., M. Billeter, G. Otting, M. Müller, W.J. Gehring, and K. Wüthrich. 1989. The structure of the *Antennapedia* homeodomain determined by NMR spectroscopy in solution: Comparison with prokaryotic repressors. *Cell* **59:** 573–580.

Rosenfeld, M.G. 1991. POU-domain transcription factors: pou-er-ful developmental regulators. *Genes Dev.* **5:** 897–907.

Rosner, M.H., M.A. Vigano, K. Ozato, P.M. Timmons, F. Poirier, P.W.J. Rigby, and L.M. Staudt. 1990. A POU-domain transcription factor in early stem cells and germ cells of the mammalian embryo. *Nature* **345:** 686–692.

Sadowski, I., J. Ma, S. Triezenberg, and M. Ptashne. 1988. GAL4-VP16 is an unusually potent transcriptional activator. *Nature* **335:** 563–564.

Schaffner, W. 1989. How do different transcription factors binding the same DNA sequence sort out their jobs? *Trends Genet.* **5:** 37–39.

Scheidereit, C., A. Heguy, and R.G. Roeder. 1987. Identification and purification of a human lymphoid-specific octamer binding protein (OTF-2) that activates transcription of an immunoglobulin promoter in vitro. *Cell* **51:** 783–793.

Scheidereit, C., J.A. Cromlish, T. Gerster, K. Kawakami, C.-G. Balmaceda, R.A. Currie, and R.G. Roeder. 1988. A human lymphoid-specific transcription factor that activates immunoglobulin genes is a homeobox protein. *Nature* **336:** 551–557.

Schöler, H.R., A.K. Hatzopolous, R. Balling, N. Suzuki, and P. Gruss. 1989. A family of octamer-specific proteins present during mouse embryogenesis: Evidence for germline-specific expression of an Oct factor. *EMBO J.* **8:** 2543–2550.

Schöler, H.R., S. Ruppert, N. Suzuki, K. Chowdhury, and P. Gruss. 1990. New type of POU domain in germ line-specific protein Oct-4. *Nature* **344:** 435–439.

Schreiber, E., P. Matthias, M.M. Müller, and W. Schaffner. 1988. Identification of a novel lymphoid-specific octamer binding protein (OTF-2B) by proteolytic clipping bandshift assay (PCBA). *EMBO J.* **7:** 4221–4229.

Scott, M.P. and A.J. Weiner. 1984. Structural relationships among genes that control development: Sequence homology between the Antennapedia, Ultrabithorax and fushi tarazu loci of *Drosophila*. *Proc. Natl Acad. Sci.* **81:** 4115–4119.

Scott, M.P., J.W. Tamkun, and G.W. Hartzell III. 1989. The structure and function of the homeodomain. *Biochim. Biophys. Acta* **989:** 25–48.

Shepherd, J.C.W., W. McGinnis, A.E. Carrasco, E.M. De Robertis, and W.J. Gehring. 1984. Fly and frog homoeo domains show homologies with yeast mating type regulatory proteins. *Nature* **310:** 70–71.

Singh, H., R. Sen, D. Baltimore, and P.A. Sharp. 1986. A nuclear factor that binds to a conserved sequence motif in transcriptional control elements of immunoglobulin genes. *Nature* **319:** 154–158.

Staudt, L.M., H. Singh, R. Sen, T. Wirth, P.A. Sharp, and D. Baltimore. 1986. A lymphoid-specific protein binding to the octamer motif of immunoglobulin genes. *Nature* **323:** 640–643.

Stern, S. and W. Herr. 1991. The herpes simplex virus *trans*-activator VP16 recognizes the Oct-1 homeo domain: Evidence for a homeo domain recognition subdomain. *Genes Dev.* **5:** 2555–2566.

Stern, S., M. Tanaka, and W. Herr. 1989. The Oct-1 homeodomain directs formation of a multiprotein-DNA complex with the HSV transactivator VP16. *Nature* **341:** 624–630.

Stoykova, A.S., S. Sterrer, J.R. Erselius, A.K. Hatzopoulos, and P. Gruss. 1992. Mini-Oct and Oct-2c: Two novel, functionally diverse murine *Oct-2* gene products are differentially expressed in the CNS. *Neuron* **8:** 541–558.

Sturm, R.A. and W. Herr. 1988. The POU domain is a bipartite DNA-binding structure. *Nature* **336:** 601–604.

Sturm, R.A., G. Das, and W. Herr. 1988. The ubiquitous octamer-binding protein Oct-1 contains a POU domain with a homeo box subdomain. *Genes Dev.* **2:** 1582–1599.

Sturm, R., T. Baumruker, B.R. Franza, Jr., and W. Herr. 1987. A 100-kD HeLa cell octamer binding protein (OBP100) interacts differently with two separate octamer-related sequences within the SV40 enhancer. *Genes Dev.* **1:** 1147–1160.

Suzuki, N., H. Rohdewohld, T. Neuman, P. Gruss, and H.R. Schöler. 1990. Oct-6: A POU transcription factor expressed in embryonal stem cells and in the developing brain. *EMBO J.* **9:** 3723–3732.

Tanaka, M. and W. Herr. 1990. Differential transcriptional activation by Oct-1 and Oct-2: Interdependent activation domains induce Oct-2 phosphorylation. *Cell* **60:** 375–386.

Tanaka, M., J.-S. Lai, and W. Herr. 1992. Promoter-selective activation domains in Oct-1 and Oct-2 direct differential activation of an snRNA and mRNA promoter. *Cell* **68:** 755–767.

Tanaka, M., U. Grossniklaus, W. Herr, and N. Hernandez. 1988. Activation of the U2 snRNA promoter by the octamer motif defines a new class of RNA polymerase II enhancer elements. *Genes Dev.* **2:** 1764–1778.

Triezenberg, S.J., R.C. Kingsbury, and S.L. McKnight. 1988. Functional dissection of VP16, the *trans*-activator of herpes simplex virus immediate early gene expression. *Genes Dev.* **2:** 718–729.

Verrijzer, C.P., A.J. Kal, and P.C. Van der Vliet. 1990a. The DNA binding domain (POU domain) of transcription factor oct-1 suffices for stimulation of DNA replication. *EMBO J.* **9:** 1883–1888.

———. 1990b. The Oct-1 homeo domain contacts only part of the octamer sequence and full oct-1 DNA binding activity requires the POU-specific domain. *Genes Dev.* **4:** 1964–1974.

Wirth, T., L. Staudt, and D. Baltimore. 1987. An octamer oligonucleotide upstream of a TATA motif is sufficient for lymphoid-specific promoter activity. *Nature* **329:** 174–178.

Wolberger, C., A.K. Vershon, B. Liu, A.D. Johnson, and C.O. Pabo. 1991. Crystal structure of a MATα2 homeodomain-operator complex suggests a general model for homeodomain-DNA interactions. *Cell* **67:** 517–528.

Xiao, P. and J.P. Capone. 1990. A cellular factor binds to the herpes simplex virus type 1 *trans*activator Vmw65 and is required for Vmw65-dependent protein-DNA complex assembly with Oct-1. *Mol. Cell. Biol.* **10:** 4974–4977.

Xiao, J.H., I. Davidson, H. Matthes, J.-M. Garnier, and P. Chambon. 1991. Cloning, expression, and transcriptional properties of the human enhancer factor TEF-1. *Cell* **65:** 551–568.

Yang, J., M.M. Müller-Immerglück, K. Seipel, L. Janson, G. Westin, W. Schaffner, and U. Pettersson. 1991. Both Oct-1 and Oct-2A contain domains which can activate the ubiquitously expressed U2 snRNA genes. *EMBO J.* **10:** 2291–2296.

Yuo, C.-Y., M. Ares, Jr., and A.M. Weiner. 1985. Sequences required for 3′ end formation of human U2 small nuclear RNA. *Cell* **42:** 193–202.

42
Retinoid Receptors as Transcription Factors

David J. Mangelsdorf and Ronald M. Evans
Gene Expression Laboratory, Howard Hughes Medical Institute
The Salk Institute for Biological Studies
La Jolla, California 92037

OVERVIEW

The process by which retinoic acid (RA) and its congeners elicit their effects on vertebrate development and physiology is mediated by ligand-activated transcription factors that are members of the nuclear receptor superfamily. Thus far, two distinct classes of retinoid receptor genes have been detected, the retinoic acid receptors (RARs) and the retinoid X receptors (RXRs); each subclass contains three separate genes. An analysis of RAR and RXR ligand specificity, target gene specificity, and patterns of expression suggests that each receptor pathway has both overlapping and unique functions. The ability of the retinoid receptors to interact with other nuclear receptors as well as other classes of transcription factors further increases the diversity and complexity of retinoic acid responses.

INTRODUCTION

In 1913, a nutritive factor was discovered as a lipid component of butter, egg yolk, and cod liver oil that in vertebrate animals was found to be essential for growth (McCollum and Davis 1913; Osborne and Mendel 1913). The factor was subsequently isolated and called vitamin A. Today, vitamin A and its natural and synthetic derivatives (the retinoids) are known to play essential roles in vision, reproduction, epithelial differentiation, hematopoiesis, bone development, and pattern formation during embryogenesis (Sporn et al. 1984). There is also considerable evidence to suggest that retinoids have potent antiproliferative effects and may be effective in the treatment of a variety of human diseases, including cancer (Ong and Chytil 1983; Sporn et al. 1984). Although vitamin A participates in many diverse and apparently unrelated functions, it is

Transcriptional Regulation.
Copyright 1992 Cold Spring Harbor Laboratory Press 0-87969-410-6/92 $3 + 00

known that this diversity is, in part, regulated by various retinoid metabolites (Fig. 1). In the visual cycle, retinal is the photoreactive component of rhodopsin. Its involvement in vision is a well-understood biochemical process that can be described as a cascade of chemical reactions (Wald 1968). The actions of other retinoids, however, are less well understood. Although retinol is believed to be responsible for the reproductive effects of the vitamin, it is clear that almost all of the other effects seen in growth, differentiation, and development are due to all-*trans* RA and/or closely related metabolites (Sporn et al. 1984).

RA Physiology

One of the earliest effects of all-*trans* RA action can be seen in the developing vertebrate embryo (Maden 1985; Brockes 1989; Eichele 1989). During embryogenesis, one way in which individual cells determine their fate is by registering positional information in the context of an embryonic field that generates a unique structure such as a vertebrate limb. In the chick limb, anterior-posterior patterning appears to be controlled by a region of cells known as the zone of polarizing activity (ZPA). The observation that RA not only can substitute for the ZPA (Tickle et al. 1982; Summerbell 1983), but also is apparently present in a concentration gradient across the developing limb bud (Thaller and Eichele 1987) has led to the hypothesis that RA is a vertebrate morphogen. In addition to being able to specify the anterior-posterior axis of the developing chick limb (Tickle et al. 1982), RA is able to reset positional information

Vitamin A = Retinol
(fertilization)

CH₂OH

Retinal
(vision)

CHO

All-Trans Retinoic Acid
(growth and differentiation)

COOH

Retinyl esters
(storage)

9-Cis Retinoic Acid
(growth and differentiation)

COOH

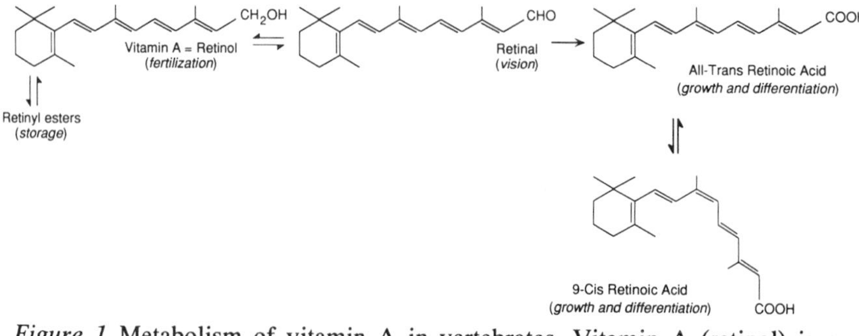

Figure 1 Metabolism of vitamin A in vertebrates. Vitamin A (retinol) is acquired through the diet where it may be interconverted to its storage form in the liver or to the aldehyde form (retinal). Retinal not only is required for the visual process, but also serves as the precursor to retinoic acid through an irreversible reaction. Retinoic acid and possibly other metabolites are responsible for the effects seen in morphogenesis, growth, and development.

during regeneration of an amputated newt limb (Maden 1982). RA is also capable of modulating anteroposterior transformation in the *Xenopus* central nervous system (Durston et al. 1989) and body axis (Sive et al. 1990). Recently, a ZPA-like activity has been discovered in the floor plate of the developing chick central nervous system (Hornbruch and Wolpert 1986; Wagner et al. 1990) that can synthesize several retinoids, including RA and didehydroretinoic acid (ddRA), suggesting that these compounds may function as neuronal morphogens. Teratogenic effects of RA in utero on limbs, spinal cord, and cranial facial structures further implicate this substance in mammalian development. In vitro, RA has been shown to induce differentiation of embryonic carcinoma (EC) (Strickland and Mahdavi 1978), keratinocytes (Fuchs and Green 1981), neuroblastoma (Haussler et al. 1983), and promyelocytic leukemia cells (Breitman et al. 1980). This action of retinoids has important implications for "differentiation therapy" in the treatment of human cancer. Finally, there is a rapidly growing literature showing that RA directly regulates the expression of several classes of transcription factors, including the proteins encoded by the *Hox* loci (Colberg-Poley et al. 1985; LaRosa and Gudas 1988; Oliver et al. 1990; Simeone et al. 1990). In this review, we focus on these latter effects, specifically on the mechanism by which RA and its congeners are able to elicit a diversity of biological responses at the level of gene transcription. We consider first the structure/function relationships and hormone specificities of the retinoid receptors. Then we examine how these ligand-dependent factors interact with their cognate target DNA and the transcriptional machinery to direct the regulation of gene networks.

RA RECEPTORS

One fundamental question in retinoid biology (and in hormonal signaling processes in general) is how a group of closely related and simple compounds can mediate diverse and complex responses. Multicellular organisms have evolved two basic strategies for mediating the translation of an extracellular signal into a transcriptional response at the target cell (Fig. 2). In one mechanism, the stimulus (e.g., a small peptide or growth factor) binds to a cell-surface receptor. Transduction of this signal to the nucleus is then accomplished by one of a myriad of second messages. The many examples of signals that operate via a second messenger are demonstrated by the high genetic and phenotypic variation of their receptors and pathways (Herschman 1989). A second mechanism cells have evolved to process an extracellular stimulus is through an intracellular receptor. In this pathway, the blood-borne signals are small lipophilic

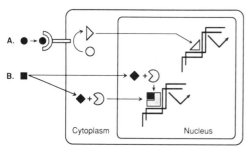

Figure 2 Signal transduction in higher animals. (*A*) The signal, usually a soluble peptide hormone or growth factor, binds to its receptor on the target cell's surface. Ligand binding triggers a series of enzymatic events, such as a change in intracellular calcium or the phosphorylation state of a protein, which in turn may act as second messengers to the nucleus. (*B*) Lipid-soluble hormones such as steroids, vitamin D, thyroid hormone, and retinoic acid penetrate the cell membrane and bind to an intracellular receptor. In this pathway the liganded receptor itself becomes the signal to the nucleus, where it directly interacts with the transcriptional machinery.

molecules, such as steroids, that are either actively or passively transported through the cell membrane where they bind cytosolic or nuclear receptors. The liganded receptor complex is a functionally active transcription factor that binds specifically to the regulatory region of target genes. In contrast to the cell-surface receptors, the intracellular receptors belong to one highly conserved family of proteins (Evans 1988; Green and Chambon 1988). Thus, from the characterization of one of these receptor pathways a unified mechanism can be derived by which the whole class of intracellular receptors can be studied. To date, nuclear receptors have been discovered for steroids, retinoids, and thyroid hormone (Evans 1988; Green and Chambon 1988).

Cellular Retinoic Acid Binding Protein

Because all-*trans* RA is a small lipophilic molecule that can apparently modulate gene expression, its mechanism of action has long been hypothesized to be analogous to that of steroid and thyroid hormones. This notion led to a biochemical "hunt" for an RA receptor. In the late 1970s a cellular retinoic acid binding protein (CRABP) was discovered (Chytil and Ong 1978). CRABP is a small cytoplasmic protein (M_r 15.5 K) that binds all-*trans* RA selectively and with high affinity ($K_d = \sim 4$ nM) (Ong and Chytil 1978). It is known that at least two species of this protein exist, and the genes for both have been isolated by molecular cloning techniques (Shubeita et al. 1987; Wei et al. 1987; Giguere et al. 1990a). These two closely related proteins, CRABP I and CRABP II, show distinct patterns of expression in the adult as well as during development (Dollé et al. 1989; Perez-Castro et al. 1989; Giguere et al. 1990a). For example, in the developing chick limb bud, CRABP I is expressed in a gradient across the limb which is inversely proportional to the endogenous concentration gradient of all-*trans* RA (Maden et al. 1988). Despite these descriptors, however, there is no direct evidence that CRABP can regulate transcription or that it is critical for receptor function. It is clear that some cells that respond to all-*trans* RA lack the binding protein and that in these cells CRABP is not required for RA transport (Haussler et al. 1984; Jetten et al. 1987; Mangelsdorf et al. 1990). Furthermore, CRABP bears no structural or evolutionary resemblance to steroid hormone receptors. Although the role of CRABP is at present unknown, the fact that this highly conserved protein is found in multiple species and shows a specific pattern of expression suggests that its function is important. It has been speculated that CRABP could act as a buffering system to regulate the intracellular concentration of all-*trans* RA and thereby provoke or inhibit a particular response. This hypothesis is consistent with the results of Maden et al. (1988) in the chick limb bud in which CRABP is found in an anterior-posterior gradient. However, synthetic retinoids that do not bind CRABP are still capable of mimicking RA-induced morphogenesis, suggesting that all-*trans* RA effects do not require CRABP (Tamura et al. 1990). A potential role for CRABP in the conversion of all-*trans* RA to other metabolites has also been proposed. In this scheme, CRABP would function as a shuttle protein to deliver all-*trans* RA to the appropriate metabolic enzymes in a fashion similar to the retinol-binding proteins in the intestine (Ong et al. 1987; Blomhoff et al. 1990).

True RARs

The initial characterization and biochemical analysis of CRABP led many investigators to believe that these proteins were the cognate receptors for all-*trans* RA. However, the identification of a true RAR did not come about from a biochemical characterization of the protein, but rather through its evolutionary relatedness to the nuclear receptors. In 1987, Petkovitch et al. and Giguere et al. independently isolated a human cDNA encoding an RA receptor protein similar to the nuclear hormone receptors. The human RAR (hRARα) has a DNA-binding and ligand-binding domain that is structurally and functionally conserved with other members of the nuclear receptor superfamily and is able to activate transcription of target genes in an all-*trans* RA-dependent fashion (see Fig. 4a) (Evans 1988). The discovery of this RAR was pivotal to the understanding of the mechanism of all-*trans* RA action because it demonstrated, for the first time, the existence of a retinoid-responsive transcription factor. Subsequently, additional RAR-related genes have been isolated, and now at least three different RAR subtypes (RARα, RARβ, RARγ) are known (see Fig. 6 and below). The ligand-binding domains of the RARs are highly conserved (>75% amino acid identity, see Fig. 6), suggesting that they all arose from a common ancestral RAR gene. These RAR isoforms are expressed in distinct patterns throughout development and in the mature organism (see below), indicating that they may mediate different functions. Thus, it appears that the diversity of effects by all-*trans* RA on cells can be explained in part by the diversity of all-*trans* RA receptors. With the discovery of multiple RAR genes, one important question is whether all the actions of vitamin A are mediated by these receptors or whether additional retinoid substrates and regulatory pathways exist.

RX RECEPTORS

A Novel Retinoid Response Pathway

At the same time the subfamily of RARs and their roles in retinoid action were first being investigated, several studies were being initiated to identify ligands for other receptor-like proteins. The fact that nuclear receptors share a common structure suggests the existence of a superfamily of genes whose products may be ligand-responsive transcription factors. Since 1987, at least 15 new gene products have been identified in both vertebrates and *Drosophila* which are known members of this nuclear receptor superfamily (Milbrandt 1987; Chang and Kokontis 1988; Giguere et al. 1988; Miyajima et al. 1988, 1989; Hamada et al. 1989; Lazar et al. 1989; Wang et al. 1989; Oro et al. 1992). Because initially the ligands for these receptor-like proteins are unknown, they are referred to as "orphan" receptors (XRs). The surprising discovery that there are many such orphan receptors has opened new directions in endocrine research and may lead to the identification of novel regulatory systems.

Figure 3 describes two methods that have been successfully employed to characterize the ligand- and DNA-binding specificities of orphan receptors (Giguere et al. 1987; Petkovitch et al. 1987; Mangelsdorf et al. 1990). Both methods are based on the observation that the molecular structure of nuclear receptors is conserved and that one receptor domain can be exchanged for another to create a functional hybrid (Green and

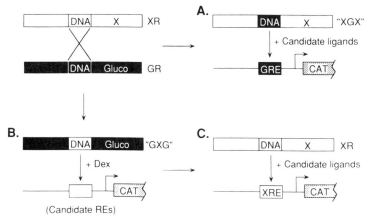

Figure 3 The *cis/trans* assay. Two strategies were developed to analyze orphan receptors. (*A*) In the first strategy the DNA-binding domain GR is substituted into the orphan receptor (XR) to make the chimera XGX. When co-expressed in cultured cells with a reporter plasmid containing a glucocorticoid response element (GRE), the reporter gene (e.g., CAT, chloramphenicol acetyltransferase) is expressed only in the presence of ligand X. (*B*) In the second strategy the chimera GXG is constructed and co-expressed with reporter genes containing candidate orphan receptor response elements (XREs). In the presence of the synthetic glucocorticoid, dexamethasone (Dex), the hybrid receptor GXG will only activate expression of the reporter gene when it contains the correct XR response element. (*C*) Once the XRE has been identified, the wild-type orphan receptor can be used (as in *A*) to screen for candidate ligands. These two assays allow the search for both the cognate ligand and response element of an orphan receptor.

Chambon 1987, 1988; Evans 1988; Umesono et al. 1988; Thompson and Evan 1989). In one strategy, the DNA-binding domain of an orphan receptor is substituted with the corresponding region from the glucocorticoid receptor (GR) (Fig. 3A). The resulting chimera will now stimulate a glucocorticoid-responsive promoter when exposed to the appropriate ligand. This hybrid receptor approach was used to functionally identify the human retinoic acid receptor (hRARα) (Giguere et al. 1987; Petkovitch et al. 1987). In the second strategy, the GR DNA-binding domain is replaced with that of the orphan receptor to form a hybrid receptor responsive to the synthetic glucocorticoid, dexamethasone (Fig. 3B). This glucocorticoid-inducible chimeric receptor will now activate transcription of a reporter gene that contains a *cis*-element responsive to the orphan receptor. Once the *cis*-responsive element for the orphan receptor is known, the need for the chimera is eliminated and the wild-type receptor can be used in the ligand screening assay (Fig. 3C). Utilizing this strategy, it was discovered that one of the human orphan receptors represented a second class of retinoid-responsive transcription factor, the human retinoid X receptor (hRXRα, Fig. 4b) (Mangelsdorf et al. 1990). A striking observation to come from the cloning of RXR is the apparent dissimilarity of its sequence to that of the RARs, considering they both respond to all-*trans* RA (Fig. 4). In fact, RAR is more similar to the thyroid hormone receptor (TR) than it is to RXR, suggesting that the response to RA by these two receptor systems has evolved through distinct pathways. This observation further underscores the importance and complexity of retinoid action in physiology and, coupled with the presence of a growing list of orphan receptors, leads to the speculation that other retinoid receptors may exist.

The discovery in RXR of a second retinoid transduction pathway has led us to investigate its functional properties and determine its relationship to the RARs. An understanding of the differences and similarities of the RAR and RXR systems requires knowledge of the diversity of the family members, their patterns of expression, and their pharmacology in response to cognate ligands. The isolation of cDNAs encoding three mouse RXR proteins, termed mRXRα, β, and γ (see Fig. 6), has been reported (Mangelsdorf et al. 1992). As is also true with the RAR subfamily, the RXR proteins are closely related to each other both in their DNA-binding and ligand-binding domains. Their homologies in-

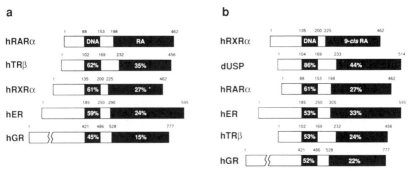

Figure 4 Schematic amino acid comparison of RAR and RXR with other members of the nuclear receptor superfamily. Primary amino acid sequences have been aligned on the basis of regions of maximum similarity, with the percentage identity indicated for the DNA-binding and ligand-binding domains in relation to *a*, hRARα (Giguere et al. 1987; Petkovitch et al. 1987) or *b*, hRXRα (Mangelsdorf et al. 1990). (hTRβ) Human thyroid hormone receptor β (Weinberger et al. 1986); (hER) human estrogen receptor (Green et al. 1986); (hGR) human glucocorticoid receptor (Hollenberg et al. 1985); (dUSP) *Drosophila ultraspiracle* (Oro et al. 1990).

dicate that these receptors are likely to regulate common target sequences and respond to common ligands. However, they differ markedly in their amino-terminal domains, which could confer distinct *trans*-activation functions. Interestingly, although there is no apparent insect homolog of the RARs, a *Drosophila* homolog of the RXR gene has been identified which maps to the *ultraspiracle* (*usp*) locus (Oro et al. 1990). Although *usp* does not respond to retinoids, its homology with RXR indicates the ancient evolutionary origin of this gene family and indeed may indicate that RXRs preceded RARs as the original retinoid signaling system. In this respect, it will be of interest to discover the ligand for *usp*.

A New Hormone: 9-*cis* RA

Human RXRα, like the RARs, was originally identified by its ability to respond to all-*trans* RA; similarly, murine RXR subtypes are also activated by all-*trans* RA. The initial observation that all-*trans* RA was the most potent inducer of both RAR and RXR suggested that it might also be the natural ligand for both of these receptors. However, there was circumstantial evidence for ligands that might discriminate between RAR and RXR. Thus, although RAR and RXR respond with a similar rank order of potency to the naturally occurring metabolites of vitamin A (retinoic acid > retinal > retinyl acetate > retinol), there are distinct pharmacological differences with respect to the synthetic retinoids (Mangelsdorf et al. 1990). For example, the benzoic acid retinoid derivative, TTNPB, displays potent all-*trans* RA-like activity with hRARα but only 10% of this response with hRXRα. Furthermore, hRARα has at least a tenfold higher sensitivity to all-*trans* RA than does hRXRα, whose response was not saturated even at 10^{-5} M all-*trans* RA. Indeed, we have been unable to demonstrate high-affinity binding of [^{3}H]all-*trans* RA to RXR extracted from cells transfected with RXR expression plasmid. In contrast, under similar conditions, all-*trans* RA binds with high affinity (K_d = 4 nM) to the RAR proteins (Ishikawa et al. 1990; Yang et al. 1991).

One explanation for the lack of high-affinity binding of all-*trans* RA to RXR is that the true ligand may be a distinct retinoid metabolite. In studies of vitamin D action, for example, 25-hydroxyvitamin D_3 was first proposed as the active vitamin D receptor (VDR) ligand. It was not until the discovery of a more polar metabolite specifically bound to chromatin (Haussler et al. 1968) that 1, 25-dihydroxyvitamin D_3 was identified as the true hormone. In the case of RA metabolites, Thaller and Eichele (1990) have demonstrated that 3,4-didehydroretinoic acid has potent morphogenic effects in the developing chick limb bud, where it is present at a concentration six times that of all-*trans* RA. Moreover, 3,4-dihydroretinoic acid can differentially activate RXRs and RARs in a fashion similar to all-*trans* RA (Blumberg et al. 1992; Mangelsdorf et al. 1992). These studies implied that all-*trans* RA might serve as a pro-hormone that would be metabolized to retinoid X and subsequently led to an intensive search to identify the RXR ligand. We and other workers have demonstrated that 9-*cis* RA, which is converted from all-*trans* RA in cells, is a naturally occurring, high-affinity ligand for the human RXRα (Heyman et al. 1992; Levin et al. 1992). 9-*cis* RA *trans*-activates RXRα up to 40 times more efficiently than does all-*trans* RA and binds to RXR with high affinity (K_d = 11.7 nM). Similarly, 9-*cis* RA is also retinoid X for the mouse RXR α, β, and γ subtypes (Mangelsdorf et al. 1992).

Although RXRs may interact with RARs (see below), they may also function independently. Expression of RXRα in *Drosophila* Schneider cells is sufficient to reconstitute retinoid responsiveness. Thus, not only do the RXRs bind and respond to 9-*cis* RA, but they also are able to activate target genes in the absence of other RAR gene products. Furthermore, the RXRs are capable of activating through the recently described response element in the CRBPII gene, which is not induced by the RARs (Fig. 5) (Mangelsdorf et al 1991). These results indicate that the RXRs are bona fide members of the nuclear receptor family and, together with the discovery of the new vertebrate hormone, 9-*cis* RA, define a second retinoid signaling pathway.

A point of potential physiological significance is that 9-*cis* RA binds to and *trans*-activates not only RXRs, but also RARs, and may thus serve as a common or "bifunctional" ligand. Conversion of the all-*trans* to the 9-*cis* isomer could provide a novel means for differential cell-specific regulation of the activity of these retinoid pathways. The hypothesis that 9-*cis* RA may be functionally distinct from its all-*trans* precursor raises the interesting possibility that regulation of its isomerization could be a key step in retinoid physiology. Whether or not this reaction is catalyzed by an enzyme is unknown, but it is intriguing to note a dark cycle reaction in the visual system in which a membrane-bound isomerase converts the all-*trans* isomer into the photolabile 11-*cis* isomer (Bernstein et al. 1987; Rando 1990).

TARGET GENE SPECIFICITY
The 3-4-5 Rule

Members of the receptor superfamily modulate target gene expression by binding either as homodimers or heterodimers to hormone response ele-

a) RXRE

		1	
	----->		----->
DR-1	AGGTCA	G	AGGTCA
rCRBPII	AGGTCA	C	AGGTCA
hApoAI	AGGGCA	A	GGGTCA
cOVAL	GTGTCA	A	AGGTCA

b) VDRE

		3	
	----->		----->
DR-3	AGGTCA	AGG	AGGTCA
rOST	GGGTGA	ATG	AGGACA
hOST	GGGTGA	ACG	GGGGCA
mSPP-1	GGTTCA	CGA	GGTTCA

c) TRE

		4	
	----->		----->
DR-4	AGGTCA	CAGG	AGGTCA
rMH	AGGTGA	CAGG	AGGACA
rME	GGGTTA	GGGG	AGGACA
MLV	GGGTCA	TTTC	AGGTCC

d) RARE

		5	
	----->		----->
DR-5	AGGTCA	CCAGG	AGGTCA
mRARβ	GGTTCA	CCGAA	AGTTCA
mCP-H	AGGTCA	CTGAC	AGGGCA
hADH3	GGGTCA	TTCAG	AGTTCA

Figure 5 Direct repeats serve as HREs for RXR, VDR, TR, and RAR. The respective consensus direct repeats (DR-1, DR-3, DR-4, DR-5) are shown for each hormone response system followed by known HREs from various cognate target genes. (*a*) Retinoid X response elements (RXREs) are DR-1 HREs. (rCRBPII) Rat cellular retinol-binding protein type II gene promoter (shown are only two of the four tandem repeats found in this response element) (Mangelsdorf et al. 1991); (cOVAL) chicken ovalbumin gene promoter (Wang et al. 1989); (hApoAI) human apolipoprotein AI gene promoter (Rottman et al. 1991). (*b*) Vitamin D response elements (VDREs) are DR-3 HREs. (rOST) Rat osteocalcin gene promoter (Demay et al. 1990); (hOST) human osteocalcin gene promoter (Ozono et al. 1991); (mSPP-1) mouse osteopontin gene promoter (Noda et al. 1990). (*c*) Thyroid hormone response elements (TREs) are DR-4 HREs. (rMHC) Rat cardiac myosin heavy-chain α gene promoter (Izumo and Mahdavi 1988); (rME) rat malic enzyme gene promoter (Petty et al. 1990); (MLV) Moloney leukemia virus long terminal repeat (Sap et al. 1989). (*d*) Retinoic acid response elements (RAREs) are DR-5 HREs. (mRARβ) Mouse RARβ gene promoter (Sucov et al. 1990); (mCPH) mouse complement factor H gene promoter (Muños-Cánoves et al. 1990); (hADH3) human alcohol dehydrogenase gene promoter (Duester et al. 1991).

ments (HREs). We have described the properties of direct repeats of consensus half-site sequence AGGTCA as minimal HREs for the nonsteroid members of the nuclear receptor family (Umesono et al. 1991).

Receptor specificity for binding and activation is determined at least in part by the number of nucleotides separating the two half-sites. Spacers of 3, 4, or 5 nucleotides have been shown to serve as optimal HREs for the VDRs, TRs, and RARs, respectively, a pattern denoted as the "3-4-5 rule" (Umesono et al. 1991). We have also characterized an HRE present in the upstream regulatory region of the CRBPII gene that confers selective responsiveness to the RXR (Mangelsdorf et al. 1991). Termed the CRBPII-RXRE, this RXR-specific HRE consists of four tandemly arranged AGGTCA repeats separated by a single nucleotide, filling one of the spacing options left unoccupied by the 3-4-5 rule. Several HREs for these receptors are listed in Figure 5.

Our studies imply that knowledge of receptors' half-site spacing preferences can be exploited as part of a strategy to elucidate functional interactions between members of the superfamily, including the orphan receptors (see below). In addition, by searching data bases, genes can be identified containing sequences in their regulatory regions related to HREs of distinct half-site spacing, which would follow the 3-4-5 rule or fill other spacing options. An example of how this strategy can be used successfully is represented by the CRBPII-RXRE (Mangelsdorf et al. 1991), which was first discovered by screening a GenBank data base for sequences containing the AGGTCA motif. Thus, this approach has led to the identification of target genes, which have provided important insights into the complex, physiological networks regulated by hormonal signals (see below).

RXR Interacts Directly with the VDR, TR, and RAR

Accessory factors present in nuclear extracts appear to be necessary for high-affinity binding of the RAR, TR, and VDR to their cognate HREs (Murray and Towle 1989; Glass et al. 1990; Liao et al. 1990; Yang et al. 1991). It was proposed that these accessory factors might be members of the receptor family which stimulate receptor binding through heterodimer formation (Glass et al. 1990). Indeed, we and other workers have recently found that RXR functions as a common heterodimeric partner for the VDR, TR, and RAR (Yu et al. 1991; Kliewer et al. 1992a; Leid et al. 1992; Zhang et al. 1992). It also forms a weaker heterodimer with the orphan receptor, COUP (Kliewer et al. 1992b). These results emerged from our initial finding of a functional interaction between RXR and RAR and COUP (Mangelsdorf et al. 1991; Kliewer et al. 1992b). Cotransfection of either RAR or COUP was shown to efficiently repress RXR-mediated *trans*-activation through the CRBPII-RXRE (Mangels-

dorf et al. 1991; Kliewer et al. 1992b). Cotransfection experiments performed with a variety of RAR mutants revealed that this repression of
RXR activity was mediated through the carboxy-terminal region of RAR,
which includes the dimerization domain, suggesting the possibility of a
physical interaction between RAR and RXR (Kliewer et al. 1992a. In
fact, RAR and RXR form heterodimers in solution and interact cooperatively at target HREs, including the retinoic acid response element
(RARE) of the RARβ promoter and the CRBPII-RXRE. Thus, the signaling pathways mediated by the two families of retinoid receptors converge through direct RAR-RXR interactions.

As in the case of RAR, RXR interacts cooperatively with the VDR
and TR in binding to target HREs and forms stable solution heterodimers
with the two receptors (Yu et al. 1991; Kliewer et al. 1992a). This ability
of RXR to interact with receptors responsive to a variety of ligands establishes a central role for RXR in modulating multiple hormonal pathways. As discussed above, two additional subtypes of RXR, termed
RXRβ and RXRγ, have also been isolated (Mangelsdorf et al. 1992), and
these too can interact with other nuclear receptors. Thus, the interaction
of multiple forms of RXR with nuclear receptors responsive to a diversity of signaling molecules likely provides the repertoire of transcription
factor activities necessary to regulate the battery of hormone-responsive
genes. It remains unclear why the VDR, TR, and RAR interact with a
common partner, particularly since the actions of vitamin D and thyroid
hormone do not appear to be retinoid-dependent. Apparently, only one
partner of the heterodimer needs to be occupied by ligand, although this
supposition has yet to be tested.

Interactions with Other Factors

In addition to heterodimer function, recent studies indicate that the activity of the RAR may be modulated by the nuclear transcription factor
AP-1. AP-1 is a complex of the proto-oncoproteins Jun and Fos, whose
activity is stimulated by tumor promoters and growth factors. It was observed in the regulation of the human osteocalcin gene that agents
stimulating AP-1 synthesis block the action of RA (Schüle et al. 1990a).
Reciprocally, RA treatment is capable of inhibiting the action of AP-1.
Inspection of the osteocalcin promoter revealed that within the proximity
of the vitamin D and RA response element is a perfect AP-1-binding site.
Although the mechanism of this mutual inhibition by RA and AP-1 is not
yet clear, these two distinct regulatory systems are able to impose a type
of "check and balance" system on each other's activities, which in the

context of this particular promoter requires both AP-1 and RA response elements. This phenomenon, whereby two different classes of regulatory factors modulate expression by interacting with a common response element, has been referred to as cross-coupling (Schüle et al. 1990a).

A second example of such communication between factors implicates protein-protein interactions between a nuclear hormone receptor and AP-1 (Diamond et al. 1990; Jonat et al. 1990; Lucibello et al. 1990; Schüle et al. 1990b; Yang-Yen et al. 1990). In these studies, functional antagonism of AP-1-induced expression could be demonstrated in the presence of GR. The inhibition of AP-1 activation of the collagenase promoter by GR is hormone-dependent, but, surprisingly, although it requires the GR DNA-binding domain, the ability of the GR to bind DNA is not required (Schüle et al. 1990b; Yang-Yen et al. 1990). Thus, GR is able to inhibit a wide variety of AP-1-responsive promoters even though it cannot bind to the AP-1 response element. Similarly, it was shown that the oncoprotein Jun could block GR-induced expression of a GRE-containing promoter but that this inhibition did not involve the DNA-binding domain of Jun (Schüle et al. 1990b). Thus, cross-coupling appears to be a mechanism by which retinoid and other nuclear receptors can regulate the function of other transcription factors through both DNA-binding and DNA-binding-independent protein-protein interactions. One important future question is to determine the nature of the interaction and whether it is mediated by a conserved structural motif common to all nuclear receptors.

TISSUE DISTRIBUTION AND EXPRESSION SPECIFICITY

Although the RARs and RXRs can regulate distinct target genes, they may also regulate common target genes. One way to infer the roles of these receptors and their ligands is to examine their patterns of expression and their regulation. As illustrated in Figure 6, the pleiotropic effects of retinoids might be explained in part by the patterns of expression of various RAR and RXR genes. In aggregate, in the adult organism the RARs and RXRs are widely (if not universally) expressed. In general, this pattern reflects a perdurance of that observed *in situ* in the embryo.

Detailed studies of RAR expression by in situ hybridization techniques (Dollé et al. 1989; Noji et al. 1989; Osumi-Yamashita et al. 1990; Ruberte et al. 1990; Smith and Eichele 1991) imply a role for each RAR subtype during embryonic development and limb formation. In the developing mouse embryo, RARα is ubiquitously expressed at low levels. RARβ transcripts, however, are restricted to specific regions such as the

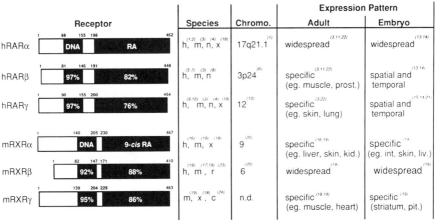

Figure 6 Comparative analysis of the RAR and RXR family of retinoid responsive transcription factors. Primary amino acid sequences have been aligned as in Fig. 4 in relation to either hRARα or mRXRα. "Species" indicates in which organisms each receptor has been identified ([c] chicken; [h] human; [m] mouse; [n] newt; [r] rat; [x] *Xenopus*). "Chromo." indicates the human chromosome location. "Expression pattern" indicates the general distribution of each receptor mRNA in the adult and embryo. For a more detailed analysis, see the text and the references listed below. References are as follows: (1) Pet-kovitch et al. 1987; (2) Giguere et al. 1987; (3) Zelent et al. 1989; (4) Ragsdale et al. 1989; (5) de Thé et al. 1987; (6) Brand et al. 1988; (7) Benbrook et al. 1988; (8) Giguere et al. 1989; (9) Krust et al. 1989; (10) Ishikawa et al. 1990; (11) de Thé et al. 1989; (12) Rees et al. 1989; (13) Dollé et al. 1989; (14) Osumi-Yamashita et al. 1990; (15) Ruberte et al. 1990; (16) Mangelsdorf et al. 1990; (17) Hamada et al. 1989; (18) Blumberg et al. 1992; (19) Mangelsdorf et al. 1992; (20) D. Mangelsdorf et al., unpubl. (21) Giguere et al. 1990b; (22) Kastner et al. 1990; (23) Yu et al. 1991; (24) Rowe et al. 1991.

interdigital mesenchyme, mesenchyme surrounding the inner ear epi-thelium (Dollé et al. 1989), and the developing nervous system (Smith and Eichele 1991). A potential role in neurogenesis (Simeone et al. 1990; Smith and Eichele 1991) is further strengthened by the finding that all-*trans* RA can be synthesized in the developing neural floor plate (Wag-ner et al. 1990). In contrast, RARγ gene expression is detected in all mesenchyme giving rise to bones and facial cartilage, and in differentiat-ing squamous keratinizing epithelia (Osumi-Yamashita et al. 1990; Ruberte et al. 1990). This nonoverlapping distribution of RARβ and RARγ suggests that they may have distinct developmental functions. Be-cause of its expression in the interdigital mesenchyme during the time of digit separation, it has been proposed that RARβ may function in regulat-ing programmed cell death (Dollé et al. 1989).

In situ hybridization and Northern analyses have also been employed to reveal RXR expression patterns. Although there is no absolute correlation between the individual RAR and RXR subtypes, several interesting similarities are emerging. For example, both RARα and RXRβ are found in almost all tissues, whereas RARβ and γ and RXRα and γ are much more restricted. Although RXRβ shows no striking pattern, somewhat elevated expression is observed in the anterior extensions of the spinal cord and hindbrain (Mangelsdorf et al. 1992). RXRα shows abundant expression in liver, kidney, spleen, and a variety of visceral tissues (Mangelsdorf et al. 1990, 1992) that are in marked distinction to the RAR subtypes, which are found in very low levels in these corresponding sites (Giguere et al. 1987; Brand et al. 1988; Zelent et al. 1989; Kastner et al. 1990). This pattern led us to propose that RXRα may be involved in retinoid metabolism, a hypothesis that was further bolstered by the demonstration that the CRBPII gene (Mangelsdorf et al. 1991) is RXR responsive. CRBPII helps to absorb dietary retinol and assist in its transfer to chylomicrons and subsequent transport to the liver. Since high levels of retinoids are teratogenic, especially to the early embryo, the abundant early expression of RXRα in the decidua and placenta (Mangelsdorf et al. 1992) may indicate that RXRα has a role in feedback regulation of retinoid uptake and storage in the embryo. The expression of RXRα in organs such as the liver, kidney, and intestine suggests an additional role for retinoids in physiological homeostasis. Interestingly, RXRα and RARγ are both abundantly expressed in the epidermis (Kastner et al. 1990; Mangelsdorf et al. 1992), indicating that these two receptors are likely to be responsible for the dermatologic effects of retinoids.

RXRγ expression appears to be rather restricted, accumulating most abundantly in muscle and brain (Mangelsdorf et al. 1992). In the chicken, a homolog of RXRγ has been shown to be expressed in the developing peripheral nervous system (Rowe et al. 1991). The CNS pattern of RXRγ expression in the mouse is prominent in the embryonic enlage to the caudate putamen (basal ganglia), the major target of dopaminergic innervation by the substantia nigra. Interestingly, both RXRγ and RARβ are coexpressed in the motor neurons of the spinal cord, again suggesting a selective coexpression between these two receptor systems. Prominent expression of RXRγ in the pituitary is also found, suggesting a potential role for retinoids in the regulatory cascade associated with hypophyseal differentiation.

These studies suggest that the RAR and RXR families play critical roles in diverse aspects of development, from embryo implantation to organogenesis, limb development, and central nervous system differentiation, as well as in adult physiology and metabolism.

RA-CONTROLLED GENE EXPRESSION

Autoregulation

One mechanism by which RA may coordinate complex gene expression is through the direct autoregulation of the retinoid receptors themselves. It now appears that all three RAR subtypes may be RA inducible. The evidence is most advanced for the RARβ gene, which displays the most dramatic induction and contains an RA response element (RARE, Fig. 5) in its promoter (de Thé et al. 1990b; Sucov et al. 1990). The propagation of a RA-specific autoregulatory loop has potential biological advantages. One example is the effect RA has on anterior/posterior patterning, both along the body axis and in the developing limb bud. In the development of axial structures in the *Xenopus* embryo, increasing doses of RA cause a progressive reduction in anterior structures (Durston et al. 1989; Sive et al. 1990). In the developing chick limb, RA is able to mimic the polarizing activity that specifies the anterior/posterior pattern of digit formation (Tickle et al. 1982; Summerbell 1983). These results have led to the proposal that RA is a morphogen, and in support of this it has been reported that RA exists in a shallow concentration gradient across the developing limb bud (Thaller and Eichele 1987). Morphogenic gradients have been implicated in pattern formation in several systems (Slack 1987). Although the role of RA as a morphogen is still controversial (Noji et al. 1991; Tabin 1991; Wanek et al. 1991), one way these effects of RA may be amplified is through the up-regulation of RAR. Since target gene activation requires both ligand and receptor, a small increase in RA concentration could lead to a concomitant increase in RARβ, resulting in a disproportionately larger biological response. Although such a response would be dependent on the sensitivity of the RARβ promoter to RA, recent evidence utilizing transgenic mice expressing the *lacZ* gene driven from a βRARE-containing promoter show that in the developing mouse embryo the βRARE is dramatically responsive to endogenous concentrations of RA (Rossant et al. 1991).

It is not yet known whether RXR expression is also RA-dependent. However, as mentioned above, the discovery of an RXR response element in the CRBPII promoter strongly suggests that 9-*cis* RA may play an autoregulatory role in its own synthesis. The ability to autoregulate both the hormone and its receptor has the potential to provide an exquisite and sensitive mechanism for governing other gene networks.

Regulation of Gene Networks

The vertebrate homologs of the *Drosophila* homeobox (Hox) proteins are thought to specify positional information during embryogenesis. The mammalian Hox genes are organized into four distinct chromosomal loci each containing a cluster of as many as nine genes (Acampora et al. 1989; Boncinelli et al. 1989). Expression of the Hox2 cluster occurs sequentially in a 3′ to 5′ direction, which coincides with the anterior/posterior boundaries of the rhombomere segments in the hindbrain (Murphy et al. 1989; Wilkinson et al. 1989; for review, see Lewis 1989). The nine genes of the human Hox2 cluster are differentially activated in cultured EC cells when exposed to increasing concentrations of RA (Simeone et al. 1990). Thus, the 3′ genes, defining the anterior boundaries, are most sensitive to RA stimulation. The 5′ (posterior) genes are only fractionally induced and require higher concentrations of RA to observe this effect. Interestingly, RARβ is present in the hindbrain (Smith and Eichele 1991) and is also induced by RA in a concentration-dependent manner in EC cells. These studies support a role for RA in controlling hindbrain development through its regulation of Hox2 gene transcription. With other genes, there is also evidence that RA regulation of Hox expression in *Xenopus* may be coupled to other growth factors (Cho and DeRobertis 1990).

RA-induced differentiation of embryonic stem cells may operate similarily. For example, the pluripotent mouse EC cells, P19, can be induced to differentiate into three different phenotypes depending on the concentration of RA in which they are grown (Edwards and McBurney 1983). Nanomolar concentrations of RA yield cardiac muscle phenotypes, whereas 10 nM and >100 nM RA induce skeletal muscle and neuron phenotypes, respectively. Thus, RA gradients established early in the developing embryo may be partly responsible for the commitment of stem cells to differentiate into multiple phenotypes. In this scenario, one might envision RARs and RXRs to be expressed early in the embryo and help establish an RA gradient by regulating expression of RA metabolizing enzymes and other retinoid receptors. Both classes of retinoid receptors have been detected in the *Xenopus* egg, supporting this hypothesis (Blumberg et al. 1992).

HUMAN DISEASE

The cloning of the retinoid receptor genes has allowed an evaluation of their roles in development, physiology, and human disease. Of particular interest are their potential roles as proto-oncogenes, i.e., genes that through mutation could contribute to oncogenic transformation. This possibility is given force by the previous discovery that the v-*erbA* oncogene, which contributes to an avian erythroleukemia, is a mutated derivative of the TR (Sap et al. 1986; Weinberger et al. 1986). It facilitates oncogenic transformation of cells by blocking the action of the endogenous TR and thus prevents erythroblasts from differentiating in response to triiodothyronine (Zenke et al. 1990). On the basis of these observations, it is not surprising that an association between the RARα gene and the etiology of acute promyelocytic leukemia (APL) has recently been demonstrated.

APL is distinguished, in 90% of affected individuals, by a reciprocal chromosome 15:17 translocation in which the t(15;17) breakpoint occurs in the *RARα* gene itself (Borrow et al. 1990; de Thé et al. 1990a; Longo et al. 1990). High doses of RA will induce complete clinical remission in APL patients (Huang et al. 1988), suggesting that a mutant form of the *RARα* gene interacts or contributes to leukemogenesis and simultaneously provides a molecular marker for identifying leukemic promyelocytes. It has been shown that the translocation results in a fusion between the *RARα* gene and a region on chromosome 15 referred to as *PML*, which originally was named *myl* (de Thé et al. 1990a). The translocation is balanced and reciprocal and, in additon to the wild-type RARα and PML, generates two novel abnormal fusion gene products, RAR-PML and PML-RAR. The PML-RAR protein contains most of the wild-type PML protein fused to the functional DNA-binding and ligand-binding domains of the RAR. As discussed below, it is believed that the PML-RAR fusion (and not the RAR-PML fusion) contributes to the disease state (de Thé et al. 1991; Kakizuka et al. 1991).

The wild-type PML proteins contain at least four potentially interesting structural motifs, including a proline-rich amino terminus, a cysteine-rich portion, a potential α-helical region, and a leucine zipper region that shows homology with the leucine zipper of the Fos family (Kakizuka et al. 1991). Because the Fos leucine zipper mediates dimerization, the presence of this related sequence in PML raises the further possibility that the PML or PML-RAR protein may be part of a homodimer or heterodimer complex. As mentioned above, the PML-RAR fusion includes most of these potentially important regions, whereas the reciprocal fusions only include a highly truncated segment of the PML protein.

Among the four structural regions, the most striking is the cysteine-rich segment, which we have referred to as the "cysteine-chapel motif." Data base searches have identified several proteins with almost perfect conservation of several amino acids in this region, the most notable of which are the cysteines found in the first of three clusters in PML (Kakizuka et al. 1991). Although the function of this region has yet to be clearly demonstrated, the fact that several of these proteins are known DNA-binding proteins and transcription factors suggests that PML may bind DNA through this cysteine-rich domain, and thus make it a strong candidate for a transcription factor.

As one approach to the question of how the t(15;17) translocation contributes to APL, the activities of the wild-type RARα and the PML-RAR fusion protein have been compared. In one typical experiment, plasmids driving expression of either wild-type RARα or PML-RAR were transfected into HL60 cells and assayed for activation of two different RARE-containing reporters (Kakizuka et al. 1991). The results revealed that PML-RAR is an RA-dependent transcription factor and may activate as well as or even better than wild-type RAR through an RARE-containing promoter. These findings suggest PML-RAR does not contribute to APL through the RAR pathway, although PML-RAR can differ markedly from RARα in cell-type specificity of its activation profiles. The basis for this variation is not known and requires further investigation.

In view of the structural features of PML-RAR, it is most likely that this fusion product interferes with either the RAR or the PML transcriptional pathway (Fig. 7). For example, PML-RAR may block either one of these pathways in the absence of RA. In the presence of RA, the fusion protein could be activated and the block would be released. Assuming that the PML-RAR does not interfere with the endogenous RAR pathway, we propose a model in which PML-RAR functions as a dominant-negative inhibitor of the endogenous PML pathway and thereby blocks promyelocytic differentiation (Fig. 7). This idea is not without precedent. It has previously been shown that heterologous transcription factors fused to the ligand-binding domain of steroid receptors lose their normal activation properties and become hormone dependent. For example, the transforming activity of the *myc* protein becomes estrogen-dependent when fused to the estrogen receptor (Picard et al. 1988; Eilers et al. 1989). For PML-RAR, the t(15;17) translocation may place the PML product under control of the RAR ligand-binding domain. The abnormal

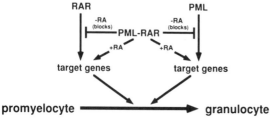

Figure 7 Proposed model for the genesis of APL. The model indicates how the aberrant PML-RAR fusion protein might contribute to the leukemogenesis in APL patients. Also shown are the sites of action of RA, which is an effective therapy for sending the disease into complete remission. For more discussion, see text.

fusion protein might block function of wild-type PML by forming non-productive heterodimers or by blocking target DNA sites. Addition of RA would reverse this inhibition by releasing the block or transforming the fusion receptor to an activated state. This model provides a simple explanation for the striking therapeutic effect of RA in PML. A conclusive test will require the identification of PML-RAR target genes crucial for leukemogenesis.

PERSPECTIVES AND CONCLUSION

The discovery by Giguere et al. (1987) and Petkovich et al. (1987) of a human RA receptor in a vertebrate system offered the hope of analyzing the mechanisms of morphogenesis by identifying a set of developmentally controlled genes. This discovery was made more meaningful by the recognition that the RAR was a member of the steroid/thyroid hormone receptor superfamily. This association suggested that the mechanisms of action of retinoids are, by analogy, similar to those of steroid and thyroid hormones. Accordingly, the RAR is proposed to be a sequence-specific DNA-binding transcription factor whose activity is controlled by RA. Subsequent to the identification of the initial RARα, two additional genes (β and γ) were identified that comprise the RA receptor subfamily. Mangelsdorf et al. (1990) identified the retinoid X receptors, which represent a second evolutionary pathway for mediating retinoid responsiveness. RXRs are also part of the steroid/thyroid hormone receptor superfamily but are not part of the RAR subfamily. Indeed, it appears that there are three distinct RXR genes also referred to as α, β, and γ. Thus, in aggregate, six retinoid-responsive transcription factors have been identified, each of which may play a critical role in orchestrating embryonic development and adult physiology.

Family Ties

One obvious challenge is to understand the rationale for multiple receptors in each subfamily. Do they serve interactive and interdependent functions, or are they redundant? The same sort of question can be proposed for the two retinoid subfamilies themselves. For example, is RXR a redundant pathway to the RAR, or are these two subfamilies serving fundamentally different roles? One approach to these questions is to understand the temporal-spatial patterns of expression of these molecules during embryonic development and in the adult. A second is to identify the target genes of each of these molecules and, indeed, to simply know whether they all recognize common sequences or have distinct specificities. Because the function of a protein must be intimately related to its structure, it can be argued that the differences between the RXRs and RARs indicate fundamentally different functions because of their inherent structural dissimilarities.

The relatively weak homology of the RARs and RXRs indicates that their genes diverged long ago, yet converged on utilization of similar ligands, possibly reflecting the increased demand of more complex organisms. Although understanding the origins of these two gene families may seem tangential to understanding their significance, this may represent a limited view. By tracing these two genes back in history, we may be better able to link them with their original biological functions. Because evolution proceeds via adaptation and selection, it is likely that their original functions will be informative about their modern roles. Thus, identification of invertebrate homologs may contribute greatly in advancing this frontier.

Knowing that the receptors are sequence-specific, retinoid-dependent transcription factors does not explain how they control morphological diversity or cell fate. For example, the receptors may represent the tip of a hierarchical cascade that activates a limited set of regulatory genes, or they may stimulate directly a large fraction of downstream functions. Again, a key approach is to identify target genes. Ultimately, it is the genes that are being regulated that produce the changes in cell function that are triggered by retinoids. If these genes can be identified, we will have greatly advanced our understanding of how receptors contribute to morphological diversity.

Retinoid Relatives

Although the focus of this chapter has been on all-*trans* RA, the discovery of 9-*cis* RA as a high-affinity ligand for the RXRs stresses the point that there are many gaps in our knowledge of retinoid metabolism that need to be filled. It seems likely that these two receptors, which are known to respond differently to two different RA isomers, may show differential activity to other retinoid metabolites as well. Already there is evidence to suggest that all-*trans* and 9-*cis* RA are not the only metabolites responsible for all of the effects attributed to vitamin A. The finding that 3,4-didehydroretinoic acid (Thaller and Eichele 1990) is an abundant molecule that activates RXRs and RARs indicates that it too may play an important morphogenic role. There is the intriguing possibility that other orphan receptors also have retinoid ligands. This possibility is made more compelling by the discovery of the novel, bioactive retinoid metabolite 14-hydroxy-*retro*-retinol (Buck et al. 1991). This retinol derivative is specific in inducing lymphocyte proliferation. RA isomers cannot substitute for this activity and, likewise, 14-hydroxy-*retro*-retinol does not activate RARs or RXRs (D.J. Mangelsdorf and J. Buck, per. comm.). This discovery opens the door for other potential retinoid signaling pathways. In this context, it is notable that vitamin A (retinol) itself is virtually inactive. Thus, it is clear that in the future it will be essential to characterize the enzymes that convert vitamin A to other potentially active metabolic products. One critical question is whether there are specific retinoid metabolizing enzymes that are expressed in a spatially and developmentally regulated pattern that corresponds to the known developmental sites of retinoid action. In principle, the sites of production of such converting enzymes would provide a road map to the organizational signaling centers throughout the body. The cloning of such enzymes would not only be highly desirable, but also might provide us with the tools to begin to identify the next layer of biological organization of the embryo.

Genetic Analysis

The cumbersome genetics of vertebrate systems implies that this route is unlikely to be revealing about RAR or RXR function. However, via homologous recombination, it is possible to use cloned DNA to alter genomic sequences and to derive transgenic mice harboring the mutant allele (Capecchi 1989). This gene "knock-out" approach, in principle, allows a systematic analysis of RAR and RXR function. It may also be useful for the introduction of mutations that modify (instead of eliminate) receptor function. This will allow the roles of individual domains to be assessed. Another approach is to generate dominant-negative alleles of receptors (Pratt et al. 1990; Espeseth et al. 1990; R.A. Heyman et al., in prep.) that interfere with wild-type receptor activity and effectively block the normal action of RA. By targeting these dominant-negative receptors to specific cell types in transgenic mice, the tissue-specific function of RARs and RXRs may be identified. Thus, as shown in this chapter, the RARs and RXRs are interesting not only as molecular machines to modulate transcriptional programs, but also as key molecules in the activation of developmental and physiological cascades. These studies may help to open up a new era in understanding the molecular basis not only of embryonic development, but also of human disease.

ACKNOWLEDGMENTS

The authors thank Drs. Kazuhiko Umesono, Richard Heyman, Bruce Blumberg, and Steven Kliewer for their contributions to this manuscript, and Elaine Stevens for administrative assistance. Portions of this manuscript, including unpublished observations, are being published elsewhere in other forms. D.J.M. is a staff scientist at the Salk Institute for Biological Studies; R.M.E. is an investigator of the Howard Hughes Medical Institute at the Salk Institute. This work was supported by the Howard Hughes Medical Institute, National Institutes of Health, National Cancer Institute, and the Mathers Foundation.

REFERENCES

Acampora, D., M. D'Esposito, A. Faiella, M. Pannese, E. Migliaccio, F. Morelli, A. Stornaiuolo, V. Nigro, A. Simeone, and E. Boncinelli. 1989. The human HOX gene family. *Nucleic Acids Res.* **17:** 10385–10402.

Benbrook, D., E. Lernhardt, and M. Pfahl. 1988. A new retinoic acid receptor identified from a hepatocellular carcinoma. *Nature* **333:** 669–672.

Bernstein, P.S., W.C. Law, and R.R. Rando. 1987. Isomerization of all-*trans*-retinoids to 11-*cis*-retinoids in vitro. *Proc. Natl. Acad. Sci.* **84:** 1849–1853.

Blomhoff, R., M.H. Green, T. Berg, and K.R. Norum. 1990. Transport and storage of vitamin A. *Science* **250:** 399-404.

Blumberg, B., D.J. Mangelsdorf, J.A. Dyck, D.A. Bittner, R.M. Evans, and E.M. DeRobertis. 1992. Multiple retinoid-responsive receptors in a single cell: Families of RXRs and RARs in the *Xenopus* egg. *Proc. Natl. Acad. Sci.* **89:** 2321–2325.

Boncinelli, E., D. Acampora, M. Pannese, M. D'Esposito, R. Somma, G. Gaudino, A. Storaiuolo, M. Cafieco, A. Faiella, and A. Simeone. 1989. Organization of human class I homeobox genes. *Genome* **31:** 728–743.

Borrow, J., A.D. Goddard, D. Sheer, and E. Solomon. 1990. Molecular analysis of acute promyelocytic leukemia breakpoint cluster region on chromosome 17. *Science* **249:** 1577–1580.

Brand, N., M. Petkovich, A. Krust, P. Chambon, H. de Thé, A. Marchio, P. Tiollais, and A. Dejean. 1988. Identification of a second human retinoic acid receptor. *Nature* **332:** 850–853.

Breitman, T.R., S.E. Selonick, and S.J. Collins. 1980. Induction of differentiation of the human promyelocytic leukemia cell line (HL-60) by retinoic acid. *Proc. Natl. Acad. Sci.* **77:** 2936–2940.

Brockes, J.P. 1989. Retinoids, homeobox genes, and limb morphogenesis. *Neuron* **2:** 1285–1294.

Buck, J., F. Derguini, E. Levi, K. Nakanishi, and U. Hammerling. 1991. Intracellular signaling by 14-hydroxy-4,14-*retro*-retinol. *Science* **254:** 1654–1656.

Capecchi, M. 1989. Altering the genome by homologous recombination. *Science* **244:** 1288–1292.

Chang, C. and J. Kokontis. 1988. Identification of a new member of the steroid receptor super-family by cloning and sequence analysis. *Biochem. Biophys. Res. Commun.* **155:** 971–977.

Cho, K. W. Y. and E. M. DeRobertis. 1990. Differential activation of *Xenopus* homeobox genes by mesoderm-inducing growth factors and retinoic acid. *Genes Dev.* **4:** 1910–1916.

Chytil, F. and D.E. Ong. 1978. Cellular vitamin A binding proteins. *Vitam. Horm.* **36:** 1–32.

Colberg-Poley, A.M., S.D. Voss, and P. Gruss. 1985. Expression of murine genes containing homeo box sequences during visceral and parietal endoderm differentiation of embryonal carcinoma stem cells. *Cold Spring Harbor Symp. Quant. Biol.* **50:** 285–290.

Demay, M. B., J. M. Gerardi, H. F. DeLuca, and H. M. Kronenberg. 1990. DNA sequences in the rat osteocalcin gene that bind the 1,25-dihydroxyvitamin D_3 receptor and confer responsiveness to 1,25-dihydroxyvitamin D_3. *Proc. Natl. Acad. Sci.* **87:** 369–373.

de Thé, H., A. Marchio, P. Tiollais, and A. Dejean. 1987. A novel steroid thyroid hormone receptor-related gene inappropriately expressed in human hepatocellular carcinoma. *Nature* **330:** 667–670.

————. 1989. Differential expression and ligand regulation of the retinoic acid receptor α and β genes. *EMBO J.* **8:** 429–433.

de Thé, H., C. Chomienne, M. Lanotte, L. Degos, and A. Dejean. 1990a. The t(15;17) translocation of actue promyelocytic leukaemia fuses the retinoic acid receptor α gene to a novel transcribed locus. *Nature* **347:** 558–561.

de Thé, H., M. Vivanco-Ruiz, P. Tiollais, H. Stunnenberg, and A. Dejean. 1990b. Identification of a retinoic acid responsive element in the retinoic acid receptor β receptor gene. *Nature* **343:** 177–180.

de Thé, H., C. Lavau, A. Marchio, C. Chomienne, L. Degos, and A. Dejean. 1991. The *myl-RARa* fusion mRNA generated by the t(15;17) translocation in acute promyelocytic leukemia encodes a functionally altered retinoic acid receptor. *Cell* **66:** 675–684.

Diamond, M.I., J.N. Miner, S.K. Yoshinaga, and K.R. Yamamoto. 1990. Transcription factor interactions: Selectors of positive or negative regulation from a single DNA element. *Science* **249:** 1266–1272.

Dollé, P., E. Ruberte, P. Kastner, M. Petkovich, C.M. Stoner, L.J. Gudas, and P. Chambon. 1989. Differential expression of genes encoding α, β and γ retinoic acid receptors and CRABP in the developing limbs of the mouse. *Nature* **342:** 702–705.

Duester, G., M. L. Shean, M. S. McBride, and M. J. Stewart. 1991. Retinoic acid response element in the human alcohol dehydrogenase gene *ADH3*: Implications for regulation of retinoic acid synthesis. *Mol. Cell. Biol.* **11:** 1638–1646.

Durston, A.J., J.P.M. Timmermans, W.J. Hage, H.F.J. Kendriks, N.J. de Vries, M. Heideveld, and P.D. Nieuwkoop. 1989. Retinoic acid causes an anteroposterior transformation in the developing central nervous system. *Nature* **340:** 140–144.

Edwards, M.K.S. and M.W. McBurney. 1983. The concentration of retinoic acid determines the differentiated cell types formed by a teratocarcinoma cell line. *Dev. Biol.* **98:** 187–191.

Eichele, G. 1989. Retinoids and vertebrate limb pattern formation. *Trends Genet.* **5:** 246–251.

Eilers, M., D. Picard, K.R. Yamamoto, and J.M. Bishop. 1989. Chimaeras of Myc oncoprotein and steroid receptors cause hormone-dependent transformation of cells. *Nature* **340:** 66–68.

Espeseth, A.S., S.P. Murphy, and E. Linney. 1989. Retinoic acid receptor expression vector inhibits differentiation of F9 embryonal carcinoma cells. *Genes Dev.* **3:** 1647–1656.

Evans, R.M. 1988. The steroid and thyroid hormone receptor superfamily. *Science* **240:** 889–895.

Fuchs, E. and H. Green. 1981. Regulation of terminal differentiation of cultured human keratinocytes by vitamin A. *Cell* **25:** 617–625.

Giguere, V., E.S. Ong, R.M. Evans, and C.J. Tabin. 1989. Spatial and temporal expression of the retinoic acid receptor in the regenerating amphibian limb. *Nature* **337:**

566–569. (Addendum **341:** 80.)

Giguere, V., E.S. Ong, P. Segui, and R.M. Evans. 1987. Identification of a receptor for the morphogen retinoic acid. *Nature* **330:** 624–629.

Giguere, V., N. Yang, P. Segui, and R.M. Evans. 1988. Identification of a new class of steroid hormone receptors. *Nature* **331:** 91–94.

Giguere, V., S. Lyn, P. Yip, C.-H. Siu, and S. Amin. 1990a. Molecular cloning of cDNA encoding a second cellular retinoic acid-binding protein. *Proc. Natl. Acad. Sci.* **87:** 6233–6237.

Giguere, V., M. Shago, R. Zirngibl, P. Tate, J. Rossant, and S. Varmuza. 1990b. Identification of a novel isoform of the retinoic acid receptor γ expressed in the mouse embryo. *Mol. Cell. Biol.* **10:** 2335–2340.

Glass, C.K., O.V. Devary, and M.G. Rosenfeld. 1990. Multiple cell type-specific proteins differentially regulate target sequence recognition by the α retinoic acid receptor. *Cell* **63:** 729–738.

Green, S. and P. Chambon. 1987. Oestradiol induction of a glucocorticoid-responsive gene by a chimaeric receptor. *Nature* **325:** 75–78.

————. 1988. Nuclear receptors enhance our understanding of transcription regulation. *Trends Genet.* **4:** 309–314.

Green, S., P.Walter, V. Kumar, A. Krust, J.-M. Bornert, P. Argos, and P. Chambon. 1986. Human oestrogen receptor cDNA: Sequence, expression and homology to v-*erb*-A. *Nature* **320:** 134–139.

Hamada, K., S.L. Gleason, B.-Z., Levi, S. Hirschfeld, E. Apopela, and K. Ozato. 1989. H-2RIIBP, a member of the nuclear hormone receptor superfamily that binds to both the regulatory element of major histocompatibility class I genes and the estrogen response element. *Proc. Natl. Acad. Sci.* **86:** 8289–8293.

Haussler, M.R., J.F. Myrtle, and A.W. Norman. 1968. The association of a metabolite of vitamin D_3 with intestinal mucosa chromatin, *in vivo. J. Biol. Chem.* **243:** 4055–4064.

Haussler, M., N. Sidell, M. Kelly, C. Donaldson, A. Altman, and D. Mangelsdorf. 1983. Specific high-affinity binding and biologic action of retinoic acid in human neuroblastoma cell lines. *Proc. Natl. Acad. Sci.* **80:** 5525–5529.

Haussler, M.R., C.A. Donaldson, M.A. Kelly, D.J. Mangelsdorf, G.T. Bowden, W.J. Meinke, F.L. Meyskens, and N. Sidell. 1984. Identification and quantitation of intracellular retinol and retinoic acid binding proteins in cultured cells. *Biochim. Biophys. Acta* **803:** 54–62.

Herschman, H.R. 1989. Extracellular signals, transcriptional responses and cellular specificity. *Trends Biochem. Sci.* **14:** 455–458.

Heyman, R.A., D.J. Mangelsdorf, J.A. Dyck, R.B. Stein, G. Eichele, R.M. Evans, and C. Thaller. 1992. 9-*cis* retinoic acid is a high affinity ligand for the retinoid X receptor. *Cell* **68:** 397–406.

Hollenberg, S.M., C. Weinberger, E.S. Ong., G. Cerelli, A. Oro, R. Lebo, E.B. Thompson, M.G. Rosenfeld, and R.M. Evans. 1985. Primary structure and expression of a functional human glucocorticoid receptor cDNA. *Nature* **318:** 635–641.

Hornbruch, A. and L. Wolpert. 1986. Positional signalling by Hensen's node when grafted to the chick limb bud. *J. Embryol. Exp. Morphol..* **94:** 257–265.

Huang, M.E., Y.C. Ye, S.R. Chen, J.R. Chai, J.X. Lu, L. Zhoa., L.J. Gu, and Z.Y. Wang. 1988. Use of all-*trans* retinoic acid in the treatment of acute promyelocytic leukemia. *Blood* **72:** 567–572.

Ishikawa, T., K. Umesono, D.J. Mangelsdorf, H. Aburatani, B.Z. Stanger, Y. Shibasaki, M. Imawari, R.M. Evans, and F. Takaku. 1990. A functional retinoic acid receptor encoded by the gene on human chromosome 12. *Mol. Endocrinol.* **4:** 837–844.

Izumo, S. and V. Mahdavi. 1988. Thyroid hormone receptor α isoforms generated by alternative splicing differentially activate myosin HC gene expression. *Nature* **334:** 539–542.

Jetten, A.M., K. Anderson, M.A. Deas, H. Kaagechika, R. Lotan, J.I. Rearick, and K. Shudo. 1987. New benzoic acid derivatives with retinoic activity: Lack of direct correlation between biological activity and binding to cellular retinoic acid binding protein. *Cancer Res.* **47:** 3523–3527.

Jonat, C., H.J. Rahmsdorf, K.-K. Park, A.C.B. Cato, S. Gebel, H. Ponta, and P. Herrlich. 1990. Antitumor promotin and antiinflammation: Down-modulation of AP-1 (fos/jun) activity by glucocorticoid hormone. *Cell* **62:** 1189–1204.

Kakizuka, A., W.H. Miller, Jr., K. Umesono, R.P. Warrell, Jr., S.R. Frankel, V.V.V.S. Murty, E. Dmitrovsky, and R.M. Evans. 1991. Chromosomal translocation t(15;17) in human acute promyelocytic leukemia fuses RARα with a novel putative transcription factor, PML. *Cell* **66:** 663–674.

Kastner, P., A. Krust, C. Mendelsohn, J.M. Garnier, A. Zelent, P. Leroy, A. Staub, and P. Chambon. 1990. Murine isoforms of retinoic acid receptor γ with specific patterns of expression. *Proc. Natl. Acad. Sci.* **87:** 2700–2704.

Kliewer, S.A., K. Umesono, D.J. Mangelsdorf, and R.M. Evans. 1992a. Retinoid X receptor interacts with nuclear receptors in retinoic acid, thyroid hormone and vitamin D signaling. *Nature* **355:** 446–449.

Kliewer, S.A., K. Umesono, R. Heyman, D.J. Mangelsdorf, J.A. Dyck, and R.M. Evans. 1992b. Retinoid X receptor-COUP-TF interactions modulate retinoic acid signaling. *Proc. Natl. Acad. Sci.* **89:** 1448–1452.

Krust, A., P. Kastner, M. Petkovich, A. Zelent, and P. Chambon. 1989. A third human retinoic acid receptor, hRAR-γ. *Proc. Natl. Acad. Sci.* **86:** 5310–5314.

LaRosa, G.J. and L.J. Gudas. 1988. Early retinoic acid-induced F9 teratocarcinoma stem cell gene ERA-1: Alternate splicing creates transcripts for a homeobox-containing protein and one lacking the homeobox. *Mol. Cell. Biol.* **8:** 3906–3917.

Lazar, M.A., R.A. Hodin, D.S. Darling, and W.W. Chin. 1989. A novel member of the thyroid/steroid hormone receptor family is encoded by the opposite strand of the rat c-*erbAa* transcriptional unit. *Mol. Cell. Biol.* **9:** 1128–1136.

Leid, M., P. Kastner, R. Lyons, H. Nakshatri, M. Saunders, T. Zacharewski, J.-Y. Chen, A. Staub, J.-M. Garnier, S. Mader, and P. Chambon. 1992. Purification, cloning, and RXR identity of the HeLa cell factor with which RAR or TR heterodimerizes to bind target sequences efficiently. *Cell* **68:** 377–395.

Levin, A.A., L.J. Sturzenbecker, S. Kazmer, T. Bosakowski, C. Huselton, G. Allenby, J. Speck, C. Kratzeisen, M. Rosenberger, A. Lovey, and J.F. Grippo. 1992. 9-*cis* Retinoic acid stereoisomer binds and activates the nuclear receptor RXRα. *Nature* **355:** 359–361.

Lewis, J. 1989. Genes and segmentation. *Nature* **341:** 382–383.

Liao, J., K. Ozono, T. Sone, D. P. McDonnell, and J. W. Pike. 1990. Vitamin D receptor interaction with specific DNA requires a nuclear protein and 1,25-dihydroxyvitamin D_3. *Proc. Natl. Acad. Sci.* **87:** 9751–9755.

Longo, L., P.P. Pandolfi, A. Biondi, A. Rambaldi, A. Mencarelli, F. Lo Coco, D. Diverio, L. Pegoraro, G. Avanzi, A. Tabilio, D. Xangrilli, M. Alcalay, E. Donti, F. Grignani, and P.G. Pelicci. 1990. Rearrangements and aberrant expression of the retinoic acid receptor α gene in acute promyelocytic leukemias. *J. Exp. Med.* **172:** 1571–1575.

Lucibello, F.C., E.P. Slater, K.U. Jooss, M. Beato, and R. Müller. 1990. Mutual transrepression of fos and the glucocorticoid receptor: Involvement of a functional domain in fos which is absent in fosB. *EMBO J.* **9:** 2827–2834.

Maden, M. 1982. Vitamin A and pattern formation in the regenerating limb. *Nature* **295**: 672–675.

———. 1985. Retinoids and the control of pattern in limb development and regeneration. *Trends Genet.* **1**: 103–107.

Maden, M., D.E. Ong, D. Summerbell, and F. Chytil. 1988. Spatial distribution of cellular protein binding to retinoic acid in the chick limb bud. *Nature* **335**: 733–735.

Mangelsdorf, D.J., E.S. Ong, J.A. Dyck, and R.M. Evans. 1990. Nuclear receptor that identifies a novel retinoic acid response pathway. *Nature* **345**: 224–229.

Mangelsdorf, D.J., K. Umesono, S.A. Kliewer, U. Borgmeyer, E.S. Ong, and R.M. Evans. 1991. A direct repeat in the cellular retinol-binding protein type II gene confers differential regulation by RXR and RAR. *Cell* **66**: 555–561.

Mangelsdorf, D.J., U. Borgmeyer, R.A. Heyman, J.Y. Zhou, E.S. Ong, A.E. Oro, A. Kakizuka, and R.M. Evans. 1992. Characterization of three RXR genes that mediate the action of 9-*cis* retinoic acid. *Genes Dev.* **6**: 329–344.

McCollum, E.V. and M. Davis. 1913. The necessity of certain lipins in the diet during growth. *J. Biol. Chem.* **15**: 167–175.

Milbrandt, J. 1987. A nerve growth factor-induced gene encodes a possible transcriptional regulatory factor. *Science* **238**: 797–799.

Miyajima, N., R. Horiuchi, Y. Shibuya, S. Fukushige, K. Matsubara, K. Toyoshima, and T. Yamamoto. 1989. Two *erbA* homologs encoding proteins with different T_3 binding capacities are transcribed from opposite DNA strands of the same genetic locus. *Cell* **57**: 31–39.

Miyajima, N., Y. Kadowaki, S. Fukushige, S. Shimizu, K. Semba, Y. Yamanashi, K. Matsubara, K. Toyoshima, and T. Yamamoto. 1988. Identification of two novel members of *erbA* superfamily by molecular cloning: The gene products of the two are highly related to each other. *Nucleic Acids Res.* **16**: 11057–11074.

Muños-Cánoves, P., D. P. Vik, and B. F. Tack. 1990. Mapping of a retinoic acid responsive element in the promoter region of the complement factor H gene. *J. Biol. Chem.* **265**: 20065–20068.

Murphy, P., D.R. Davidson, and R.E. Hill. 1989. Segment-specific expression of a homeobox-containing gene in the mouse hindbrain. *Nature* **341**: 156–159.

Murray, M. B. and H. C. Towle. 1989. Identification of nuclear factors that enhance binding of the thyroid hormone receptor to a thyroid hormone response element. *Mol. Endocrinol.* **3**: 1434–1442.

Noda, M., R. L. Vogel, A. M. Craig, J. Prahl, H. F. DeLuca, and D. T. Denhardt. 1990. Identification of a DNA sequence responsible for binding of the 1,25-dihydroxyvitamin D_3 receptor and 1,25-dihydroxyvitamin D_3 enhancement of mouse secreted phosphoprotein 1 (*Spp-1* or osteopontin) gene expression. *Proc. Natl. Acad. Sci.* **87**: 9995–9999.

Noji, S., T. Yamaai, E. Koyama, T. Nohno, and S. Taniguchi. 1989. Spatial and temporal expression pattern of retinoic acid receptor genes during mouse bone development. *FEBS Lett.* **257**: 93–96.

Noji, S., T. Nohno, E. Koyama, K. Muto, K. Ohyama, Y. Aoki, K. Tamura, K. Osugi, H. Ide, S. Taniguchi, and T. Saito. 1991. Retinoic acid induces polarizing activity but is unlikely to be a morphogen in the chick limb bud. *Nature* **350**: 83–86.

Oliver, G., E.M. DeRobertis, L. Wolpert, and C. Tickle. 1990. Expression of a homeobox gene in the chick wing bud following application of retinoic acid and grafts of polarizing region tissue. *EMBO J.* **9**:3093–3099.

Ong, D.E. and F. Chytil. 1978. Cellular retinoic acid-binding protein from rat testis. *J. Biol. Chem.* **253**: 4551–4554.

————. 1983. Vitamin A and cancer. *Vitam. Horm.* **40:** 105–144.

Ong, D.E., B. Kakkad, and P.N. MacDonald. 1987. Acyl-CoA-independent esterification of retinol bound to cellular retinol-binding protein (type II) by microsomes from rat small intestine. *J. Biol. Chem.* **262:** 2729–2736.

Oro, A.E., M. McKeown, and R.M. Evans. 1990. Relationship between the product of the *Drosophila ultraspiracle* locus and the vertebrate retinoid X receptor. *Nature* **347:** 298–301.

————. 1992. The *Drosophila* nuclear receptors: New insight into the actions of nuclear receptors in development. *Curr. Opin. Genet. Dev.* **2:** 269–274.

Osborne, T.B. and L.B. Mendel. 1913. The relation of growth to the chemical constituents of the diet. *J. Biol. Chem.* **15:** 311–326.

Osumi-Yamashita, N., S. Noji, T. Nohno, E. Koyama, H. Doi, K. Eto, and S. Taniguchi. 1990. Expression of retinoic acid receptor genes in neural crest-derived cells during mouse facial development. *FEBS Lett.* **264:** 71–74.

Ozono, K., J. Liao, S. A. Kerner, R. A. Scott, and J. W. Pike. 1991. The vitamin D-responsive element in the human osteocalcin gene. *J. Biol. Chem.* **265:** 21881–21888.

Perez-Castro, A.V., L.E. Toth-Rogler, L. Wei, and M. Chi Nguyen-Huu. 1989. Spatial and temporal pattern of expression of the cellular retinoic acid-binding protein and the cellular retinol-binding protein during mouse embryogenesis. *Proc. Natl. Acad. Sci.* **86:** 8813–8817.

Petkovich, M., N.J. Brand, A. Krust, and P. Chambon. 1987. A human retinoic acid receptor which belongs to the family of nuclear receptors. *Nature* **330:** 444–450.

Petty, K. J., B. Desvergne, T. Mitsuhashi, and V.M. Nikodem. 1990. Identification of a thyroid hormone response element in the malic enzyme gene. *J. Biol. Chem.* **265:** 7395–7400.

Picard, D., S.J. Salser, and K.R. Yamamoto. 1988. A movable and regulable inactivation function within the steroid binding domain of the glucocorticoid receptor. *Cell* **54:** 1073–1080.

Pratt, M.A.C., J. Kralova, and M.W. McBurney. 1990. A dominant negative mutation of the retinoic acid receptor gene in a retinoic acid-nonresponsive embryonal carcinoma cell. *Mol. Cell. Biol.* **10:** 6445–6453.

Ragsdale, C.W., Jr., M. Petkovich, P.B. Gates, P. Chambon, and J.P. Brockes. 1989. Identification of a novel retinoic acid receptor in regenerative tissues of the newt. *Nature* **341:** 654–657.

Rando, R.R. 1990. The chemistry of vitamin A and vision. *Angew. Chem. Int. Ed. Engl.* **29:** 461–480.

Rees, J.L., A.K. Daly, and C.P.F. Redfern. 1989. Differential expression of the α and β retinoic acid receptors in tissues of the rat. *Biochem. J.* **259:** 917–919.

Rossant, J., R. Zirngibl, D. Cado, M. Shago, and V. Giguere. 1991. Expression of a retinoic acid-response element-*hsplacZ* transgene defines specific domains of transcriptional activity during mouse embryogenesis. *Genes Dev.* **5:** 1333–1344.

Rottman, J.N., R.L. Widom, B. Nadal-Ginard, V. Mahdavi, and S.K. Karathanasis. 1991. A retinoic acid responsive element in the apolipoprotein AI gene distinguishes between two different retinoic acid response pathways. *Mol. Cell. Biol.* **11:** 3814–3820.

Rowe, A., N.S.C. Eager, and P.M. Brickell. 1991. A member of the RXR nuclear receptor family is expressed in neural-crest-derived cells of the developing peripheral nervous system. *Development* **111:** 771–778.

Ruberte, E., P. Dolle, A. Krust, A. Zelent, G. Morriss-Kay, and P. Chambon. 1990. Specific spatial and temporal distribution of retinoic acid receptor gamma transcripts during mouse embryogenesis. *Development* **108:** 213–222.

Sap, J., A. Muños, J. Schmitt, H. Stunnenberg, and B. Vennström. 1989. Repression of transcription mediated at a thyroid hormone response element by the v-*erb-A* oncogene product. *Nature* **340:** 242–244.

Sap, J., A. Muñoz, K. Damm, Y. Goldberg, J. Ghysdael, A. Leutz, H. Beug, and B. Vennström. 1986. The c-*erb-A* protein is a high-affinity receptor for thyroid hormone. *Nature* **324:** 635–640.

Schüle, R., K. Umesono, D.J. Mangelsdorf, J. Bolado, J.W. Pike, and R.M. Evans. 1990a. Jun-fos and receptors for vitamins A and D recognize a common response element in the human oestocalcin gene. *Cell* **61:** 497–504.

Schüle, R., P. Rangarajan, S. Kliewer, L.J. Ransone, J. Bolado, N. Yang, I.M. Verma, and R.M. Evans. 1990b. Functional antagonism between oncoprotein c-*jun* and the glucocorticoid receptor. *Cell* **62:** 1217–1226.

Shubeita, H.E., J.F. Sambrook, and A.M. McCormick. 1987. Molecular cloning and analysis of functional cDNA and genomic clones encoding bovine cellular retinoic acid-binding protein. *Proc. Natl. Acad. Sci.* **84:**5645–5649.

Simeone, A., D. Acampora, L. Arcioni, P.W. Andrews, E. Boncinelli, and F. Mavillo. 1990. Sequential activation of *HOX2* homeobox genes by retinoic acid in human embryonal carcinoma cells. *Nature* **346:** 763–766.

Sive, H.L., B.W. Draper, R.M. Harland, and H. Weintraub. 1990. Identification of a retinoic acid-sensitive period during primary axis formation in *Xenopus laevis*. *Genes Dev.* **4:** 932–942.

Slack, J.M.W. 1987. Morphogenetic gradients-past and present. *Trends Biochem. Sci.* **12:** 200–204.

Smith, S.M. and G. Eichele. 1991. Temporal and regional differences in the expression pattern of distinct retinoic acid receptor-β transcripts in the chick embryo. *Development* **111:** 245–252.

Sporn, M.B., A.B. Roberts, and D.S. Goodman, eds. 1984. *The retinoids*, vol. 1 and 2. Academic Press, New York.

Strickland, S. and V. Mahdavi. 1978. The induction of differentiation in teratocarcinoma stem cells by retinoic acid. *Cell* **15:** 393–403.

Sucov, H.M., K.K. Murakami, and R.M. Evans. 1990. Characterization of an autoregulated response element in the mouse retinoic acid receptor type β gene. *Proc. Natl. Acad. Sci.* **87:** 5392–5396.

Summerbell, D. 1983. The effect of local application of retinoic acid to the anterior margin of the developing chick limb. *J. Embryol. Exp. Morphol.* **78:** 269–289.

Tabin, C. J. 1991. Retinoids, homeoboxes, and growth factors: Toward molecular models for limb development. *Cell* **66:** 199–217.

Tamura, K., H. Kagechika, Y. Hashimoto, K. Shudo, K. Ohsugi, and H. Ide. 1990. Synthetic retinoids, retinobenzoic acids, Am80, Am580 and Ch55 regulate morphogenesis in chick limb bud. *Cell Differ. Dev.* **32:** 17–26.

Thaller, C. and G. Eichele. 1987. Identification and spatial distribution of retinoids in the developing chick limb bud. *Nature* **327:** 625–628.

———. 1990. Isolation of 3,4-didehydroretinoic acid, a novel morphogenetic signal in the chick wing bud. *Nature* **345:** 815–819.

Thompson, C.C. and R.M. Evans. 1989. *trans*-Activation by thyroid hormone receptors: Functional parallels with steroid hormone receptors. *Proc. Natl. Acad. Sci.* **86:** 3494–3498.

Tickle, C., B.M. Alberts, L. Wolpert, and J. Lee. 1982. Local application of retinoic acid to the limb bud mimics the action of the polarising region. *Nature* **296:** 564–565.

Umesono, K., K.K. Murakami, C.C. Thompson, and R.M. Evans. 1991. Direct repeats as selective response elements for the thyroid hormone, retinoic acid, and vitamin D_3 receptors. *Cell* **65:** 1255–1266.

Umesono, K., V. Giguere, C.K. Glass, M.G. Rosenfeld, and R.M. Evans. 1988. Retinoic acid and thyroid hormone induce gene expression through a common responsive element. *Nature* **336:** 262–265.

Wagner, M., C. Thaller, T. Jessell, and G. Eichele. 1990. Polarizing activity and retinoid synthesis in the floor plate of the neural tube. *Nature* **345:** 819–822.

Wald, G. 1968. The molecular basis of visual excitation. *Nature* **219:** 800–807.

Wanek, N., D.M. Gardiner, K. Muneoka, and S.V. Bryant. 1991. Conversion by retinoic acid of anterior cells into ZPA cells in the chick wing bud. *Nature* **350:** 81–83.

Wang, L.-H., S.Y. Tsai, R.G. Cook, W.G. Beattie, M.-J. Tsai, and B.W. O'Malley. 1989. COUP transcription factor is a member of the steroid receptor superfamily. *Nature* **340:** 163–166.

Wei, L.-N., J.R. Mertz, D.S. Goodman, and M. Chi Nguyen-Huu. 1987. Cellular retinoic acid- and cellular retinol-binding proteins: Complementary deoxyribonucleic acid cloning, chromosomal assignment, and tissue specific expression. *Mol. Endocrinol.* **1:** 526–538.

Weinberger, C., C.C. Thompson, E.S. Ong, R. Lebo, D.J. Gruol, and R.M. Evans. 1986. The c-*erb*-A gene encodes a thyroid hormone receptor. *Nature* **324:** 641–646.

Wilkinson, D.G., S. Bhatt, M. Cook, E. Boncinelli, and R. Krumlauf. 1989. Segmental expression of Hox-2 homeobox-containing genes in the developing mouse hindbrain. *Nature* **341:** 405–409.

Yang, N., D.J. Mangelsdorf, R. Schüle, and R.M. Evans. 1991. Characterization of DNA-binding and retinoic acid binding properties of retinoic acid receptor. *Proc. Natl. Acad. Sci.* **88:** 3559–3563..

Yang-yen, H.-F., J.-C. Chambard, Y.-L. Sun, T. Smeal, T.J. Schmidt, J. Drouin, and M. Karin. 1990. Transcriptional interference between c-*jun* and the glucocorticoid receptor: Mutual inhibition of DNA binding due to direct protein-protein interaction. *Cell* **62:** 1205–1215.

Yu, V.C., C. Delsert, B. Andersen, J.M. Holloway, O. V. Devary, A.M. Naar, S.Y. Kim, J.M. Boutin, C.K. Glass, and M.G. Rosenfeld. 1991. RXRβ: A coregulator that enhances binding of retinoic acid, thyroid hormone, and vitamin D receptors to their cognate response elements. *Cell* **67:** 1251–1266.

Zelent, A., A. Krust, M. Petkovich, P. Kastner, and P. Chambon. 1989. Cloning of murine α and β retinoic acid receptors γ and a novel receptor predominantly expressed in skin. *Nature* **339:** 714–717.

Zenke, M., A. Muñoz, J. Sap, B. Vennström, and H. Beug. 1990. V-*erbA* oncogene activation entails the loss of hormone-dependent regulator activity of c-*erbA*. *Cell* **61:** 1035–1049.

Zhang, X., B. Hoffmann, P.B. Tran, G. Graupner, and M. Pfahl. 1992. Retinoid X receptor is an auxiliary protein for thyroid hormone and retinoic acid receptors. *Nature* **355:** 441–446.

43

Combinatorial Regulation at a Mammalian Composite Response Element

Keith R. Yamamoto, David Pearce,
Jay Thomas, and Jeffrey N. Miner
Department of Biochemistry and Biophysics
PIBS Biochemistry and Molecular Biology Program
University of California
San Francisco, California 94143-0448

OVERVIEW

Transcriptional regulators from different factor families can interact at composite response elements to effect combinatorial control. We describe studies of plfG, a composite element at which the glucocorticoid receptor and AP-1 factors interact and either enhance or repress transcription, depending on the subunit composition of AP-1. Three general conclusions emerge: (1) Very closely related members of a regulatory factor family can be functionally distinguished at a composite element; (2) discrete "composite specificity domains" can be localized within a particular factor that distinguish it from other members of the same family in the context of a given element and cell type; and (3) the DNA sequence to which a factor binds may affect factor conformation, in turn serving as a determinant of subsequent protein-protein interactions.

INTRODUCTION

The positions and rates of transcription initiation by RNA polymerase II are specified in part by two classes of DNA sequence elements: *promoters*, which influence the composition and activity of the basal transcription machinery, and *response elements*, which bind protein factors that sense physiological signals and modulate positively or negatively the efficiency of initiation from linked promoters; response elements and promoters can be interdigitated or widely separated on the DNA. In this chapter, we consider the implications of two generalities that have emerged from studies of response elements and the regulatory

Transcriptional Regulation.
Copyright 1992 Cold Spring Harbor Laboratory Press 0-87969-410-6/92 $3 + 00

factors that bind to them. First, response elements are commonly aggregates of recognition sequences for multiple sequence-specific regulatory factors. In principle, such clustered binding sites for regulatory factors could serve as junction points for *combinatorial regulation*, at which factors from distinct signaling pathways could communicate to produce patterns of regulation distinct from the actions of the individual factors and from the simple sum of their individual effects. Such sites are termed *composite response elements* (Diamond et al. 1990; Miner and Yamamoto 1991). Second, the sequence-specific regulatory factors are encoded by multigene families in which the family members recognize common or closely related DNA response elements with qualitatively or even quantitatively similar regulatory consequences. Taken at face value, this implies that closely related family members might be redundant. We consider the possibility that they might be functionally distinct in the context of composite response elements.

The glucocorticoid receptor (GR) is a member of the nuclear receptor superfamily (Evans 1988; Amero et al. 1992). Upon association with hormonal ligands, the receptor migrates to the cell nucleus, binds to glucocorticoid response elements (GREs) through Cys_2-Cys_2 zinc fingers (Luisi et al. 1991; Schmidt and Berg; Wright; both this volume), and enhances or represses transcription in a hormone-dependent, cell-type- and promoter-specific fashion. One well-characterized class of GREs comprises imperfect palindromes bearing hexamer half-sites separated by three base pairs (Evans 1988; Beato 1989). At such elements, termed "simple" GREs, GR alone is sufficient to confer hormonal regulation, and it effects enhancement but not repression of transcription (Godowski et al. 1988; Miner et al. 1991). Hence, when the receptor acts at a simple GRE, its DNA-binding domain serves solely to bring its activation domain close to the promoter to be regulated (Ptashne 1988).

The receptors for four different steroid hormones: glucocorticoid, mineralocorticoid, progesterone, and androgen, all bind to and enhance transcription from simple GREs (Fig. 1) (Chandler et al. 1983; Arriza et al. 1987; Otten et al. 1988), whereas it is clear that these hormones evoke physiological responses that are completely distinct. For example, mineralocorticoids and glucocorticoids can elicit opposing effects on ion transport within a single tissue (Bastl et al. 1989; Turnamian and Binder 1989) or even within a single cell type or individual cell (Joels and De Kloet 1990). Therefore, the specificity and complexity of hormone effects must derive by other means. This inferred requirement for additional determinants of hormonal regulation can be illustrated in another way: The glucocorticoid receptor is expressed and functional in virtually all mammalian cell types, but a distinct combination of genes is gluco-

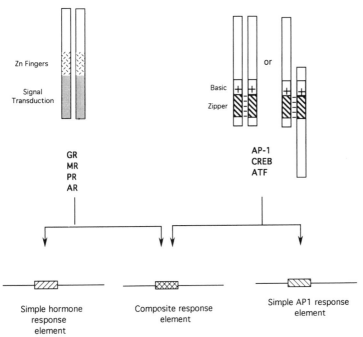

Figure 1 Steroid receptors and AP-1 factors function separately at their respective response elements and interact at cognate composite response elements. Diagrams of the nuclear receptor and bZIP factors are shown; simple bZIP factors form obligate dimers through their zipper domains and can be either homodimeric or heterodimeric. Representative members of the steroid receptor subfamily (GR, glucocorticoid receptor; MR, mineralocorticoid receptor; PR, progesterone receptor; AR, androgen receptor) and the AP-1 subfamily (AP-1, activator protein 1; CREB, cAMP response element binding protein; ATF, activating transcription factor) are listed below their respective superfamilies. In each case, these subfamily factors bind independently to their cognate simple response elements and enhance transcription. In addition, particular members within each subfamily can interact via protein-protein and protein-DNA interactions at composite response elements to produce regulatory effects that are distinct from those conferred by one factor alone at simple elements. In particular, subfamily members with similar activities at a simple response element can display strikingly different activities at a composite response element. They also provide an explicit mechanism for cross talk between separate signal transduction pathways. (Reprinted, with permission, from Miner and Yamamoto 1991.)

corticoid-regulated in each cell type. Thus, the receptor alone is not sufficient to define its spectrum of activities. In principle, both types of specificity might be accomplished at composite response elements, where in contrast to the situation at simple elements, receptor action is contingent on communication between receptor and nonreceptor factors. Within such a framework, receptors that are indistinguishable at simple response elements might function in strikingly distinct ways.

Here we describe recent studies of a composite response element, plfG, which normally resides within the regulatory region of the proliferin gene. Mordacq and Linzer (1989) demonstrated that proliferin expression is regulated by AP-1, which mediates responses to the phorbol ester TPA, and by GR, which footprinted a 25-bp sequence upstream of the gene. When the footprinted sequence, denoted plfG, was fused to a minimal heterologous promoter, it behaved as a composite response element: GR bound but was inactive in the absence of co-occupying AP-1; in the presence of AP-1, the receptor either enhanced or repressed transcription, depending on the subunit composition of AP-1 (Diamond et al. 1990).

AP-1 factors represent a second family of sequence-specific regulatory proteins. They function as obligate dimers that recognize specific AP-1 consensus sites through "basic zipper" (bZIP) DNA-binding motifs (Kerppola and Curtan 1991; Curran and Vogt; McKnight; both this volume). Each AP-1 family member carries a bZIP region that is closely homologous to either c-Jun or c-Fos, the two prototype representatives of the family (Kerppola and Curran 1991); c-Jun-like proteins generally can homodimerize or heterodimerize across the AP-1 family, whereas c-Fos-like proteins heterodimerize with the Jun subclass, but do not dimerize within the Fos subclass (Vogt and Bos 1990; O'Shea et al. 1992). The various AP-1 dimers all recognize, albeit with different affinities, the AP-1 consensus-binding site (Fig. 1) and can stimulate, albeit with different efficiencies, initiation from nearby promoters (Abate et al. 1991; Kerppola and Curran 1991).

Are the individual members of regulatory gene families, in particular those most closely related, functionally distinct within the cell or are they merely redundant? In this chapter, we first summarize our approach to this question in the context of AP-1 and steroid receptor actions at plfG. Second, we describe the identification of specific factor domains that determine family member selectivity at composite elements. Third, we consider the general features of molecular interactions that specify combinatorial regulation. Our findings imply that the oligomerization state of a transcriptional regulator can be specifically modulated and that the precise DNA sequence encountered by a DNA-binding factor plays a role in determining its regulatory fate. We suggest that regulators may contain multiple "composite specificity domains," which are putative interactive surfaces that integrate context information and generate combinatorial control.

A COMPOSITE ELEMENT DISCRIMINATES MEMBERS
OF TWO DIFFERENT FACTOR FAMILIES

A striking characteristic of the plfG composite element is its capacity to confer either positive or negative regulation by glucocorticoids (Diamond et al. 1990). This was first observed as a cell-specificity phenomenon: The hormone-receptor complex repressed plfG-linked reporter gene expression in CV-1 cells, enhanced its expression in HeLa cells, and had no effect in F9 cells; in contrast, a simple GRE conferred hormone-dependent enhancement in all cell lines tested. By cotransfection of expression vectors for c-Jun, c-Fos, or both, Diamond et al. (1990) showed that the *ratio* of intracellular c-Jun and c-Fos could specify the direction of hormonal regulation from plfG (but not from a simple GRE): If the AP-1 bound at plfG was composed predominantly of c-Jun homodimers, glucocorticoids enhanced transcription from plfG; if instead AP-1 was predominantly c-Jun/c-Fos heterodimers, GR repressed transcription; finally, plfG-linked promoters in the absence of AP-1 were inactive and unaffected by glucocorticoids.

Mutational studies implied that the DNA-binding domains, and presumably DNA binding, both by the receptor and by AP-1 were essential for regulation at plfG; moreover, chemical cross-linking and coimmunoprecipitation experiments demonstrated a specific protein-protein interaction between GR and c-Jun (Diamond et al. 1990). These findings suggested that the receptor might bind to plfG in the absence of AP-1 (indeed, GR binds with similar affinity to plfG and to a simple GRE in vitro; S.-T. Jeng and K.R. Yamamoto, unpubl.), but that it might function only in conjunction with bound AP-1 (Fig. 1) and that it might sense AP-1 subunit composition by direct interaction. Furthermore, related family members, in this case c-Jun and c-Fos, which display qualitatively similar activities when dimerized with c-Jun at a simple AP-1 site (Vogt and Bos 1990; Abate et al. 1991; Kerppola and Curran 1991), were shown to be distinct with respect to their specification of glucocorticoid regulation at plfG (Miner and Yamamoto 1991; Miner et al. 1991).

The finding that qualitative differences between AP-1 family members could be detected at plfG prompted us to test whether this same element might also distinguish steroid receptors that behave similarly at simple GREs. Specifically, we compared GR with the mineralocorticoid receptor (MR); they share 94% identity in their zinc finger DNA-binding domains and 60% identity in their hormone-binding regions. Not surprisingly, both receptors bind to and enhance transcription from simple GREs, and their ligand-binding specificities are overlapping (both respond to corticosterone, an important physiological regulator), albeit nonidentical (Arriza et al. 1987; Pearce and Yamamoto 1993). However, despite these close similarities, the two receptors mediate different physiological effects, even evoking opposing regulatory effects in the same cell type (Bastl et al. 1989; Turnamian and Binder 1989; Joels and De Kloet 1990; Laplace et al. 1992).

Pearce and Yamamoto (1993) compared the activities of MR and GR on plfG3:CAT, a reporter bearing three tandem plfG composite elements fused to a minimal promoter driving CAT. At a 10:1 ratio of cotrans-fected c-Fos:c-Jun expression vectors in F9 cells (which lack endogenous AP1 activity), MR had no effect on plfG3:CAT, whereas GR strongly repressed transcription. Thus, the composite element was GR-specific under these conditions. In contrast, both MR and GR enhanced transcrip-tion from a simple GRE in these cells, and their activities at that locus were unaffected by transfection of c-Fos and c-Jun.

COMPOSITE SPECIFICITY DOMAINS

To search for a discrete polypeptide region responsible for the differen-tial behavior of these receptors, GR-MR chimeras were constructed and introduced into F9 cells under conditions in which GR but not MR represses plfG3:CAT (Pearce and Yamamoto 1993). We found that chimeras containing a segment of GR upstream of its DNA-binding domain (aa 105–440) were competent for repression at plfG (Fig. 2). Notably, this GR amino-terminal region conferred repression activity on chimeras bearing either the MR or GR DNA-binding domains, consistent with the view that both MR and GR occupy the composite element, but that only GR functions under these conditions. In parallel experiments, both intact MR and amino-terminal deletion mutants of MR failed to repress under these conditions, demonstrating that the MR amino terminus does not inhibit a cryptic repressing function residing elsewhere on MR (Fig. 2B). Finally, fusions of the MR amino terminus to the GR DNA- and ligand-binding domains (MR 604.GR) did not repress, in-dicating that GR does not contain additional repression domains outside the amino-terminal region. We conclude that the plfG composite element indeed distinguishes members of the steroid receptor subfamily and that we can define a "composite specificity domain" within the GR amino-terminal segment that discriminates GR from MR with respect to repres-sion of c-Jun/c-Fos activity at plfG in F9 cells (Pearce and Yamamoto 1993).

The composite specificity domain identified in our experiments resides within a region that heretofore has not been correlated with a unique function. The amino-terminal segments of the nuclear receptor family are highly divergent in size and sequence, and even the most

A

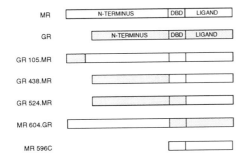

B

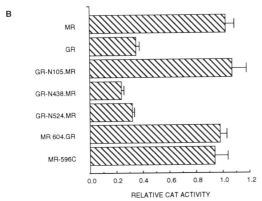

Figure 2 A composite specificity domain within GR that selectively confers repression of c-Jun/c-Fos action at plfG. GR sequences were fused in frame at homologous sites to MR sequences and expressed under control of the RSV enhancer/promoter in transient transfection experiments. F9 cells were transfected with expression vectors for either MR, GR, or GR.MR chimeras as shown, together with plfG:CAT, c-Jun expression vector, an excess of c-Fos expression vector, and an internal control plasmid. Data are presented as CAT activities in the presence of 1 μM corticosterone, expressed relative to CAT activity in the absence of hormone, which is assigned a value of 1.0. (Reprinted, with permission, from Pearce and Yamamoto 1993.)

closely related receptors, such as MR and GR, display extensive differences in this region (Patel et al. 1989). In contrast, the DNA- and ligand-binding domains of the nuclear receptor superfamily likely evolved as a single unit from a common ancestor (Amero et al. 1992). Thus, we can speculate that these receptors may first have acquired the capacity to enhance transcription at simple elements, with specificity determined solely by DNA-binding characteristics. The subfamily now represented by GR, MR, PR, and AR may have been defined by a shift in DNA-binding specificity that separated their sequence recognition properties from those of other receptors such as estrogen receptor (ER), TR, and RAR. By this view, the capacity for combinatorial regulation might have been acquired only later, as the various family members became associated with novel amino-terminal exons that permitted communication with other factors at composite response elements. Such evolutionary alterations would vastly increase the regulatory diversity of these molecules.

Implicit in this scheme is the notion that other composite specificity domains, defining other novel surfaces for protein-protein interaction, would be detected in different experimental or physiological contexts. Such surfaces would not by necessity be limited to the amino-terminal segments of these receptors; indeed, preliminary results suggest that GR-mediated enhancement from plfG may be determined by a distinct composite specificity domain within or downstream from the zinc finger region (D. Pearce, unpubl.).

The same protein chimera strategy was used to identify composite specificity domains within AP-1 subunits (Miner and Yamamoto 1992). We first tested chimeras between c-Jun and c-Fos (Cohen and Curran 1990), as shown in Figure 3A. The expression vector for each chimera was cotransfected with a c-Jun expression vector into F9 cells; as ex-

Figure 3 A composite specificity domain within AP-1 that specifies distinct receptor functions at plfG. (*A*) Domains of c-Jun and c-Fos were exchanged as described previously (Cohen and Curran 1990); numbers below diagrams give positions of amino acid residues that define the borders of various domains. FFFJ (amino terminus + bZIP): c-Jun aa 317-334; c-Fos aa 1-199; JFFJ(bZIP): c-Jun aa 1-248 and 317-334; c-Fos aa 128-199; JJFJ (zipper): c-Jun aa 1-280 and 317-334; c-Fos aa 164-199. Intact c-Jun and c-Fos and the chimera were cloned into mammalian expression vectors (RSV and CMV) for transfection experiments. (*B*) Chimeric c-Jun and c-Fos proteins were tested for their effects on plfG:CAT expression, alone and together with receptor and hormone, in transfected F9 cells. Each chimera was cotransfected with PlfG:CAT, 6RGR expression plasmid, and a β-galactosidase expression vector as an internal control. Each reaction also contained additional c-Jun expression vector to provide a dimer partner for each listed construct. Dexamethasone was added where indicated (hatched bars) for 24 hr; solid bars lacked hormone; aliquots for each pair were taken from the same DNA precipitate. CAT activity was normalized to β-galactosidase activity and expressed as relative CAT activity. Each data point represents an average of four experiments. (Reprinted, with permission, from Miner and Yamamoto 1992.)

pected, all stimulated transcription both from a "simple" consensus AP-1 site and from plfG in the absence of GR. When GR acted at plfG3 in conjunction with either c-Jun/c-Fos, c-Jun/FFFJ, or c-Jun/JFFJ heterodimers (see diagrams in Figs. 3A), transcription was repressed, suggesting that the amino- and carboxy-terminal regions of c-Jun are not sufficient as determinants of positive glucocorticoid regulation under these conditions. However, when the basic region of c-Jun replaced that of c-Fos (as in JJFJ), the receptor functioned as an activator. Thus, in the

A

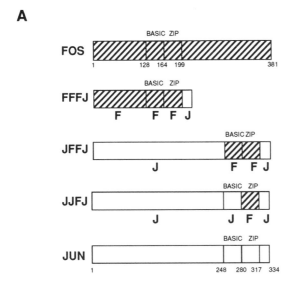

B

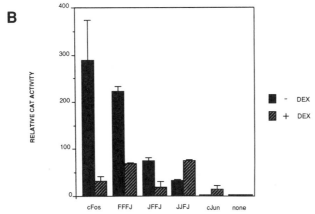

Figure 3 (See facing page for legend.)

context of a c-Jun/c-Fos chimera heterodimerized with c-Jun, the basic regions of the AP-1 subunits appear to be determinants of composite specificity (Fig. 3B). In fact, the c-Fos basic and zipper region alone (together with cotransfected c-Jun) appeared to be a sufficient determinant of receptor-mediated repression at plfG (J.N. Miner, unpubl.).

The functional connection between nuclear receptors and the AP-1 family extends beyond GR and c-Jun/c-Fos; other members of these factor families appear to collaborate in regulatory interactions at other genes (Kourides and Gurr 1989; Thukral et al. 1989; Jonat et al. 1990; Nicholson et al. 1990; Miner et al. 1991; Miner and Yamamoto 1991; Pearce and Yamamoto 1993; Imai et al. 1993). The c-Fos-related antigen Fra1 (Cohen and Curran 1988; Cohen et al. 1989) is immunologically related to c-Fos and is conserved particularly strongly within the bZIP region. Like c-Fos, Fra1 enhances transcription by heterodimerization with c-Jun and subsequent binding to a consensus simple AP-1 site (Cohen and Curran 1988; Cohen et al. 1989) or to plfG (Miner and Yamamoto 1992). Fra1 is also similar to c-Fos in its failure to dimerize, bind DNA, or enhance transcription in the absence of Jun. However, Fra1 was found to differ strikingly from c-Fos in its functional effect on GR action at the composite element. Remarkably, c-Jun/Fra1 dimers specified transcriptional enhancement by the receptor. Thus, Fra1 has the dimerization, DNA-binding, and transcriptional activation properties of c-Fos at the composite element, but its functional interaction with GR is opposite to that seen with c-Fos. Studies with c-Fos/Fra1 chimeras revealed that a precise replacement of the basic region of c-Fos with that of Fra1 specified receptor-mediated activation, whereas intact c-Fos specified repression (Miner and Yamamoto 1992). Remarkably, FRFF (Fig. 4) differs from c-Fos by only four chemically conservative amino acid substitutions.

Molecular, genetic, and structural analyses of the basic regions in bZIP factors indicate that these segments are α-helical and that they make sequence-specific DNA contacts (Landschulz et al. 1988, 1989; Rauscher et al. 1988; Vinson et al. 1989; Abate et al. 1990; O'Neil et al. 1990; Patel et al. 1990; Weiss et al. 1990). In fact, by alignment with the determined crystal structure of GCN4 (Ellenberger et al. 1992), another bZIP protein, it was deduced that the four critical residues that determine the composite specificity of c-Fos and Fra1 reside within this "DNA recognition helix" and that they are solvent-accessible, positioned on the helical surface away from the DNA (Miner and Yamamoto 1992). In principle, such a region could interact with other regulatory factors such as GR that are bound contiguously on the DNA.

One interpretation of these results is that the four c-Fos-specific

cFos   EKRRIRRERNKMAAAKCRNRRR

Fra 1   ERRRVRRERNKLAAAKCRNRRK

Figure 4 Helical representation of the basic regions of c-Fos and Fra1. Three of the four amino acid residues of c-Fos and Fra1 that appear to be critical for composite specificity by GR at plfG reside on one surface of the basic region α-helix, as indicated by hatch marks between the c-Fos and Fra1 sequences and extending to their putative location on the helix. By alignment of this region with the crystal structure of the basic region helix of another bZIP protein, GCN4 (Ellenberger et al. 1992), we infer that the residues that contact DNA are positioned below the helix and that the upper surface residues, including three of those that differ between c-Fos and Fra1, are solvent accessible. The fourth difference, R-K, is also shown on the sequence but is outside the helical region and therefore could not be precisely assigned. (Reprinted, with permission, from Miner and Yamamoto 1992.)

amino acid residues of the basic helix might comprise a signal (when bound together with c-Jun at plfG) for the receptor to repress transcription. Conversely, the four Fra1-specific residues might signal the receptor to confer enhancement. Intriguingly, recent results (see below) suggest that the Fra1-type patch is necessary but not sufficient for receptor-mediated enhancement at plfG and that, in the absence of a functional "enhancement signal" perhaps requiring specifically positioned c-Jun or Fra1, hormone-dependent repression is the default behavior for GR at this element.

RECEPTOR/AP-1 COMPLEXES

Using a receptor-specific monoclonal antibody (Gametchu and Harrison 1984), we carried out coimmunoprecipitation assays to identify regions of AP-1 necessary for contact with GR in vitro. We found that deletions of the c-Jun bZIP region abrogated the receptor/c-Jun interaction, implying that the c-Jun DNA-binding domain is involved in the GR interaction (Diamond et al. 1990). Furthermore, c-Fos coprecipitated with the receptor only in the presence of c-Jun, perhaps indicating that c-Fos is merely tethered to the c-Jun/receptor complex through its leucine zipper interaction with c-Jun. Indeed, the c-Fos leucine zipper was crucial for c-Fos interaction with the c-Jun/GR complex, whereas mutations in the c-Fos basic region that block its specific DNA binding had no effect binding to c-Jun/GR (Miner and Yamamoto 1992). This supports the tethering model but leaves unresolved the role of the composite specificity domain mapped to the c-Fos and Fra1 basic helix. Conceivably, GR may interact selectively with Fra1 at this position; alternatively, a different cellular factor may monitor the specificity domain.

COMPOSITE ELEMENTS ARE REGULATORY JUNCTION POINTS

Taken together, these findings established that the plfG composite response element functions as a "junction point" for combinatorial regulation, a sequence at which particular members of two (or more) distinct regulatory factor families interact, and the information embodied in composite specificity domains is interpreted. Thus, composite elements in general might resolve the apparently redundant behavior of factor family members at simple response elements. At present, we know little about the mechanisms by which these domains function, or about the nature or limits of their specificities. However, we predict that experimental detection of composite specificity domains will depend strongly on both the cellular context and the nature of the composite element. For example, MR likely harbors composite specificity domains that have not been revealed in the contexts examined here.

MOLECULAR DETERMINANTS OF COMPOSITE REGULATION

Steroid receptors are likely to engage in composite interactions with factor families other than AP-1, and such interactions are accomplished at composite elements with sequences that differ from plfG. Other composite GREs, such as those associated with the α-fetoprotein (Guertin et al. 1988; Zhang et al. 1991), prolactin (Sakai et al. 1988), and phosphoenolpyruvate carboxykinase (PEPCK) (Imai et al. 1990, 1993; Lucas et al. 1991) genes, also differ substantially from the simple GRE consensus sequence, and indeed from each other. AP-1 has been implicated as a functional nonreceptor factor at the α-fetoprotein element (Zhang et al. 1991), whereas different, as-yet-unidentified factors appear to collaborate with GR in the regulation of prolactin and PEPCK gene expression. Given this information, it was important to assess in general the roles of protein-protein interactions, protein-DNA interactions, and composite element sequence organization in specifying composite regulation.

We have considered three ways in which GR might communicate with other factors at composite elements (Fig. 5). These schemes are not mutually exclusive nor do they encompass all possible mechanisms (for example, we do not consider here models in which distortion or bending of DNA by one factor affects the action of another). Nevertheless, they may provide focal points for future study. In the first model, distinct sequences recognized by the receptor might induce or stabilize altered GR conformations, which in turn might specify, for example, homodimerization of GR at simple GREs or heterotypic association with AP-1 at a composite element (Fig. 5A). A second scheme invokes cooperative DNA binding: Neither GR nor the cognate nonreceptor factor alone

A. DNA Sequence Alters Functional Properties of Factor

B. Factor Interaction Increases DNA Affinity

C. Binding Proximity Facilitates Novel Factor Interaction

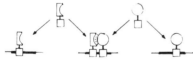

Figure 5 Models for factor communication at composite response elements. (*A*) DNA sequence alters functional properties of factor. GR monomers bind specifically to either a simple or a composite element, each of which induces a distinct allosteric transition in receptor structure. At the simple element, the conformational change facilitates GR dimerization (and enhancement activity); at the composite element, the conformational change facilitates interaction of GR with a nonreceptor factor, yielding composite regulation. (*B*) Factor interaction increases DNA affinity. Neither factor binds independently with high affinity to the DNA element. Together, they bind cooperatively, yielding composite regulation. (*C*) Binding proximity facilitates novel factor interaction. The two factors bind independently to the DNA element. Once bound, their close proximity facilitates a specific interaction between the factors, yielding composite regulation. In the case of plfG, for example, an interaction of the activation domains of GR and c-Jun/c-Fos that results in their mutual inhibition would be consistent with experimental findings.

would bind avidly to the composite element, but specific interaction of their DNA-binding domains might stabilize the ternary complex (Fig. 5B). Cooperative interactions between factors from different families have been observed, for example, in the case of the yeast regulators α2 and MCM1 (Johnson, this volume). A third hypothesis implicates factor interactions that alter their regulatory functions rather than their DNA affinities (Fig. 5C); for example, the transcriptional activating domains of GR and c-Jun/c-Fos might interact specifically at plfG, thereby abrogating the activities of both factors without affecting ternary complex formation.

To begin to distinguish among these three models, we first tested whether GR bound at plfG would repress AP-1 derivatives carrying heterologous activating domains (Fig. 6). For this experiment, a DNA fragment encoding only the bZIP DNA-binding domain of c-Fos was fused either to the strong acidic activating region from the herpesvirus VP16 protein (Triezenberg et al. 1988) or to the amino-terminal region of

A

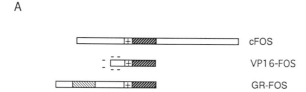

B

AP1 Derivative	CAT Activity	
	-	+ Dex
cFOS + cJUN	24	3
VP-FOS + cJUN	23	4
GR-FOS + cJUN	19	4
FRA1 + cJUN	9	33

Figure 6 GR-mediated repression of heterologous activating domains at plfG. (*A*) Diagrams depict fusions of the c-Fos basic and zipper region (bZIP) with the acidic activating region of the herpesvirus activator, VP16, or with the GR amino-terminal activation domain, enh2. Intact c-Fos is shown for orientation. (*B*) Fusions were tested by cotransfection with intact c-Jun into F9 cells; similar results were obtained using just the bZIP region of c-Jun instead of intact c-Jun. The results are expressed as relative CAT activity (normalized to a β-galactosidase expression plasmid as an internal control).

GR itself, which contains an activating domain denoted *enh2* (Godowski et al. 1988). Expression vectors encoding these constructs were transfected into F9 cells together with a reporter carrying plfG and a c-Jun expression vector. Figure 6 shows that GR inhibited each of these heterologous activating domains and that the extents of inhibition were similar to the repression of intact c-Fos/c-Jun heterodimers. Repression of the GR-Fos chimera by GR at plfG seemed particularly remarkable, as GR binding to contiguous *simple* GREs provoked precisely the opposite consequence, strongly synergistic enhancement of transcription (Kakidani and Ptashne 1988; Strähle et al. 1988). As a control in this experiment (Fig. 6), we confirmed that GR enhances transcription in the presence of Fra1/c-Jun heterodimers, consistent with the idea that GR is not merely "squelching" (Gill and Ptashne 1988). We conclude from this experiment that composite regulation at plfG is unlikely to be determined by specific interactions between GR and segments of AP-1 outside the bZIP DNA-binding region (Fig. 5C).

In a second experiment, we tested whether GR bound at plfG could trigger composite regulation by collaborating with a heterologous activator bound at a remote site (Fig. 7). Thus, five tandem binding sites for the hybrid activator protein GAL4.VP16 (Sadowski et al. 1988) were introduced into a reporter about 40 bp upstream of a single plfG element; similar results were obtained in a construct bearing the plfG sequence upstream of the five GAL4.VP16 sites (J.N. Miner, unpubl.). As expected, c-Jun/c-Fos alone or GAL4.VP16 alone activated this reporter promoter, and c-Jun/c-Fos transfected together with GAL4.VP16 resulted in strong synergistic activation (Fig. 7). Addition of hormone confirmed that GR repressed c-Jun/c-Fos activity at the plfG element in this construct. Indeed, GR also repressed activation by GAL4.VP16 in the absence of c-Jun/c-Fos and even repressed the synergistic activation by c-Jun/c-Fos together with GAL4.VP16 (Fig. 7). As a control, GR did not affect GAL4.VP16 activity in a reporter construct bearing the five tandem GAL4.VP16 sites but lacking plfG. These results argue against several specific modes of composite regulation: (1) cooperative binding, in which a GR-AP-1 interaction increases the fractional occupancy of plfG (Fig. 5B); (2) factor positioning, in which the plfG sequence defines precisely the relative orientations of GR and AP-1 on the DNA (Fig. 5B); and (3) factor-specific interaction, in which GR and AP-1 contain complementary interacting surfaces that modify their respective activities rather than their DNA affinities (Fig. 5C).

Such observations leave open the possibility that the nucleotide sequence of plfG might affect receptor conformation, thereby facilitating combinatorial interactions with nonreceptor factors and producing com-

A

(GAL)$_5$-plfG-CAT

	P ADH

(GAL)$_5$ plfG   CAT

(GAL)$_5$-CAT

	P GLOB

(GAL)$_5$ CAT

B

Reporter	Activator		CAT Activity	
	AP1	GAL-VP	-	+ Dex
(GAL)$_5$-plfG-CAT	-	-	0.3	0.4
	+	-	4.0	2.1
	-	+	4.9	1.3
	+	+	76	1.5
(GAL)$_5$-CAT	-	-	0.7	nd
	-	+	516	345

Figure 7 Repression of heterologous activators bound at remote sites by GR bound at plfG. Reporter constructs are diagramed in *A*; similar results were obtained when the relative positions of the (GAL)$_5$ and plfG elements were reversed. Reporters were cotransfected, as indicated, with AP-1 (c-Jun + excess c-Fos), GAL4.VP16, or both, either in the absence or presence of hormone; a GR expression vector was also transfected in all cases. Relative CAT activities (normalized to β-galactosidase) are presented in *B*; nd indicates not determined.

posite rather than simple regulation (Fig. 5A). In fact, biochemical and structural studies (Härd et al. 1990; Perlmann et al. 1990; Luisi et al. 1991) imply that GR binding at a palindromic simple GRE induces a conformational change that produces a stable dimer interface and results in receptor dimerization (see below). To date, no direct studies have tested whether GR undergoes a distinct conformational change at plfG; however, the results of genetic experiments described in the next section suggest indirectly that the receptor may fold differently when bound at simple and composite elements.

Together, these findings are consistent with the notion that composite regulation by GR at plfG may be specified not only by protein-protein interactions, perhaps involving composite specificity domains, but also by protein-DNA interactions in which the plfG sequence might serve as an allosteric effector of GR conformation. Particularly striking is the discovery that GR bound at plfG could repress a heterologous activator bound at a remote site separated from plfG itself (Fig. 7); notably, replacement of the plfG sequence by a simple GRE produced strong synergy between GR and AP-1 (see Kakidani and Ptashne 1988; J.N. Miner, unpubl.). It is apparent from these findings that repression (or perhaps more accurately, "anti-enhancement") is the "default" behavior of GR bound at plfG. That is, plfG-bound GR in general blocks the action of various activators in various sequence contexts; in contrast, in order for the plfG/GR complex to activate transcription, its default repression behavior must be overridden by a novel interaction of GR with a c-Jun homodimer or Fra1/c-Jun heterodimer precisely positioned with GR at plfG. This is in striking contrast to GR activity at simple GREs, where enhancement, rather than repression, is the default behavior of DNA-bound GR (Godowski et al. 1988; W. Matsui and D. Pearce, unpubl.).

GR OLIGOMERIZATION AT SIMPLE AND COMPOSITE ELEMENTS

Two lines of evidence suggest that GR undergoes a conformational change upon binding to a palindromic simple GRE. First, comparison of the three-dimensional structure of the GR DNA-binding domain in solution (solved by NMR spectroscopy; Härd et al. 1990) with the structure of the DNA-binding domain complexed with a simple GRE (solved by X-ray crystallography; Luisi et al. 1991) suggests conformational differences, especially in a region that contains residues directly involved in DNA binding and dimerization (Luisi et al. 1991; J. Thomas, unpubl.). It was proposed that this region may be reconfigured when it contacts DNA and that one consequence of this transition is stabilization of the dimer interface. Second, whereas two GR monomers bind highly cooperatively to a palindromic simple GRE (LaBaer 1989; Dahlman-Wright et al. 1991) forming a stable dimer (LaBaer 1989; Luisi et al. 1991; J. Thomas, unpubl.), the receptor is predominantly monomeric in solution (Perlmann et al. 1990). Indeed, there was no evidence of dimerization even at the millimolar subunit concentrations used for the solution structure analysis (Härd et al. 1990), whereas dimers formed on the DNA even if specific DNA contacts were limited only to a single half-site (Luisi et al. 1991).

As an indirect measure of the conformation of GR bound to plfG, we mutated particular amino acid residues predicted from the crystal structure to mediate dimerization and compared the activities of these mutants on a palindromic simple GRE and at plfG. As shown in Table 1, mutations at the dimer interface had no effect on monomer binding to the simple GRE (confirming that the mutations do not alter DNA binding per

Table 1   Effects of mutations in the GR dimer interface on GR binding and activity

Receptor	DNA binding		Activity		
	monomer	dimer	simple GRE (activation)	plfG (repression)	plfG (activation)
WT	100	100	100	100	100
R479A	93	43	31	127	40
N491A	91	16	23	112	28
N491A/R479A	133	12	6	202	9

Two GR residues predicted from crystallographic studies to reside at the dimer interface, R479 and N491, were mutated to alanine and tested singly and in combination for DNA-binding activity at a consensus half-site (monomer) or at a palindromic simple GRE (dimer), and for regulatory activity in cotransfection experiments with reporters linked to a simple GRE or to the plfG composite element. For repression, c-Jun and c-Fos were cotransfected; for activation at plfG, c-Jun was cotransfected. Activities are reported as percent of wild type.

se) but strongly compromised cooperative association of the second monomer and led to a parallel decrease in enhancement from the simple GRE in vivo. At the plfG element, receptor-mediated repression of c-Jun/c-Fos activity was unaffected, or perhaps slightly strengthened, by the dimer mutants; in contrast, receptor-mediated enhancement of c-Jun homodimer activity, as with enhancement from the simple GRE, was abrogated by mutation of the dimer interface. Three implications emerge from these observations: (1) Default GR activity at a simple GRE (enhancement) requires receptor dimerization; (2) default GR activity at plfG (repression) can be conferred by the monomeric receptor; and (3) binding of c-Jun (or c-Jun/Fra1) at plfG can override the default behavior of the receptor at plfG by driving GR into a conformation that favors dimerization and transcriptional enhancement.

CONCLUSIONS AND PERSPECTIVES

It has long been evident that much of the phenotypic complexity of cells and organisms reflects the elaboration of a large number of specific patterns of gene expression by various combinations of a relatively small number of regulatory factors. The collaboration of regulators at composite response elements such as plfG likely represents one general class of mechanisms by which this combinatoriality is achieved; it is apparent that composite elements provide facile and versatile junction points for integrating information from multiple signaling systems. Given its importance, there are doubtless many ways to accomplish cross talk between regulators; even in the case of the nuclear receptor family alone, several different schemes for interfamily communication have been presented (Jonat et al. 1990; Lucibello et al. 1990; Schüle et al. 1990; Yang-yen et al. 1990; Karin 1991). In any case, investigations of plfG have helped to illuminate three notions that could be considered in a somewhat broader context; these concern mechanisms of cell-specific regulation, the types of functional surfaces on transcriptional regulators, and the role of DNA as an effector of regulatory factor function.

Our early studies of plfG were motivated by the finding of cell specificity of receptor function. This response element evoked GR-mediated enhancement in one cell line and GR-mediated repression in another (Diamond et al. 1990). Subsequent investigation revealed that the factor responsible for the cell specificity, AP-1, is itself virtually ubiquitous. Thus, the cell-specific behavior (positive or negative regulation) of GR, a factor that itself is produced in nearly all cell types, is produced not by the cell-specific *production* of particular AP-1 subunits, but rather by their *functional ratio*. Such a scheme yields a pleasing biological parsimony in which specificity emerges from communication between factors that are neither constrained to cell-specific expression nor dedicated merely to interacting with each other (Miner and Yamamoto 1991). Indeed, we speculate that physiological control over the ratio of c-Jun and c-Fos, for example, may normally be imposed not by altering their relative expression levels, as we have done experimentally, but rather by more subtle means. Imagine, for example, that phosphorylation of a particular serine residue of c-Fos abrogates its functional interaction with GR but leaves unaffected its communication with numerous other factors. This would provide regulatory inputs for additional signaling networks and would utilize AP-1 to govern GR function, while still allowing it independently to participate in other regulatory events in the same cell.

The finding that closely related members of a given regulatory factor family can be distinguished functionally at a composite element presaged the existence of composite specificity domains. These specific polypeptide segments determine factor behavior in a composite context, such as the activity versus inactivity distinction of GR and MR, or the specification of positive or negative GR regulation, as with Fra1 and c-Fos, at plfG. It seems likely that each factor contains multiple specificity domains and that different domains come into play in different sequence and cellular contexts.

In the simplest view, composite specificity domains may correspond to interaction surfaces for particular factors bound either at the response element or at the promoter. The specificity domains described here, for example, might correspond to direct contact points between GR and AP-1, or to sites of binding or modification by unidentified components that modulate the affinity or activity of the GR/AP-1 interaction. In any case, these findings imply that each regulatory factor might contain multiple important functional domains in addition to the well-established DNA-binding, dimerization, and activation/repression regions that are commonly considered. We suggest that these novel functional domains likely constrain further the rate of evolution of regulatory factors, or at least impose added pressure for their coevolution, and thus contribute to the remarkable evolutionary conservation of the transcription machinery and its regulators (Guarente and Bermingham-McDonogh 1992; Guarente, this volume).

It is implicit in the notion of combinatorial regulation that regulatory factors must engage in specific interactions with a range of other regulators in the cell. Within a given factor family, it is apparent that various homo- and heterodimers contribute to this combinatorial specification (Lamb and McKnight 1991; Banuett 1992; Mangelsdorf and Evans, this volume). Studies of composite elements such as plfG indicate that interactions *between* factor families also play key roles. The multiplicity of these putative interactions implies that many of them are likely to be transient, perhaps occurring only at the DNA elements at which they function. In this view, the DNA itself might be "passive," increasing the local concentration of the interactants, or it might be "active," inducing conformational changes in one or more binding factors that signal a particular protein-protein interaction fate.

One speculative model is that GREs, both simple and composite, may have both passive and active functions. Thus, we suggest that after binding hormone in the cytoplasm, the GR enters the nucleus and binds to DNA predominantly as a monomer and that the sequence context of the binding site may serve as an allosteric effector of receptor conformation that determines, for example, whether GR will homodimerize and enhance transcription or instead form a heterotypic complex with c-Jun and c-Fos and repress transcription. According to this scheme, the plfG sequence might induce a GR conformation that precludes dimerization and enhancement (in the absence of c-Jun or c-Jun/Fra1), but that favors interaction with cellular cofactors that inhibit the function of the initiation apparatus; in yeast, such an activity has been ascribed to the products of two genes, *SSN6* and *TUP1* (Johnson, this volume). Clearly, this notion that specific DNA sequences may trigger allosteric changes in protein structure requires direct experimental examination beyond the inferences drawn from the binding properties of GR at simple GREs (Luisi et al. 1991). Nevertheless, the idea may have heuristic value for further analyses of the mechanisms of combinatorial transcriptional regulation.

ACKNOWLEDGMENTS

We thank the members of the Yamamoto laboratory for stimulating suggestions and criticisms throughout the course of this work and M. del Mar Vivanco Ruiz for comments on the manuscript; we also thank A. Cordano and B. Maler for help with preparation of the text and figures, respectively. Research in our laboratory was supported by grants from the National Institutes of Health and the National Science Foundation; J.N.M. was a postdoctoral fellow of the American Cancer Society and the Leukemia Society; D.P. held a National Institutes of Health Physician Scientist award.

REFERENCES

Abate, C., D. Luk, and T. Curran. 1991. Transcriptional regulation by Fos and Jun in vitro: Interaction among multiple activator and regulatory domains. *Mol. Cell. Biol.* **11:** 3624–3632.

Abate, C., D. Luk, R. Gentz, F.R. Rauscher III, and T. Curran. 1990. Expression and purification of the leucine zipper and DNA-binding domains of Fos and Jun: Both Fos and Jun contact DNA directly. *Proc. Natl. Acad. Sci.* **87:** 1032–1036.

Amero, S.A., R.H. Kretsinger, N.D. Moncrief, K.R. Yamamoto, and W.R. Pearson. 1992. The origin of nuclear receptor proteins: A single precursor distinct from other transcription factors. *Mol. Endocrinol.* **6:** 3–7.

Arriza, J.L., C. Weinberger, G. Cerelli, T.M. Glaser, B.L. Handelin, D.E. Housman, and R.M. Evans. 1987. Cloning of human mineralocorticoid receptor complementary DNA: Structural and functional kinship with the glucocorticoid receptor. *Science* **237:** 268–275.

Banuett, F. 1992. *Ustilago maydis*, the delightful blight. *Trends Genet.* **8:** 174–180.

Bastl, C.P., G. Schulman, and E.J. Cragoe. 1989. Low-dose glucocorticoids stimulate electroneural NaCl absorption in rat colon. *Am. J. Physiol.* **257:** F1027–F1038.

Beato, M. 1989. Gene regulation by steroid hormones. *Cell* **56:** 335–344.

Chandler, V.L., B.A. Maler, and K.R. Yamamoto. 1983. DNA sequences bound specifically by glucocorticoid receptor in vitro render a heterologous promoter hormone responsive in vivo. *Cell* **33:** 489–499.

Cohen, D.R. and T. Curran. 1988. *fra-1*: A serum-inducible, cellular immediate early gene that encodes a *fos*-related antigen. *Mol. Cell. Biol.* **8:** 2063–2069.

———. 1990. Analysis of dimerization and DNA binding functions in Fos and Jun by domain-swapping: Involvement of residues outside the leucine zipper/basic region. *Oncogene* **5:** 929–939.

Cohen, D.R., P.C.P. Ferreira, R. Gentz, B.R. Franza, Jr., and T. Curran. 1989. The product of a *fos*-related gene, *fra-1*, binds cooperatively to the AP-1 site with Jun: Transcription factor AP-1 is comprised of multiple protein complexes. *Genes Dev.* **3:** 173–184.

Dahlman-Wright, K., A. Wright, J.-Å. Gustafsson, and J. Carlstedt-Duke. 1991. Interaction of the glucocorticoid receptor DNA-binding domain with DNA as a dimer is mediated by a short segment of five amino acids. *J. Biol. Chem.* **266:** 3107–3112.

Diamond, M., J.N. Miner, S.K. Yoshinaga, and K.R. Yamamoto. 1990. Transcription factor interactions: Selectors of positive or negative regulation from a single DNA element. *Science* 249: 1266–1272.

Ellenberger, T.E., C.J. Brandl, K. Struhl, and S.C. Harrison. 1992. The GCN4 basic-region-leucine zipper binds DNA as a dimer of uninterrupted α-helices: Crystal structure of the protein-DNA complex. *Cell* 71: 1223–1227.

Evans, R.M. 1988. The steroid and thyroid hormone receptor superfamily. *Science* 240: 889–895.

Gametchu, B. and R.W. Harrison. 1984. Characterization of a monoclonal antibody to the rat liver glucocorticoid receptor. *Endocrinology* 114: 274–279.

Gill, G. and M. Ptashne. 1988. Negative effect of the transcriptional activator GAL4. *Nature* 334: 721–724.

Godowski, P.J., D. Picard, and K.R. Yamamoto. 1988. Signal transduction and transcriptional regulation by glucocorticoid receptor-LexA fusion proteins. *Science* 241: 812–816.

Guarente, L. and O. Bermingham-McDonogh. 1992. Conservation and evolution of transcriptional mechanisms in eukaryotes. *Trends Genet.* 8: 27–31.

Guertin, M., H. LaRue, D. Bernier, O. Wrange, M. Chevrette, M.-C. Gingras, and L. Belanger. 1988. Enhancer and promoter elements direction activation and glucocorticoid repression of the a_1-fetoprotein gene in hepatocytes. *Mol. Cell. Biol.* 8: 1398–1407.

Härd, T., E. Kellenbach, R. Boelens, B.A. Maler, K. Dahlman, L.P. Freedman, J. Carlstedt-Duke, K.R. Yamamoto, J.-Å. Gustafsson, and R. Kaptein. 1990. Solution structure of the glucocorticoid receptor DNA-binding domain. *Science* 249: 157–160.

Imai, E., J.N. Miner, J. Mitchell, K.R. Yamamoto, and D.K. Granner. 1993. Glucocorticoid receptor-CREB interaction and the response of the PEPCK gene to glucocorticoids. *J. Biol. Chem.* (in press).

Imai, E., P.-E. Stromstedt, P.G. Quinn, J. Carlstedt-Duke, J.-Å. Gustafsson, and D.K. Granner. 1990. Characterization of a complex glucocorticoid response unit in the phosphoenolpyruvate carboxykinase gene. *Mol. Cell. Biol.* 10: 4712–4719.

Joels, M. and E.R. De Kloet. 1990. Mineralocorticoid receptor-mediated changes in membrane properties of rat CA1 pyramidal neurons in vitro. *Proc. Natl. Acad. Sci.* 87: 4495–4498.

Jonat, C., H.J. Rahmsdorf, P. Herrlich, K.-K. Park, A.C.B. Cato, S. Gebel, and H. Ponta. 1990. Antitumor promotion and antiinflammation: Down-modulation of AP-1 (fos/jun) activity by glucocorticoid hormone. *Cell* 62: 1189–1204.

Kakidani, H. and M. Ptashne. 1988. GAL4 activates gene expression in mammalian cells. *Cell* 52: 161–167.

Karin, M. 1991. Signal transduction and gene control. *Curr. Opin. Cell Biol.* 3: 467–473.

Kerppola, T.K. and T. Curran. 1991. Transcription factor interactions: Basics on zippers. *Curr. Opin. Struct. Biol.* 1: 71–79.

Kourides, I.A. and J.A. Gurr. 1989. Regulation of the transfected human glycoprotein hormone α-subunit gene by dexamethasone and thyroid hormone. *DNA* 8: 473–480.

LaBaer, J. 1989. "A detailed analysis of the DNA-binding affinity and sequence specificity of the glucocorticoid receptor DNA-binding domain." Ph.D. thesis, University of California, San Francisco.

Lamb, P. and S.L. McKnight. 1991. Diversity and specificity in transcriptional regulation: The benefits of heterotypic dimerization. *Trends Biochem. Sci.* 16: 417–422.

Landschulz, W.H., P.F. Johnson, and S.L. McKnight. 1988. The leucine zipper: A hypothetical structure common to a new class of DNA binding proteins. *Science* 240: 1759–1764.

————. 1989. The DNA binding domain of the rat liver nuclear protein C/EBP is bipartite. *Science* **243:** 1681–1688.

Laplace, J.R., R.F. Husted, and J.B. Stokes. 1992. Cellular responses to steroids in the enhancement of Na^+ transport by rat collecting duct cells in culture; differences between glucocorticoid and mineralocorticoid hormones. *J. Clin. Invest.* **90:** 1370–1378.

Lucas, P.C., R.M. O'Brien, J.A. Mitchell, C.M. Davis, E. Imai, B.M. Forman, H.H. Samuels, and D.K. Granner. 1991. A retinoic acid response element is part of a pleiotropic domain in the phospho*enol*pyruvate carboxykinase gene. *Proc. Natl. Acad. Sci.* **88:** 2184–2188.

Lucibello, F.C., E.P. Slater, K.U. Jooss, M. Beato, and R. Müller. 1990. Mutual transrepression of Fos and the glucocorticoid receptor: Involvement of a functional domain in Fos which is absent in FosB. *EMBO J.* **9:** 2827–2834.

Luisi, B.F., W.X. Xu, Z. Otwinowski, L.P. Freedman, K.R. Yamamoto, and P.B. Sigler. 1991. Crystallographic analysis of the interaction of the glucocorticoid receptor with DNA. *Nature* **352:** 497–505.

Miner, J.N. and K.R. Yamamoto. 1991. Regulatory crosstalk at composite response elements. *Trends Biochem. Sci.* **16:** 423–426.

————. 1992. The basic region of AP1 specifies glucocorticoid receptor activity at a composite response element. *Genes Dev.* **6:** 2491–2501.

Miner, J.N., M.I. Diamond, and K.R. Yamamoto. 1991. Joints in the regulatory lattice: Composite regulation by steroid receptor-AP1 complexes. *Cell Growth Differ.* **2:** 525–530.

Mordacq, J.C. and D.I.H. Linzer. 1989. Co-localization of elements required for phorbol ester stimulation and glucocorticoid repression of proliferin gene expression. *Genes Dev.* **3:** 760–769.

Nicholson, R.C., S. Mader, S. Nagpal, M. Leid, C. Rochette-Egly, and P. Chambon. 1990. Negative regulation of the rat stromelysin gene promoter by retinoic acid is mediated by an AP1 binding site. *EMBO J.* **9:** 4443–4454.

O'Neil, K.T., R.H. Hoess, and W.F. DeGrado. 1990. Design of DNA-binding peptides based on the leucine zipper motif. *Science* **249:** 774–778.

O'Shea, E.K., R. Rutkowski, and P. Kim. 1992. Mechanism of specificity in the Fos-Jun oncoprotein heterodimer. *Cell* **68:** 699–708.

Otten, A.D., M.M. Sanders, and G.S. McKnight. 1988. The MMTV LTR promoter is induced by progesterone and dihydrotestosterone but not by estrogen. *Mol. Endocrinol.* **2:** 143–147.

Patel, L., C. Abate, and T. Curran. 1990. Altered protein conformation on DNA binding by Fos and Jun. *Nature* **347:** 572–575.

Patel, P.D., T.G. Sherman, D.J. Goldman, and S.J. Watson. 1989. Molecular cloning of a mineralocorticoid (type I) receptor complementary DNA from rat hippocampus. *Mol. Endocrinol.* **3:** 1877–1885.

Pearce, D. and K.R. Yamamoto. 1993. Mineralocorticoid and glucocorticoid receptor activities are distinguished by nonreceptors factors at a composite element. *Science* (in press).

Perlmann, T., P. Eriksson, and Ö. Wrange. 1990. Quantitative analysis of the glucocorticoid receptor-DNA interaction at the mouse mammary tumor virus glucocorticoid response element. *J. Biol. Chem.* **265:** 17222–17229.

Ptashne, M. 1988. How eukaryotic transcriptional activators work. *Nature* **365:** 683–689.

Rauscher, F.J., III, D.R. Cohen, T. Curran, T.J. Bos, P.K. Vogt, D. Bohmann, R. Tjian, and B.R. Franza, Jr. 1988. Fos associated protein p39 is the product of the *jun* proto-oncogene. *Science* **240:** 1010–1016.

Sadowski, I., J. Ma, S. Triezenberg, and M. Ptashne. 1988. Gal4-VP16 is an unusually potent transcriptional activator. *Nature* **335:** 563–564.

Sakai, D.D., S. Helms, J. Carlstedt-Duke, J.A. Gustafsson, F.M. Rottman, and K.R. Yamamoto. 1988. Hormone-mediated repression: A negative glucocorticoid response element from the bovine prolactin gene. *Genes Dev.* **2:** 1144–1154.

Schüle, R., P. Rangarajan, S. Kliewer, L.J. Ransone, J. Bolado, N. Yang, I.M. Verma, and R.M. Evans. 1990. Functional antagonism between oncoprotein c-Jun and the glucocorticoid receptor. *Cell* **62:** 1217–1226.

Strähle, U., W. Schmid, and G. Schütz. 1988. Synergistic action of the glucocorticoid receptor with transcription factors. *EMBO J.* **7:** 3389–3395.

Thukral, S.K., M.A. Tavianini, H. Blumberg, and E.T. Young. 1989. Localization of a minimal binding domain and activation regions in yeast regulatory protein ADR1. *Mol. Cell. Biol.* **9:** 2360–2369.

Triezenberg, S.J., R.C. Kingsbury, and S.L. McKnight. 1988. Functional dissection of VP16, a *trans*-activator of herpes simplex virus immediate early gene expression. *Genes Dev.* **2:** 718–729.

Turnamian, S.G. and H.J. Binder. 1989. Regulation of active sodium and potassium transport in the distal colon of the rat, role of the aldosterone and glucocorticoid receptors. *J. Clin. Invest.* **84:** 1924–1929.

Vinson, C.R., P.B. Sigler, and S.L. McKnight. 1989. Scissors-grip model for DNA recognition by a family of leucine zipper proteins. *Science* **246:** 911–916.

Vogt, P.K. and T.J. Bos. 1990. *jun:* Oncogene and transcription factor. *Adv. Cancer Res.* **55:** 1–2.

Weiss, M.A., T. Ellenberger, C.R. Wobbe, J.P. Lee, S.C. Harrison, and K. Struhl. 1990. Folding transition in the DNA-binding domain of GCN4 on specific binding to DNA. *Nature* **347:** 575–578.

Yang-yen, H.-F., J.-C. Chambard, Y.-L. Sun, T. Smeal, T.J. Schmidt, J. Drouin, and M. Karin. 1990. Transcriptional interference between c-Jun and the glucocorticoid receptor: Mutual inhibition of DNA binding due to direct protein-protein interaction. *Cell* **62:** 1205–1215.

Zhang, X.-K., J.-M. Dong, and J.-F. Chiu. 1991. Regulation of α-fetoprotein gene expression by antagonism between AP-1 and the glucocorticoid receptor at their overlapping binding site. *J. Biol. Chem.* **266:** 8248–8254.

44
Positive and Negative Control of Human Interferon-β Gene Expression

Tom Maniatis, Lisa-Anne Whittemore, Wei Du, Chen-Ming Fan,
Andrew D. Keller, Vito J. Palombella, and Dimitrios N. Thanos
Department of Biochemistry and Molecular Biology
Harvard University, Cambridge, Massachusetts 02138

OVERVIEW

Expression of the human interferon-β (IFN-β) gene is transiently induced by virus infection. The regulatory sequences required for this on/off switch are located within a 100-bp regulatory element located immediately upstream of the start site of transcription. This region contains at least three distinct virus-inducible elements and two negative regulatory elements. The mechanism of virus induction is thought to involve the inactivation or displacement of repressor proteins bound to the negative elements, and combinatorial interactions between virus-inducible factors that specifically bind to the three distinct positive regulatory elements. The gene is then turned off after induction by virus-inducible repressors that bind to the positive control elements. In this review, we summarize our current understanding of the organization of the IFN-β gene promoter and recent studies of transcriptional activators and repressors that bind to specific sites within the promoter.

INTRODUCTION

The IFN-β gene is highly inducible by virus or double-stranded RNA (for review, see DeMaeyer and DeMaeyer-Guignard 1988). Prior to virus induction, the level of IFN-β gene mRNA is too low to be detected, but within hours after infection, over 2000 transcripts per cell are produced. Virus induction is transient, however, since the level of IFN-β mRNA peaks 6–12 hours after induction, then decreases rapidly. This burst of mRNA synthesis leads to the transient production of IFN-β, a secreted protein that binds to a specific cell-surface receptor. The bound receptor triggers a signal transduction pathway leading to the activation of a large number of genes encoding antiviral proteins. Virus induction of the IFN-

Transcriptional Regulation.
Copyright 1992 Cold Spring Harbor Laboratory Press 0-87969-410-6/92 $3 + 00

β gene and IFN induction of antiviral genes have provided useful models for studying the mechanisms involved in gene induction and repression. In this review, we focus on the first step of the antiviral response: virus induction of the IFN-β gene.

Studies of the effects of promoter mutations on IFN-β gene expression in vivo have led to the precise localization of the DNA sequences required for virus induction (for review, see Maniatis et al. 1987; Maniatis 1988; Taniguchi 1988). A relatively small DNA fragment containing a surprisingly complex arrangement of positive and negative regulatory elements is capable of conferring transient virus induction on heterologous promoters. Attempts to identify the transcriptional regulatory proteins that specifically interact with this DNA fragment have led to the unexpected observation that individual elements within the IFN-β promoter are recognized by a number of different proteins. Determining which of these proteins are involved in the regulation of IFN-β gene expression has proved to be a formidable challenge. In this chapter, we describe our current understanding of the organization of IFN-β regulatory sequences and summarize recent progress in the identification and characterization of proteins that bind to the IFN-β promoter.

A comparison of the kinetics of accumulation of IFN-β mRNA with changes in the rate of transcription of the IFN-β gene indicates that transient induction of the IFN-β gene is due, at least in part, to transcriptional activation followed by postinduction repression of transcription (Whittemore and Maniatis 1990a). The kinetics of induction and decay of IFN-β mRNA can be altered by cycloheximide (CHX), an inhibitor of protein synthesis (for review, see DeMaeyer and DeMaeyer-Guignard 1988). In the presence of CHX or other metabolic inhibitors, virus induces the IFN-β gene to higher levels, and the level of IFN-β mRNA remains high late after induction. This phenomenon, called superinduction, is characteristic of many highly inducible genes (for review, see Brawerman 1989). Nuclear run-on transcription experiments indicate that CHX blocks transcriptional repression of the IFN-β gene, since in the presence of CHX, the rate of transcription remains high up to 24 hours after induction (Whittemore and Maniatis 1990a). CHX may therefore block the synthesis of a transcriptional repressor involved in postinduction turnoff of the IFN-β gene. CHX may also stabilize IFN-β mRNA, but the magnitude of the CHX-specific increase in transcription observed in nuclear transcription experiments indicates that any posttranscriptional effect is small.

Although the IFN-β gene is clearly turned off at the transcriptional level, rapid degradation of the transcript is also essential for the postinduction decrease in IFN-β mRNA (Whittemore and Maniatis

1990a). Analysis of fusion gene constructs in stably transfected mouse C127 cells indicates that there are two distinct destabilizers in the IFN-β transcript. One destabilizer is located in the 3′ untranslated region and is similar to the AU-rich "destabilizer" found in many other highly inducible genes (for review, see Brawerman 1989). The other destabilizer is located 5′ to the translation stop codon and, on the basis of a sequence comparison, is different from the AU-rich destabilizer. The destabilizers of the IFN-β transcript, although necessary for postinduction repression, do not appear to be regulated. Thus, postinduction repression of the IFN-β gene is the result of a combination of transcriptional repression and constant rapid decay of IFN-β transcripts.

ORGANIZATION OF THE IFN-β REGULATORY SEQUENCES

As shown in Figure 1A, the IFN-β gene promoter contains both positive and negative regulatory elements located within the 200 bp 5′ to the start site of transcription. Although many of these elements have been studied in isolation, the intact IFN-β promoter requires specific combinations of both positive and negative elements for proper regulation. The precise requirements for inducible expression vary with cell type, which may reflect varying concentrations of regulatory factors in these cells. Most of the studies described below have been performed in stably transformed mouse C127 cells using a bovine papillomavirus (BPV) vector or in mouse L cells by transient assay.

Two negative regulatory domains (NRDs) have thus far been identified. The 5′ end point of NRDII is located between −210 and −104. When this region of the IFN-β promoter is deleted, the basal level of transcription increases five- to tenfold (Zinn et al. 1983). Genomic footprinting studies in human MG63 cells reveal differences in the DNase digestion pattern in this region (−94 to −167) before and after induction (Zinn and Maniatis 1986). NRDI is also necessary for repression prior to induction (Goodbourn et al. 1986; Goodbourn and Maniatis 1988). Point mutations and deletions between −55 and −37 increase the basal level of transcription, and this region represses constitutive transcription when placed immediately upstream of a heterologous promoter. However, the precise 5′ end point of NRDI has not been identified, since NRDI overlaps a positive regulatory domain, and mutations in this overlapping region affect both basal and inducible levels of transcription. A genomic footprint is found between −55 and −37 of the IFN-β promoter in uninduced but not in induced human MG63 cells (Zinn and Maniatis 1986), suggesting that a repressor is bound to NRDI before induction and released or displaced after virus induction.

A.

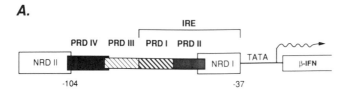

B.   PRDI :   A G A A G T G A A A G T G

        IRS: A G A A G T G A A A C T G

        HEX :   A A G T G A A A G T G A

Figure 1 (*A*) Organization of IFN-β gene regulatory sequences: The IFN-β transcript is denoted by an arrow, and numbers refer to distance in nucleotides from
the start site of transcription. The TATAA box (TATA), IFN gene regulatory
element (IRE), positive regulatory domains (PRD), and negative regulatory
domains (NRD) are labeled. Each box refers to a regulatory domain as specified.
See text for details and references. (*B*) The nucleotide sequence of PRDI (Goodbourn and Maniatis 1988), two copies of the hexamer (HEX) (Fujita et al. 1985),
and the IRS (taken from Wathelet et al. 1988). To align the sequences, PRDI has
been extended by one nucleotide at the 3 ′ end. N = G, A, T, or C; Y = C or T.

The negative regulatory domains were identified using a BPV vector
to stably transform mouse C127 cells (Zinn et al. 1983; Goodbourn et al.
1986; Goodbourn and Maniatis 1988). In these experiments, the transfected gene is carried on an extrachromosomal plasmid at a constant
copy number. Similar results were obtained with stably transfected HeLa
cells (Burstein 1986). However, NRD mutations do not alter the basal
level of transcription in transient expression experiments (Fujita et al.
1987; S. Goodbourn and T. Maniatis, unpubl.). These observations suggest that the repressors which interact with NRDI and NRDII are present
at low levels and can be sequestered by excess DNA in transient expression experiments. Alternatively, a specific chromatin structure may be
required for NRD-dependent repression, and the transfected genes in
transient assays may not acquire the necessary chromatin conformation.

    Four distinct positive regulatory domains have been identified
(PRDI–PRDIV, Fig. 1A). Although single copies of each of these
regulatory elements are not detectably inducible by virus, multimerized
copies of each or certain combinations of single copies are sufficient to
confer virus induction on heterologous promoters.

    PRDI was mapped by deletion and point mutation analysis between
−77 and −64 (Goodbourn and Maniatis 1988) and contains two copies of

the hexamer sequence AAGTG(A/G) (Fig. 1B) (Fujita et al. 1985). For the purpose of this discussion, we assume that one copy of PRDI is functionally equivalent to two copies of the hexamer (Goodbourn and Maniatis 1988; Keller and Maniatis 1988). However, we note that comparative studies that would rigorously establish this point have not been carried out. Besides being a virus-inducible element, multiple copies of the hexamer silence transcription when placed between the SV40 enhancer and a TATA box (Kuhl et al. 1987; Fan and Maniatis 1989). This silencing effect is reversed upon virus induction. Presumably, constitutive repressors that bind to PRDI are displaced by positive regulatory proteins upon induction.

The *interferon response sequence* (IRS) is a promoter element found in many IFN-inducible genes (for review, see Vilcek 1991). As shown in Figure 1B, the IRS of the H-2K^b gene promoter differs by only one nucleotide from PRDI. Although a promoter containing multiple copies of PRDI is induced by IFN-α/β and IFN-γ as well as by poly(I)-poly(C) and virus (Fan and Maniatis 1989 and unpubl.; MacDonald et al. 1990), the intact IFN-β promoter is not IFN-inducible. Conversely, a promoter containing multiple copies of the IRS is induced by IFN, as well as by poly(I)-poly(C) and virus (Wathelet et al. 1988; Fan and Maniatis 1989). Some, but not all, IFN-inducible genes are induced by poly(I)-poly(C) or virus (Wathelet et al. 1989). The possibility that the activation of PRDI or the IRS following virus infection is indirectly mediated by induced IFN has been ruled out by performing the virus inductions in cells which lack IFN-α and IFN-β genes (M. Wathelet et al., in prep.; A. Keller and T. Maniatis, unpubl.). These experiments indicate that although PRDI and the IRS in isolation are coordinately regulated, their regulation is distinct in the context of the intact promoters. Differences in activity of the intact promoters may be the result of negative regulatory domains that preclude binding of some positive regulatory factors.

PRDII, which is located between –66 and –55, was identified as a virus-inducible element distinct from PRDI by deletion and point mutation analysis in mouse C127 cells (Goodbourn et al. 1986; Goodbourn and Maniatis 1988) and by experiments which show that multiple copies of PRDII function as a virus-inducible enhancer on a heterologous promoter (Fan and Maniatis 1989; Fujita et al. 1989b; Visvanathan and Goodbourn 1989). Since PRDII overlaps NRDI, point mutations in this region affect both basal and inducible expression (Goodbourn et al. 1986; Goodbourn and Maniatis 1988). PRDII, in contrast to PRDI, does not silence transcription from the SV40 enhancer and is not inducible by IFN (Fan and Maniatis 1989). PRDII is also a stronger transcription element than PRDI and acts as a constitutive enhancer in C127 cells. The sequence of PRDII is similar to the asymmetric κB site consensus found in many enhancers (for review, see Lenardo and Baltimore 1989). The region between –77 and –37, which contains PRDI, PRDII, and NRDI, is sufficient to confer virus inducibility on a heterologous promoter in C127 cells (Goodbourn et al. 1985). This region, the interferon gene regulatory element (IRE), is necessary in all cell types tested, but is not sufficient in some cells, for virus-inducible expression.

PRDIII is a regulatory element located between –89 and –77. This region is necessary in addition to the IRE for virus induction in HeLa cells (Burstein 1986) and mouse L cells (Fujita et al. 1985, 1987; LeBlanc et al. 1990), but it is not necessary in mouse C127 cells. The high degree of similarity between the sequence of PRDI and PRDIII, and the observation that most proteins that bind PRDI also bind PRDIII, indicate that PRDIII is a variant of PRDI. Presumably, cells that require this element contain insufficient levels of PRDI-binding factor to activate a promoter containing only one PRDI site. Cooperative binding of this factor to the combined PRDI-PRDIII sites may therefore be sufficient to activate transcription in combination with PRDII.

Sequences located between –104 and –91 are required for virus induction in mouse L929 cells (Fujita et al. 1985) but not in C127 cells (Zinn et al. 1983). This region, which we have designated PRDIV, contains a binding site for the Oct family of transcription factors (for review, see Garcia-Blanco et al. 1989) and a binding site for the ATF/CREB family of transcription factors (Hai et al. 1988, 1989; Du and Maniatis 1992). However, mutations that decrease Oct-1 binding in vitro do not decrease the level of induction in mouse L929 cells, and multiple copies of the Oct-1 site are not virus-inducible (Du and Maniatis 1992). Thus, Oct family proteins do not appear to play a role in PRDIV-dependent virus induction. In contrast, base substitutions that interfere with ATF binding decrease the level of virus induction in mouse L929 cells, and multiple copies of PRDIV confer both cAMP and virus inducibility on a heterologous promoter (Du and Maniatis 1992). Work is in progress to identify the protein(s) involved in virus induction of PRDIV and to determine whether there is a relationship between virus and cAMP inducibility.

REGULATORY ELEMENTS REQUIRED FOR POSTINDUCTION REPRESSION

As discussed above, postinduction repression of the IFN-β gene occurs at the transcriptional level. Furthermore, the IRE fused to a heterologous gene can be appropriately induced and repressed at the transcriptional level in C127 cells (Whittemore and Maniatis 1990a). Thus, the regulatory elements involved in postinduction repression must be contained within the IRE. One candidate for the postinduction repressor-binding site is NRDI, since mutations in this site increase the basal level of transcription (Goodbourn et al. 1986). However, the kinetics of induction and decay of IFN-β mRNA are not affected by a deletion that removes most of the NRDI site (Whittemore and Maniatis 1990b). Thus, NRDI is not necessary for the normal shutoff of the IFN-β gene, indicating that the factors involved in postinduction repression are distinct from those involved in repression prior to induction.

The NRDI deletion mutant contains one copy each of PRDI and PRDII, indicating that one or both of these elements mediate postinduction repression. In fact, we find that multimers of either PRDI or PRDII are sufficient for postinduction repression (Whittemore and Maniatis 1990b). Thus, both elements function as positive and negative regulatory sequences. In addition, transcription induction mediated through both PRDI and PRDII can be superinduced in the presence of CHX. Therefore, CHX blocks the postinduction repression of both PRDI and PRDII, and it appears that a virus-inducible gene is involved in the postinduction repression of each of these elements. DNA-binding experiments using nuclear extracts from cells infected with virus indicate that there are CHX-sensitive DNA-binding activities that interact specifically with PRDI and PRDII. The existence of such DNA-binding activities is consistent with a model in which virus-inducible repressors displace the inducers acting on PRDI and PRDII, thereby repressing IFN-β gene transcription late after induction. One candidate for a PRDII postinduction repressor and two candidates for a PRDI repressor are discussed below.

PROTEINS THAT BIND TO THE IFN-β PROMOTER

Several experimental approaches have been taken to identify proteins that bind to the IFN-β gene promoter, including gel shift and footprinting experiments. Genes encoding these DNA-binding proteins have also been cloned by screening cDNA expression libraries.

These approaches have thus far failed to identify factors that bind specifically to NRDI or NRDII. In contrast, a large number of proteins that bind to each of the four positive regulatory domains have been identified (Fig. 2). However, it has been difficult to determine which of these proteins, if any, are directly involved in the regulation of IFN-β gene expression. Virus induction does not require protein synthesis but does alter the binding of factors to the IFN-β promoter (Zinn and Maniatis 1986). Thus, the regulatory factors involved in virus induction are likely to require posttranslational modification in order to bind the IFN-β promoter. Some or all of these factors involved in virus-mediated induction of the IFN-β promoter may therefore not be detected by screening bacterial expression libraries. Below, we summarize our current understanding of the proteins that bind specifically to IFN-β gene regulatory elements.

Proteins That Bind to PRDI

As shown in Figure 2, a number of PRDI-binding activities have been identified. Many of these activities are related to each other (IRF-related), but two are distinct (PRDI-BF1 and PRDI-BF2). Since PRDIII is similar to PRDI, and the PRDI-binding factors which have been tested bind to PRDIII, we will not discuss PRDIII-binding factors separately.

IRF-1

IRF-1 was isolated from a λgt11 cDNA library with a DNA probe containing multiple copies of the canonical hexamer sequence (5'-AAGTGA-3'; Miyamoto et al. 1988). The cDNA clone encodes a 37-kD protein that binds to PRDI in a manner indistinguishable from that of a previously characterized binding activity (Fujita et al. 1988) detected in nuclear tracts derived from mouse L929 cells. Since point mutations in PRDI that decrease the affinity of this binding activity in vitro significantly decrease the level of virus induction in vivo, it was suggested that IRF-1 plays an important role in virus induction of the IFN-β gene

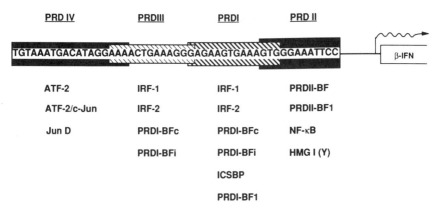

Figure 2 Proteins that bind to the positive regulatory domains of the IFN-β gene promoter: The sequences of the positive regulatory domains are shown within the boxes and the proteins that bind to these regions are listed under the corresponding boxes. Several gel shift activities that bind to PRDI, but may be identical to the factors listed, are not shown in the figure. See text for details and references.

(Fujita et al. 1988). Sequence analysis of IRF-1 reveals that the protein is largely hydrophobic but contains a stretch of basic amino acids within a hydrophilic region near the amino terminus. The carboxy-terminal region of the protein is acidic and rich in serine and threonine (Miyamoto et al. 1988).

High-level expression of an IRF-1 cDNA in monkey COS cells results in the activation of endogenous IFN-α and IFN-β genes (Fujita et al. 1989a). However, the level of IFN-β production is low compared to that obtained with virus induction. The effect on IFN-α expression is unexpected, since IRF-1 binds weakly to the IFN-α promoters tested, and virus infection of COS cells does not induce the endogenous IFN-α gene. Furthermore, in cotransfection experiments, IRF-1 activates a promoter containing multimerized copies of the hexamer sequence AAGTGA, but has only a weak stimulatory effect on the intact IFN-β promoter (Miyamoto et al. 1988; Harada et al. 1989; LeBlanc et al. 1990; MacDonald et al. 1990). Although these experiments show that IRF-1 is capable of stimulating transcription of promoters containing multiple copies of the hexamer sequence, they do not necessarily indicate that IRF-1 plays a role in virus induction of the endogenous IFN-β gene.

IRF-1 mRNA is induced by virus and IFN-α/β or IFN-γ (Fujita et al. 1989c; Harada et al. 1989; Pine et al. 1990). The kinetics of viral induction indicate that IRF-1 mRNA and IFN-β mRNA reach peak levels at approximately the same time. As would be expected for a newly synthesized protein, the virus- and IFN-induced gel shift activity that corresponds to IRF-1 is sensitive to CHX (Pine et al. 1990; L.-A. Whittemore et al., unpubl.). Since the IFN-β gene and IFN-α/β-inducible genes are induced in the presence of CHX in most cell types (for review, see DeMaeyer and DeMaeyer-Guignard 1988; Goldfeld and Maniatis 1989), the CHX-sensitive inducibility of IRF-1 cannot account for the activation of IFN-β or IFN-α/β activated genes. Although IRF-1 is currently the best-characterized candidate for a PRDI-dependent activator of IFN-β expression, it is possible that the true activator has not yet been identified. IRF-1 may be involved in virus induction, but may require a posttranslational modification that has not yet been detected. This modification would be required for transcriptional activation, but not for binding to the IFN-β promoter. Alternatively, the constitutive activity of IRF-1 may be sufficient for virus induction of the IFN-β gene, but repressors prevent IRF-1 binding prior to virus induction. It is also possible that IRF-1 is not involved in virus induction but may regulate the expression of other genes containing PRDI or IRS sequences. For example, IRF-1 may be involved in IFN-γ induction of IFN-stimulated genes. Consistent with this possibility is the fact that IRF-1 protein is highly induced by

IFN-γ (Pine et al. 1990) and that IFN-γ induction of most IFN-stimulated genes requires protein synthesis (Pine et al. 1990; for review, see DeMaeyer and DeMaeyer-Guignard 1988).

IRF-2

A second IRF-1-like binding factor was isolated by cross-hybridization with an IRF-1 cDNA probe (Harada et al. 1989). This protein, designated IRF-2, is homologous to IRF-1 at its amino terminus and has a molecular mass of 39.5 kD. IRF-2 binds specifically to multiple copies of the hexamer with an affinity that is approximately 5 times greater than that of IRF-1. Interestingly, there is no difference in the binding affinities of IRF-1 and IRF-2 for the intact IFN-β promoter, suggesting that these proteins recognize the sequences surrounding PRDI or that they recognize the single base pair difference between PRDI and two copies of the hexamer. Like IRF-1, IRF-2 mRNA is inducible by virus and IFN (Harada et al. 1989). Despite these similarities, the two proteins appear to have different functions.

IRF-2 has no effect on transcription of cotransfected reporter genes containing multiple hexamer sites, but it does block IRF-1-dependent transcription activation. Transfected IRF-2 also decreases the transcriptional activity of the SV40 enhancer when multiple hexamer sites are inserted between the enhancer and the TATA box (Kuhl et al. 1987; Fujita et al. 1988; MacDonald et al. 1990). Thus, in these assays, IRF-2 functions as a repressor. However, transfected IRF-2 has no effect on the intact IFN-β promoter in mouse L929 cells, and it is not known whether IRF-2 can repress transcription in virus-induced cells.

Recent experiments indicate that there is a correlation between IRF expression and virus induction of the IFN-β gene during mouse embryonal carcinoma (EC) cell differentiation (Harada et al. 1990). IFN-α and IFN-β genes are refractory to virus induction in undifferentiated (D⁻) EC cells but are highly inducible in differentiated (D⁺) cells. Neither IRF-1 nor IRF-2 is expressed in D⁻ EC cells, but both genes are induced by virus in D⁺ EC cells. Thus, the IFN-β and IRF genes appear to be coordinately regulated in EC cells.

ISGFs

The interferon-stimulated gene factors ISGF1, ISGF2, and ISGF3 are gel shift activities that bind to the ISRE (*i*nterferon-*s*timulated gene *r*egulatory *e*lement) of several interferon-stimulated genes (Levy et al. 1988). ISGF1 is a constitutive factor that binds to PRDI and the ISRE and may be identical to IRF-2. ISGF2 is an IFN-α/β- and IFN-γ-inducible factor whose induction is blocked by CHX. This factor also binds to PRDI and recently has been shown to be identical to IRF-1 (Pine et al. 1990). In addition, gel shift activities called IBP-1 (Blanar et al. 1989), Factor M, and Factor G (Imam et al. 1990) may be identical to IRF-1/ISGF2, and the gel shift activity called C1-C2 (Rutherford et al. 1988) may contain IRF-1/ISGF2 and IRF-2.

ISGF3, which may be identical to the gel shift activity called Factor E (Imam et al. 1990), is a multicomponent cytoplasmic factor that is assembled and transported to the nucleus upon induction with IFN-α (Levy et al. 1989). Thus, in contrast to IRF-1, the activity of ISGF3 is dependent on induction. ISGF3 activates the ISRE in an in vitro transcription assay (Fu et al. 1990), indicating that it is a positive regulator of IFN-inducible gene expression. Since ISGF3 does not bind to PRDI (Raj et al. 1989), it is not likely to have a role in IFN-β gene expression.

PRDI-BF$_c$

PRDI-BF$_c$ is detected in nuclear extracts from human MG63 cells (Keller and Maniatis 1988). This factor binds to the same sequence and displays the same methylation interference pattern as IRF-1 and IRF-2. In addition, PRDI-BF$_c$ binding is affected by the same mutations in PRDI that affect the binding of IRF-1 and IRF-2. Like IRF-2, the level of PRDI-BF$_c$-binding activity does not change significantly upon induction with virus or poly(I)-poly(C) (Keller and Maniatis 1988; Harada et al. 1989). The apparent molecular mass of PRDI-BF$_c$, determined by UV cross-linking experiments, is approximately 50 kD (V. Palombella et al., unpubl.). Anti-IRF-2 polyclonal antibodies were recently shown to bind specifically to PRDI-BF$_c$ in gel shift experiments (V. Palombella and T. Maniatis, unpubl.). Thus, PRDI-BF$_c$ and IRF-2 appear to be the same protein.

PRDI-BF$_i$

PRDI-BF$_i$ is not detected in nuclear extracts from uninduced cells, but it is present in extracts from cells treated with virus or poly(I)-poly(C) and CHX (Keller and Maniatis 1988). In some cell types, PRDI-BF$_i$ is also highly induced by CHX alone (V. Palombella and T. Maniatis, unpubl.). Since PRDI-BF$_i$ is induced in the absence of protein synthesis, it must be generated by posttranslational modification of a preexisting protein. The molecular mass of PRDI-BF$_i$ is approximately 24,000–29,000 kD, and the protein is recognized by anti-IRF-2 antibodies. Thus, PRDI-BF$_i$ may be either a proteolytic digestion product of IRF-2 or a smaller protein that shares antigenic determinants with IRF-2 (V. Palombella and T.

Maniatis, unpubl.). Experiments are in progress to distinguish between these possibilities. In either case, the postinduction modification of PRDI-BF$_i$ may be involved in virus induction of the IFN-β gene. If PRDI-BF$_i$ is a proteolyzed form of IRF-2, the induced cleavage may inactivate the negative regulatory activity of IRF-2. Thus, IRF-2 may be eliminated as an antagonist of positive regulatory proteins that interact with PRDI, or it may be converted to an activator. An alternative possibility is that intact IRF-2 is a repressor, but the proteolyzed form is an activator. However, truncated forms of IRF-2 do not activate transcription in cotransfection experiments (V. Palombella and T. Maniatis, unpubl.).

ICSBP

Interferon consensus sequence binding protein (ICSBP) was isolated from a murine λZAP expression library using a concatenated IFN consensus sequence (ICS) (Driggers et al. 1990). The ICS, which is equivalent to the IRS, is responsible for IFN-mediated induction of major histocompatibility complex (MHC) class I genes (Shirayoshi et al. 1988; Driggers et al. 1990). The ICSBP gene encodes a protein of 424 amino acids (48 kD), and the amino terminus of ICSBP, which contains the DNA-binding domain, has significant sequence similarity to the amino-terminal sequences of IRF-1 and IRF-2. In contrast, the carboxy-terminal region of ICSBP has no sequence similarity to either IRF-1 or IRF-2. In addition to binding the ICS of MHC class I genes, ICSBP binds the IRS of other IFN-inducible genes and the PRDI element of the IFN-β gene. Because of the similarities between IRF-1, IRF-2, and ICSBP, Driggers et al. (1990) conclude that ICSBP is a member of the IRF gene family. However, unlike IRF-1 and IRF-2, ICSBP is predominantly expressed in cells of the lymphoid/macrophage lineages. The role of ICSBP in the virus-inducible expression of the IFN-β gene and the IFN-regulated expression of MHC class I genes is not known.

PRDI-BF1

PRDI-BF1 was identified by screening a human λgt11 cDNA library with a probe containing multiple hexamer sites (Keller and Maniatis 1991). This 88-kD protein contains five zinc fingers near its carboxyl terminus which bind DNA (Fig. 3). The protein also contains a serine/threonine-rich region and acidic regions whose functions have yet to be established. DNA sequence analysis of the PRDI-BF1 cDNA reveals that PRDI-BF1 is not related to the IRF family of PRDI-binding proteins. Although both PRDI-BF1 and the IRF family of proteins bind

PRDI-BF1

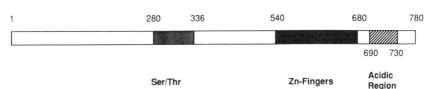

Figure 3 Structure of the PRDI-BF1 protein: The locations of the serine/threonine-rich region (shaded box), the acidic region (cross-hatched box), and zinc fingers (filled box) are indicated. The amino acids are numbered from the amino terminus (1–780) (Keller and Maniatis 1991).

to PRDI, the DNA sequences required for binding are different. Methylation of guanines at positions –72 and –70 interferes with both PRDI-BF1 and IRF binding. However, methylation of the guanine at –66 interferes completely with PRDI-BF1 binding but only partially with IRF binding (Harada et al. 1989). Significantly, this nucleotide distinguishes PRDI from the IRS. As predicted from the methylation interference patterns, IRF proteins bind to both PRDI and IRS with approximately equal affinities, whereas PRDI-BF1 binds to PRDI with a higher affinity than to the ISRE (Keller and Maniatis 1991).

Cotransfection studies indicate that PRDI-BF1 is a potent repressor of PRDI-dependent transcriptional activation. PRDI-BF1 is capable of blocking virus induction of the intact IFN-β promoter or of a synthetic promoter containing multiple copies of PRDI (Keller and Maniatis 1991). As predicted from the aforementioned in vitro binding studies, PRDI-BF1 is only a weak repressor of ISRE-dependent virus induction. Interestingly, PRDI-BF1 can block the activity of the SV40 enhancer by a 500-fold ratio when PRDI sites are placed between the enhancer and promoter. However, PRDI-BF1 does not block transcription when the PRDI sites are positioned more than 15 bp upstream of the TATA box. Thus, PRDI-BF1 appears to block transcription in this context by interfering with the binding or activity of factors bound to the TATA box and can mediate this effect only when the PRDI sites are close to the TATA box. By analogy, PRDI-BF1 may repress PRDI-dependent transcription by interfering with the binding or activity of transcription factors bound to PRDI and to sites immediately adjacent to PRDI.

The PRDI-BF1 gene is induced by virus in human MG63 cells. PRDI-BF1 mRNA is present at low levels prior to induction, increases as early as 4 hours postinduction, and then continues to increase for the next

20 hours. The highest levels of PRDI-BF1 mRNA correspond to the period of postinduction repression of the IFN-β gene. Thus, PRDI-BF1 may be a repressor that is synthesized over the course of viral infection and shuts down transcription of the IFN-β gene late after induction.

As discussed above, IRF-2 is also a virus-inducible transcriptional repressor. However, IRF-2 differs from PRDI-BF1 in many respects. In particular, PRDI-BF1, which binds to PRDI but not to the IRS, is virus-inducible but not IFN-inducible. IRF-2, which binds to both PRDI and the IRS, is both virus- and IFN-inducible (Harada et al. 1989). Furthermore, although there is an inverse correlation between the levels of PRDI-BF1 and IFN-β mRNA during the shutoff phase of virus induction, IRF-2 and IFN-β mRNA are coordinately regulated by virus. These differences are consistent with PRDI-BF1's having a role in postinduction repression of the IFN-β gene and IRF-2's having a negative role prior to or early in the induction of IFN and/or IFN-responsive genes.

Proteins That Bind to PRDII

Several proteins bind specifically to PRDII, including PRDII-BF (Keller and Maniatis 1988), PRDII-BF1 (Fan and Maniatis 1990), NF-κB (Fujita et al. 1989b; Hiscott et al. 1989; Lenardo et al. 1989; Visvanathan and Goodbourn 1989), and HMG I(Y) (D. Thanos and T. Maniatis, in prep.). Only two of these proteins, NF-κB and HMG (I)Y, have been implicated in IFN-β gene expression.

PRDII-BF

PRDII-BF was identified in nuclear extracts from human MG63 cells using the IFN-β promoter as a probe in gel shift experiments (Keller and Maniatis 1988). This factor is present in extracts prepared from cells before and after virus induction, and the level does not increase upon induction. UV cross-linking experiments reveal that PRDII-BF exhibits a monomer molecular mass of approximately 65 kD. Single base mutations in PRDII that decrease the level of virus induction significantly decrease the affinity of PRDII for PRDII-BF (Keller and Maniatis 1988). PRDII-BF has not been further characterized, and the gene encoding this protein has not been cloned.

PRDII-BF1

PRDII-BF1 was identified by screening a λgt11 human cDNA library with a probe containing multiple copies of PRDII (Fan and Maniatis 1990). Sequence analysis of this protein reveals that it corresponds to the cDNA clones designated HIV-EP1 (Maekawa et al. 1989) and MBP1 (Baldwin et al. 1990). The full-length PRDII-BF1 cDNA clone (9.5 kb) contains an open reading frame of 8151 nucleotides, encoding a protein of 298 kD, the largest sequence-specific DNA-binding protein yet identified. A remarkable feature of this protein is that it contains two sets of TFIIIA-type zinc finger motifs separated by 1640 amino acids (Fig. 4). The amino acid sequences of the two sets of zinc fingers are 70% similar, suggesting that they recognize the same DNA sequence. This possibility has been confirmed by experiments which show that bacterially produced fusion proteins containing either set of zinc fingers bind independently to PRDII or an H-2K^b gene promoter element, with a fourfold higher affinity for the latter site (Fan and Maniatis 1990).

A protein with two separate DNA-binding domains that recognize the same DNA sequence is unprecedented. At least three different *Drosophila* transcriptional regulatory proteins contain separated zinc finger motifs (Tautz et al. 1987; Reuter et al. 1990; Fasano et al. 1991). However, it is not known if these DNA-binding domains interact with the same or different recognition sequences. Bacterial proteins containing two DNA-binding domains that interact with different DNA sequences have been reported (Moitoso de Vargas et al. 1988; Mizuuchi and Mizuuchi 1989). In these cases, the proteins are involved in the assembly of multicomponent protein-DNA complexes required for recombination processes involving DNA insertion and excision. It is possible that PRDII-BF1 plays a similar role in assembling multiprotein transcription complexes.

The prediction that PRDII-BF1 binds simultaneously to two linked binding sites was recently tested using a truncated version of the protein expressed in bacteria. This truncated protein, which contains both sets of zinc fingers, coordinately binds to two linked PRDII and/or H-2K^b sites when the sites are separated by as many as 54 bp or as few as 6 bp. Intact PRDII-BF1 also binds coordinately to two binding sites separated by ap-

Figure 4 Structure of the PRDII-BF1 protein: The locations of the acidic region (cross-hatched box) and zinc fingers (filled boxes) are indicated. The amino acids are numbered from the amino terminus (1–2797) (Fan and Maniatis 1990).

proximately 500 bp (C.-M. Fan and T. Maniatis, unpubl.). This complex has been visualized by electron microscopy (Y.H. Wang et al., in prep.) and appears as a looped structure. The size of the protein bound to the loop junction suggests that PRDII-BF1 binds as both a monomer and a dimer. This possibility is confirmed by gel filtration and glycerol gradient experiments, which indicate that PRDII-BF1 is capable of forming a complex at least twice as large as its predicted molecular weight (C.-M. Fan and T. Maniatis, unpubl.). Thus, PRDII-BF1 may form multimers that bind at least four cognate sequences at the same time.

DNase I footprinting experiments on the intact human IFN-β promoter reveal that there are indeed four binding sites for the PRDII-BF1 protein. The protein not only binds to PRDII, but also coordinately binds to one site within NRDI, another site over the TATA box, and a third site between the TATA box and the start site of transcription (C.-M. Fan and T. Maniatis, unpubl.). Thus, PRDII-BF1, by forming multimers, acquires the ability to cover most of the IFN-β promoter.

PRDII-BF1 is virus-inducible, and maximal levels of PRDII-BF1 mRNA are observed at the time when the IFN-β gene is being switched off. Recent studies show that PRDII-BF1 can repress transcription of PRDII-containing promoters in cotransfection experiments. These observations suggest PRDII-BF1 may mediate postinduction repression by blocking access of positive-acting transcription factors.

NF-κB

NF-κB was first identified as a B-cell-specific nuclear protein that binds to the κB site of the immunoglobulin kappa chain (Igκ) gene enhancer (Sen and Baltimore 1986a,b). Subsequently, NF-κB was shown to be present in the cytoplasm of many cell types, complexed to an inhibitor protein designated IκB (Baeuerle and Baltimore 1988). Stimulation of these cells with a variety of agents, such as phorbol esters, cAMP, or lipopolysaccharide, leads to the dissociation of the NF-κB/IκB complex and the appearance of NF-κB-binding activity in the nucleus. NF-κB-binding sites have been identified in a large number of promoters and enhancers (Lenardo and Baltimore 1989).

Purified NF-κB consists of two subunits, p50 and p65 (proteins of 50 and 65 kD) (Kawakami et al. 1988; Baeuerle and Baltimore 1989). Although both p50 and p65 contribute to sequence-specific DNA binding, only p65 is required for IκB association and inhibition (Baeuerle and Baltimore 1989; Urban and Baeuerle 1990). The cDNA sequence encoding p50 contains an open reading frame (ORF) capable of encoding a 105-kD protein (Ghosh et al. 1990; Kieren et al. 1990), and the p50-

coding sequence is located at the amino terminus of the ORF. Recently, pulse-chase experiments have shown that the p50 is produced by proteolytic processing of p105 (Fan and Maniatis 1991). The amino acid sequence of the carboxyl terminus of p105 is similar to IκB (Haskill et al. 1991) in that both contain the "ankyrin" repeats, which are found in some proteins involved in tissue differentiation and cell cycle regulation (Lux et al. 1990). The level of p105 mRNA is inducible by mitogens (Bours et al. 1990), and nuclear NF-κB-binding activity correlates with B-cell differentiation (Sen and Baltimore 1986b). Both p50 and p65 are members of the *rel* gene family (Ghosh et al. 1990; Kieren et al. 1990; Nolan et al. 1991; Ruben et al. 1991), and they both bind DNA. However, they display different recognition properties (Urban et al. 1991). Several other *rel*-related polypeptides have also been shown to bind to the κB site (Ballard et al. 1990). c-*rel* and v-*rel*, as well as NF-κB p50 and p65, display different transcriptional activities (Inoue et al. 1991; Fan and Maniatis 1991). Strikingly, the *Drosophila dorsal* gene product is homologous to the *rel* family members (Steward 1987) and displays sequence-specific activation and repression of target genes (Ip et al. 1991; Thisse et al. 1991). The above observations suggest that NF-κB belongs to the evolutionarily conserved *rel/dorsal* family of transcription factors.

A number of observations indicate that NF-κB or other members of the *rel* gene family may play an important role in the PRDII-dependent virus induction of the IFN-β gene (Fujita et al. 1989b; Hiscott et al. 1989; Lenardo et al. 1989; Visvanathan and Goodbourn 1989). First, NF-κB binds specifically to the PRDII site of the IFN-β promoter, and PRDII mutations that decrease virus induction in vivo also decrease the affinity of NF-κB for PRDII in vitro (Lenardo et al. 1989; Visvanathan and Goodbourn 1989). Second, studies of promoters containing multiple κB or PRDII sites indicate that the two sites are functionally interchangeable (Hiscott et al. 1989; Lenardo et al. 1989; LeBlanc et al. 1990). Both elements function as constitutive enhancers in B cells and virus-inducible enhancers in fibroblasts. Finally, and perhaps most significantly, the binding and nuclear localization of NF-κB is activated by virus or poly(I)-poly(C) (Fujita et al. 1989b; Hiscott et al. 1989; Lenardo et al. 1989; Visvanathan and Goodbourn 1989). This conclusion is strengthened by the observation that virus infection of pre-B lymphocytes induces the endogenous IFN-β and Igκ genes (Lenardo et al. 1989). However, activation of NF-κB by LPS treatment induces the Igκ genes but not the IFN-β genes. Thus, nuclear NF-κB activity appears to be necessary, but clearly is not sufficient, for virus induction.

An obvious possibility is that dsRNA activates NF-κB through activation of the dsRNA-dependent kinase. Other protein kinases, such as protein kinase A and protein kinase C, phosphorylate IκB and lead to the dissociation of the NF-κB/IκB complex (Shirakawa and Mizel 1989; Ghosh and Baltimore 1990). In the context of this idea, it is of interest that 2-aminopurine, an inhibitor of dsRNA-dependent kinase in vitro, blocks virus induction of the intact IFN-β gene (Marcus and Sekellick 1988; Zinn et al. 1988; Wathelet et al. 1989), as well as a promoter containing two copies of PRDII (L.-A. Whittemore and T. Maniatis, unpubl.). However, attempts to show that dsRNA-dependent kinase activates or that 2-aminopurine blocks the induction of NF-κB have thus far failed.

HMG I(Y)

Yet another protein that binds to PRDII was identified by screening a human λgt11 library with multiple copies of PRDII. Two distinct cDNA clones were recovered. Both cDNAs encode high mobility group (HMG) proteins. HMGs are basic low-molecular-weight chromatin-associated proteins (for review, see Bustin et al. 1990). One cDNA encodes HMG I and the other encodes HMG Y, an isoform of HMG I, which differs from HMG I by the absence of 11 amino acids. The functional significance of this difference is not known. HMG I(Y) cDNA clones were first isolated by Reeves and co-workers (Johnson et al. 1988) on the basis of the amino acid sequence of the purified proteins and subsequently isolated from a human λgt11 library using an octamer protein-binding site as a probe (Eckner and Birnsteil 1989). As shown in Figure 5, both HMG I and HMG Y contain a basic amino acid motif repeated three times and an acidic region located close to the carboxyl terminus of the protein.

Antisense inhibition experiments have provided evidence for direct involvement of HMG I(Y) in IFN-β gene regulation (D. Thanos and T. Maniatis, in prep.). Cotransfection of a mammalian expression vector containing the HMG I(Y) cDNA in the antisense orientation reduces the basal level of expression and blocks virus induction from reporter plasmids containing either the intact IFN-β promoter or multiple PRDII sites linked to CAT (D. Thanos and T. Maniatis, in prep.). No significant effect is observed when the HMG I(Y) sense plasmid is cotransfected in a similar experiment, nor does antisense HMG I(Y) affect the basal or virus-induced expression of a reporter plasmid containing multiple copies of PRDI. Thus, the block to virus induction is specific to the HMG I(Y) antisense plasmid and to PRDII.

Gel shift experiments indicate that HMG I(Y) has the unusual property of binding to PRDII but not to the κB element. Antisense HMG I(Y)

HMG I

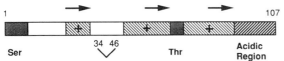

Figure 5 Structure of the HMG I protein: The locations of the serine-rich, threonine-rich, and the acidic regions are indicated. The basic regions are denoted by reverse cross-hatched boxes and plus signs. Arrows indicate repeats within the basic regions. The amino acids are numbered from the amino terminus (1–107), and the v indicates amino acids that are missing in the HMG Y protein (Johnson et al. 1988).

has no effect on κB-dependent virus induction, whereas PRDII-dependent induction is blocked (D. Thanos and T. Maniatis, in prep.). Thus, HMG I(Y) is required for PRDII- but not κB-dependent virus induction, suggesting that HMG I(Y) alters the DNA or chromatin structure of PRDII to allow a functional NF-κB/PRDII complex to form.

The relationship between HMG I(Y) and NF-κB binding at PRDII was investigated by comparing the effects of single base mutations on HMG I(Y) and on NF-κB binding (Lenardo et al. 1989; Visvanathan and Goodbourn 1989; D. Thanos and T. Maniatis, in prep.) with the effects of the same mutations on virus induction in vivo (Goodbourn and Maniatis 1988). In general, mutations in the AT-rich region in the middle of the PRDII-binding site (GGGAAATTCC) have the strongest negative effect on HMG I(Y) binding, whereas mutations in the GC-rich flanking sequence primarily reduce binding to NF-κB. Significantly, both types of mutations decrease the level of virus induction in vivo. These observations suggest that both NF-κB binding and HMG I(Y) binding are required for induction, but that the two proteins interact with different regions of PRDII. This possibility is supported by the demonstration that HMG I(Y) binds to the minor groove of duplex DNA (Solomon et al. 1986), whereas NF-κB contacts bases in the major groove (Sen and Baltimore 1986a). Work is in progress to determine whether NF-κB and HMG I(Y) can simultaneously bind to PRDII.

At present, the requirement of HMG I(Y) for virus induction is not understood. Cotransfection of HMG I(Y) does not significantly enhance the level of virus induction of transfected reporter genes in HeLa cells, suggesting that endogenous HMG I(Y) is not limiting or that HMG I(Y) is not a transcription activator. The latter possibility is supported by the observation that cotransfection of a mammalian expression vector containing a GAL4/HMG I(Y) fusion gene does not stimulate expression of reporter genes containing GAL4-binding sites before or after virus induction (D. Thanos and T. Maniatis, unpubl.). As mentioned above, it is possible that HMG I(Y) alters the DNA structure or chromatin configuration of the promoter in such a way that NF-κB may then activate transcription. Overexpression of NF-κB heterodimer in cells without virus induction leads to the activation of transcription mediated by PRDII to the same extent as virus induction, suggesting that induction of PRDII per se is dependent on the nuclear appearance of NF-κB, not further modification of HMG I(Y) and/or NF-κB proteins after virus treatment.

The possibility that HMG I(Y) alters the structure of DNA is suggested by similarities between this protein and a bacterial protein termed integration host factor (IHF) (White et al. 1989; for reviews, see Friedman 1988; Nash 1990). Like HMG I(Y), IHF is a small basic protein that binds specifically to AT-rich sequences in DNA through the minor groove. IHF binding induces a bend or kink in DNA, and this protein-DNA interaction plays a critical role in a variety of biological processes, including site-specific recombination and gene expression. IHF mediates both positive and negative control of gene expression in *Escherichia coli* (Griffo et al. 1989; Giladi et al. 1990), and IHF-induced DNA bending may facilitate interactions between RNA polymerase and a transcription factor that regulates a nitrogen fixation operon in *Klebsiella pneumoniae* (Hoover et al. 1990). We are currently carrying out experiments to determine whether HMG I(Y) bends DNA and whether this bending facilitates the binding and/or transcriptional activity of NF-κB.

Proteins That Bind to PRDIV

The sequence of PRDIV is similar to the DNA sequences recognized by the ATF family of proteins. The ATF family of proteins are leucine zipper proteins that bind to a group of cAMP-inducible and adenovirus E1A-responsive sequence elements (Hai et al. 1988, 1989). We have shown that ATF-2, a cellular transcription factor that is activated by adenovirus E1A protein (Liu and Green 1990), binds specifically to PRDIV (Du and Maniatis 1992). Single base mutations in PRDIV that interfere with ATF-2 binding decrease virus induction of the intact IFN-β promoter in mouse L929 cells (Du and Maniatis 1992), suggesting that ATF-2 or a protein with related binding characteristics is involved in virus induction. To determine whether the transcriptional activity of ATF-2 is stimulated by virus induction, we cotransfected a mammalian expression vector containing a GAL4/ATF-2 fusion gene with a reporter gene containing multiple GAL4-binding sites and tested for virus induction, cAMP induction, and E1A stimulation. As expected from previous experiments (Liu and Green 1990), the GAL4/ATF-2 fusion responded to E1A. However, this fusion did not respond to virus or cAMP induction. Thus, although ATF-2 binds specifically to PRDIV, it does not appear to be involved in PRDIV-dependent virus induction. On the basis of the similarity between PRDIV and ATF-binding sites, PRDIV may be recognized by other proteins in the leucine zipper family of transcription factors. Recently, we found that NF-IL6, a member of the C/EBP family of transcription factors, also binds to PRDIV (W. Du and T. Maniatis, unpubl.). Experiments are in progress to identify the protein(s) involved in virus induction of PRDIV.

CONCLUSIONS AND PERSPECTIVES

Studies of IFN-β gene regulation have led to significant advances in our understanding of the general mechanisms of eukaryotic gene regulation. For example, characterization of the IFN-β promoter provided one of the first examples of an inducible enhancer (Goodbourn et al. 1985). In addition, studies of distinct IFN-β promoter elements demonstrated striking differences between the transcriptional activities of single and multiple copies of these elements (Fujita et al. 1987; Fan and Maniatis 1989; MacDonald et al. 1990). Evidence for negative control in higher eukaryotic gene regulation was also provided by studies of the IFN-β promoter (Goodbourn et al. 1986; Zinn and Maniatis 1986), and further experiments indicated that different factors must be involved in pre- and postinduction repression (Whittemore and Maniatis 1990b). The negative regulatory elements NRDI and NRDII are involved in stable repression of the gene prior to induction, whereas postinduction repression is mediated by the same elements required for induction (PRDI and PRDII). Thus, these IFN-β promoter elements function in both positive and negative control during virus induction.

Another important concept to emerge from studies of IFN-β gene regulation is the combinatorial mechanism of virus induction (Goodbourn and Maniatis 1988; Fan and Maniatis 1989). Maximal levels of virus induction in some cell types require at least four distinct regulatory elements that are not detectably inducible in isolation. The requirement for multiple independent pathways of activation, in conjunction with negative control mechanisms, results in highly stringent control of IFN-β gene expression.

Studies of IFN-β gene expression have also indicated the limitations of biochemical and "reverse genetic" approaches in studying gene regulation. The naive view entertained at the outset of our study was that an understanding of gene regulation could be achieved by identifying the sequences required for regulation and subsequently identifying the proteins that bind specifically to those sequences. The cloning and characterization of genes encoding those proteins would then allow biochemical studies that would reveal mechanistic details of gene regulation. Although this approach provided valuable information regarding the organization of the promoter and led to the identification and cloning of genes that encode proteins that bind specifically to the promoter, it has not led to the definitive identification of the IFN-β gene regulatory proteins. A large number of different proteins bind to individual IFN-β promoter elements, and these elements are found in other genes that are not virus-inducible. Unambiguous identification of IFN-β regulatory proteins may therefore require a genetic approach involving selective inactivation of the genes that encode these proteins.

As discussed above, a number of different positive and negative regulatory proteins bind specifically to the IFN-β promoter. Thus far, two candidates for a PRDI-specific positive regulatory protein have been identified: IRF-1 and PRDI-BF$_i$. Although a number of observations are consistent with the possibility that IRF-1 is involved in IFN-β gene regulation, direct evidence has not yet been obtained. If IRF-1 is involved in virus induction, its activity must be altered by a virus-inducible posttranslational modification that has yet to be detected. IRF-1 is clearly not sufficient for virus induction of IFN-β, but a virus activated form of IRF-1 may synergize with regulatory proteins bound to another region of the IFN-β promoter such as PRDII. It is also possible that IRF-1 is involved in regulating other genes that contain PRDI-like elements in their promoters.

PRDI-BF$_i$ is the only known PRDI-binding factor that is modified upon virus induction. Thus far, there is no evidence that this protein is a transcriptional activator. In fact, preliminary studies suggest that PRDI-BF$_i$ may be a truncated form of IRF-2. If this is the case, virus induction may involve altering the balance of IRF-1 and IRF-2 competition for PRDI in favor of IRF-1. We are currently determining the structure of PRDI-BF$_i$ as a first step in testing this possibility.

There is considerable evidence that NF-κB or another member of the NF-κB family plays a role in PRDII-dependent virus induction. HMG I(Y) is also required for induction of PRDII but is probably not a transcription activator. On the basis of the observations discussed above, we believe that HMG I(Y) may alter the DNA structure of the IFN-β promoter to allow the formation of a functional NF-κB/PRDII complex. This interesting mechanism, which plays an important role in prokaryotic gene regulation, is unprecedented in the regulation of higher eukaryotic gene expression.

The factor(s) that activates PRDIV in response to virus induction has not been identified. The most likely candidate for a PRDIV regulatory protein is a member of the ATF family of transcription factors. An interesting possibility, suggested by the behavior of PRDIV, is that there is an overlap in the regulatory pathways of virus and cAMP induction.

The postinduction decrease in IFN-β mRNA levels is the result of transcriptional repression and rapid turnover of IFN-β mRNA. Since protein synthesis is necessary for postinduction repression, virus-inducible CHX-sensitive activities must be involved. Both PRDI-BF1 and IRF-2 are candidates for PRDI repressors. The kinetics of virus induction for PRDII-BF1 suggest that it may be a postinduction repressor of PRDII. However, attempts to demonstrate that PRDII-BF1 blocks virus induction of the IFN-β promoter have thus far failed.

Is the complexity of the IFN-β promoter exceptional, or is it an indication of the general mechanisms required to achieve the high degree of specificity characteristic of gene activation in higher eukaryotes? Relatively simple mechanisms appear to be involved in heat shock and hormone induction of gene expression. However, studies of growth-factor-regulated genes and developmentally regulated *Drosophila* genes have uncovered more complex arrangements of positive and negative regulatory elements. IFN-β gene regulation may therefore continue to provide a useful model for studying complex molecular interactions required for specific gene activation in higher eukaryotes.

ACKNOWLEDGMENTS

We are grateful to Marc Wathelet and M. Aleida Leza for their useful critical comments on the text.

REFERENCES

Baeuerle, A.S. and D. Baltimore. 1988. IκB: A specific inhibitor of the NF-κB transcription factor. *Science* **242:** 540–545.

————. 1989. A 65 kD subunit of active NF-κB is required for inhibition of NF-κB by IκB. *Genes Dev.* **3:** 1689–1698.

Baldwin, A.S., Jr., K.P. LeClair, H. Singh, and P.A. Sharp. 1990. A large protein containing zinc finger domains binds to related sequence elements in the enhancers of the class I major histocompatibility complex and kappa immunoglobulin genes. *Mol. Cell. Biol.* **10:** 1406–1414.

Ballard, D.W., W.H. Walker, S. Doerre, P. Sista, J.A. Molitor, E.P. Dixon, N.J. Peffer, M. Hannick, and W.C. Greene. 1990. The v-*rel* oncogene encodes a κB enhancer protein that inhibits NF-κB function. *Cell* **63:** 803–814.

Blanar, M.A., A.S. Baldwin, Jr., R.A. Flavell, and P.A. Sharp. 1989. A gamma-interferon-induced factor that binds the interferon response sequence of the MHC class I gene, H-2K^b. *EMBO. J.* **8:** 1139–1144.

Bours, V., J. Villalobos, P.R. Burd, K. Kelly, and U. Siebenlist. 1990. Cloning of a mitogen-inducible gene encoding a κB DNA-binding protein with homology to the *rel* oncogene and to cell-cycle motifs. *Nature* **348:** 76–80.

Brawerman, G. 1989. mRNA decay: Finding the right targets. *Cell* **57:** 9–10.

Burstein, H. 1986. "Regulatory sequence requirements for human β-interferon gene expression." Undergraduate thesis, Harvard University, Cambridge, Massachusetts.

Bustin, M., D.A. Lehn, and D. Landsman. 1990. Structural features of the HMG chromosomal proteins and their genes. *Biochim. Biophys. Acta* **1049:** 231–243.

DeMaeyer, E. and J. DeMaeyer-Guignard. 1988. *Interferons and other regulatory cytokines.* Wiley, New York.

Driggers, P.H., D.L. Ennist, S.L. Gleason, W.-H. Mak, M.S. Marks, B.-Z. Levi, J.R. Flanagan, E. Appella, and K. Ozato. 1990. An interferon γ-regulated protein that binds the interferon-inducible enhancer element of the major histocompatibility complex class I genes. *Proc. Natl. Acad. Sci.* **87:** 3743–3747.

Du, W. and T. Maniatis. 1992. An active transcription factor/cAMP response element binding protein is required for virus induction of the human interferon β-gene. *Proc. Natl. Acad. Sci.* **89:** (in press).

Eckner, R. and M.L. Birnsteil. 1989. Cloning of cDNAs coding for human HMG I and HMG Y proteins: Both are capable of binding to the octamer sequence motif. *Nucleic Acids Res.* **17:** 5947–5959.

Fan, C.-M. and T. Maniatis. 1989. Two different virus-inducible elements are required for human β-IFN gene regulation. *EMBO. J.* **8:** 101–110.

——— . 1990. A DNA-binding protein containing two widely separated zinc finger motifs that recognize the same DNA sequence. *Genes Dev.* **4:** 29–42.

———.1991. Generation of p50 subunit of NF-κB by processing of p105 through an ATP-dependent pathway. *Nature* **354:** 395–398.

Fasano, L., L. Roder, N. Core, E. Alexandre, C. Vola, B. Jacq, and S. Kerridge. 1991 . The gene *teashirt* is required for the development of *Drosophila* embryonic trunk segments and encodes a protein with widely spaced zinc finger motifs. *Cell* **64:** 63–79.

Friedman, R.L. 1988. Integration host factor: A protein for all reasons. *Cell* **55:** 545–554.

Fu, X.-Y., D.S. Levy, S.A. Veals, D.E. Levy, and J.E. Darnell, Jr. 1990. ISGF3, the transcriptional activator induced by interferon α, consists of multiple interacting polypeptide chains. *Proc. Natl. Acad. Sci.* **87:** 8555–8559.

Fujita, T., S. Ohno, H. Yasumitsu, and T. Taniguchi. 1985. Delimination of DNA sequences required for the regulated expression of human interferon-β gene. *Cell* **41:** 489–496.

Fujita, T., H. Ahibuya, H. Hotta, K. Yamanishi, and T. Taniguchi. 1987. Interferon β gene regulation: Tandemly repeated sequences of a synthetic 6 bp oligomer function as a virus inducible enhancer. *Cell* **49:** 357–367.

Fujita, T., Y. Kimura, M. Miyamoto, E.L. Barsoumian, and T. Taniguchi. 1989a. Induction of endogenous IFN-α and IFN-β genes by a regulatory transcription factor, IRF-1. *Nature* **337:** 270–272.

Fujita, T., M. Miyamoto, Y. Kimura, J. Hammer, and T. Taniguchi. 1989b. Involvement of a *cis*-element that binds as H2TF/NF-κB-like factor(s) in the virus-induced interferon-β gene expression. *Nucleic Acids Res.* **17:** 3335–3346.

Fujita, T., F.L. Reis, N. Watanabe, Y. Kimura, T. Taniguchi, and J. Vilcek. 1989c. Induction of the transcription factor IRF-1 and interferon-β mRNAs by cytokines and activators of second-messenger pathways. *Proc. Natl. Acad. Sci.* **86:** 9936–9940.

Fujita, T., J. Sakakibara, Y. Sudo, M. Miyamoto, Y. Kimura, and T. Taniguchi. 1988. Evidence for a nuclear factor(s), IRF-1, mediating induction and silencing properties to human IFN-β gene regulatory elements. *EMBO J.* **7:** 3397–3405.

Garcia-Blanco, M.A., R.G. Clerc, and P.A. Sharp. 1989. The DNA-binding homeo domain of the Oct-2 protein. *Genes Dev.* **3:** 739–745.

Ghosh, S. and D. Baltimore. 1990. Activation in vitro of NF-κB by phosphorylation of its inhibitor IκB. *Nature* **344:** 678–682.

Ghosh, S., A.M. Gifford, L.R. Riviere, P. Tempst, G.P. Nolan, and D. Baltimore. 1990. Cloning of the p50 DNA binding subunit of NF-κB: Homology to *rel* and *dorsal. Cell* **62:** 1019–1029.

Giladi, H., M. Gottesman, and A.B. Oppenheim. 1990. Integration host factor stimulates the phage lambda pL promoter. *J. Mol. Biol.* **213:** 109–121.

Goldfeld, A.E. and T. Maniatis. 1989. Coordinate viral induction of tumor necrosis factor α and interferon β in human B cells and monocytes. *Proc. Natl. Acad. Sci.* **86:** 1490–1494.

Goodbourn, S. and T. Maniatis. 1988. Overlapping positive and negative regulatory domains of the human β-interferon gene. *Proc. Natl. Acad. Sci.* **85:** 1447–1451.

Goodbourn, S.E.Y., H. Burstein, and T. Maniatis. 1986. The human β-interferon gene enhancer is under negative control. *Cell* **45:** 601–610.

Goodbourn, S.E.Y., K. Zinn, and T. Maniatis. 1985. Human β-interferon gene expression is regulated by an inducible enhancer element. Cell **41:** 509–520.

Griffo, G., A.B. Oppenheim, and M.E. Gottesman. 1989. Repression of the λ p*cin* promoter by integration host factor. *J. Mol. Biol.* **209:** 55–64.

Hai, T., L. Fang, W.J. Coukas, and M.R. Green. 1989. Transcription factor ATF cDNA clones: An extensive family of leucine zipper proteins able to selectively form DNA-binding heterodimers. *Genes Dev.* **3:** 2083–2090.

Hai, T., L. Fang, A. Alegretto, M. Karin, and M.R. Green. 1988. A family of immunologically related transcription factors that includes multiple forms of ATF and AP-1. *Genes Dev.* **2:** 1216–1226.

Harada, H., K. Willison, J. Sakakibara, M. Miyamoto, T. Fujita, and T. Taniguchi. 1990. Absence of the type I IFN system in EC cells: Transcriptional activator (IRF-1) and repressor (IRF-2) genes are developmentally regulated. *Cell* **63:** 303–312.

Harada, H., T. Fujita, M. Miyamoto, Y. Kimura, M. Maruyama, A. Furia, T. Miyata, and T. Taniguchi. 1989. Structurally similar but functionally distinct factors, IRF-1 and IRF-2, bind to the same regulatory elements of IFN and IFN-inducible genes. *Cell* **58:** 729–739.

Haskill, S., A.A. Berg, S.M. Tompkins, J.S. Morris, A.D. Yurochko, A. Sampson-Johannes, K. Mondal, P. Ralph, and A.S. Baldwin, Jr. 1991. Characterization of an immediate-early gene induced in aberrant monocytes that encodes IκB-like activity. *Cell* **65:** 1281–1289.

Hiscott, J., D. Alper, L. Cohen, J.-F. LeBlanc, L. Sportza, A. Wong, and S. Xanthoudakis. 1989. Induction of human interferon gene expression is associated with a nuclear factor that interacts with the NF-κB site of the human immunodeficiency virus enhancer. *J. Virol.* **63:** 2557–2566.

Hoover, T.R., E. Santero, S. Porter, and S. Kustu. 1990. The integration host factor stimulates interaction of RNA polymerase with NIFA, the transcriptional activator for nitrogen fixation operons. *Cell* **63:** 11–22.

Imam, A.M.A., A.M. Ackrill, T.C. Dale, I.M. Kerr, and G.R. Stark. 1990. Transcription factors induced by interferons α and γ. *Nucleic Acids Res.* **18:** 6573–6579.

Inoue, J., L.D. Kerr, L.J. Ransone, E. Bengal, T. Hunter, and I.M. Verma. 1991. c-*rel* activates but v-*rel* represses transcription from κB sites. *Proc. Natl. Acad. Sci.* **88:** 3715–3719.

Ip, Y.T., R. Kraut, M. Levin, and C.A. Rushlow. 1991. The dorsal morphogen is a sequence-specific DNA-binding protein that interacts with a long-range repression element in *Drosophila*. *Cell* **64:** 439–446.

Johnson, K.R., D.A. Lehn, T.S. Elton, P.J. Barr, and R. Reeves. 1988. Complete murine cDNA sequence, genomic structure, and tissue expression of the high mobility group protein HMG-I(Y). *J. Biol. Chem.* **263:** 18338–18342.

Kawakami, K., C. Scheidereit, and R.G. Roeder. 1988. Identification and purification of a human immunoglobulin-enhancer-binding protein (NF-κB) that activates transcription from a human immunodeficiency virus type 1 promoter *in vitro*. *Proc. Natl. Acad. Sci.* **85:** 4700–4704.

Keller, A. and T. Maniatis. 1988. Identification of an inducible factor that binds to a positive regulatory element of the human β-interferon gene. *Proc. Natl. Acad. Sci.* **85:** 3309–3313.

———. 1991. Identification and characterization of a novel repressor of β-interferon gene expression. *Genes Dev.* **5:** 868–879.

Kieren, M., V. Blank, F. Logeat, J. Vandekerckhove, F. Lottspeich, O. LeBail, M.B. Urban, P. Kourilsky, P. Baeuerle, and A. Israel. 1990. The DNA binding subunit of NF-κB is identical to factor KBF-1 and homologous to the *rel* oncogene product. *Cell* **62:** 1007–1018.

Kuhl, D., J. de la Fuente, M. Chaturvedi, S. Parimoo, J. Ryals, F. Meyer, and C. Weissman. 1987. Reversible silencing of enhancers by sequences derived from the human IFN-α promoter. *Cell* **50:** 1057–1069.

LeBlanc, J.-F., L. Cohen, S. Rodrigues, and J. Hiscott. 1990. Synergism between distinct enhanson domains in viral induction of the human beta interferon gene. *Mol. Cell. Biol.* **10:** 3987–3993.

Lenardo, M. and D. Baltimore. 1989. NF-κB: A pleiotropic mediator of inducible and tissue-specific gene control. *Cell* **58:** 227–229.

Lenardo, M., C.-M. Fan, T. Maniatis, and D. Baltimore. 1989. The involvement of NF-κB in β-interferon gene regulation reveals its role as a widely inducible mediator of signal transduction. *Cell* **57:** 287–294.

Levy, D.E., D.S. Kessler, R. Pine, and J.E. Darnell, Jr. 1989. Cytoplasmic activation of ISGF3, the positive regulator of interferon-α-stimulated transcription, reconstituted in vitro. *Genes Dev.* **3:** 1362–1371.

Levy, D.E., D.S. Kessler, R. Pine, N. Reich, and J.E. Darnell, Jr. 1988. Interferon-induced nuclear factors that bind a shared promoter element correlate with positive and negative transcriptional control. *Genes Dev.* **2:** 383–393.

Liu, F. and M.R. Green. 1990. A specific member of the ATF transcription factor family can mediate transcription activation by the adenovirus E1A protein. *Cell* **61:** 1217–1224.

Lux, S.E., K.M. John, and V. Bennett. 1990. Analysis of cDNA for human erythrocyte ankyrin indicates a repeated structure with homology to tissue-differentiation and cell-cycle control proteins. *Nature* **344:** 36–42.

MacDonald, N., D. Kuhl, D. Maguire, D. Naf, P. Gallant, A. Goswamy, H. Hug, H. Bueler, M. Chaturvedi, J. de la Fuente, H. Ruffner, F. Meyer, and C. Weissman. 1990. Different pathways mediate virus inducibility of the human IFN-α1 and IFN-β genes. *Cell* **60:** 767–779.

Maekawa, T., T. Sakura, T. Sudo, and S. Ishii. 1989. Putative metal finger structure of the human immunodeficiency virus type I enhancer binding protein HIV-EP1. *J. Biol. Chem.* **264:** 14591–14593.

Maniatis, T. 1988. Mechanisms of human B-interferon gene regulation. *Harvey Lect.* **82:** 71–104.

Maniatis, T., S. Goodbourn, and J.A. Fischer. 1987. Regulation of inducible and tissue-specific gene expression. *Science* **236:** 1237–1245.

Marcus, P.I. and M.J. Sekellick. 1988. Interferon induction by viruses. XVI. 2-aminopurine blocks selectively and reversibly an early stage in interferon induction. *J. Gen. Virol.* **69:** 1637–1645.

Miyamoto, M., T. Fujita, Y. Kimura, M. Maruyama, H. Harada, Y. Sudo, T. Miyata, and T. Taniguchi. 1988. Regulated expression of a gene encoding a nuclear factor, IRF-1, that specifically binds to IFN-β gene regulatory elements. *Cell* **54:** 903–913.

Mizuuchi, M. and K. Mizuuchi. 1989. Efficient Mu transposition requires interaction of transposase with a DNA sequence at the Mu operator: Implications for regulation. *Cell* **58:** 399–408.

Moitoso de Vargas, L., C.A. Pargellis, N.M. Hasan, E.W. Bushman, and A. Landy. 1988. Autonomous DNA-binding domains of λ integrase recognize two different sequence families. *Cell* **54:** 923–929.

Nash, H.A. 1990. Bending and supercoiling of DNA at the attachment site of bacteriophage λ. *Trends Biochem. Sci.* **15:** 222–227.

Nolan, G.P., S. Ghosh, H.C. Liou, P. Tempst, and D. Baltimore. 1991. DNA binding and IκB inhibition of the cloned p65 subunit of NF-κB, a *rel* related polypeptide. *Cell* **64:** 961–969.

Pine, R., T. Decker, D.S. Kessler, D.E. Levy, and J.E. Darnell, Jr. 1990. Purification and cloning of interferon-stimulated gene factor 2 (ISGF2): ISGF2 (IRF-1) can bind to the promoters of both beta interferon and interferon-stimulated genes but is not a primary transcriptional activator of either. *Mol. Cell. Biol.* **10:** 2448–2457.

Raj, N.B.K., J. Engelhardt, W.-C. Au, D.E. Levy, and P.M. Pitha. 1989. Virus infection and interferon can activate gene expression through single synthetic element, but endogenous genes show distinct regulation. *J. Biol. Chem.* **264:** 16658–16666.

Reuter, G., M. Giarre, J. Farah, J. Gausz, A. Spierer, and P. Spierer. 1990. Dependence of position-effect variegation in *Drosophila* on dose of a gene encoding an unusual zinc-finger protein. *Nature* **344:** 219–223.

Ruben, S.M., P.J. Dillon, R. Schreck, T. Henkel, C.-H. Chen, M. Maher, P.A. Baeuerle, and C.A. Rosen. 1991. Isolation of a *rel*-related human cDNA that potentially encodes the 65kD subunit of NF-κB. *Science* **251:** 1490–1493.

Rutherford, M.N., G.E. Hannigan, and B.R.G. Williams. 1988. Interferon-induced binding of nuclear factors to promoter elements of the 2-5A synthetase gene. *EMBO J.* **7:** 751–759.

Sen, R. and D. Baltimore. 1986a. Multiple nuclear factors interact with the immunoglobulin enhancer sequences. *Cell* **46:** 705–716.

———. 1986b. Inducibility of κ immunoglobulin enhancer-binding protein NF-κB by a post-translational mechanism. *Cell* **47:** 921–928.

Shirakawa, F. and S.B. Mizel. 1989. In vitro activation and nuclear translocation of the NF-κB catalyzed by cAMP-dependent protein kinase and protein kinase C. *Mol. Cell. Biol.* **9:** 2424–2430.

Shirayoshi, Y., P.A. Burke, E. Appella, and K. Ozato. 1988. Interferon-induced transcription of a major histocompatibility class I gene accompanies binding of inducible nuclear factors to the interferon consensus sequence. *Proc. Natl. Acad. Sci.* **85:** 5884–5888.

Solomon, M.J., F. Strauss, and A. Varshavsky. 1986. A mammalian high mobility group protein recognizes any stretch of six A-T base pairs in duplex DNA. *Proc. Natl. Acad. Sci.* **83:** 1276–1280.

Steward, R. 1987. Dorsal, an embryonic polarity gene in *Drosophila*, is homologous to the vertebrate proto-oncogene, c-*rel*. *Science* **238:** 692–694.

Taniguchi, T. 1988. Regulation of cytokine gene expression. *Annu. Rev. Immunol.* **6:** 439–464.

Tautz, D., R. Lehmann, H. Schnurch, R. Schuh, E. Seifert, A. Kienlin, K. Jones, and H. Jackle. 1987. Finger protein of novel structure encoded by *hunchback*, a second member of the gap class of *Drosophila* segmentation genes. *Nature* **327:** 383–389.

Thisse, C., F. Perrin-Schmitt, C. Stoetzel, and B. Thisse. 1991. Sequence-specific transactivation of *Drosophila twist* gene by the *dorsal* gene product. *Cell* **65:** 1191–1201.

Urban, M.B. and P.A. Baeuerle. 1990. The 65-kD subunit of NF-κB is a receptor for IκB and a modulator of DNA-binding specificity. *Genes Dev.* **4:** 1975–1984.

Urban, M.B., R. Schreck, and P.A. Baeuerle. 1991. NF-κB contacts DNA by a heterodimer of the p50 and p65 subunit. *EMBO J.* **10:** 1817–1825.

Vilcek, J. 1991. Interferons. In *Peptide growth factors and their receptors: Handbook of experimental pharmacology* (ed. M.A. Sporn and A.B. Roberts), vol. 95 (II), pp. 3–38. Springer-Verlag, New York.

Visvanathan, K.V. and S. Goodbourn. 1989. Double-stranded RNA activates binding of NF-κB to an inducible element in the human β-interferon promoter. *EMBO J.* **8:** 1129–1138.

Wathelet, M.G., I.M. Clauss, F.C. Paillard, and G.A. Huez. 1988. Regulation of interferon-inducible genes by interferon, poly(rI)-poly(rC), and viruses. In *The biology of the interferon system* (ed. Y. Kawade and S. Kobayashi), pp. 11–17. Kodansha Scientific, Tokyo.

———. 1989. 2-Aminopurine selectively blocks the transcriptional activation of cellular genes by virus, double-stranded RNA, and interferons in human cells. *Eur. J. Biochem.* **184:** 503–509.

White, S.W., K. Appelt, K.S. Wilson, and I. Tanaka. 1989. A protein structural motif that bends DNA. *Proteins* **5:** 281–288.

Whittemore, L.-A. and T. Maniatis. 1990a. Postinduction turnoff of beta-interferon gene expression. *Mol. Cell. Biol.* **64:** 1329–1337.

———. 1990b. Postinduction repression of the β-interferon gene is mediated through two positive regulatory domains. *Proc. Natl. Acad. Sci.* **87:** 7799–7803.

Zinn, K. and T. Maniatis. 1986. Detection of factors that interact with the human β-interferon regulatory region in vivo by DNAase I footprinting: Dissociation and binding correlate with gene activity. *Cell* **45:** 611–618.

Zinn, K., D. DiMaio, and T. Maniatis. 1983. Identification of two distinct regulatory regions adjacent to the human β-interferon gene. *Cell* **34:** 865–879.

Zinn, K., A. Keller, L.-A. Whittemore, and T. Maniatis. 1988. 2-Aminopurine selectively inhibits the induction of β-interferon, c-*fos*, and c-*myc* gene expression. *Science* **240:** 210–213.

45

The Bicoid Morphogen: Concentration-dependent Transcriptional Activation of Zygotic Target Genes during Early *Drosophila* Development

Wolfgang Driever[1]
Max-Planck-Institut für Entwicklungsbiologie
Abteilung III Genetik, D-7400 Tübingen, Germany

OVERVIEW

The *Drosophila* maternal gene *bicoid* encodes a homeodomain protein, Bicoid, which activates various zygotic genes at distinct threshold concentrations in the embryo. Bicoid is distributed in a concentration gradient along the anterior-posterior axis of the embryo. The structures of target gene promoters appear to specify their spatially restricted responses: Genes with high-affinity binding sites for Bicoid are active at low concentrations of Bicoid (in the thoracic region), whereas those with low-affinity sites for Bicoid appear to be expressed only in more anterior positions (the head region) where high Bicoid concentrations prevail. Investigation of Bicoid will reveal how a continuous gradient of a single regulator can achieve discretely different regulatory effects within its field of distribution.

INTRODUCTION

Control of Early Development in the *Drosophila* Embryo

During embryonic development of *Drosophila melanogaster*, a hierarchy of genes acts to specify the body pattern (Nüsslein-Volhard and Wieschaus 1980; Akam 1987; Ingham 1988). The fertilized egg develops first as a polynucleated syncytium to form, after about 2.5 hours of development, a peripheral layer of blastoderm nuclei. At this stage, the earliest genes to be transcribed in the embryo (zygotic genes) already display local regions of expression that reflect the organization of the embryonic

---

[1]Present address: Cardiovascular Research Center, Massachusetts General Hospital, Thirteenth Street, Building 149, Charlestown, Massachusetts 02129.

axis. Thus, information that initiates the process of pattern formation must preexist in the egg.

Genetic analysis has demonstrated that maternal gene products (transcribed during oogenesis) regulate the establishment of regional identity in the early *Drosophila* embryo (Nüsslein-Volhard et al. 1987). These studies reveal that four maternal gene systems are sufficient to generate the basic body pattern. For the anterior-posterior axis, the anterior system regulates development of head and thorax, the posterior system controls development of the abdomen, and the terminal system specifies the unsegmented regions at the anterior and posterior tips of the embryo, the acron and the telson (Fig. 1A,B). The dorsoventral axis is established by a single system of maternal effect genes. Molecular analyses have revealed that the maternal genes employ different mechanisms to generate an uneven distribution of transcription factors which initiates the earliest regionalized pattern of zygotic gene expression.

For the anterior system, which is best understood in molecular terms, a single protein, the product of the *bicoid* gene, is distributed in a concentration gradient along the anterior-posterior axis, with a high point at the anterior tip of the embryo. Bicoid protein (in the following called Bicoid) acts as a concentration-dependent transcriptional activator of zygotic gene expression.

The key gene of the posterior system, *nanos*, negatively controls translation and transcript stability of an initially equally distributed suppressor of abdominal development, *hunchback* (Hülskamp et al. 1989; Irish et al. 1989; Struhl 1989).

The *torso* receptor tyrosine kinase transmits a signal into the egg that will lead via a kinase cascade to region-specific activation of zygotic transcription factors in the termini of the embryo (Klingler et al. 1988; Casanova and Struhl 1989; Sprenger et al. 1989).

For the dorsoventral axis, a complex cascade of maternal effect genes regulates the subcellular localization of the *dorsal* gene product, a *rel* homologous transcription factor, and thus establishes a gradient of nuclear (ventral side of the embryo) versus cytoplasmic (dorsal side) localization of the *dorsal* protein (Anderson 1987; Steward et al. 1988; Roth et al. 1990).

In this chapter, I report the data that have accumulated during the last few years on how the Bicoid protein, a maternally derived transcription factor, can act as a morphogen to specify distinct domains of zygotic gene expression within the head and thorax of the early *Drosophila* embryo. The exciting feature of Bicoid is its concentration-dependent action: At high concentrations of Bicoid (in the head region of the syncytial blastoderm) more genes appear to get activated than at further posterior

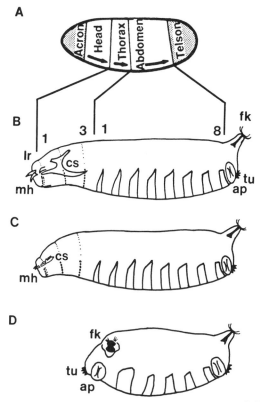

Figure 1 Blastoderm fate map of the *Drosophila* embryo and structures affected by mutations in the maternal gene *bicoid*. (*A*) At the syncytial blastoderm stage, when a layer of a few thousand nuclei has been formed over the yolk, patterns of zygotic gene expression reveal that the principal regions of the embryo are already determined. The drawing shows which parts of the blastoderm will give rise to certain parts of the embryo: the acron (the anteriormost, nonsegmented part of the head), the gnathal or segmented region of the head, the thorax, the abdomen, and the telson (the posterior nonsegmented region of the embryo). (*B*) Schematic drawing of the cuticular structures of a wild-type first-instar larva. The projections of the origin of these structures on the blastoderm fate map are shown. Most of the head is involuted and forms internal sclerotized structures like the cephalopharyngeal skeleton (cs). The labrum, a small dent-like structure anterior and dorsal to the cs, derives from the acron. (*C*) Cuticle phenotype of a weak *bcd* allele. Only the anteriormost structures, derivatives of the acron, like the labrum, are missing. The cs is severely reduced. (*D*) Cuticle phenotype of a strong *bcd* allele. Head and thorax are completely missing and replaced by a duplicated telson. Anterior is to the top, ventral left. (A1–A8) First to eighth abdominal segments; (ap) anal plates; (cs) cephalopharyngeal skeleton; (fk) filzkörper; (mh) mouth hooks; (lr) labrum; (T1–T3) first to third thoracic segments; (tu) tuft. (Modified from Nüsslein-Volhard et al. 1987.)

positions, where low Bicoid concentrations prevail. An inevitable prerequisite to the understanding of the function of Bicoid as a transcriptional regulator in the embryo is a basic knowledge of its role during embryogenesis, as elucidated initially by genetic experiments. Therefore, I first describe the evidence that established Bicoid as a morphogen in the embryo. Second, I concentrate on experiments which suggest that Bicoid acts as a transcriptional activator.

bicoid and Its Role in Anterior Development

Discovered in genetic screens for maternal mutations affecting pattern formation in *Drosophila, bicoid (bcd)* mutants displayed severe effects on anterior development of the embryo (Fig. 1) (Frohnhöfer and Nüsslein-Volhard 1986). In the allelic series, three groups of *bcd* mutations have been defined according to their severity of phenotype: (1) Weak alleles affect the anteriormost structures of the head, the labral derivatives; (2) intermediate alleles show a strong reduction of head structures and often also affect the second and third thoracic segment; and (3) embryos from females homozygous mutant for strong *bcd* alleles develop neither head nor thorax and carry a duplication of the posteriormost structure, the telson, at the anterior end. Thus, with increasing allelic strength a larger portion of the anterior half of the blastoderm fate map becomes deleted, and the strongest alleles often also show defects in the anterior abdominal segments. The duplication of telson structures at the anterior end of the embryo can be considered as a homeotic transformation: Telson appears to be the basic state specified by the terminal system of genes; in the presence of *bcd* activity, telson is transformed into anterior terminal structures, the acron.

Experiments involving transplantation of cytoplasm from various regions of wild-type embryos into embryos from *bcd* mutant females demonstrated that the *bcd* activity is localized at the anterior tip of the freshly laid egg (Frohnhöfer and Nüsslein-Volhard 1986; Frohnhöfer et al. 1986). Depending on the amount of material transplanted, anterior cytoplasm from wild-type donor embryos can rescue progressively more anterior structures in recipient embryos from *bcd* mutant females; similarly, the higher the *bcd* gene dosage in the maternal genome of donor embryos, the more structures can be rescued with a constant amount of cytoplasm. Thus, a graded requirement for *bcd* activity could be established: The rescue of head structures depends on transplanting more *bcd* activity than is sufficient for the induction of thoracic structures.

A graded requirement for *bcd* activity is also reflected by the shift of positions on the blastoderm fate map (e.g., the border between head and thorax, which can be monitored by a morphological marker, the head-fold, or the expression pattern of the segmentation genes) that are caused by a variation of the *bcd* gene dosage in the female (Frohnhöfer and Nüsslein-Volhard 1986, 1987). Females that carry additional copies of the gene deposit more *bcd* activity into the embryo, and the headfold develops at a more posterior position, when compared to wild type, whereas embryos from females with just one functional copy of the *bcd* gene have the headfold at more anterior positions. Thus, the quantity of the *bcd* gene product determines not only *which* structures will develop in the anterior of the embryo, but also *where* they will develop.

LOCALIZED *BCD* MRNA ACTS AS THE SOURCE FOR THE BICOID MORPHOGEN GRADIENT

bcd mRNA Localization in the Embryo

The isolation of the *bcd* gene allowed the investigation of the molecular nature of the localized *bcd* activity identified in the *Drosophila* embryo (Frigerio et al. 1986; Berleth et al. 1988). The *bcd* gene is transcribed exclusively during oogenesis in the nurse cell nuclei, and there is no evidence for any zygotic expression in the embryo. The nurse cells are a cluster of germ-line-derived cells located at the prospective anterior pole of the cell that differentiates into the oocyte. The nurse cells synthesize most of the material (except the yolk) that is going to constitute the oocyte. This material is transported through a system of specialized channels, the ring-channels, into the oocyte. St. Johnston et al. (1989) give a detailed description of *bcd* mRNA distribution in the ovariole, leading to the final localization at the anterior pole of the egg and early embryo (Fig. 2a) (Frigerio et al. 1986; Berleth et al. 1988). *bcd* mRNA, like some other maternal mRNAs, disappears rapidly during cellularization at about 3 hours of development, suggesting that a common mechanism controls the stability of these mRNAs in the embryo.

It appears that a complex and highly regulated mechanism accounts for the anterior cytoplasmic localization of *bcd* mRNA in the egg. A model has been proposed (Berleth et al. 1988; St. Johnston et al. 1989) suggesting that *bcd* mRNA during oogenesis may be bound by specific RNA-binding proteins (the maternal gene *exuperantia* may code for such a protein) and linked by other proteins (e.g., the product of the maternal gene *swallow*) to the cytoskeleton (Pokrywka and Stephenson 1991). Whereas *exuperantia* may be specifically involved in the initiation of *bcd* mRNA localization (Macdonald et al. 1991; Marcey et al. 1991), the

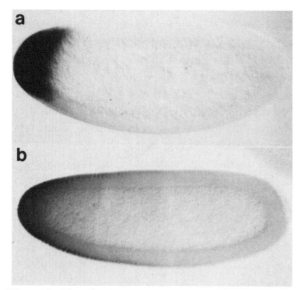

Figure 2   bicoid mRNA and protein distribution in the *Drosophila* embryo. In situ detection of *bcd* mRNA (*a*) and Bicoid protein (*b*) in whole-mount embryos at the syncytial blastoderm stage. (*b* modified from St. Johnston et al. 1989.) Although *bcd* mRNA is strictly localized to the anterior tip of the embryo, the Bicoid gradient spreads over more than half of the embryo. Anterior at left, dorsal at top.

function of *swallow* appears to be more general, because it also affects cellularization and nuclear movements (Stephenson et al. 1988). Mutations in either *exuperantia* or *swallow* abolish the strict anterior localization of *bcd* mRNA and result in the formation of very shallow gradients of *bcd* mRNA in the embryo. The *staufen* gene product appears to be involved in the maintenance of anterior *bcd* mRNA localization after egg deposition: In embryos from mutant *staufen* females, *bcd* mRNA that appeared properly localized during oogenesis starts to diffuse and slowly forms a gradient. The *staufen* protein has been shown to colocalize with *bcd* mRNA at the anterior tip of the egg in a *bcd* mRNA-dependent fashion. Thus, *staufen* has been suggested to interact with *bcd* mRNA (St. Johnston et al. 1991). Embryos mutant for either of the three genes affecting *bcd* mRNA localization develop head phenotypes similar to weak *bcd* alleles (Schüpbach and Wieschaus 1986; Stephenson et al. 1988). *staufen* is also involved in specifying posterior development.

   Macdonald and Struhl (1988) investigated which parts of the *bcd* mRNA are involved in its localization. Using a series of deletions as well as fusion genes with parts of *bcd* mRNA reintroduced into the germ line, they conclude that a sequence of about 625 nucleotides in the 3'-untranslated region of the *bcd* mRNA is necessary and sufficient for localization of the RNA in the anterior half of the *Drosophila* embryo. The identified region is suggested to form extensive secondary structure, some portions of which appear to be conserved among various *Drosophila* species (Seeger and Kaufman 1990; Macdonald 1990).

The *bicoid* Protein Gradient

The *bcd* mRNA codes for a 489-amino-acid protein, Bicoid, the domain structure of which is considered in more detail below. Bicoid starts to be translated from the localized *bcd* mRNA soon after egg deposition and diffuses to form a concentration gradient along the anterior-posterior axis with a maximum at the anterior tip of the embryo (Fig. 2b) (Driever and Nüsslein-Volhard 1988a). The protein is concentrated within the nuclei. During the rapid early nuclear cleavages, the *Drosophila* embryo is a single large polynucleated cell. Thus, up to and during the syncytial blastoderm stage, when transcription of zygotic genes begins, the diffusion of Bicoid is not limited by any cell boundaries. When measured at the syncytial blastoderm stage, the shape of the gradient indicates an exponential decay of the Bicoid concentration toward the posterior. From immunostain intensities, it was estimated that the Bicoid concentration changes by 2 to 3 orders of magnitude within the anterior half of the embryo (Driever and Nüsslein-Volhard 1988a).

The simplest model for the establishment of the Bicoid gradient in the embryo is synthesis from a localized source (the *bcd* mRNA), diffusion within the embryo, and a constant rate of proteolytic degradation throughout the embryo. Indeed, in less than 1 hour after the RNA has disappeared, Bicoid is no longer detected, arguing for a rather short half-life of the protein.

Bicoid Concentration Determines Position in the Anterior Half of the Embryo

A variation in the *bcd* gene dosage has a striking effect on the positioning of morphological landmarks in the gastrulating embryo. The headfold, a transverse invagination at the border between the prospective head region and the thorax, is located at 64% (±1%) egg length (0% is the posterior pole) in wild type. It shifts anteriorward (to 73% egg length) in embryos from females carrying only one functional copy of the *bcd* gene. In contrast, it is positioned at progressively more posterior positions in embryos from females with three (59% egg length), four

(56% egg length), six (53% egg length), and eight (about 50% egg length) functional copies of the *bcd* gene (Frohnhöfer and Nüsslein-Volhard 1986; Berleth et al. 1988). The same shifts on the fate map can already be detected at the blastoderm stage by analyzing the expression patterns of very early expressed zygotic genes, e.g., the pair rule gene *even-skipped* (Driever and Nüsslein-Volhard 1988b) or the gap gene *hunchback* (Struhl et al. 1989).

The analysis of Bicoid distribution in embryos from females with an increasing number of functional copies of the *bcd* gene demonstrates that the amount of Bicoid is proportional to the *bcd* gene copy number. With increasing gene dosage, higher concentrations of Bicoid can be detected not only at the anterior tip, but also at more posterior positions (Driever and Nüsslein-Volhard 1988b). The shifts on the blastoderm fate map, as monitored by the *even-skipped* and *hunchback* expression patterns (Driever and Nüsslein-Volhard 1988b; Struhl et al. 1989), follow the shifts in Bicoid concentration. Therefore, the absolute concentration of Bicoid determines at least one position along the anterior-posterior axis on the fate map.

Experiments in which, by genetic means, not only the overall level, but also the shape, of the Bicoid gradient were modified reveal that not only one, but at least two different regions on the embryonic fate map are specified by Bicoid in a concentration-dependent manner. Changes of the shape of the Bicoid gradient are observed in embryos from females mutant for any of the genes involved in *bcd* mRNA localization and result in severe phenotypic defects (Driever and Nüsslein-Volhard 1988b).

The most revealing example are embryos from *exuperantia staufen* double-mutant females. They do not have a Bicoid gradient but show very low Bicoid levels (equivalent to thoracic levels in wild type) throughout the embryo and develop solely thoracic structures but no head or other structures (Gaul and Jäckle 1989; Schüpbach and Wieschaus 1986). The blastoderm embryos express *hunchback* (as a marker for thorax) but not *Deformed* (as a marker for head development; Jack and McGinnis 1990). When four extra copies of the *bcd* gene are introduced genetically into such females, Bicoid is still homogeneously distributed in the embryos, but at a higher concentration level (corresponding to the concentrations normally found in the head region of wild-type blastoderm stage embryos); the embryos develop head structures but no thoracic or other structures. These embryos express *Deformed* (W. Driever, in prep.). Thus, low concentrations of Bicoid autonomously define thorax (expression of the *hunchback* gene), whereas high levels of Bicoid define head (expression of the *Deformed* gene).

The conclusion from such experiments is that the Bicoid concentration provides positional information to the embryo: A low concentration is required for thoracic development, and higher concentrations are required in the anterior third of the embryo to delimit the region of gnathal development. Thus, Bicoid fits the classic definition of a "morphogen" as a "particular kind of inducing factor characterized by the evocation of different cellular behaviors at different concentrations" (Slack 1987). The interpretation of the continuous information, provided by a gradient, into several discrete cell states can be explained by postulating the existence of a series of concentration thresholds (Lewis et al. 1977). In the case of Bicoid, as soon as Bicoid concentration is above a certain threshold for thoracic development, nuclei express thorax-specific genes, and in more anterior regions, where the concentration is above the threshold for head development, gnathal fate is expressed.

TRANSCRIPTIONAL CONTROL OF ZYGOTIC GENE EXPRESSION BY *BICOID*

The *bicoid* Protein

Some rare cDNAs indicate that the primary *bcd* transcript may be subject to differential splicing (Berleth et al. 1988). The most abundant cDNA (I) derives from an mRNA that has the capacity to code for a 489-amino-acid protein with a homeodomain in the amino-terminal third. Another cDNA (II) derives from the fusion of the first and fourth exon (with the capacity to code for a 149-amino-acid protein lacking the homeodomain), whereas a third splicing variant (III) utilizes a splice acceptor site for the third exon located 15 nucleotides further 5': The conceptual protein would have five additional amino acids in front of the homeodomain. Differential splicing is frequently observed for transcripts of *Drosophila* homeotic genes (e.g., *Ultrabithorax*; O'Connor et al. 1988; Kornfeld et al. 1989).

The injection of in-vitro-transcribed *bcd* mRNAs of the most abundant type I into the anterior tip of embryos from females homozygous mutant for strong *bcd* alleles can rescue the mutant phenotype completely and gives rise to hatching larvae that develop to adulthood (Driever et al. 1990). Similarly, the injection of *bcd* mRNA into the posterior tip of wild-type embryos can lead to the development of a complete second head and thorax at the posterior end of the embryo. These data demonstrate that type I mRNA, and thus only one *bcd* protein species, is necessary and sufficient for the induction of anterior development. The other mRNAs (and thus protein species) may be aberrant splicing products, a view that is supported by the finding that the

Drosophila pseudoobscura bicoid gene lacks the alternate splice acceptor site at the third exon necessary to generate type III mRNAs (Seeger and Kaufman 1990). Bicoid therefore is considered here as the 489-amino-acid protein.

The domain organization of Bicoid is depicted in Figure 3. At the amino-terminal end of the protein, a histidine- and proline-rich "paired-repeat" is located (Frigerio et al. 1986). This repeat is based on the hexanucleotide sequence $CA^T/_C\ CCG$. Repeats of this type are found in many genes in *Drosophila*, often in the proximity of homeodomains. Incidentally, *bcd* has been cloned due to cross-hybridization of this region with the *paired* gene (Frigerio et al. 1986). A function of the prd-repeat is not known. The Bicoid homeodomain is only distantly related to the other classes of homeodomains (Scott et al. 1989); implications of this feature for its DNA-binding specificity are considered in the next chapter. Carboxy-terminal to the homeodomain is a serine- and threonine-rich region that fulfills the criteria for a PEST sequence (Rogers et al. 1987). PEST sequences have been suggested to be involved in the regulation of protein stability. For Bicoid, a deletion of the PEST sequence does not affect protein stability (Fig. 3) (W. Driever, unpubl.). In the middle of the protein are two glutamine repeats (opa- or M-repeat; McGinnis et al. 1984), whereas the carboxy-terminal part carries a concentration of negative charges. In other proteins, both glutamine-rich and acidic sequences have been shown to contribute to transcriptional activation (Hope and Struhl 1986; Ma and Ptashne 1987a; Courey and Tjian 1988). A weak (perhaps insignificant) sequence similarity to an RNA recognition motif (Rebagliati 1989) exists in the carboxy-terminal domain.

Polyclonal as well as monoclonal antibodies specific for Bicoid recognize several protein species, ranging in apparent molecular weight from 56,000 to 60,000 on developmental Western blots of early embryo extracts (Driever and Nüsslein-Volhard 1988b). The apparent molecular weight is slightly higher than the molecular mass of 54 kD calculated from the deduced sequence. Bicoid is phosphorylated in *Drosophila* Schneider cells (Driever and Nüsslein-Volhard 1989), suggesting that it might also be phosphorylated in the embryo. Whether other modifications take place is not known.

DNA-binding Specificity of *bicoid* Protein

The presence of a homeodomain (McGinnis et al. 1984; Scott and Weiner 1984) in the amino-terminal third of Bicoid suggests that it has a sequence-specific DNA-binding activity (Laughon and Scott 1984; Desplan et al. 1985) which might act to regulate the expression of

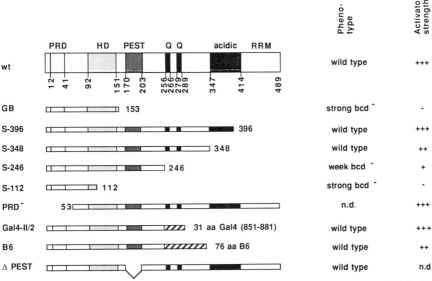

Figure 3 Functional domains of Bicoid. The structures of wild-type Bicoid (wt) and various mutant Bicoid proteins are drawn in the left part of the figure. Numbers below the bar give the positions of amino acids in the protein. The domains of Bicoid as judged from the primary structure of the protein are (PRD) paired repeat, a histidine- and proline-rich motif (Frigerio et al. 1986); (HD) homeodomain; a PEST sequence rich in proline, glutamic acid, serine, and threonine (flanked by positively charged amino acids) that has been suggested to be involved in regulation of protein stability; (Q) a glutamine repeat; an acidic domain; and the RRM RNA recognition motif (Rebagliati 1989). Except for *bcd* GB, a strong chemically induced allele of *bcd* (sequence data from Struhl et al. 1989), all other Bicoid derivatives have been generated in vitro (Driever et al. 1989b; Struhl et al. 1989; W. Driever unpubl.). The column "Phenotype" categorizes the cuticular patterns obtained in embryos from females which (in addition to being homozygous mutant for a strong *bcd* allele) carry a *bcd* minigene expressing the respective Bicoid derivative (Driever et al. 1990, and unpubl.); except for GB, the chemically induced strong allele, and Gal4-II/2, where the phenotype has been tested by injection of mRNAs coding for the *bcd*-Gal4-II/2 fusion protein into embryos from mutant *bcd* females (see Driever et al. 1989b). For classification of phenotypes, see Fig. 1. The column "Activator strength" simplifies data obtained in various assay systems on the activity of Bicoid to mediate transcriptional activation. Assays in yeast: GB and PRD⁻ (Struhl et al. 1989); for the other proteins, assays both in yeast and *Drosophila* (Driever et al. 1989b). (n.d.) Not determined.

zygotic target genes. The earliest zygotic genes expressed in distinct spatial domains along the anterior-posterior axis are the gap genes (Nüsslein-Volhard and Wieschaus 1980). The phenotype of mutations in the gap gene *hunchback* (*hb*; deletion of gnathal and thoracic segments;

Lehmann and Nüsslein-Volhard 1987) and the expression pattern of *hb* mRNA in *bcd* mutant embryos (Tautz et al. 1987; Schröder et al. 1988; Tautz 1988) suggest that *hb* may be one of the targets for regulation by *bcd*. The expression of the 2.9-kb transcript from the *hb* P2 promoter in the anterior half of the embryo (see Fig. 6) is absent in embryos from *bcd* mutant females. DNA-binding studies with the *hb* promoter were performed to test whether Bicoid directly regulates *hb* expression.

Bicoid binds in vitro to several sites in the upstream region of the *hb* gene (Figs. 4 and 5A) (Driever and Nüsslein-Volhard 1989). These sites define a consensus binding sequence for Bicoid: TCTAATCCC. Two classes of binding sites exist: The "A"-type resembles the consensus sequence closely (1 or 2 exchanges; not affecting the TAATC core). The "X"-type can contain up to 4 base exchanges compared to the consensus sequence and appears less well protected in footprint assays. At high Bicoid concentrations, binding could be observed to a variety of sequences having TAAT, CTAA, or TAATC elements in common with the consensus. These findings can be interpreted as the consensus representing a high-affinity binding site, whereas the other sequences are bound with lower affinities. The three A-type sites and the X3 site in the *hb* promoter are conserved in *Drosophila virilis* (Treier et al. 1989).

strong bcd sites	A1	A C G T A A T C C C C
	A2	C T C T A A T C C A G
	A3	A T C T A A T C C C T
weak bcd sites	B1	T G C T A A T C T G A
	B2	C T T T A A T C C C A
	X1	T G C T A A G C T G G
	X2	C G C T A A G C T C C
	X3	G G A T C A T C C A A

consensus (strong sites)   T C T A A T C C C

en, eve, ftz sites   T C A A T T A A A T
Ubx, Antp sites   (T A A)$_n$

Figure 4 DNA-binding specificity of the Bicoid protein. The sequences of Bicoid-binding sites identified in the *hunchback* promoter were aligned to define a consensus binding site for Bicoid. The location of these binding sites with respect to the transcription start is indicated in Fig. 5. "B" binding sites are located about 1 kb further upstream. For comparison, the binding sequences of other homeodomain proteins are given below (Beachy et al. 1988; Desplan et al. 1988; Driever and Nüsslein-Volhard 1989).

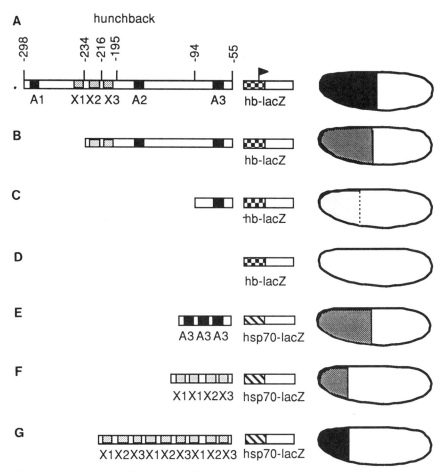

Figure 5 Bicoid-binding sites define Bicoid-dependent expression domains in the early embryo. Fusion genes that carry different parts of the *hunchback* promoter fused to a *lacZ* reporter gene, introduced into the germ line by P-transformation, drive expression of β-galactosidase in distinct domains within the embryo (Driever et al. 1989a). Shaded areas within the embryos represent the expression domains and relative levels of expression. In *C*, the posterior border of expression (dotted line) cannot be determined precisely due to the low level of expression. "A" means A-type binding sites and "X" means X-type binding sites (see text and Fig. 3).

The consensus sequence for Bicoid binding to DNA is different from those sequences identified for other homeodomain proteins, many of which bind in vitro to one single type of sequence (Fig. 3) (Beachy et al. 1988; Desplan et al. 1988; Hoey and Levine 1988; Müller et al. 1988). Indeed, as far as has been tested, other homeodomain proteins do not bind to the Bicoid consensus site (Hanes and Brent 1989; Treisman et al. 1989). The Bicoid homeodomain is diverged from other homeodomain families: It has only 42% protein homology with the Antennapedia homeodomain (Frigerio et al. 1986). Within homeodomain helix 3, which forms the second helix of the helix-turn-helix motif and in Engrailed has been shown to provide contacts to DNA (Kissinger et al. 1990), amino acids 1, 2, 4, and 9 differ between Bicoid and Antennapedia. In contrast to bacterial helix-turn-helix proteins, where amino acids at positions 1, 2, 5, and 6 form the critical contacts with the operator sequence (Wharton and Ptashne 1985; Anderson et al. 1987; Aggarwal et al. 1988), in the Bicoid homeodomain, position 9 of helix 3 (which is amino acid 50 of the homeodomain) appears to be crucial for DNA-binding specificity (Hanes and Brent 1989; Treisman et al. 1989). By single amino acid exchanges at position 9, the Bicoid-dependent transcriptional activation function could be switched to respond to Antp class binding sites in a yeast assay (Hanes and Brent 1989). Furthermore, *paired* protein carrying a lysine (like Bicoid) at position 9 (mutated from a serine) binds to the Bicoid consensus site in vitro (Treisman et al. 1989). A more detailed analysis of bcd binding to variants of the consensus binding site (Hanes and Brent 1991) suggests that homeodomain binding sites consist of two subsites: (1) a common TAAT core element and (2) specificity determining bases that lie 3′ to it. The closest base at the 3′ end of the TAAT element (TAATN) appears to contribute most to the binding specificity. The fact that nonsymmetric base substitutions in one half of the site switch specificity suggests that each site is bound by a single Bicoid monomer.

Transcriptional Activation

When tested in *Drosophila* embryos or cell culture (Driever and Nüsslein-Volhard 1989), as well as in yeast (Driever et al. 1989b; Hanes and Brent 1989; Struhl et al. 1989), Bicoid activates transcription depending on the presence of Bicoid-binding sites in the promoter region. The primary structure of Bicoid (Fig. 3) shows elements that are believed to be involved in transcriptional activation: glutamine-rich domains (Courey and Tjian 1988) as well as an acidic domain (Hope and Struhl 1986; Ma and Ptashne 1987a). The contribution of different domains of Bicoid to the activation function appears to depend to a certain degree on the test system used to measure the activator strength.

In yeast, Bicoid is a relatively weak activator when compared to GCN4 (6 times less active; Struhl et al. 1989) or GAL4 (more than 10 times less active; Driever et al. 1989b). In these studies, data from terminal deletion derivatives of Bicoid reveal that both the carboxyl terminus with the acidic region and a serine- and threonine-rich region (around the PEST sequence) contribute to activation, whereas the PRD repeat and the Q repeats are inactive (Struhl et al. 1989; Driever et al. 1989b).

When tested in *Drosophila* Schneider cells, the carboxy-terminal 150 amino acids, including the acidic domain, contribute about 80%, and the serine-threonine-rich region contributes about 20% of the activity. A transient assay in early *Drosophila* embryos, where mRNA coding for Bicoid derivatives was injected into embryos transgenic for a hb-CAT reporter gene, reveals that the glutamine-rich region also contributes to the activation function in embryos (Driever et al. 1989b).

The activities of Bicoid derivatives have been tested in embryos from mutant *bcd* females by injection of mRNAs (Driever et al. 1989b) or expression from modified *bcd* genes that had been introduced into the germ line (W. Driever, unpubl.). In both assays, wild-type protein as well as truncated versions lacking the acidic domain (see Fig. 3) can rescue the mutant phenotype completely. A derivative bcd1-246 also lacking the glutamine-rich region is able to rescue only partially; still, most structures, except the labrum, are formed. However, there is no specific requirement for the glutamine-rich region: Its function can be substituted by fusing heterologous acidic activation domains (polypeptides with an overall acidic character that had been identified as activating domains in yeast; Ma and Ptashne 1987b) to bcd1-246. Some of these fusion proteins, e.g., bcd(1-246)-B6 (B6 is a peptide with a net charge of −8 that had been selected from random bacterial sequences due to its ability to activate transcription in yeast when fused to the DNA-binding portion of GAL4), can rescue the *bcd* mutant phenotype both in mRNA injection experiments and in transgenic animals (W. Driever, unpubl.).

Struhl et al. (1989) conclude that the region between the homeodomain and the Q repeats is important for activation, because in the strong *bcd* allele, GB, Bicoid truncates right after the homeodomain (Fig. 3), whereas truncation at amino acid 257 in the allele *bcd* 111 results in a weak mutant phenotype. The PEST part of this serine- and threonine-rich region that contributes to activation in all test systems is not of dominant importance for the morphogenetic performance of Bicoid, because a derivative carrying a deletion of the PEST sequence (ΔPEST, Fig. 3) can still rescue the mutant phenotype. A possible role of posttranslational modifications has to be investigated, because Bicoid is phosphorylated in *Drosophila* cells.

Although sufficient evidence has accumulated that Bicoid is a transcriptional activator with its activator function located in the carboxy-terminal two thirds of the protein, no single domain of the protein appears to act as the prevailing activation domain. Thus, one can speculate that there is a more complex contribution of different parts of the protein to the surface that might interact with the transcriptional apparatus. If specific adapters (Berger et al. 1990) exist (e.g., for the glutamine-rich sequence, which is active in embryos but not in cell lines, or for the acidic sequence), they can be functionally replaced by each other in the embryo: The B6 sequence substitutes for the Q repeats. It is quite surprising that such a delicate morphogenetic process as the one directed by Bicoid can be performed by severely modified proteins. The homeodomain appears to provide all the specificity, whereas there is a high degree of freedom for what sequences provide the activation function. Indeed, all chemically induced mutations that delete parts of the homeodomain itself (Struhl et al. 1989) give rise to strong mutant phenotypes, whereas mutations in other parts of the protein are found in hypomorphic alleles.

Determination of Domains of Zygotic Gene Expression

How do the molecular properties of Bicoid, sequence-specific DNA binding and transcriptional activation, act to translate the continuous information provided by the concentration gradient into discrete domains of zygotic gene expression? The introduction of *lacZ* fusion genes into the germ line of *Drosophila* allows the analysis of the contribution of Bicoid-binding sites to the determination of the posterior border of *hb* expression in the syncytial blastoderm embryo (Fig. 5) (Schröder et al. 1988; Driever et al. 1989a; Struhl et al. 1989). A *hb* fragment of about 250 bp located upstream of the TATA box is sufficient to direct a *hb*-like *lacZ* expression pattern in the early embryo (Fig. 5A). This fragment acts as an enhancer-like element, since it specifies the same expression pattern when fused in reverse orientation or at a 1-kb distance from a reporter gene. There is no specific requirement for the proximal part of the *hb* promoter, since it can be functionally replaced by the HSP70 promoter (Driever et al. 1989a; Struhl et al. 1989). *hb* itself has no autocatalytic influence on its own expression, since the *hb lacZ* fusion genes are expressed in homozygous mutant *hb⁻* embryos similar to wild type.

A progressive deletion of Bicoid-binding sites from the 5′ end of the 250-bp regulatory fragment results in a progressive reduction of the expression level (an estimated 100:20:1 ratio when fusion genes in Figure 5A, B, and C are compared). In addition, the posterior border of expression becomes less sharp and slightly shifted toward the anterior (with only one binding site present in the construct shown in Fig. 5C, the level of expression is so low that the border of expression cannot be determined precisely). Thus, the Bicoid-binding sites appear to contribute in an additive or even synergistic way to the level of *hb* expression. The apparent sharpening of the expression border with an increasing number of Bicoid-binding sites could simply be explained by an increased level of *hb* expression within the anterior domain. On the other hand, a cooperative effect of binding could explain both the increased level and the shifted border. Small differences in the binding affinities of the A1, A2, and A3 sites for Bicoid could contribute to the observed shift of the border (Fig. 5A–C).

Not only the Bicoid-binding sites in the proximal half of the regulatory 243-bp *hb* fragment, but also parts of this fragment carrying only distal Bicoid sites direct Bicoid-dependent expression in the early embryo (Struhl et al. 1989). Interestingly, when Struhl et al. used promoter fragments that carry one A-type and three X-type binding sites, they reported a posteriorward shift of the border of expression with increasing number of such fragments fused to the reporter gene. It appears that at a low number of A-type sites (only one), the X-type sites determine the expression domain in the anterior quarter, whereas with multiple fragments carrying altogether more A-type sites, the A-type sites direct expression in larger domains. Struhl et al. (1989) suggest cooperative effects to be responsible for the observed shifts.

The contribution of the different types of Bicoid sites to the fusion gene expression has been analyzed in experiments illustrated in Figure 5E–G (Driever et al. 1989a). Although A-type binding sites direct expression in the anterior half of the embryo, X-type binding sites, even when present in many copies, restrict expression to the anterior quarter of the embryo only. Here, too, the level of expression rises with increasing number of Bicoid sites.

The footprint characteristics of the different binding sites suggest that Bicoid has a higher affinity for A-type than for X-type binding sites. Taking into account the Bicoid gradient in the embryo, one can conclude that high-affinity binding sites allow activation of a target gene even at low Bicoid concentrations (in the middle of the embryo), whereas low-affinity binding sites delimit expression to more anterior positions where high Bicoid levels prevail. Thus, the affinity of Bicoid-binding sites present in the promoter of a target gene would determine its domain of expression in the early embryo.

Target Genes Regulated by *bicoid*

The phenotypes of mutations in *bcd* and *hb* are not identical. Elimination of *hb* in the zygote affects the formation of the thorax and the posterior gnathal segments, although anterior head structures are formed. In contrast, *bcd* is required maternally for the development of the entire anterior half of the embryo and the anterior abdomen. Thus, *bcd* must regulate at least one target gene other than *hb*. Several different approaches were taken to identify *bcd* target genes.

A number of zygotic mutations affect structures in the anterior part of the head or the anterior abdomen (Fig. 6) (Nüsslein-Volhard et al. 1984; Wieschaus et al. 1984a; Jürgens et al. 1986). *Krüppel (Kr)* mutant embryos (Wieschaus et al. 1984b) are deficient in the anterior abdomen and thorax. The anterior border of the central *Kr* domain shifts anteriorward with decreasing *bcd* activity (Gaul and Jäckle 1987), suggesting a negative role of *bcd* in regulating the anterior *Kr* border. Detailed genetic analysis (Hülskamp et al. 1990), however, demonstrates that *bcd*, together with the maternal *hb*, is a positive regulator of *Kr* expression. The anteriorward shift of *Kr* with reduced *bcd* activity appears to be due to the anterior shift of a *bcd*-dependent, so far unidentified negative regulator of *Kr* expression (Hülskamp et al. 1990; the gene *giant* might be a candidate: see below). *Krüppel* itself is distributed in a gradient and acts in a concentration-dependent manner (Stanojevic et al. 1989; Pankratz et al. 1990). The level of the *Krüppel* gradient is enhanced by

Figure 6 Bicoid acts as a morphogen in the early embryo. (*A*) Model explaining how a gradient of the transcriptional activator Bicoid could activate *hunchback* (carrying high-affinity Bicoid sites) even at low Bicoid concentrations in the middle of the embryo, whereas a gene X that is involved in head patterning is only expressed at high concentrations of Bicoid, because it has binding sites with lower affinity in its regulatory region. (*B*) Zygotic target genes for Bicoid regulation. (*Top*) Segmental organization of the *Drosophila* embryo. (Ac) Unsegmented acronal region; (Lr) labrum; (He) segmented head region; (PrI) preantennal segment I; (PrII) preantennal segment II, (An) antennal segment; (Ic) intercalary segment; (Md) mandibular segment; (Mx) maxillary segment; (La) labial segment. (Adapted from Cohen and Jürgens [1990] and Ingham [1990]); (Th) thorax; (Ab) abdomen; (Te) unsegmented telson. (*Bottom*) Regions of the fate map affected by some putative targets for Bicoid (open boxes) and their expression domains (light gray, gray, and black areas for expression domains at early cleavage stage, syncytial, and cellular blastoderm, respectively): (*otd*) orthodenticle, (*ems*) empty spiracles, (*btd*) buttonhead, (*gt*) giant, (*hb*) hunchback, (*Kr*) Krüppel, (*mat cad*) maternal caudal. Positions in the anterior of the head are not perfectly colinear with the fate map. See text for details and references. For *hb*, the hatched area shows the structures deleted when both the maternal and the zygotic contribution are mutant. Borders of *Krüppel* and *hunchback* expression domains are indicated to be graded (Stanojevic et al. 1989).

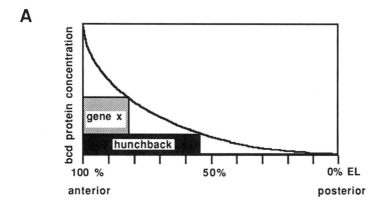

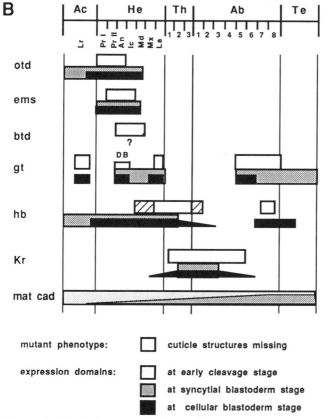

Figure 6 (See facing page for legend.)

bcd. Different *Kr* concentrations determine elements of the anterior abdominal pattern, providing an explanation for the abdominal defects in *bcd* mutant embryos. Hoch et al. (1990) and Jacob et al. (1991) have identified two *bcd*-responsive elements in the *Krüppel* promoter by analyzing *Krüppel*/lacZ fusion gene expression in early embryos. One 142-bp element containing both Bicoid and hunchback protein-binding sites is able to drive *Krüppel*-like expression in the center of the embryo (Hoch et al. 1991). It is supposed that *bcd* and *hb* act as redundant activator systems to specify *Krüppel* expression.

The identification of other target genes for *bcd* in the anterior head region is complicated by the way head development proceeds: Many genes affecting head patterning distort the complex involution of the head and render a detailed analysis difficult. Investigation of the expression pattern of segmentation genes, which are expressed very early in a segmental fashion as well as in several patches in the head, in embryos mutant for zygotic genes that affect head development allowed the determination of both the region of the blastoderm embryo that is affected by these head genes and their position within the hierarchy of genetic interactions (Cohen and Jürgens 1990). The genes *orthodenticle (otd*; Finkelstein and Perrimon 1990), *empty spiracles (ems*; Dalton et al. 1989), and *buttonhead (btd*; Cohen and Jürgens 1990) delete distinct, sequential regions of the head, anterior to the gnathal region affected by *hb*. For *otd* and *ems*, it has been shown that their expression domains shift with a variation in *bcd* gene dosage. The striped expression of *otd* is established by a *bcd*-dependent activation of *otd*, first in a domain covering the whole anterior third of the embryo; slightly later, genes of the terminal system turn off *otd* expression at the very tip of the embryo.

otd, ems, and *btd*, and possibly one more gene expressed posteriorly to *ems*, may confer the patterning function of *bcd* in the head. *Deformed* (Regulski et al. 1987) is expressed posterior to *ems*, and it has been suggested that at least a part of the *Deformed* domain may be under *bcd* control (Jack and McGinnis 1990). Additional gene(s) have to execute the function of *bcd* in transforming posterior terminal to acronal fate in the unsegmented anterior terminus of the embryo. Bicoid appears to activate transcription not only of gap genes, but has recently been shown to be involved in the activation of stripe 2 expression of the pair rule gene *even skipped* (Small et al. 1991; Stanojevic et al. 1991). Both Bicoid and *hunchback* protein are responsible for activation of *even skipped* stripe 2 expression, whereas *giant* and *Krüppel*, by interfering with binding or activity of Bicoid and hunchback activation at overlapping or neighboring sites, determine the anterior and posterior borders of *even skipped* stripe 2 expression.

A less specific approach to characterize putative *bcd*-responsive genes has been the expression of Bicoid in third-instar larval salivary glands to detect immunohistochemically Bicoid binding to discrete bands of polytene chromosomes (W. Driever, unpubl.). The number of chromosomal bands that bind Bicoid is strongly dependent on the level of Bicoid expression: The expression of Bicoid from the hsp70 promoter following a weak heat shock results in binding to few bands (10–20); expression from the salivary-gland-specific sgs-3 promoter (Martin et al. 1989) results in binding to more than a hundred bands, whereas a strong heat shock in hsp70bcd larvae leads to a near-homogeneous staining of the chromosomes (and is lethal to the larvae). The pattern of bands obtained at low levels of expression is reproducible and includes chromosomal positions that might correlate with the loci *hb, Kr, gt, otd,* and *btd*. However, the level of expression at which this pattern arises is ambiguous, and therefore the data do not present any proof for a direct role of Bicoid in regulating the expression of these genes. Of all the signals, the immunostain at the *giant* locus (Mohler et al. 1989) is most prominent. Bicoid can bind to two elements in the *giant* promoter (W. Driever, unpubl.). The actual role of *giant* in head formation is less clear: It has been proposed to act as a gap gene anterior to *hb*, although the mutant phenotype affects three separate elements of the head (Fig. 6) (Mohler et al. 1989) and regions in the posterior abdomen. The anterior *giant* domain is not expressed in embryos from females mutant for *bcd* (Eldon and Pirrotta 1991; Kraut and Levine 1991a,b).

It is possible that *bcd* regulates the expression domains of gap genes as well as of genes specifying segmental identity in the head by acting either alone (e.g., to specify *hb* pattern) or in combination with other transcription factors (e.g., with maternal *hb* to determine the *Krüppel* domain).

BICOID AND POSTTRANSCRIPTIONAL CONTROL OF THE MATERNAL *CAUDAL* MRNA

A less well understood function of Bicoid is its involvement in the posttranscriptional control of maternal *caudal* (*cad*) expression. *cad* is expressed by both the maternal and the zygotic genome. The maternal *cad* transcript and protein (containing a homeodomain) are first uniformly distributed in the egg, but during early cleavage stages, *cad* protein, and successively *cad* mRNA, disappear from the anterior such that shallow gradients of *cad* mRNA and protein form (Fig. 6) (Mlodzik et al. 1985; Macdonald and Struhl 1986; Mlodzik and Gehring 1987a). This posttranscriptional control depends on *bcd* activity, since in embryos from *bcd* mutant females, maternal *cad* mRNA and protein remain uniformly distributed in the embryo. The gradient formation is independent of zygotic transcription and proceeds normally in unfertilized eggs (Macdonald and Struhl 1986; Mlodzik and Gehring 1987b). Thus, a function of zygotic gene products in mediating *cad* gradient formation can be excluded. Rebagliati (1989) suggested the presence of an RNA recognition motif in the carboxy-terminal portion of Bicoid. This sequence similarity is most likely not functional, since it is not conserved in *Drosophila pseudoobscura* (Seeger and Kaufman 1990). Whether Bicoid has both DNA- and RNA-binding activity is an open question. The Bicoid homeodomain is unique among all other characterized homeodomains so far, as it has a highly positively charged, arginine-rich stretch of amino acids (amino acids 141–148: KNRRRHK) just adjacent to helix 3 of the homeodomain. Site-specific mutations within this sequence, or its exchange against the amino acid sequence found at the homologous position in the *Antennapedia* homeodomain, do not interfere with transcriptional activation of zygotic genes and thus are able to induce normal wild-type development in embryos from females homozygous mutant for *bcd*[E1] when introduced as a modified *bcd* transgene (W. Driever and F. Sprenger, unpubl.). Initial observations indicate that *cad* RNA gradient formation does not proceed normally in embryos from females carrying these transgenes as the only source of Bicoid activity. Similar argininerich regions of some proteins have been implied to confer sequence-specific RNA-binding activity to the protein (Tat binding to TAR RNA: Roy et al. 1990; Weeks et al. 1990; Rev binding to RRE RNA and N binding to *nut* mRNA: Lazinski et al. 1989). It is striking that sequences in the maternal *cad* mRNA leader 5′ to the ATG could theoretically fold to give secondary structures containing a Bicoid-binding sequence deviating only in one position from the DNA-binding consensus (W. Driever and F. Sprenger, unpubl.). Further investigations are necessary to show if the Bicoid homeodomain indeed harbors an RNA-binding function.

CONCLUSIONS AND PERSPECTIVES

The genetic and molecular analysis of early pattern formation in the *Drosophila* embryo in general, and especially our knowledge about the *bicoid* gene, provide us with insights into the molecular mechanisms by which maternally derived molecules define the establishment of the earliest regional identities in a higher eukaryotic embryo. The *bicoid* gene product, distributed in a concentration gradient, is a transcriptional activator that acts as a morphogen by differential spatial activation of target genes within the embryo. Expression domains of some *bcd*-dependent zygotic genes are defined by the number and affinity of Bicoid-binding sites in their promoters only (e.g., *hunchback*). Other target genes depend on activation by Bicoid, whereas the limits of expression are determined by neighboring repressors (e.g., domains of *Krüppel* or *even skipped stripe 2*).

The ideas discussed below may help to understand how "simple" transcription factors can control processes as complicated as pattern formation during early embryogenesis. Some conclusions may be oversimplified, and other thoughts are well known from the analysis of organisms less complex than *Drosophila*.

Why is it important to consider that Bicoid can bind to a number of variants of its consensus binding sequence, albeit probably with very different affinities? The absolute concentration of *trans*-acting factors in a nucleus may vary by several orders of magnitude (at least 2–3 orders of magnitude for Bicoid in the *Drosophila* embryo). Thus, two genes with different types of binding sites for a single transcriptional regulator could respond to different concentrations of the regulator. Hence, groups of nuclei in a concentration gradient of the regulator could activate, for example, different subsets of genes.

Variants (deviating in as many as 4 bases) of a 9-bp consensus binding sequence can be found statistically every few kilobases within the genome. Single weak activator molecules (like Bicoid) bound to such random sites may have no adverse effect on cellular survival. Target genes in their promoters contain clusters of binding sites (which are unlikely to be present in the genome at random), allowing the binding of several activator molecules and thereby increasing the expression level manyfold. One can speculate about the minimum number of Bicoid-binding sites necessary to obtain a "reasonable" activation of a target gene, and I estimate that for Bicoid at least three binding sites are necessary to get a substantial expression level (as judged from the fusion gene experiments described above). On the other hand, single Bicoid-binding sites could act together with binding sites for other transcription factors and cooperate to induce effective levels of target gene expression. *Krüppel* regulation may be an example, since *bcd* and *hb* both contribute to *Krüppel* activation in the central domain (Hoch et al. 1990).

Probably the most prominent problem to be addressed in the Bicoid system is the following: How is it possible to generate a sharp decision between the on and the off state of a target gene within a concentration gradient of the regulator? In the *Drosophila* embryo, the posterior border of *hb* expression can be described as a steep expression gradient over four to five nuclei with a 20- to 50-fold (or even stronger) change in *hb* transcription rate, whereas Bicoid concentration varies only 2- to 3-fold (and possibly even less) over the same region of four to five nuclei. Therefore, minor concentration changes indeed define activation thresholds. Simple binding of an activator to its sites and linear activation are certainly not sufficient to explain such sharp on/off decisions. How then is the continuous information provided by the Bicoid gradient translated into distinct step-like on and off decisions of zygotic gene expression?

By far, the best-investigated case of a molecular switch is the binding of the λ repressor to the right operator of bacteriophage λ during the regulation of the λ life cycle (Ptashne 1986). Cooperative mechanisms are employed to generate a switch between the lysogenic and the lytic states of λ. The repressor, depending on its concentration, is present either in monomeric or DNA-binding dimeric form (one monomer cooperatively "helps" the other to bind DNA); repressor dimers bind cooperatively (one dimer "helps" a second to bind) to adjacent sites in the operator. λ repressor binding to the operator therefore can be described by a sigmoidal binding curve: A fewfold drop in repressor concentration is sufficient to efficiently induce synthesis of cro and start the lytic cycle.

In the case of Bicoid, the generation of sharp thresholds is not yet understood. Are similar cooperative mechanisms employed by Bicoid during early development? No data exist as to whether Bicoid is present in monomer-oligomer equilibria or whether it binds cooperatively to DNA. The presence of multiple Bicoid-binding sites in the *hb* promoter may allow cooperative interactions to take place. Indeed, the analysis of embryos carrying reporter genes with increasing numbers of binding sites points to a more than additive effect of additional binding sites on the transcription rate, as discussed above. Besides cooperative DNA binding, such effects may also be due to synergistic protein-protein interactions of several Bicoid molecules each with components of the transcriptional complex (Courey et al. 1989; Carey et al. 1990). Carey et al. describe this type of synergism as follows: "two (or as much as 5 to 10) molecules of an activator (or of different activators), bound to adjacent sites on DNA, simultaneously contact an as-yet-unidentified target protein. The interaction energies would add, leading to an exponential increase in the affinity of the target for multiple activators; the exponential increase in affinity would generate a synergistic increase in transcription." Further experiments will have to unravel whether cooperativity is involved in the generation of sharp borders of expression for target genes of Bicoid.

What are the remaining problems concerning the role of Bicoid in transcriptional control, and how may they be addressed? A major pitfall is our lack of understanding of the actual DNA-binding mechanism of Bicoid: Are monomers or oligomers binding to DNA, and does cooperativity play a role? In vitro experiments to solve these problems have been hampered by the difficulty of expressing Bicoid (in the various systems tested) to levels that would make an isolation of the protein feasible (T. Hoey et al., pers. comm.). Since other homeodomain proteins are easy to express, the putative RNA-binding function of Bicoid may inhibit expression at high levels. Both DNA-binding studies and in vitro transcription experiments will help to investigate whether cooperativity is involved in the Bicoid system. The second major topic on Bicoid is the investigation of how other target genes besides *hb* are regulated by Bicoid. This will finally reveal the mechanisms that are used in the embryo to define multiple domains of zygotic gene expression with the information provided by the concentration profile of the Bicoid gradient.

Gradient mechanisms like the one discussed for Bicoid are not restricted to syncytial cell states like the *Drosophila* embryo. The subcellular localization (e.g., the balance between cytoplasmic and nuclear localization) of a transcriptional regulator could be influenced through signals from outside a cell (as in the *dorsal* system in *Drosophila*; Roth et al. 1990), or the activity of transcription factors could be regulated (e.g., by phosphorylation) by means of a signal-receptor tyrosine kinase cascade (as suggested for the *torso* system; Sprenger et al. 1989), thereby generating fields of differential activity of transcriptional regulators within a tissue, although the protein concentration itself may be identical in all cells of the field. One may envision such fields to be dependent on the extracellular concentration of diffusible ligands or even on differential activation of voltage-gated channels in electrically stimulated fields. Work on vertebrate pattern formation will reveal the importance of graded fields of activity of transcriptional regulators for vertebrate development.

ACKNOWLEDGMENTS

I especially thank Christiane Nüsslein-Volhard, in whose laboratory most of the work reported here has been performed, as well as Mary Mullins, Helen Doyle, Dominique Ferrandon, and Siegfried Roth for their critical reviews of the manuscript.

REFERENCES

Aggarwal, A.K., D.W. Rodgers, M. Drottar, M. Ptashne, and S.C. Harrison. 1988. Recognition of a DNA operator by the repressor of phage 434: A view at high resolution. *Science* **242:** 899–907.

Akam, M. 1987. The molecular basis for metameric pattern in the *Drosophila* embryo. *Development* **101:** 1–22.

Anderson, J.E., M. Ptashne, and S.C. Harrison. 1987. Structure of the repressor-operator complex of bacteriophage 434. *Nature* **326:** 846–852.

Anderson, K.V. 1987. Dorsal-ventral pattern genes of *Drosophila*. *Trends Genet.* **3:** 91–97.

Beachy, P.A., M.A. Krasnow, E.R. Gavis, and D.S. Hogness. 1988. An Ultrabithorax protein binds sequences near its own and the Antennapedia P1 promoter. *Cell* **55:** 1069–1081.

Berger, S.L., W.D. Cress, A. Cress, S.J. Triezenberg, and L. Guarente. 1990. Selective inhibition of activation but not basal transcription by the acidic activation domain of VP16: Evidence for transcriptional adaptors. *Cell* **61:** 1199–1208.

Berleth, T., M. Burri, G. Thoma, D. Bopp, S. Richstein, G. Frigerio, M. Noll, and C. Nüsslein-Volhard. 1988. The role of localization of bicoid RNA in organizing the anterior pattern of the *Drosophila* embryo. *EMBO J.* **7:** 1749–1756.

Carey, M., Y.-S. Lin, M.R. Green, and M. Ptashne. 1990. A mechanism for synergistic activation of a mammalian gene by *GAL4* derivatives. *Nature* **345:** 361–364.

Casanova, J. and G. Struhl. 1989. Localized surface activity of *torso*, a receptor tyrosine kinase, specifies terminal body pattern in *Drosophila*. *Genes Dev.* **3:** 2025–2038.

Cohen, S.M. and G. Jürgens. 1990. Mediation of *Drosophila* head development by gap-like segmentation genes. *Nature* **346:** 482–485.

Courey, A.J. and R. Tjian. 1988. Analysis of Sp1 in vivo reveals multiple transcriptional domains, including a novel glutamine rich activation motif. *Cell* **55:** 887–898.

Courey, A.J., A.D. Holtzman, S.P. Jackson, and R. Tjian. 1989. Synergistic activation by the glutamine rich domains of human transcription factor Sp1. *Cell* **59:** 827–836.

Dalton, D., R. Chadwick, and W. McGinnis. 1989. Expression and embryonic function of *empty spiracles*: A *Drosophila* homeo box gene with two patterning functions on the anterior posterior axis of the embryo. *Genes Dev.* **3:** 1940–1956.

Desplan, C., J. Theis, and P.H. O'Farrell. 1985. The *Drosophila* developmental gene *engrailed* encodes a sequence specific DNA binding activity. *Nature* **318:** 630–635.

———. 1988. The sequence specificity of homeo domain-DNA interaction. *Cell* **54:** 1081–1090.

Driever, W. and C. Nüsslein-Volhard. 1988a. A gradient of bicoid protein in *Drosophila* embryos. *Cell* **54:** 83–93.

———. 1988b. The bicoid protein determines position in the *Drosophila* embryo in a concentration dependent manner. *Cell* **54:** 95–104.

———. 1989. Bicoid protein, a positive regulator of hunchback transcription in the early *Drosophila* embryo. *Nature* **337:** 138–143.

Driever, W., V. Siegel, and C. Nüsslein-Volhard. 1990. Autonomous determination of anterior structures in the early *Drosophila* embryo by the bicoid morphogen. *Development* **109:** 811–820.

Driever, W., G. Thoma, and C. Nüsslein-Volhard. 1989a. Determination of spatial domains of zygotic gene expression in the *Drosophila* embryo by the affinity of binding site for the bicoid morphogen. *Nature* **340:** 363–367.

Driever, W., J. Ma, C. Nüsslein-Volhard, and M. Ptashne. 1989b. Rescue of *bicoid*-mutant *Drosophila* embryos by bicoid fusion proteins containing heterologous activating sequences. *Nature* **342:** 149–154.

Eldon, E.D. and V. Pirrotta. 1991. Interactions of the *Drosophila* gap gene *giant* with maternal and zygotic pattern-forming genes. *Development* **111:** 367–378.

Finkelstein, R. and N. Perrimon. 1990. The orthodenticle gene is regulated by *bicoid* and *torso* and specifies *Drosophila* head development. *Nature* **346:** 485–488.

Frigerio, G., M. Burri, D. Bopp, S. Baumgartner, and M. Noll. 1986. Structure of the segmentation gene paired and the *Drosophila* PRD gene set as part of a gene network. *Cell* **47:** 735–746.

Frohnhöfer, H.G. and C. Nüsslein-Volhard. 1986. Organization of anterior pattern in the *Drosophila* embryo by the maternal gene *bicoid*. *Nature* **324:** 120–125.

Frohnhöfer, H.G. and C. Nüsslein-Volhard. 1987. Maternal genes required for the anterior localization of *bicoid* activity in the embryo of *Drosophila*. *Genes Dev.* **1:** 880–890.

———. 1986. Manipulating the anteroposterior pattern of the *Drosophila* embryo. *J. Embryol. Exp. Morphol.* **97:** 169–179.

Gaul, U. and H. Jäckle. 1987. Pole region dependent repression of the *Drosophila* gap gene *Krüppel* by maternal gene products. *Cell* **51:** 549–555.

———. 1989. Analysis of maternal effect combinations elucidates regulation and function of the overlap of *hunchback* and *Krüppel* gene expression in the *Drosophila* blastoderm embryo. *Development* **107:** 651–662.

Hanes, S.D. and R. Brent. 1989. DNA specificity of the bicoid activator protein is determined by homeodomain recognition helix residue 9. *Cell* **57:** 1275–1283.

———. 1991. A genetic model for interaction of the homeodomain recognition helix with DNA. *Science* **251:** 426–430.

Hoch, M., E. Seifert, and H. Jäckle. 1991. Gene expression mediated by *cis* acting sequences of the *Krüppel* gene in response to the *Drosophila* morphogens *bicoid* and *hunchback*. *EMBO. J.* **10:** 2267–2278.

Hoch, M., C. Schröder, E. Seifert, and H. Jäckle. 1990. *cis* acting control elements for *Krüppel* expression in the *Drosophila* embryo. *EMBO J.* **9:** 2587–2595.

Hoey, T. and M. Levine. 1988. Divergent homeo box proteins recognize similar DNA sequences in *Drosophila*. *Nature* **332:** 858–861.

Hope, I.A. and K. Struhl. 1986. Functional dissection of a eucaryotic transcriptional activator protein, GCN4 of yeast. *Cell* **46:** 885–894.

Hülskamp, M., C. Pfeifle, and D. Tautz. 1990. A morphogenetic gradient of hunchback protein organizes the expression of the gap genes *Krüppel* and *Knirps* in the early *Drosophila* embryo. *Nature* **346:** 577–580.

Hülskamp, M., C. Schröder, C. Pfeifle, H. Jäckle, and D. Tautz. 1989. Posterior segmentation of the *Drosophila* embryo in the absence of a maternal posterior organizer gene. *Nature* **338:** 629–632.

Ingham, P.W. 1988. The molecular genetics of embryonic pattern formation in the *Drosophila* embryo. *Nature* **335:** 25–34.

———. 1990. The X, Y, Z of head development. *Nature* **346:** 412–413.

Irish, V., R. Lehmann, and M. Akam. 1989. The *Drosophila* posterior group gene *nanos* functions by repressing *hunchback* activity. *Nature* **338:** 646–648.

Jack, T. and W. McGinnis. 1990. Establishment of the *Deformed* expression stripe requires the combinatorial action of coordinate, gap and pair-rule proteins. *EMBO J.* **9:** 1187–1198.

Jacob, Y., S. Sather, J.R. Martin, and R. Ollo. 1991. Analysis of *Krüppel* control elements reveals that localized expression results from the interaction of multiple subelements. *Proc. Natl. Acad. Sci.* **88:** 5912–5916.

Jürgens, G., R. Lehmann, M. Schardin, and C. Nüsslein-Volhard. 1986. Segmental organization of the head in the embryo of *Drosophila melanogaster*. *Wilhelm Roux's Arch. Dev. Biol.* **193:** 359–377.

Kissinger, C.R., L. Beishan, E. Martin-Blanco, T. Kornberg, and C.O. Pabo. 1990. Crystal structure of an *engrailed* homeodomain-DNA complex at 2.8 Å resolution: A framework for understanding homeodomain-DNA interactions. *Cell* **63:** 579–590.

Klingler, M., M. Erdélyi, J. Szabad, and C. Nüsslein-Volhard. 1988. Function of *torso* in determining the terminal anlagen of the *Drosophila* embryo. *Nature* **335:** 275–277.

Kornfeld, K., R.B. Saint, P.A. Beachy, P.J. Harte, P.A. Peattie, and D.S. Hogness. 1989. Structure and expression of a family of *Ultrabithorax* mRNAs generated by alternative splicing and polyadenylation in *Drosophila*. *Genes Dev.* **3:** 243–258.

Kraut, R. and M. Levine. 1991a. Spatial regulation of the gap gene *giant* during *Drosophila* development. *Development* **111:** 601–609.

————. 1991b. Mutually repressive interactions between the gap genes *giant* and *Krüppel* define middle body regions of the *Drosophila* embryo. *Development* **111:** 611–621.

Lazinski, D., E. Grzadzielska, and A. Das. 1989. Sequence specific recognition of RNA hairpins by bacteriophage antiterminators requires a conserved arginine-rich motif. *Cell* **59:** 207–218.

Laughon, A. and M.P. Scott. 1984. Sequence of a *Drosophila* segmentation gene: Protein structure homology with DNA-binding proteins. *Nature* **310:** 25–31.

Lehmann, R. and C. Nüsslein-Volhard. 1987. *hunchback*, a gene required for segmentation of an anterior and posterior region of the *Drosophila* embryo. *Dev. Biol.* **119:** 402–417.

Lewis, J., M.W. Slack, and L. Wolpert. 1977. Thresholds in development. *J. Theor. Biol.* **65:** 579–590.

Ma, J. and M. Ptashne. 1987a. Deletion analysis of *GAL4* defines two transcriptional activating segments. *Cell* **48:** 847–853.

————. 1987b. A new class of yeast transcriptional activators. *Cell* **51:** 113–119.

Macdonald, P.M. 1990. bicoid mRNA localization signal: Phylogenetic conservation of function and RNA secondary structure. *Development* **110:** 161–171.

Macdonald, P.M. and G. Struhl. 1986. A molecular gradient in early *Drosophila* embryos and its role in specifying the body pattern. *Nature* **324:** 537–545.

————. 1988. *cis*-acting sequences responsible for anterior localization of bicoid mRNA in *Drosophila* embryos. *Nature* **336:** 595–598.

Macdonald, P.M., S.K. Luk, and M. Kilpatrick. 1991. Protein encoded by the *exuperantia* gene is concentrated at sites of *bicoid* mRNA accumulation in *Drosophila* nurse cells but not oocytes or embryos. *Genes Dev.* **5:** 2455–2466.

Marcey, D., W.S. Wakins, and T. Hazelrigg. 1991. The temporal and spatial distribution pattern of maternal exuperantia protein: Evidence for a role in establishment but not maintenance of *bicoid* mRNA localization. *EMBO J.* **10:** 4259–4266.

Martin, M., A. Giangrande, C. Ruiz, and G. Richards. 1989. Induction and repression of the *Drosophila Sgs-3* glue gene are mediated by distinct sequences in the proximal promoter. *EMBO J.* **8:** 561–568.

McGinnis, W., M.S. Levine, E. Hafen, A. Kuroiwa, and W.J. Gehring. 1984. A conserved DNA sequence in homeotic genes of *Drosophila* Antennapedia and bithorax complexes. *Nature* **308:** 428–433.

Mlodzik, M. and W. Gehring. 1987a. Expression of the *caudal* gene in the germ line of *Drosophila*: Formation of an RNA and protein gradient during early embryogenesis. *Cell* **48:** 465–478.

————. 1987b. Hierarchy of the genetic interactions that specify the anteroposterior segmentation pattern of the *Drosophila* embryo as monitored by caudal protein expression. *Development* **101:** 421–435.

Mlodzik, M., A. Fjose, and W. Gehring. 1985. Isolation of *caudal,* a *Drosophila* homeobox containing gene with maternal expression, whose transcripts form a concentration gradient at the pre-blastoderm stage. *EMBO J.* **4:** 2961–2969.

Mohler, J., E.D. Eldon, and V. Pirrotta. 1989. A novel spatial transcription pattern associated with the segmentation gene, *giant*, of *Drosophila*. *EMBO J.* **8:** 1539–1548.

Müller, M., M. Affolter, W. Leupin, G. Otting, K. Wüthrich, and W.J. Gehring. 1988. Isolation and sequence specific DNA binding of the *Antennapedia* homeodomain. *EMBO J.* **7:** 4299–4304.

Nüsslein-Volhard, C. and E. Wieschaus. 1980. Mutations affecting segment number and polarity in *Drosophila*. *Nature* **287:** 795–801.

Nüsslein-Volhard, C., H.G. Frohnhöfer, and R. Lehmann. 1987. Determination of anterioposterior polarity in *Drosophila*. *Science* **238:** 1675–1681.

Nüsslein-Volhard, C., E. Wieschaus, and H. Kluding. 1984. Mutations affecting the pattern of the larval cuticle in *Drosophila melanogaster*. I. Zygotic loci on the second chromosome. *Wilhelm Roux's Arch. Dev. Biol.* **193:** 267–282.

O'Connor, M.B., R. Binari, L.A. Perkins, and W. Bender. 1988. Alternative RNA products from the *Ultrabithorax* domain of the bithorax complex. *EMBO J.* **7:** 435–445.

Pankratz, M.J., E. Seifert, N. Gerwin, B. Billi, U. Nauber, and H. Jäckle. 1990. Gradients of *Krüppel* and *Knirps* gene products direct pair-rule gene stripe patterning in the posterior region of the *Drosophila* embryo. *Cell* **61:** 309–317.

Pokrywka, N.J. and E.C. Stephenson. 1991. Microtubules mediate the localization of *bicoid* mRNA during *Drosophila* oogenesis. *Development* **113:** 55–66.

Ptashne, M. 1986. *A genetic switch.* Cell and Blackwell Scientific, Cambridge, Massachusetts.

Rebagliati, M. 1989. An RNA recognition motif in the bicoid protein. *Cell* **58:** 231–232.

Regulski, M., N. McGinnis, R. Chadwick, and W. McGinnis. 1987. Development and molecular analysis of *Deformed*, a homeotic gene controlling *Drosophila* head development. *EMBO J.* **6:** 767–777.

Rogers, S., R. Wells, and K. Rote. 1987. Amino acid sequences common to rapidly degraded proteins: The PEST hypothesis. *Science* **234:** 364–368.

Roth, S., D. Stein, and C. Nüsslein-Volhard. 1990. A gradient of nuclear localization of the dorsal protein determines dorsoventral pattern in the *Drosophila* embryo. *Cell* **59:** 1189–1202.

Roy, S., U. Delling, C.-H. Chen, C.A. Rosen, and N. Sonenberg. 1990. A bulge structure in HIV-1 TAR RNA is required for Tat binding and Tat-mediated *trans*-activation. *Genes Dev.* **4:** 1365–1373.

Schröder, C., D. Tautz, E. Seifert, and H. Jäckle. 1988. Differential regulation of two transcripts from the *Drosophila* gap segmentation gene *hunchback*. *EMBO J.* **7:** 2881–2888.

Schüpbach, T. and E. Wieschaus. 1986. Maternal-effect mutations altering anterior posterior pattern in the *Drosophila* embryo. *Wilhelm Roux's Arch. Dev. Biol.* **195:** 302–317.

Scott, M.P. and A.J. Weiner. 1984. Structural relationships among genes that control development: Sequence homology between the Antennapedia, Ultrabithorax, and fushi tarazu loci of *Drosophila*. *Proc. Natl. Acad. Sci.* **81:** 4115–4119.

Scott, M.P., J.W. Tamkan, and G.W. Hartzell III. 1989. The structure and function of the homeodomain. *Biochim. Biophys. Acta* **989:** 25–48.

Seeger, M.A. and T.C. Kaufman. 1990. Molecular analysis of the bicoid gene from *Drosophila pseudoobscura*: Identification of conserved domains within coding and noncoding regions of the bicoid mRNA. *EMBO J.* **9:** 2977–2987.

Slack, J.M.W. 1987. Morphogenetic gradients—Past and present. *Trends Biochem. Sci.* **12:** 200–204.

Small, S., R. Kraut, T. Hoey, R. Warrior, and M. Levine. 1991. Transcriptional regulation of a pair rule stripe in *Drosophila. Genes Dev.* **5:** 827–839.

Sprenger, F., L.M. Stevens, and C. Nüsslein-Volhard. 1989. The *Drosophila* gene *torso* encodes a putative receptor tyrosine kinase. *Nature* **338:** 4478–4483.

Stanojevic, D., T. Hoey, and M. Levine. 1989. Sequence specific DNA-binding of the gap proteins encoded by *hunchback* and *Krüppel* in *Drosophila. Nature* **341:** 331–335.

Stanojevic, D., S. Small, and M. Levine. 1991. Regulation of a segmentation stripe by overlapping activators and repressors in the *Drosophila* embryo. *Science* **254:** 1385–1387.

Stephenson, E.C., Y. Chao, and J.D. Fackenthal. 1988. Molecular analysis of the *swallow* gene of *Drosophila melanogaster. Genes Dev.* **2:** 1655–1665.

Steward, R., S.B. Zusman, L.H. Huang, and P. Schedl. 1988. The dorsal protein is distributed in a gradient in the early *Drosophila* embryo. *Cell* **55:** 487–495.

St. Johnston, D., D. Beuchle, and C. Nüsslein-Volhard. 1991. *Staufen*, a gene required to localize maternal RNAs in the *Drosophila* egg. *Cell* **66:** 51–63.

St. Johnston, D., W. Driever, T. Berleth, S. Richstein, and C. Nüsslein-Volhard. 1989. Multiple steps in the localization of bicoid mRNA to the anterior pole of the *Drosophila* oocyte. *Development* (suppl.) **109:** 13–19.

Struhl, G. 1989. Differing strategies for organizing anterior and posterior body pattern in *Drosophila* embryos. *Nature* **338:** 741–744.

Struhl, G., K. Struhl, and P. Macdonald. 1989. The gradient morphogen bicoid is a concentration-dependent transcriptional activator. *Cell* **57:** 1259–1273.

Tautz, D. 1988. Regulation of the *Drosophila* segmentation gene *hunchback* by two maternal morphogenetic centers. *Nature* **332:** 281–284.

Tautz, D., R. Lehmann, H. Schnürch, R. Schuh, E. Seifert, A. Kienlin, K. Jones, and H. Jäckle. 1987. Finger protein of novel structure encoded by *hunchback*, a second member of the gap class of *Drosophila* segmentation genes. *Nature* **327:** 383–389.

Treier, M., C. Pfeifle, and D. Tautz. 1989. Comparison of the gap segmentation gene *hunchback* between *Drosophila melanogaster* and *Drosophila virilis* reveals novel modes of evolutionary change. *EMBO J.* **8:** 1517–1525.

Treisman, J., P. Gönczy, M. Vashishtha, E. Harris, and C. Desplan. 1989. A single amino acid can determine the DNA binding specificity of homeodomain proteins. *Cell* **59:** 553–562.

Weeks, K.M., C. Ampe, S.C. Schultz, T.A. Steitz, and D.M. Crothers. 1990. Fragments of the HIV-1 Tat protein specifically bind TAR RNA. *Science* **249:** 1281–1285.

Wharton, R.P. and M. Ptashne. 1985. Changing the binding specificity of a repressor by redesigning an α-helix. *Nature* **316:** 601–605.

Wieschaus, E., C. Nüsslein-Volhard, and G. Jürgens. 1984a. Mutations affecting the pattern of the larval cuticle in *Drosophila melanogaster*. III. Zygotic loci on the X chromosome and fourth chromosome. *Wilhelm Roux's Arch. Dev. Biol.* **193:** 296–307.

Wieschaus, E., C. Nüsslein-Volhard, and H. Kluding. 1984b. *Krüppel*, a gene whose activity is required in the zygotic genome for normal embryonic segmentation. *Dev. Biol.* **104:** 172–186.

Chromatin/DNA Topology

46

Template Topology and Transcription

James C. Wang
Department of Biochemistry and Molecular Biology
Harvard University
Cambridge, Massachusetts 02138

OVERVIEW

For two decades it has been known that DNA supercoiling influences transcription. More recently, transcription has also been shown to affect the supercoiling of intracellular DNA. The theoretical framework and experimental results on how DNA topology and transcription are interrelated are summarized in this chapter.

INTRODUCTION

Studies on the relationship between DNA topology and transcription were initiated a few years after the discovery of supercoiled DNA. Vinograd was the first to recognize that the spatial contortion of a double-stranded DNA ring with intact strands is very sensitive to winding or unwinding of the double helix; small alterations of the helical structure of such a DNA are thus accompanied by readily measurable changes in properties that depend on its overall shape (Vinograd et al. 1965). Because of this intricate dependence, closed circular DNAs provide a tool for measuring minute changes of the double-helix structure brought about by changes in temperature, ionic environment, or the binding of other molecules (Crawford and Waring 1967; Wang 1969).

How the binding of an RNA polymerase might change the double-helix structure was of particular interest. Indirect evidence and theoretical considerations suggested that RNA polymerase might unpair a short segment of DNA, so as to copy the genetic information encoded by the exposed bases of the template strand via the Watson-Crick pairing scheme (for review, see Chamberlin 1974). To test this model, pairs of differently radiolabeled nicked DNA samples were converted by DNA ligase to the closed circular form. For each pair, one sample was ligated in the presence of RNA polymerase and the other in its absence. If RNA polymerase unwinds DNA, then after ligation and removal of bound protein, the DNA ligated in the presence of the polymerase should be underwound or negatively supercoiled relative to the DNA ligated in the absence of the polymerase; the more compact shape of the supercoiled form would in turn make it a faster sedimenting species. Measurements of the relative sedimentation rates of the differently labeled DNAs in each pair of samples, which were mixed following ligation and deproteinized prior to sedimentation analysis, indicate that the binding of a polymerase unwinds the DNA double helix by roughly one turn (Saucer and Wang 1972; see also Wang et al. 1977; Gamper and Hearst 1982). Spectroscopic measurements (Hsieh and Wang 1978), and chemical reactivity measurements at the nucleotide sequence level (Siebenlist et al. 1980; Kirkegaard et al. 1983; Sasse-Dwight and Gralla 1989), provided additional evidence for the unwinding of the DNA double helix by RNA polymerase.

Around 1972, a theoretical analysis showed that supercoiling of the DNA has a profound effect on protein binding if a protein winds or unwinds the DNA by even a fraction of a turn (Davidson 1972). Together, the unwinding measurements and the theoretical deduction provided a thermodynamic basis for earlier observations that negatively supercoiled DNAs appeared to be better templates for transcription than their nicked derivatives (Hayashi and Hayashi 1971). A more systematic examination of the effect of template supercoiling on transcription in vitro confirmed that transcription is strongly affected by supercoiling of the DNA template (Botchan et al. 1973).

Studies of the effects of DNA supercoiling on transcription received a boost in 1976 with the discovery of bacterial DNA gyrase (or bacterial DNA topoisomerase II; Gellert et al. 1976). In vitro, this enzyme catalyzes negative supercoiling of DNA in the presence of ATP; its discovery therefore strengthened the notion that intracellular DNA in eubacteria is in a negatively supercoiled state. The identification of bacterial gyrase as the target of several drugs, some of which were known as early as 1967 to depress transcription (Smith and Davis 1967), provided the first hint that the large effect of DNA supercoiling on transcription observed in vitro might be relevant in vivo. Mutations in the genes *gyrA* and *gyrB*, which encode the two subunits of the enzyme, have also been shown to affect the expression of certain genes, e.g., the *his* operon (Rudd and Menzel 1987).

Around 1980, a new line of evidence linking DNA topology and gene expression was uncovered. The *Escherichia coli topA* gene encoding DNA topoisomerase I was identified, and its chromosomal location was mapped (Sternglanz et al. 1981; Trucksis and Depew 1981). The location of the gene led to the postulate that *topA* might be identical to *supX*, a gene initially termed *su leu 500*, mutations in which were known to suppress the leucine auxotrophy resulting from an unlinked mutation that reduced the level of transcription of the leucine operon (Mukai and Margolin 1963). A few years later, the identity between *supX* and *topA* was established (Margolin et al. 1985).

A coherent picture of the relationship between DNA topology and transcription could be woven from the threads of evidence described above: namely, intracellular DNA in eubacteria is negatively supercoiled to a degree determined by the opposing actions of DNA gyrase and DNA topoisomerase I; the degree of supercoiling in turn affects the expression of various genes (for review, see Gellert 1981; Drlica 1984; Wang 1985a). Because supercoiling affects interactions between DNA and regulatory factors, as well as between DNA and RNA polymerase, it may affect the expression of different genes differently. In general, if transcription of a particular gene has a rate-limiting step associated with the formation of a certain complex, supercoiling would have a strong effect if the formation of this complex involves significant twisting or writhing of a DNA segment. Specific predictions are not possible, however, without additional information on the configuration of the DNA in this complex.

TRANSCRIPTIONAL SUPERCOILING: THE TWIN-SUPERCOILED DOMAIN MODEL

The simple picture described above for the state of supercoiling of intracellular DNA requires significant modifications, however, as a result of more recent studies based on the transcriptional supercoiling model (Liu and Wang 1987). For a matching nut and bolt, relative longitudinal displacement is always accompanied by relative rotation. Similarly, when a macromolecule tracks along a helical DNA, it is expected to circle around the DNA. If this circling motion is prevented for some reason, then the DNA has to turn around its helical axis instead. The consequence of this rotation is that the DNA segment ahead of the tracking macromolecule becomes positively supercoiled, and the DNA segment behind it becomes negatively supercoiled. Experimental results obtained in the last few years show that in *E. coli* (Wu et al. 1988), as well as in yeast (Giaever and Wang 1988), transcription may indeed be accompanied by the generation of oppositely supercoiled domains.

To appreciate the simultaneous generation of two oppositely supercoiled domains by transcription, or indeed by any process involving the translocation of a macromolecular ensemble R along DNA, it is convenient to consider a linear DNA molecule with each of its ends firmly attached to an immobile structure E, as depicted in Figure 1A. If R is not allowed to circle around the DNA as it tracks along, the helical turns in the DNA segment ahead of it will be pushed into a shorter and shorter region; the DNA segment will thus become overwound or positively supercoiled. The opposite will happen in the DNA segment behind R: The segment will become underwound or negatively supercoiled.

One could raise the legitimate objection that despite statements in textbooks that intracellular DNA is organized into topologically separate domains due to its attachment to a cellular entity at multiple sites, this popular notion has not been rigorously tested. To circumvent this objection, the structures E shown in Figure 1A can be combined into one, as depicted in Figure 1B. E depicted in Figure 1B can be viewed as a real or hypothetical entity bound to a circular DNA.

Focusing on the drawing shown in Figure 1B, the next consideration is, What are the pathways for the removal of the supercoils? There are basically two. One involves the relaxation of these supercoiled domains by DNA topoisomerases. The other involves diffusional pathways that would allow the merging of the oppositely supercoiled domains: By

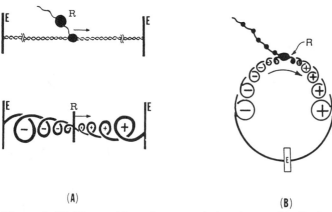

(A)   (B)

Figure 1 (*A*) The tracking of a transcriptional ensemble R along a DNA double helix (*top*) requires R to encircle around the DNA. For simplicity, the ends of the DNA segment are assumed to be attached to a cellular entity E. If R is not allowed to turn around the DNA, the DNA must be rotated around its helical axis instead, which in turn causes the overwinding or positive supercoiling of the DNA segment ahead of R, and underwinding or negative supercoiling of the DNA segment behind R (*bottom*). (*B*) The bars in *A* representing the cellular entity E at the termini of the DNA segment are combined to illustrate that E can be any DNA-bound entity, or nonexistent. See text for details. (Reprinted, with permission, from Wang 1991.)

rotating R or E shown in Figure 1B in the appropriate direction, the positive and negative supercoils can cancel each other; if E is nonexistent, then rotational diffusion of the DNA segment itself between the oppositely supercoiled domains becomes a pathway for the neutralization of positive and negative supercoils. Inside a cell, the various competing processes are expected to occur simultaneously; the supercoiled state at a particular location of intracellular DNA is thus determined by the relative rates of processes that generate or eliminate DNA supercoils at that location.

EVIDENCE SUPPORTING THE TWIN-SUPERCOILED-DOMAIN MODEL OF TRANSCRIPTIONAL SUPERCOILING

Accumulation of Positive Supercoils in *E. coli* Plasmids upon Inactivation of DNA Gyrase

It has been known since 1971 that bacterial DNA topoisomerase I preferentially relaxes negatively supercoiled DNA (Wang 1971, 1973). This specificity provides a unique tool for testing the generation of oppositely supercoiled domains in vitro or in vivo, by any process or processes. According to the model, if all DNA topoisomerases inside a cell are inactivated except one, which, like *E. coli* DNA topoisomerase I, preferentially removes negative supercoils, positive supercoils should accumulate in DNA inside the cell. The accumulation of positive supercoils in *E. coli* intracellular plasmid DNA following the inhibition of DNA gyrase was first observed by Lockshon and Morris in 1983 and interpreted in terms of the twin-supercoiled-domain model several years later (Liu and Wang 1987; Wu et al. 1988).

Several lines of evidence show that this accumulation of positive supercoils is intimately related to transcription. The final level, as well as the rate of positive supercoiling, correlates well with the extent of transcription of the plasmid; furthermore, no accumulation of positive supercoils occurs if transcription is inhibited by rifampicin at the same time as novobiocin is added (Wu et al. 1988).

In Yeast Cells Expressing *E. coli* DNA Topoisomerase I, Positive Supercoils Accumulate When Yeast DNA Topoisomerases I and II Are Inactivated

In a yeast Δ*top1top2 ts* strain, devoid of DNA topoisomerase I and expressing a temperature-sensitive DNA topoisomerase II, accumulation of positive supercoils in plasmids was also observed upon thermal inactivation of yeast DNA topoisomerase II, provided that the cells express a plasmid-borne *E. coli* DNA topoisomerase I gene (Giaever and Wang 1988). Similar to the case with *E. coli* described above, the final level, as well as the rate of positive supercoiling of a plasmid, correlates well with the extent of its transcription. Furthermore, when the same experiment was carried out with a yeast *top1top2 ts* strain with a temperature-sensitive RNA polymerase II, no accumulation of positive supercoils in the endogenous 2-μm plasmid was observed when cells expressing *E. coli* DNA topoisomerase I were shifted to a nonpermissive temperature at which both yeast DNA topoisomerase II and RNA polymerase II are inactivated (G.N. Giaever and J.C. Wang, unpubl.).

Hypernegative Supercoiling in *E. coli topA* and Yeast *top1top2 ts* Mutants

Pruss (1985) and Pruss and Drlica (1986) observed that in *E. coli topA* strains, but not in the wild-type control, the plasmid pBR322 is much more negatively supercoiled than a number of its deletion derivatives missing various segments in the region encoding tetracycline resistance. The hypernegatively supercoiled state of pBR322 in *topA* strains correlates well with the transcription of the *tet* region (Pruss and Drlica 1986).

According to the twin-supercoiled-domain model of transcriptional supercoiling, if transcription of the various plasmid-borne genes in *E. coli* leads to the formation of multiple supercoiled domains of opposite signs, hypernegative supercoiling would be expected in *topA* cells lacking DNA topoisomerase I, the major activity that preferentially removes negative supercoils, but not in *topA*+ cells. The results of Pruss and Drlica are therefore consistent with the model. Presumably, transcription of *tet* is required for the hypernegative supercoiled state because of its contribution to the frictional terms or because of the anchorage of the *tet* message to the cell membrane. The degree of negative supercoiling of the plasmid is affected by inverting the DNA segment containing the entire *tet* region (Wu et al. 1988), and the amino-terminal codons of the *tet* message appear to be important for the hypernegative supercoiling of plasmids bearing the tetracycline resistance gene (Lodge et al. 1989).

In yeast mutants lacking DNA topoisomerase I, Brill and Sternglanz (1988) observed hypernegative supercoiling of plasmids carrying transcriptionally active genes. Even in *top1top2 ts* double mutants, activation of transcription at a nonpermissive temperature for the *ts* DNA topoisomerase II induces hypernegative supercoiling. This suggests that a topoisomerase other than DNA topoisomerases I and II, or an unusual form of DNA topoisomerase II which is not thermally inactivated, may preferentially relax positively supercoiled domains in yeast.

Whereas the accumulation of positive supercoils in eubacteria and eukaryotes is almost surely due to the preferential removal of negative supercoils by a bacterial DNA topoisomerase-I-type enzyme, the causes of transcription-induced hypernegative supercoiling are less clear. In eubacteria, DNA gyrase is clearly important in removing positive supercoils. In eukaryotes, enzymes that preferentially relax positively supercoiled DNA are not known. In vivo, however, the chromatin structure may be altered differently in oppositely supercoiled domains, and differences in chromatin structure may in turn bias the relaxation of the domains by a topoisomerase. Preferential binding of molecules to the positively or negatively supercoiled region may also tilt the balance in the number of supercoils of opposite sense (Giaever and Wang 1988); RNA polymerase binding and the dependence of nucleosome formation and structure on supercoiling in eukaryotes are some additional possibilities.

There have also been reports that in *E. coli* (Figueroa and Bossie 1988), yeast (Osborne and Guarente 1988), or mammalian cells (Barsoum and Berg 1985) with wild-type DNA topoisomerase genes, plasmids undergoing active transcription seem to have lower linking numbers than do those which are less transcribed. The linking number differences observed in these cases are not as large as in the hypernegative supercoiling cases described above, however, and may be due to the unwinding of DNA by the transcriptional ensembles associated with it.

FACTORS AFFECTING TRANSCRIPTIONAL SUPERCOILING

From the above discussions, it is evident that transcription may drive DNA supercoiling in both prokaryotic and eukaryotic cells. Why transcription is accompanied by rotation of the DNA rather than the transcriptional ensemble is less clear, however. Factors that are likely to be important are summarized below.

Anchoring

In the drawing depicted in Figure 1B, imagine that R is interacting with E. The direct association with a DNA-bound entity E would anchor the transcriptional ensemble R on its template and prevent its circling around the template during transcription; RNA synthesis would thus force the DNA to turn around its helical axis. This anchoring model was first discussed in connection with the topology of the DNA template at the start of transcription, in cases where the polymerase is interacting with a DNA-bound regulatory factor (Wang 1985b, 1987).

Anchoring does not require a direct association between R and E: The two may interact separately with a large cellular structure or structures (Wang 1985b, 1987; Liu and Wang 1987). The unspecified entity E could be a regulatory factor, a DNA-bound factor that anchors to a cellular structure, or another transcriptional ensemble R. Any component of the transcriptional ensemble R, which includes the polymerase, the nascent RNA, and proteins associated with the nascent RNA, could serve as the anchor. A case of particular interest is the transcription of a membrane protein in prokaryotes: Because transcription and translation are coupled in prokaryotes, a nascent amino-terminal signal peptide of a membrane protein may be anchored on the membrane before the completion of the synthesis of the mRNA chain encoding the protein (Liu and Wang 1987; Lodge et al. 1989).

In vitro experiments show that anchoring of a polymerase to its template is sufficient to effect template supercoiling (Ostrander et al. 1990). A chimeric RNA polymerase has been constructed in which the DNA-binding domain of a yeast protein GAL4 is covalently linked, through gene fusion, to the amino terminus of phage T7 RNA polymerase. This chimeric enzyme, but not T7 RNA polymerase itself, can supercoil linear or circular DNA templates containing phage T7 promoters in the presence of all four triphosphates and excess RNase A; an example is depicted in Figure 2. Significantly, the presence of GAL4 cognate sequences on the template is not necessary for supercoiling by the chimeric enzyme, indicating that anchoring through nonspecific binding of the GAL4 domain to the DNA template is sufficient to supercoil the template during transcription.

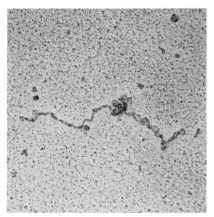

Figure 2 Supercoiling of a linear DNA by a chimeric RNA polymerase in which phage T7 RNA polymerase is fused to the DNA-binding domain of yeast GAL4 protein. (Reprinted, with permission, from Ostrander et al. 1990.)

Frictional Forces

Movements of DNA and DNA-bound macromolecules through the cellular milieu are countered by frictional forces; thus, whether the transcriptional ensembles rotate around their DNA template or the DNA template turns around its helical axis is determined by the relative magnitudes of the respective frictional forces involved. The frictional force against the movement of R is expected to increase when the nascent RNA becomes longer, when it is associated with bulky macromolecules, or when the immediate environment of R is crowded by other cellular components.

A striking and well-known example is the very active transcription of rRNA genes in frog oocytes during certain developmental stages. Figure 3 depicts electron micrographs of several heavily transcribed *Xenopus laevis* rRNA genes. For each gene, nearly 300 RNA polymerase I molecules are marching along a 10,000-bp DNA segment. Even though the RNA chains are more compact in vivo, it would seem to be a formidable exercise for the hundreds of chains, the longest of which is 10,000 nucleotides in length, to revolve around the DNA rapidly. For extremely long RNAs, such as transcripts of the *Drosophila* antennapedia region or those encoding the giant polypeptides of the myofibrillar protein titin, circling around intracellular DNA would also seem to be difficult, based on frictional consideration alone.

Interaction between any component of R and another cellular entity, such as a membrane component or a nuclear pore, would further increase the effective frictional force. Indeed, anchoring of R can be considered as a limiting case involving a large frictional term. Similarly, the frictional forces against the movements of DNA and the hypothetical entity E in Figure 1B are strongly dependent on what factors are interacting with them.

An interesting recent finding suggests that when two distal points on a DNA ring are joined by their simultaneous binding of a protein, transcriptional supercoiling of the DNA occurs more readily (Wu and Liu 1991). For *E. coli* plasmids containing one *lac* operator per monomeric plasmid, dimeric plasmids become positively supercoiled more rapidly than monomeric plasmids upon inactivation of gyrase. This "dimer effect" is observed only under conditions in which the *lac* operators are occupied by *lac* repressors, and has thus been attributed to DNA looping through dimerization of the bound tetrameric *lac* repressors. For a DNA ring in solution, linking two points by a protein presumably introduces a potential barrier: Positive and negative supercoils separated by this barrier can no longer cancel each other by rotational diffusion of the DNA between. In yeast cells expressing *E. coli* DNA topoisomerase I, a similar

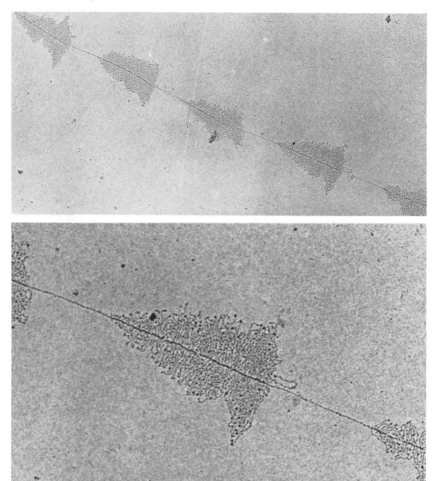

Figure 3 Electron micrographs depicting several tandemly arranged *X. laevis* rRNA genes undergoing transcription; the bottom micrograph is an enlargement of the lower-right part of the upper micrograph. These prints were kindly provided by Dr. Stephen L. McKnight.

dimer effect was observed for the 2-μm plasmid upon inactivation of the yeast DNA topoisomerases (G.N. Giaever and J.C. Wang, unpubl.); the molecular nature of this effect has yet to be elucidated.

DNA TOPOISOMERASES RESPONSIBLE FOR THE RELAXATION OF SUPERCOILED DOMAINS IN VIVO

Eubacterial Enzymes

E. coli has four known DNA topoisomerases: two type I enzymes, DNA topoisomerase I (Wang 1971) and III (Dean et al. 1983; DiGate and

Marians 1989), and two type II enzymes, DNA gyrase (DNA topoisomerase II; Gellert et al. 1976) and DNA topoisomerase IV, a newly discovered enzyme encoded by genes in the *parC* and *parE* region (Kato et al. 1990; for the closely related *Salmonella typhimurium* enzyme, see Luttinger et al. 1991).

As mentioned earlier, purified DNA topoisomerase I is well known for its specific relaxation of negative supercoils. Positively supercoiled DNA is refractory to this enzyme, unless a single-stranded region with mismatched sequences is present in the DNA (Kirkegaard and Wang 1985). Inside *E. coli* cells, the enzyme has also been shown to relax negative supercoils. For example, when DNA gyrase is inhibited by norfloxacin, intracellular plasmid DNA becomes less negatively supercoiled, as evidenced by an increment of its linking number, in a *topA*$^+$ but not in a *topA*$^-$ strain (Bliska and Cozzarelli 1987). Linking number increments were also observed by the induction of *topA* in a strain containing a plasmid-borne *topA* gene under the control of an inducible promoter (Giaever et al. 1988). The results described earlier for transcriptional supercoiling, namely, the accumulation of positive supercoils upon inhibition of gyrase in *E. coli* or inactivation of DNA topoisomerases I and II in yeast cells expressing *E. coli* DNA topoisomerase I, also argue strongly that *E. coli* DNA topoisomerase I preferentially relaxes negative supercoils in vivo.

In contrast to *E. coli* DNA topoisomerase I, the other type I enzyme, *E. coli* DNA topoisomerase III, exhibits little relaxation activity. In vitro, *E. coli* DNA topoisomerase III relaxes negatively supercoiled DNA at 52°C but not at 30°C; positively supercoiled DNA is refractory to the enzyme at all temperatures (Dean et al. 1983; DiGate and Marians 1988). In vivo, the experiment of Bliska and Cozzarelli (1987) described above indicates that DNA topoisomerase III is inefficient in relaxing negative supercoils, because intracellular plasmid DNA molecules remain negatively supercoiled upon inhibition of gyrase in a *topA*$^-$ strain. The accumulation of positive supercoils upon inhibition of gyrase (Wu et al. 1988) also shows that DNA topoisomerase III is inefficient in relaxing positive supercoils in vivo. The major biological function of *E. coli* DNA topoisomerase III is probably the unlinking of short stretches of plectonemically wound DNA strands (DiGate and Marians 1988; Wang et al. 1990; Wang 1991).

The type II enzyme *E. coli* DNA gyrase is well known for its reduction of the linking number of positively supercoiled or relaxed DNA in the presence of ATP, converting the DNA to a negatively supercoiled form (Gellert et al. 1976). Because of this property, the enzyme was thought to be the driving force for the negative supercoiling of in-

tracellular bacterial DNA; this point of view may require some modification, however, as discussed below.

In an exponentially growing *E. coli*, the total number of mRNA and
rRNA chains is of the order of 1500 (see, e.g., Watson et al. 1987). If
RNA chain elongation proceeds at a rate of 60 nucleotides per second,
then as many as 9000 negative supercoils and the same number of positive supercoils might be generated in an *E. coli* cell every second. The total number of gyrase molecules per cell is about 500 (Gellert 1981), with
an estimated turnover number of about 1–2 supercoils per second
(Sugino and Cozzarelli 1980; Maxwell and Gellert 1984; Baker et al.
1987). The total number of positive supercoils gyrase can remove is
therefore around 500–1000 per second per cell, or about one tenth of the
maximal number that could be generated in a cell undergoing active transcription. Thus, depending on how efficiently the oppositely supercoiled
domains can cancel each other by diffusional pathways, inside a cell,
gyrase might be preoccupied with the relaxation of positive supercoils,
rather than acting as a negative supercoiling enzyme. Gyrase molecules
have been found to be associated preferentially with the 3′ side of
plasmid-borne genes (Koo et al. 1990) and with several inducible
chromosomal genes following their induction (Condemine and Smith
1990); these findings are consistent with gyrase being actively engaged
in positively supercoiled regions.

The diffusional pathways presumably contribute significantly to the
removal of supercoils, however. The presence of such pathways would
explain the compensation of *E. coli topA* mutations by mutations in the
gyrase structural genes (Drlica 1984; Wang 1985a).

Little is known about the enzymological properties of the newly identified *E. coli* DNA topoisomerase IV. Unless this enzyme is also inhibited by gyrase inhibitors, the accumulation of positive supercoils in
the presence of novobiocin would suggest that DNA topoisomerase IV is
ineffective in removing positive supercoils. Similarly, because in a *topA*
strain intracellular DNA stays negatively supercoiled upon inhibition of
gyrase by norfloxacin (Bliska and Cozzarelli 1987), it can be inferred
that the DNA topoisomerase IV is also ineffective in the relaxation of
negative supercoils in vivo.

Eukaryotic Enzymes

The two best-characterized eukaryotic DNA topoisomerases are
eukaryotic DNA topoisomerase I, a type I enzyme, and DNA
topoisomerase II, a type II enzyme. Several additional topoisomerases
are known. In the yeast *Saccharomyces cerevisiae*, a gene *TOP3* has

been implicated to code for a type I enzyme on the basis of a sequence comparison with the gene (Wallis et al. 1989). The possibility that a gene *HPR1* might code for yet another topoisomerase has also been raised (Aguilera and Klein 1990). In mammalian cells, the presence of an enzyme highly homologous to, but different from, DNA topoisomerase II has been reported (Chung et al. 1989).

It is well established that purified eukaryotic DNA topoisomerase I or II readily relaxes negatively as well as positively supercoiled DNA. Results of transcriptional supercoiling in yeast have provided strong evidence that DNA topoisomerases I and II are the only enzymes that can effectively relax supercoiled DNA in vivo (Giaever and Wang 1988). Inactivation of these two enzymes in cells expressing *E. coli* DNA topoisomerase I leads to the accumulation of positive supercoils, and thus, no other enzyme in yeast can effectively relax positive supercoils. Furthermore, because the expression of the *E. coli* enzyme is needed for the accumulation of positive supercoils in the 2-μm plasmid, no endogenous yeast enzyme can effectively and specifically remove negative supercoils. As described earlier, the chromatin structure in oppositely supercoiled domains inside a cell may be different. This disparity may in turn introduce a bias in the relative rates of relaxing differently supercoiled domains, even though for purified DNA the rates of removal of positive and negative supercoils by eukaryotic DNA topoisomerase I or II are approximately equal.

It appears that the product of yeast *TOP3* gene, yeast DNA topoisomerase III, may have a weak activity for the preferential removal of negative supercoils. Accumulation of positive supercoils in extracellular rDNA rings has been observed upon inactivation of DNA topoisomerases I and II, even when the cells are not expressing *E. coli* DNA topoisomerase I. Furthermore, when a plasmid-borne *TOP3* is overexpressed, positive supercoiling of plasmids with strong RNA polymerase II promoters is also seen (R.A. Kim and J.C. Wang, unpubl.). In all cases, positive supercoiling of plasmids in the absence of the *E. coli* enzyme is less efficient, indicating that the endogenous yeast activity that preferentially relaxes negative supercoils is relatively weak.

CONCLUDING REMARKS: A VISTA OF INTRACELLULAR DNA

From the vantage point of the transcriptional supercoiling model, a chromatin fiber undergoing transcription is in a highly dynamic state. Waves of supercoils are formed and removed in the template, and these waves may influence strongly the structure of DNA and the binding of small or large molecules to it.

In a eubacterial cell, although on the average intracellular DNA is in a negatively supercoiled state, this average is a rather poor representation of a kaleidoscopic picture: Positively and negatively supercoiled regions may be interspersed at a given time, and a particular region may periodically go through various supercoiled and relaxed states. This spatial and temporal heterogeneity in the supercoiling of intracellular DNA raises many interesting questions with few answers. Does the initiation of one transcript affect reinitiation at the same promoter because of negative supercoiling of the upstream region? Does it affect transcription of adjacent genes? Do the waves of supercoils tend to synchronize a column of transcriptional ensembles marching down the same DNA template, as depicted in the dramatic example in Figure 3? If anchoring of a nascent membrane peptide is important for transcriptional supercoiling, is the expression of membrane proteins particularly sensitive to an imbalance of the intracellular levels of DNA topoisomerases? Would the expression of such a gene exert a strong influence on the expression of neighboring genes? Are the regions between convergent transcripts often in a positively supercoiled state? How does transcriptional supercoiling affect other cellular processes such as replication, recombination, and repair?

In eukaryotes, several of the key players in the supercoiling of intracellular DNA are very different from their counterparts in eubacteria. Transcription is no longer coupled to translation, and an early step in the processing of nascent RNA is the formation of ribonucleoprotein granules. Eukaryotic DNA topoisomerase II, the counterpart of bacterial gyrase, relaxes both positively and negatively supercoiled regions. Eukaryotic DNA topoisomerase I, a powerful relaxation activity for both positively and negatively supercoiled substrates, has no evolutionarily related counterpart in eubacteria. The chromatin structures differ in eukaryotes and prokaryotes. Nevertheless, there is now strong evidence that transcription in eukaryotes may drive template supercoiling just as it does in eubacteria. The differences in the DNA topoisomerases in eukaryotes and eubacteria serve as interesting examples of the different ways nature has learned to deal with the topological problems of DNA.

ACKNOWLEDGMENTS

I thank many of my present and past co-workers, especially Leroy F. Liu, T.-S. Hsieh, Guri N. Giaever, Raymond A. Kim, Marc R. Gartenberg, A. Simon Lynch, Stanley Y. Shaw, Janet Lindsley, and Joaquim Roca, for numerous discussions on topics touched upon in this chapter. The writing of this chapter also brought fond memories of the late 1960s, when experiments on the unwinding of DNA by RNA polymerase were started at the suggestion of Michael Chamberlin. Work of this laboratory on DNA topology and DNA topoisomerases has been supported mainly by grants from the National Institutes of Health and the National Science Foundation.

REFERENCES

Aguilera, A. and H.L. Klein. 1990. *HPR1*, a novel yeast gene that prevents intrachromosomal excision recombination, shows carboxy-terminal homology to the *Saccharomyces cerevisiae TOP1* gene. *Mol. Cell. Biol.* **4:** 1439–1451.

Baker, T.A., B.E. Funnell, and A. Kornberg. 1987. Helicase action of dnaB protein during replication from the *Escherichia coli* chromosomal origin *in vitro. J. Biol. Chem.* **262:** 6877–6885.

Barsoum, J. and P. Berg. 1985. Simian virus 40 minichromosomes contain torsionally strained DNA molecules. *Mol. Cell. Biol.* **5:** 3048–3057.

Bliska, J.B. and N.R. Cozzarelli. 1987. Use of site-specific recombination as a probe of DNA structure and metabolism *in vivo. J. Mol. Biol.* **194:** 205–218.

Botchan, P., J.C. Wang, and H. Echols. 1973. Effect of circularity and superhelicity on transcription from bacteriophage λ DNA. *Proc. Natl. Acad. Sci.* **70:** 3077–3081.

Brill, S.J. and R. Sternglanz. 1988. Transcription-dependent DNA supercoiling in yeast DNA topoisomerase mutants. *Cell* **54:** 403–411.

Chamberlin, M. 1974. The selectivity of transcription. *Annu. Rev. Biochem.* **43:** 721–775.

Chung, T.D.Y., F.H. Drake, K.B. Tan, S.R. Per, S.T. Crooke, and C.K. Mirabelli. 1989. Characterization and immunological identification of cDNA clones encoding two human DNA topoisomerase II isozymes. *Proc. Natl. Acad. Sci.* **86:** 9431–9435.

Condemine, G. and C.L. Smith 1990. Transcription regulates oxolinic acid-induced DNA gyrase cleavage at specific sites on the *E. coli* chromosome. *Nucleic Acids Res.* **18:** 7389–7396.

Crawford, L.V. and M.J. Waring. 1967. Supercoiling of polyoma virus DNA measured by its interaction with ethidium bromide. *J. Mol. Biol.* **25:** 23–30.

Davidson, N. 1972. Effect of DNA length on the free energy of binding of an unwinding ligand to a superhelical DNA. *J. Mol. Biol.* **66:** 307–309.

Dean, F.B., M.A. Krasnow, R. Otter, M.M. Matzuk, S.J. Spengler, and N.R. Cozzarelli. 1983. *Escherichia coli* type I topoisomerases: Identification, mechanism, and the role in recombination. *Cold Spring Harbor Symp. Quant. Biol.* **47:** 769–778.

DiGate, R.J. and K.J. Marians. 1988. Identification of a potent decatenating enzyme from *Escherichia coli. J. Biol. Chem.* **263:** 13366–13373.

———. 1989. Molecular cloning and DNA sequence analysis of *Escherichia coli topB*, the gene encoding topoisomerase III. *J. Biol. Chem.* **264:** 17924–17930.

Drlica, K. 1984. Biology of bacterial DNA topoisomerases. *Microbiol. Rev.* **48:** 273–289.

Figueroa, N. and L. Bossie. 1988. Transcription induces gyration of the DNA template in *Escherichia coli. Proc. Natl. Acad. Sci.* **85:** 9416–9420.

Gamper, H.B. and J.E. Hearst. 1982. A topological model for transcription based on unwinding angle analysis of *E. coli* RNA polymerase binary, initiation and ternary complexes. *Cell* **29:** 81–90.

Gellert, M. 1981. DNA topoisomerases. *Annu. Rev. Biochem.* **50:** 879–910.

Gellert, M., K. Mizuuchi, M. O'Dea, and H. Nash. 1976. DNA gyrase: An enzyme that introduces superhelical turns into DNA. *Proc. Natl. Acad. Sci.* **73:** 3872–3876.

Giaever, G.N. and J.C. Wang. 1988. Supercoiling of intracellular DNA can occur in eukaryotic cells. *Cell* **55**: 849–856.

Giaever, G.N., L. Snyder, and J.C. Wang. 1988. DNA supercoiling *in vivo*. *Biophys. Chem.* **29**: 7–15.

Hayashi, Y. and M. Hayashi. 1971. Template activities of the φX-174 replicative allomorphic deoxyribonucleic acids. *Biochemistry* **10**: 4212–4218.

Hsieh, T.-S. and J.C. Wang. 1978. Physicochemical studies on interactions between DNA and RNA polymerase. Ultraviolet absorption measurements. *Nucleic Acids Res.* **5**: 3337–3345.

Kato, J., Y. Nishimura, R. Imamura, H. Niki, S. Hiraga, and N. Suzuki. 1990. New topoisomerase essential for chromosome segregation in *E. coli. Cell* **63**: 393–404.

Kirkegaard, K. and J.C. Wang. 1985. Bacterial DNA topoisomerase I can relax positively supercoiled DNA containing a single-stranded loop. *J. Mol. Biol.* **185**: 625–637.

Kirkegaard, K., H. Buc, A. Spassky, and J.C. Wang. 1983. Mapping of single-stranded regions in duplex DNA at the sequence level: Single-strand-specific cytosine methylation in RNA polymerase-promoter complexes. *Proc. Natl. Acad. Sci.* **80**: 2544–2548.

Koo, H.-S., H.-Y. Wu, and L.F. Liu. 1990. Effects of transcription and translation on gyrase-mediated DNA cleavage in *Escherichia coli. J. Biol. Chem.* **265**: 12300–12305.

Liu, L.F. and J.C. Wang. 1987. Supercoiling of the DNA template during transcription. *Proc. Natl. Acad. Sci.* **84**: 7024–7027.

Lockshon, D. and D.R. Morris. 1983. Positively supercoiled plasmid DNA is produced by treatment of *Escherichia coli* with DNA gyrase inhibitors. *Nucleic Acids Res.* **11**: 2999–3017.

Lodge, J.K., T. Kasic, and D.E. Berg. 1989. Formation of supercoiling domains in plasmid pBR322. *J. Bacteriol.* **171**: 2181–2187.

Luttinger, A.L., A.L. Springer, and M.B. Schmid. 1991. A cluster of genes that affects nucleoid segregation in *Salmonella typhimurium*. *New Biol.* **3**: 687–697.

Margolin, P., L. Zumstein, R. Sternglanz, and J.C. Wang. 1985. The *Escherichia coli supX* locus is *topA*, the structural gene for DNA topoisomerase I. *Proc. Natl. Acad. Sci.* **82**: 5437–5441.

Maxwell, A. and M. Gellert. 1984. The DNA dependence of the ATPase activity of DNA gyrase. *J. Biol. Chem.* **259**: 14472–14480.

Mukai, F.H. and P. Margolin. 1963. Analysis of unlinked suppressors of an 0° mutation in *Salmonella*. *Proc. Natl. Acad. Sci.* **50**: 140–148.

Osborne, B.I. and L. Guarente. 1988. Transcription by RNA polymerase II induces changes of DNA topology in yeast. *Genes Dev.* **2**: 766–772.

Ostrander, E.O., P. Benedetti, and J.C. Wang. 1990. Template supercoiling by a chimera of yeast *GAL4* protein-phage T7 RNA polymerase. *Science* **249**: 1261–1265.

Pruss, G.J. 1985. DNA topoisomerase I mutants. Increased heterogeneity in linking number and other replicon-dependent changes in DNA supercoiling. *J. Mol. Biol.* **185**: 51–63.

Pruss, G.J. and K. Drlica. 1986. Topoisomerase I mutants: The gene on pBR322 that encodes resistance to tetracycline affects plasmid DNA supercoiling. *Proc. Natl. Acad. Sci.* **83**: 8952–8956.

Rudd, D.L. and R. Menzel. 1987. *his* operons of *Escherichia coli* and *Salmonella typhimurium* are regulated by DNA supercoiling. *Proc. Natl. Acad. Sci.* **84**: 517–521.

Sasse-Dwight, S. and J.D. Gralla. 1989. $KMnO_4$ as a probe for *lac* promoter DNA melting and mechanism *in vivo*. *J. Biol. Chem.* **264**: 8074–8081.

Saucier, J.-M. and J.C. Wang. 1972. Angular alteration of the DNA helix by *E. coli* RNA polymerase. *Nat. New Biol.* **239**: 167–170.

Siebenlist, U., R.B. Simpson, and W. Gilbert. 1980. RNA polymerase interacts homologously with two different promoters. *Cell* **20:** 269–281.

Smith, D.H. and B.D. Davis. 1967. Mode of action of novobiocin in *Escherichia coli. J. Bacteriol.* **93:** 71–79.

Sternglanz, R., S. DiNardo, K.A. Voelkel, Y. Nishimura, Y. Hirota, K. Becherer, L. Zumstein, and J.C. Wang. 1981. Mutations in the gene coding for *Escherichia coli* DNA topoisomerase I affect transcription and transposition. *Proc. Natl. Acad. Sci.* **78:** 2747–2751.

Sugino, A. and N.R. Cozzarelli. 1980. The intrinsic ATPase of DNA gyrase. *J. Biol. Chem.* **255:** 6299–6306.

Trucksis, M. and R.E. Depew. 1981. Identification and localization of a gene that specifies production of *Escherichia coli* DNA topoisomerase I. *Proc. Natl. Acad. Sci.* **53:** 1104–1111.

Vinograd, J., J. Lebowitz, R. Radloff, R. Watson, and P. Laipis. 1965. The twisted circular form of polyoma viral DNA. *Proc. Natl. Acad. Sci.* **78:** 2164–2168.

Wallis, J.W., G. Chrebet, G. Brodsky, M. Rolfe, and R. Rothstein. 1989. A hyperrecombination mutation in *S. cerevisiae* identifies a novel eukaryotic topoisomerase. *Cell* **58:** 409–419.

Wang, J.C. 1969. Variation of the average rotation angle of the DNA helix and the superhelical turns of covalently closed cyclic λ DNA. *J. Mol. Biol.* **43:** 25–39.

———. 1971. Interaction between DNA and an *Escherichia coli* protein ω. *J. Mol. Biol.* **55:** 523–533.

———. 1973. Protein ω: A DNA swivelase from *Escherichia coli*? In *DNA synthesis in vitro* (ed. R.D. Wells and R.B. Inman), pp. 163–174. University Park Press, Baltimore.

———. 1985a. DNA topoisomerases. *Annu. Rev. Biochem.* **54:** 665–697.

———. 1985b. DNA supercoiling and gene expression. *Jerus. Symp. Quantum Chem. Biochem.* **18:** 173–181.

———. 1987. DNA topoisomerases: Nature's solution to the topological ramifications of the double-helix structure of DNA. *Harvey Lect.* **81:** 93–110.

———. 1991. DNA topoisomerases: Why so many? *J. Biol. Chem.* **266:** 6659–6662.

Wang, J.C., P.R. Caron, and R.A. Kim. 1990. The role of DNA topoisomerases in recombination and genome stability: A double-edged sword? *Cell* **62:** 403–406.

Wang, J.C., J.H. Jacobsen, and J.-M. Saucier. 1977. Physicochemical studies on interactions between DNA and RNA polymerase. Unwinding of the DNA helix by *Escherichia coli* RNA polymerase. *Nucleic Acids Res.* **5:** 1225–1241.

Watson, J.D., N.H. Hopkins, J.W. Roberts, J.A. Steitz, and A.M. Weiner. 1987. *Molecular biology of the gene*, 4th edition, p. 111. Benjamin/Cummings, Menlo Park, California.

Wu, H.Y. and L.F. Liu. 1991. DNA looping alters local DNA conformation during transcription. *J. Mol. Biol.* **219:** 615–622.

Wu, H.Y., S.-H. Shyy, J.C. Wang, and L.F. Liu. 1988. Transcription generates positively and negatively supercoiled domains in the template. *Cell* **53:** 433–440.

47

Analysis of *SPT* Genes: A Genetic Approach toward Analysis of TFIID, Histones, and Other Transcription Factors of Yeast

Fred Winston
Department of Genetics
Harvard Medical School
Boston, Massachusetts 02115

OVERVIEW

Insertion mutations in *Saccharomyces cerevisiae*, caused by Ty elements or Ty long terminal repeats (δ sequences), can disrupt expression of adjacent genes by inhibiting or otherwise altering normal transcription. Selection for suppressors of these insertion mutations has resulted in the isolation of mutations that identify a large set of genes (*SPT* genes) required for normal transcription. Genetic and molecular analysis has placed most *SPT* genes into two groups. The first group includes *SPT15*, which encodes the TATA-binding factor TFIID. The second group includes *SPT11* and *SPT12*, which encode histones H2A and H2B, respectively. Each group also contains other genes that encode previously unidentified functions that are related to the functions of TFIID and histones. Most *SPT* genes identified are essential or important for growth, indicating that these genes are critical for normal transcription in vivo.

INTRODUCTION

In the yeast *S. cerevisiae* many genes involved in the regulation of gene expression have been identified by mutant isolation and analysis. In most such cases, mutants have been isolated by a particular genetic selection or screen for altered expression of a gene or of a set of genes. Subsequent analyses of the genes thus identified have led to fundamental insights into the nature of gene expression in yeast. Some prominent examples of this approach are studies on general amino acid control (Hinnebusch 1988), mating type regulation (Herskowitz and Oshima 1981; Nasmyth

Transcriptional Regulation.
Copyright 1992 Cold Spring Harbor Laboratory Press 0-87969-410-6/92 $3 + 00

and Shore 1987), regulation of *GAL* genes (Johnston 1987), and regulation of *CYC1* (Guarente 1987).

Many of the observations derived from studies of transcription in yeast have illuminated the process of transcriptional regulation in more complex eukaryotic organisms. The yeast transcription factors GAL4 and GCN4 have become model systems for the study of acidic transcriptional activators. GAL4 has been shown to activate transcription in mammalian (Kakidani and Ptashne 1988; Webster et al. 1988), dipteran (Fischer et al. 1988), and plant cells (Ma et al. 1988). Likewise, several mammalian transcription activators have been shown to function in yeast cells (see, e.g., Lech et al. 1988; Metzger et al. 1988; Schena and Yamamoto 1988). Since these mammalian factors function in yeast, they must be capable of interaction with the yeast transcriptional machinery to activate transcription. The ability of transcription factors to function in both yeast and mammalian cells suggests that there is substantial conservation of the basic mechanism for transcription throughout eukaryotes.

General transcription factors, as well as gene-specific transcriptional regulatory proteins, appear to be closely related throughout eukaryotes. RNA polymerase II is highly conserved in the number and the size of subunits (see Sentenac et al.; Corden and Ingles; both this volume). The amino acid sequences of RNA polymerase subunits that have been determined for more than one organism also show a high degree of similarity (Woychik and Young 1990). More recently, the TATA-binding factor TFIID has also been shown to be structurally and functionally conserved between yeast and other eukaryotes (Buratowski et al. 1988; Cavallini et al. 1988, 1989; Hahn et al. 1989a,b; Schmidt et al. 1989; Fikes et al. 1990; Gasch et al. 1990; Hoey et al. 1990; Hoffman et al. 1990; Horikoshi et al. 1989a,b; Kao et al. 1990; Muhich et al. 1990; Peterson et al. 1990).

One major advantage of yeast over other types of eukaryotes is the ability to test rigorously the function of a gene product in vivo. Any yeast gene, once cloned, can be tested for function in vivo by replacement of the wild-type gene with a null allele constructed in vitro. Likewise, strains that contain any other type of mutation in a gene of interest can be constructed. Therefore, functions that have been identified by biochemical analysis in vitro can be tested for their importance in vivo by gene replacement, followed by mutant analysis.

Genetic strategies can be important in the identification of genes involved in transcription. One advantage of a genetic approach is that a selection or screen for mutants can be done in a relatively unbiased manner. For example, in a system in which transcriptional regulation is being studied, properly devised selections can identify genes that encode proteins that are important at any level in the process, including DNA binding, protein modification, regulation, or signal transduction. The benefit of this type of analysis, then, is that by carrying out careful mutant hunts, one can rely on the organism itself, rather than on the bias of the investigator, to help determine which genes are important to study. In addition, the investigator does not need to rely on the abundance or in vitro stability of a protein. Different types of genetic strategies to identify important genes may also be worth while, especially in cases of functional redundancy. However, in yeast, functional redundancy has not yet been a significant problem. In the few cases in which functional redundancy is known, such as in the case of yeast histone genes (described later in this chapter), difficulties in genetic analysis can be circumvented.

In this chapter, I describe genetic strategies used to isolate particular classes of transcription mutants in yeast. The genetic selection, for suppressors of insertion mutations in promoter regions, is a powerful one. This approach has resulted in the identification of certain genes that encode proteins of known functions, allowing further study by genetic methods. Perhaps more importantly, this strategy of mutant isolation has also identified genes that encode proteins of previously unknown function; the elucidation of the activities of these newly described gene products should help to advance our understanding of transcription in eukaryotes.

SPT GENES

SPT genes were identified by selection for mutations that suppress Ty and δ insertion mutations in the 5′ noncoding regions of yeast genes (see following section). Certain of these insertion mutations, located upstream, or in the 5′ coding region, of either the *HIS4* or *LYS2* genes, were known to abolish expression of the adjacent gene, resulting in a His⁻ or Lys⁻ auxotrophy (for review, see Boeke 1989). The selection for *spt* mutants was to select for His⁺ or Lys⁺ revertants, focusing on mutations that were not closely linked to the *HIS4* or *LYS2* structural genes. This selection, described in more detail in the following section, was initially somewhat obscure, primarily because the effects of the insertion mutations on gene expression were not understood. As the biology of Ty elements came to be studied in greater detail, and as *SPT* genes and Spt⁻ mutant phenotypes were studied more extensively, the functional basis for this selection came into sharper focus. The current view is that Ty and δ insertion mutations can abolish or alter the transcription of an adjacent gene due to interference by Ty transcription signals with those of the adjacent gene. Extragenic suppressors of this interference (*spt* mutations) are mutations in *trans*-acting genes that restore utilization of a gene's transcription signals despite the presence of the insertion element.

Ty and δ Insertion Mutations

Ty elements are yeast retrotransposons: mobile genetic elements that transpose via an RNA intermediate (for review, see Boeke 1989). They are approximately 6 kb in length and are flanked by long terminal repeats, termed δ sequences, consisting of approximately 335 bp. Ty transcription initiates in the 5'δ and terminates in the 3'δ (Fig. 1). Ty transcripts have been estimated to constitute approximately 10% of total poly(A)$^+$ RNA of a haploid yeast cell. Numerous studies have identified transcription signals in both the δ sequences and the internal portion of Ty elements. δ sequences contain a TATA region required for Ty transcription as well as a weak upstream activation sequence (UAS) (Liao et al. 1987). Within the internal portion of the Ty element (the ε region) there are also transcriptional regulatory signals that can affect transcription of Ty elements (Roeder et al. 1985; Liao et al. 1987; Fulton et al. 1988; Farabaugh et al. 1989).

When a Ty element inserts in the 5' noncoding region of a yeast gene, it can alter gene transcription. In addition, homologous recombination between δ sequences that flank a Ty element can give rise to solo δ insertion mutations; these insertion mutations also alter adjacent gene transcription. The transcription signals of Ty elements, both in the δ and in the ε sequences, have been demonstrated to affect transcription of adjacent genes (Errede et al. 1985; Roeder et al. 1985; Boeke et al. 1986; Coney and Roeder 1988; Hirschman et al. 1988). These effects of Ty or solo δ insertion mutations on adjacent gene expression can be affected by several variables, including the sequence of the specific Ty element

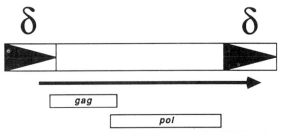

Figure 1 Ty elements are approximately 6000 bp long, flanked by long terminal repeats (δ sequences) of approximately 335 bp. Transcription initiates in the 5'δ and terminates in the 3'δ sequence (for review, see Boeke 1989).

(Roeder and Fink 1982), position of the Ty or δ element with respect to the adjacent gene (Boeke et al. 1986), and the mating type of the cell (Errede et al. 1980; Williamson et al. 1981). All these variables, although poorly understood, may be instructive as to how Ty transcription signals influence adjacent gene expression.

One insertion mutation for which inhibitory effects have been analyzed in detail is the solo δ insertion mutation *his4-912δ*. This insertion mutation is a derivative of the Ty insertion mutation *his4-912* and presumably arose by homologous recombination between the δ repeats of the Ty element (Farabaugh and Fink 1980). The *his4-912δ* insertion mutation confers a cold-sensitive His⁻ phenotype: Strains that contain *his4-912δ* are His⁻ at 23°C and 30°C and are weak His⁺ at 37°C (Chaleff and Fink 1980). The solo δ sequence of *his4-912δ* is inserted between the *HIS4* UAS and the *HIS4* TATA box (Fig. 2). Analysis of transcription of *his4-912δ* has shown that under nonpermissive conditions (in which the strain is His⁻), *HIS4* transcripts are made that initiate at the δ initiation site rather than at the wild-type *HIS4* initiation site. This mutation causes a His⁻ phenotype, presumably because the aberrant δ-initiated *HIS4* transcripts contain an AUG (from the δ sequence) and several translation termination codons upstream of the normal *HIS4* AUG. This transcript, therefore, is probably nonfunctional for translation of a *HIS4* protein. Selection for His⁺ revertants identifies *cis-* and *trans-* acting mutations that allow synthesis of a wild-type-length *HIS4* transcript.

Analyses of *cis*-acting mutations that alter transcription of *his4-912δ*

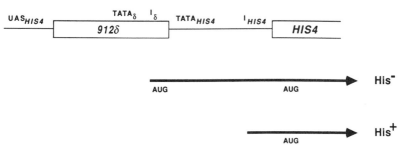

Figure 2 At *his4-912δ*, the δ sequence is inserted between the *HIS4* UAS and the *HIS4* TATA region. In *SPT⁺* genetic backgrounds, this locus produces an aberrant, long *HIS4* transcript that initiates in the δ ($I_δ$) and that contains an upstream AUG (His⁻ phenotype). In most *spt* mutants and for *cis*-acting mutations (discussed in the text), *HIS4* transcription starts at the normal *HIS4* initiation site (I_{HIS4}; His⁺ phenotype).

to allow synthesis of wild-type-length *HIS4* transcripts have indicated that the two promoters at this locus, the δ promoter and the *HIS4* promoter, are in competition with one another. The competition is probably determined by the relative "strength" of the TATA regions of the two promoters. This model is based on analysis of two classes of *cis*-acting mutations that cause a shift in transcription initiation from the δ start site to the *HIS4* start site (Hirschman et al. 1988). First, mutations in the TATA region of the δ sequence abolish initiation from the δ start site and concomitantly elevate initiation from the wild-type *HIS4* start site. Second, mutations that create additional TATA-consensus sequences flanking the normal *HIS4* TATA region increase the level of the wild-type *HIS4* transcript. Importantly, the *cis*-acting mutation in the *HIS4* TATA region that restores native transcription most effectively also decreases the level of the upstream δ-initiated transcript. These results also suggest that the promoter competition is mediated by factors that act at the TATA regions.

Isolation and Analysis of *spt* Mutants

Selection for unlinked suppressors of insertion mutations such as *his4-912δ* offers a potential means of identifying *trans*-acting factors that alter the competition between closely positioned promoters. Such factors might act directly at TATA regions or in some other way required for TATA activity. When this mutant selection was undertaken by identification of revertants of insertions at *HIS4* and at *LYS2*, a large number of unlinked suppressors were isolated. Subsequent complementation and linkage testing revealed at least 17 different genes that have been designated *SPT* genes (SPT = suppressor of Ty).

SPT genes have been identified on the basis of several related types of mutant hunts. In general, strains that contain Ty or solo δ insertion mutations at *HIS4* or at *LYS2* were used. By using three different combinations of insertion mutations, 15 different *SPT* genes were identified (Winston et al. 1984b, 1987; Fassler and Winston 1988). An additional mutant hunt, using an insertion mutation at *URA3*, identified another *SPT* gene (Natsoulis et al. 1991). Finally, a screen for genes that cause an Spt⁻ phenotype when present at high copy number has identified one additional *SPT* gene (Clark-Adams et al. 1988). Partially overlapping sets of genes were identified in all these mutant hunts. However, since some *SPT* genes are represented by very few mutant alleles, there are very likely additional genes that can mutate to confer an Spt⁻ phenotype. On the basis of results of the different mutant hunts, the particular insertion mutations used for selection of *spt* mutants are critical to the array of *spt* mutants isolated. For example, in the selection for suppressors of *his4-9128*, only 2 of approximately 200 mutations were in the *SPT3* gene (Winston et al. 1984b). In the selection for suppressors of *his4-9178*, however, the majority of *spt* mutations isolated were in *SPT3* (Winston et al. 1987; F. Winston, unpubl.).

Two types of genetic evidence suggest that products of different *SPT* genes are involved in different functional steps required for the normal expression of many genes. First, mutations in different *SPT* genes were tested for their ability to suppress a set of Ty and solo δ insertion mutations at the *HIS4* and *LYS2* genes. These *spt* mutations were shown to fall into different groups based on the different suppression patterns that they conferred (Table 1). Since the different suppression patterns occur even in cases where null alleles have been tested, this result is caused by functional differences between different *SPT* genes, rather than by allele-specific effects. Although we do not understand why there are different suppression patterns, they have been a valuable genetic tool for analysis of *spt* mutants.

Second, *spt* mutations confer additional phenotypes in addition to suppression of insertion mutations, and these phenotypes are different for different classes of *spt* mutants. For example, mutations in *SPT3, SPT7, SPT8,* and *SPT15* cause defects in both mating and sporulation (Winston et al. 1984a; Hirschhorn and Winston 1988; Eisenmann et al. 1989); some mutations in *SPT5* and *SPT6* cause temperature-sensitive lethality (Winston et al. 1984b; E.A. Malone and F. Winston, unpubl.); and some mutations in *SPT4* cause sensitivity to methyl methanesulfonate (Winston et al. 1984b). In most cases, the groups of *spt* mutations that confer similar mutant phenotypes coincide with the groups that confer

Table 1 Suppression of insertion mutations by different *spt* mutations

spt allele	*his4-9128*	*his4-9178*	*his4-917*	*lys2-1288*	*lys2-173R2*
SPT+	cs	–	–	–	+
spt3-202	+	+	+	+	–
spt15-21	+	+	+	+	–
spt6-140	+	–	–/+	+	+
spt11-1	+	–	+/–	+	+
spt13-100	–	–	+	–	+
spt14-1	–	–	+	–	+

Designations are as follows: (cs) cold sensitive; (–) His⁻ or Lys⁻ phenotype; (+) His⁺ or Lys⁺ phenotype; (–/+ and +/–) intermediate phenotypes. The insertion mutations *his4-9128, his4-9178,* and *lys2-1288* are solo δ insertion mutations. The mutation *his4-917* is a complete Ty insertion mutation. The mutation *lys2-173R2* is a revertant of a Ty insertion at *LYS2* that still contains most of a Ty element present at *LYS2* (Simchen et al. 1984; A.M. Happel and F. Winston, unpubl.).

the same pattern of suppression of insertion mutations. This result supports the idea that different groups of *SPT* genes are involved in different cellular functions.

Recent molecular analysis of *SPT* genes has revealed that three of them encode previously known products: *SPT15* encodes the TATA-binding factor TFIID, and *SPT11* and *SPT12* encode histones H2A and H2B. Since *SPT15* had been placed in a different group from *SPT11* and *SPT12* on the basis of the phenotypic criteria mentioned above, these results have allowed the majority of *SPT* genes to be grouped into either a TFIID-related group or a histone-related group. Each of these two groups then contains genes that encode known functions (TFIID or histones) and other genes that encode mystery functions but that are believed to be related, based on mutant phenotypes.

spt Mutations Alter Transcription

Since *spt* mutations restore expression of genes adjacent to Ty and δ insertion mutations, Northern analysis was undertaken to test whether phenotypic changes resulted from altered transcription initiation. In every case thus far examined, suppression by an *spt* mutation has been shown to be due to a transcriptional alteration. Although not every alteration has been characterized in detail, a variety of altered transcriptional patterns have been observed (Fig. 3). In general, the altered pattern consists of production of a new transcript, presumably by utilization of an additional initiation site, that is not used in *SPT+* strains. In the case of *his4-912δ*, which has been studied most carefully, transcription primarily initiates at the δ initiation site in *SPT+* strains and at the wild-type *HIS4* initiation site in *spt* mutants. Therefore, in this case, the *spt* mutations do not result in initiation at new sites; rather, they alter the choice between two existing initiation sites.

Despite our lack of understanding of these transcriptional changes, they have provided yet another means of grouping and characterizing *spt* mutants. In this regard, *SPT* genes fall into two distinct groups. The first group, comprising *SPT3*, *SPT7*, *SPT8*, and *SPT15*, is required for normal transcription of all the Ty1 and Ty2 elements in the yeast genome. Mutations in any of these four genes drastically reduce the level of Ty transcripts. In addition, a new Ty transcript, which initiates approximately 800 bases downstream from the normal initiation site, is synthesized at a low level (Winston et al. 1984a, 1987; D. Eisenmann et al., unpubl.). Null alleles of *SPT3* and *SPT8* (which are not essential genes) cause the same phenotype, demonstrating that the effect for mutations in these two genes is due to loss of function (Winston et al. 1984a; C. Dollard et al.,

a) *his4-912δ*

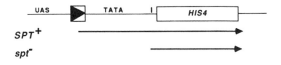

b) *his4-917δ*

c) *his4-917*

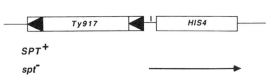

Figure 3 Transcriptional changes in *spt* mutants. Diagramed are three different insertion mutations at *HIS4*, showing the relative position of the insertion element and the *HIS4* transcription signals. The insertion elements are not drawn to scale. (*a,b*) For both *his4-912δ* and *his4-917δ*, transcription initiation is altered from one initiation site in *SPT⁺* strains to another initiation site in *spt* mutants. For some *spt* mutants, only the shorter transcript is produced; for others, both the long and short transcripts are produced (Silverman and Fink 1984; Winston et al. 1984a; Clark-Adams and Winston 1987). (*c*) For *his4-917*, there is no *HIS4* transcript in *SPT⁺* strains; a wild-type-length transcript is produced in certain *spt* mutants.

unpubl.). For the remainder of the *SPT* genes, including those in the histone-related group, mutations do not significantly reduce the level of Ty transcription, although transcription from solo δ elements is reduced (Clark-Adams et al. 1988). Interestingly, this class of *spt* mutations strongly suppresses solo δ insertion mutations and only weakly suppresses Ty insertion mutations.

SPT15, SPT3, SPT7, and SPT8: Genes That Encode TFIID and Related Functions

On the basis of the criteria outlined in the preceding sections, *SPT15*, *SPT3*, *SPT7*, and *SPT8* encode related functions. Mutations in any of these four genes abolish normal Ty transcription, cause mating and sporulation defects, and all confer the same suppression pattern for a set of Ty and δ insertion mutations. Such observations indicate that these four genes encode functionally related products.

By cloning and sequencing the *SPT15* gene, it was discovered that it encodes the TATA-binding factor TFIID (Eisenmann et al. 1989; Hahn et al. 1989a). TFIID had been identified initially from HeLa cell nuclear extracts as a function that binds directly to the TATA box and that is required for transcription initiation in vitro (Davison et al. 1983; Sawadogo and Roeder 1985; Van Dyke et al. 1988); therefore, its in vivo role was unknown. Following the discovery that yeast contains a TFIID activity that can function in place of HeLa TFIID in vitro, several laboratories purified the yeast TFIID protein and subsequently cloned the TFIID-encoding gene (Cavallini et al. 1989; Hahn et al. 1989a; Horikoshi et al. 1989a,b; Schmidt et al. 1989). The discovery that the previously identified and cloned *SPT15* gene encodes TFIID was made by comparison of the clone of *SPT15* to the clone of the gene encoding TFIID (Eisenmann et al. 1989; Hahn et al. 1989a). This comparison demonstrated that the two clones contained the same fragments of yeast DNA and that both clones were able to complement *spt15* mutations (Eisenmann et al. 1989). The discovery that *SPT15* encodes TFIID immediately allowed determination of important facts about the function of TFIID in vivo (Eisenmann et al. 1989). First, TFIID is essential for growth, since *spt15* null mutations cause inviability. Second, *spt15* missense mutations cause alterations in transcription in vivo as well as other phenotypic aberrations, as described earlier. These results proved that TFIID is an essential function, required for normal transcription in vivo as well as in vitro.

From biochemical experiments using HeLa nuclear extracts, TFIID had been shown to be one of several factors, including RNA polymerase II, required for accurate transcription initiation in vitro. TFIID was shown to bind to TATA regions and to be the only one of the general transcription factors identified that binds to DNA in a sequence-specific manner in the absence of any other general factors. Furthermore, assembly of the stable transcription initiation complex was shown to be dependent on TFIID (for review, see Sawadogo and Sentenac 1990). Biochemical experiments using yeast TFIID have confirmed these results: Purified yeast TFIID binds avidly to the TATA regions of several different genes and is able to functionally substitute for HeLa TFIID in vitro for basal level transcription (Buratowski et al. 1988; Cavallini et al. 1988; Hahn et al. 1989b; Horikoshi et al. 1989a). On the basis of in vitro analysis, therefore, the activities of TFIID include binding to TATA regions and interaction with other general transcription factors.

The finding that *spt3*, *spt7*, and *spt8* mutations confer phenotypes similar to those conferred by *spt15* mutations raises several issues pertinent to the roles played by these gene products in transcription initiation. First, what is the nature of the TFIID defect that results in altered transcription initiation? Second, are the SPT3, SPT7, and SPT8 gene products also part of the general transcription machinery? Third, are the observed *spt15* mutant phenotypes representative of *spt15* mutations in general, or are they a specific class, due to the selection by which they were isolated? The answers to these questions should help us to understand the functions of TFIID in vivo. Moreover, they may lead us to identify proteins that interact with TFIID during the process of transcription initiation.

It is tempting to speculate that *SPT3*, *SPT7*, and *SPT8* encode general transcription factors that correspond to the HeLa factors identified in vitro. Equally intriguing is the possibility that they may encode functions not yet detected in vitro. The molecular analysis of *SPT3*, *SPT7*, and *SPT8* has not shed much light on their functions. All three genes have been cloned and sequenced (Winston and Minehart 1986; C. Dollard et al., unpubl.). None of the deduced amino acid sequences reveals any marked similarity to other proteins or to motifs that would suggest a possible function. Since only a limited number of the biochemically defined general transcription factors have been purified to homogeneity and characterized at the amino acid sequence level, it remains unclear whether the SPT3, SPT7, and SPT8 gene products perform a corresponding function. We do know that *SPT7* is essential for growth, whereas *SPT3* and *SPT8* are not essential (Winston et al. 1984a; C. Dollard and F. Winston, unpubl.). These results might suggest that *SPT3* and *SPT8* are unlikely to encode general transcription factors; however, the possibility exists that either there are functionally redundant genes for some general factors or that some of them are not essential in vivo. We anticipate that further studies on the proteins encoded by these genes are likely to shed light on their functions.

Since mutations in the *SPT3*, *SPT7*, *SPT8*, and *SPT15* genes can shift transcription initiation from one site to another, it seems unlikely that the alteration in transcription initiation observed in *spt15* mutants can solely be caused by altered DNA-binding properties of a mutant TFIID product. For example, in an *spt3* mutant, the same altered transcription initiation occurs as occurs in particular *spt15* mutants. These results suggest that TFIID does not act alone to mediate the choice between initiation sites, but rather, that it is just one component necessary for the transcription machinery to initiate at the correct site. One model that can explain these results posits that at least some of the *spt15* mutants isolated as suppressors of insertion mutations encode mutant TFIID proteins that have lost the ability to interact with the products of other *SPT* genes. According to this model, one or all of those products are "specificity factors," required for initiation of transcription in δ sequences. Development of an assay for these gene products in an in vitro transcription system would constitute a major step toward understanding their functions.

SPT Genes That Encode Histones and Functionally Related Proteins

Considerable evidence has indicated that the chromatin structure of transcribed genes differs from that of nontranscribed genes. However, the role of chromatin structure in transcription remains somewhat obscure (Mathis et al. 1980; Pederson et al. 1986; Grunstein 1990). For example, we do not know whether altered chromatin structure allows transcription, or altered transcription causes a change in chromatin structure. Genetic analysis in yeast of histone genes and of other factors believed to affect chromatin structure, described in this chapter and by Grunstein et al. (this volume), have begun to address this issue.

SPT11 *and* SPT12 *Encode Histones H2A and H2B*

The identification of *SPT11* and *SPT12* as genes that encode histones H2A and H2B was an initial step in addressing the relationship between chromatin structure and transcription. Clark-Adams et al. (1988) initially showed that the *SPT11* and *SPT12* genes, identified on the basis of their ability to suppress solo δ insertion mutations when present at either high copy number or when mutant, comprised a previously identified locus that encodes histones H2A and H2B (*HTA1-HTB1*). Reminiscent of other *spt* mutations, genetic lesions at this locus, including a deletion that removes both genes, alter the pattern of transcription initiation around δ insertion sites. This result demonstrated that altered levels of histones cause a change in the pattern of transcription initiation near the insertion loci. (In yeast, there are four histone loci: Two loci contain divergently transcribed genes that encode histones H2A and H2B; two loci contain divergently transcribed genes that encode histones H3 and H4 [Table 2]. Since each histone gene is duplicated, deletion of one gene does not cause lethality.)

Table 2 Suppression of insertion mutations by histone genes in high copy number

Histone locus on plasmid	Histones encoded	*his4-912δ*	*lys2-128δ*
None	none	cs	–
HTA1-HTB1	H2A, H2B	+	+
HTA2-HTB2	H2A, H2B	+	+
HHT1-HHF1	H3, H4	+	–/+
HHT2-HHF2	H3, H4	+	–/+
HTA1-HTB1, *HHT1-HHF1*	H2A, H2B, H3, H4	–	–
HTA1	H2A	–	–
HTB1	H2B	–	–

Designations are as follows: (cs) cold sensitive; (–) His⁻ or Lys⁻ phenotype; (+) His⁺ or Lys⁺ phenotype.

Analysis of strains that overproduce various combinations of histones suggests that an imbalance of histone dimers causes suppression of insertion mutations and aberrant transcription. If either a gene pair that encodes histones H2A and H2B, or a gene pair that encodes histones H3 and H4, is placed on a high copy number plasmid, suppression of insertion mutations is observed (Table 2) (Clark-Adams et al. 1988). In the case of the H2A-H2B pair, it was shown that if only one of the two genes on the high copy number plasmid was functional, then there was no "high copy number phenotype," demonstrating that overexpression of both genes is required for elaboration of the mutant phenotype. When genes that encode all four histone genes are placed on a high copy number plasmid, there also is no suppression of insertion mutations. Therefore, the mutant phenotype is not caused by an absolute overproduction of histones, but instead by an imbalance of subunits. These results fit well with the previous work of Meeks-Wagner and Hartwell (1986), who showed that a high copy number of histone gene pairs caused chromosome instability.

In addition to suppression of insertion mutations, deletion of one of the two H2A-H2B-encoding gene pairs (*HTA1-HTB1*) causes a number of additional mutant phenotypes. Norris and Osley (1987) showed that deletion of this locus affects heat shock response, growth, sporulation, germination, and exit from stationary phase. Norris et al. (1988) also demonstrated that in (*hta1-htb1*)Δ strains, nucleosome phasing was disrupted at some loci, raising the distinct possibility that all the mutant phenotypes observed were caused by altered chromatin structure.

Recent work has shown that the (*hta1-htb1*)Δ mutation also causes another phenotype: suppression of the loss of certain transcriptional activators required for transcription of the *SUC2* gene (Clark-Adams et al. 1988; J.N. Hirschhorn et al., unpubl.). Extensive genetic and molecular analysis identified five genes required for *SUC2* transcription. These genes fall into two groups: *SNF1* and *SNF4* comprise one group, and *SNF2*, *SNF5*, and *SNF6* comprise the other group (for review, see Carlson 1987). Deletion of *HTA1-HTB1* suppresses the loss of members of one group (*SNF2*, *SNF5*, and *SNF6*), but not loss of members of the other group. This result, in showing that effects on gene expression caused by histone subunit imbalance suppress the loss of a specific set of regulatory proteins, ties together the respective roles of the two components. That is, certain transcriptional activators (e.g., SNF2, SNF5, and SNF6) may function by interaction with chromatin. Perhaps their specific function is to facilitate binding of general transcription factors (such as TFIID) or to somehow loosen or dislodge nucleosomes in the vicinity of the *SUC2* gene. Examination of chromatin structure of *SUC2* in wild-type, *snf*, and (*hta1-htb1*)Δ mutant backgrounds will begin to address this issue.

Many studies regarding the effect of altered chromatin structure on transcription have been conducted under conditions in which the levels of wild-type histone proteins are either increased or decreased (Han et al. 1987; Clark-Adams et al. 1988; Han and Grunstein 1988). However, no systematic and general mutant analysis has been undertaken on histone-encoding genes. Part of the reason for this may be technical. It is obviously more cumbersome to do genetic analysis on duplicated genes, since recessive phenotypes will be hidden. Development of more sophisticated genetic strategies for the study of histone function, such as those described by Grunstein et al. (this volume), are likely to be richly rewarded by significant information about the role of histones and chromatin structure in transcription.

SPT4, SPT5, *and* SPT6 *Encode Proteins Functionally Related to H2A and H2B*

SPT5 and *SPT6* are essential genes of *S. cerevisiae* whose function appears to be related to histones. The phenotypes caused by *spt5* and *spt6* mutations are very similar to those caused by mutations in *SPT11* and *SPT12* (*HTA1* and *HTB1*): the same pattern of suppression of Ty and δ insertion mutations; suppression of *snf2*, *snf5*, and *snf6* mutations; and suppression of deletions of the *SUC2* UAS region. In addition, high copy number clones of *SPT5*, *SPT6*, and *SPT11-SPT12* all confer an Spt⁻

mutant phenotype (Neigeborn et al. 1986, 1987; Clark-Adams and Winston 1987; Happel et al. 1991; Swanson et al. 1991; M.S. Swanson and F. Winston, unpubl.).

On the basis of the phenotypes of *spt5* and *spt6* mutants, wild-type *SPT5* and *SPT6* appear to constitute negative regulators of transcription. Mutations in *SPT5* and *SPT6* were initially identified as suppressors of the δ insertion mutation, *his4-912δ* (Winston et al. 1984b). For *SPT6*, mutations were also isolated as extragenic suppressors of the defect in *SUC2* transcription caused by *snf2* and *snf5* mutations (Neigeborn et al. 1986). In addition, *spt6* mutations were isolated as variants that relieved glucose repression of transcription of *ADH2* (Denis and Malvar 1990). In each case, *spt5* and *spt6* mutations allow transcription to occur in the presence of a *cis*- or *trans*-acting mutation or a growth condition that impairs promoter function. The identification of *SPT5* and *SPT6* as negative regulators is supported by the observation that a diploid cell that contains *SPT6*+ on one chromosome and a null allele of *SPT6* on the other homolog exhibits an Spt⁻ phenotype (Clark-Adams and Winston 1987). The same phenotype is observed for *spt5* null mutations (Swanson et al. 1991). In these cases, then, a reduction in wild-type *SPT5* or *SPT6* gene dosage causes an Spt⁻ phenotype; this result is consistent with the model that SPT5 and SPT6 act in a negative fashion.

Thus far, molecular analysis of *SPT5* and *SPT6* has provided little information regarding their functions. Both genes encode large proteins, localized to the yeast nucleus (Swanson et al. 1990, 1991). Based on the DNA sequence, the SPT6 gene product is approximately 168 kD and has an extremely acidic segment of 484 amino acids at its amino-terminal end. The sequence does not show significant similarity to amino acid sequences of other proteins, with the exception of a number of generally acidic proteins. The DNA sequence of the *SPT5* gene predicts a protein with similarities to the SPT6 protein. The predicted SPT5 protein is also large (1063 amino acids), with two striking features: a very acidic amino terminus (like SPT6) and a glycine-rich, carboxy-terminal amino acid repeat (Swanson et al. 1991). The acidic nature of the SPT5 and SPT6 gene products is consistent with the idea that they interact with histone proteins, which are unusually basic. Indeed, some other highly acidic proteins have been shown to be chromatin-associated (Earnshaw 1987). In fact, the very acidic proteins nucleoplasmin and N1/N2 associate with histone proteins and have been shown to be important for chromatin assembly in vitro (Kleinschmidt et al. 1985). Another chromatin-associated protein, nucleolin, has both an acidic amino terminus and a glycine-rich carboxyl terminus, similar to SPT5 (Lapeyre et al. 1987).

Genetic studies have indicated that *SPT5* and *SPT6* interact with each other and with one other gene, *SPT4*. First, strains that carry mutations in any two of these three genes are inviable under conditions in which the single mutants are viable (Winston et al. 1984b). Second, recessive mutations in these three genes fail to complement each other in diploid strains (M.S. Swanson and F. Winston, unpubl.). This phenotype is often indicative of physical interaction between gene products (Stearns and Botstein 1988; Hayes et al. 1989). The unlinked noncomplementation phenotype is not exhibited by any other *spt* mutants, including *spt11* and *spt12*. These results, taken together with the fact that *SPT5* or *SPT6* on a high copy number plasmid confers an Spt⁻ mutant phenotype, predicts that the SPT4, SPT5, and SPT6 proteins form a complex. Overproduction of SPT5 or SPT6 might result in altered stoichiometry, thereby reducing the effective level of the functional complex. This result is similar to the phenotype caused by overexpression of histone gene pairs (Clark-Adams et al. 1988). The level of functional complexes has also been shown to be important in other processes, including bacteriophage morphogenesis (Floor 1970; Sternberg 1976).

Summary: SPT *Genes and Chromatin*

Studies of *spt* mutants have provisionally identified two types of complexes that are required for proper chromatin structure as it pertains to transcription. The first complex is made up of nucleosomes, composed of histones H2A, H2B, H3, and H4. Gene dosage experiments have demonstrated that proper stoichiometry of histones is required for normal transcription (Clark-Adams et al. 1988). In addition, Norris et al. (1988) have demonstrated that altered histone subunit stoichiometry can disrupt chromatin at particular loci.

   The second complex believed to be required for proper chromatin structure is the predicted complex consisting of the products of the *SPT4*, *SPT5*, and *SPT6* genes. We suggest that this complex is somehow involved in the establishment or maintenance of proper chromatin structure. The possible roles for the proposed SPT4-SPT5-SPT6 complex include assembly of nucleosomes, transport or processing of histones, or actual physical association with chromatin. Experiments that address whether chromatin structure is actually altered in these mutants, and whether the SPT4, SPT5, and SPT6 gene products are physically associated with chromatin, will represent an important step toward elucidating their mechanistic functions.

SPT13 and SPT14

Two *SPT* genes that do not fall into either the TFIID-related group or the histone-related group are *SPT13* and *SPT14*. These two genes are grouped separately because mutations in both genes confer a pattern of suppression of Ty and δ insertion mutations that is strikingly different from those of other *spt* mutations. Mutations in *SPT13* and in *SPT14* suppress the effects of intact Ty insertion mutations, yet fail to suppress solo δ insertion mutations (Table 1) (Fassler and Winston 1988).

DNA sequence analysis of *SPT13* has shown that it is the same gene as *GAL11* (Suzuki et al. 1988; Fassler and Winston 1989). *gal11* mutants were first isolated as strains that exhibit a leaky Gal⁻ phenotype (Nogi and Fukasawa 1980). Recent analysis has shown that *spt13/gal11* mutants have several other mutant phenotypes, including reduced transcription of α-specific genes and of the *PYK1* (pyruvate kinase) gene, increased transcription of Ty elements, defective growth on nonfermentable carbon sources, and a severe sporulation defect (Fassler and Winston 1989; Nishizawa et al. 1990). All these phenotypes suggest that *SPT13/GAL11* is required for normal expression of a large number of genes. Since *SPT13* is not essential for growth (indeed, *spt13* null mutants grow in the laboratory at a near-normal rate), it seems likely either that its function is not significantly required for the transcription of any essential gene or that its function is partially redundant. A screen to identify genes that, when mutant, confer inviability in conjunction with *spt13* null mutations might identify genes that encode functions related to SPT13/GAL11.

Although the DNA sequence of *SPT13* has yet to provide insight into the activity of its protein product, it contains motifs that can be tested for function. The predicted protein product is 107 kD and contains stretches of polyglutamine, poly(glutamine-alanine), and a region that could form an α-helix-β-turn-α-helix structure (Suzuki et al. 1988). Deletion analysis of *SPT13* will be able to test the functional roles of these motifs.

One model for SPT13/GAL11 function hypothesizes its role as both a positive and negative transcriptional regulator that acts in conjunction with other transcription factors. Experiments have demonstrated that it is required for transcription of α-specific genes and of *PYK1*. Such results tentatively define SPT13 as a transcriptional activator. These results have also led to the suggestion that it works in conjunction with RAP1, a protein also required for transcription of the same set of genes (Shore and Nasmyth 1987; Chambers et al. 1989). Conversely, *spt13* mutations also cause an increase in the level of Ty transcription and allow transcription of genes repressed by Ty insertion mutations. These results tentatively define SPT13 as a negative transcription factor. Given that RAP1 has been shown to be required for repression of transcription in one context (silent mating type cassettes; Shore and Nasmyth 1987) and activation at others (see above), one can imagine that, at a number of genes, RAP1 and SPT13 might interact to regulate transcription in different ways. (The role of RAP1 in Ty transcription has not yet been examined.) Recent work also suggests that SPT13 interacts with GAL4 to increase the expression of most *GAL* genes (Himmelfarb et al. 1990).

CONCLUSIONS AND PERSPECTIVES

The isolation of *spt* mutants has provided a fertile source of transcription mutants to study. These mutants have provided the first demonstration that TFIID is required for transcription in vivo and that altered levels of histones cause a change in transcription in vivo. Continued analysis of *SPT* genes, including those that encode known functions and those that encode unknown functions, should continue to yield valuable information concerning transcriptional regulation in living cells.

The study of *spt* mutants has allowed placement of most of the *SPT* genes into either a TFIID-related group or a histone-related group. Although the spectrum of mutant phenotypes for the two groups is different, the functions of the gene products are likely related in vivo. For example, recent evidence from in vitro experiments suggests that TFIID binding and transcriptional activation can be affected by chromatin structure (Workman and Roeder 1987; Workman et al. 1990). Further studies, in vivo and in vitro, must be undertaken to address the interaction of factors such as TFIID with chromatin and other components of the transcription initiation machinery.

Genetic studies of transcription in yeast have identified protein factors that have not yet been characterized by in vitro transcription systems. The identification of additional components important for transcription in vitro, coupled with further genetic and biochemical analysis of *spt* mutants and other transcription mutants, should help to elucidate the identity and functions of components required for transcription initiation in vivo. By using a combined approach of in vitro and in vivo analysis, we can hope to understand both the mechanistic function of these transcription factors and the roles they play during cellular growth.

ACKNOWLEDGMENTS

This work was supported by National Institutes of Health grants GM-32967 and GM-45720, National Science Foundation grant DCB-8451649, and a grant from the Stroh Brewery Company to F.W.

REFERENCES

Boeke, J.D. 1989. Transposable elements in *Saccharomyces cerevisiae*. In *Mobile DNA* (ed. D.E. Berg and M.M. Howe), pp. 335–374. American Society for Microbiology, Washington, D.C.

Boeke, J.D., C.A. Styles, and G.R. Fink. 1986. *Saccharomyces cerevisiae SPT3* gene is required for transposition and transpositional recombination of chromosomal Ty elements. *Mol. Cell. Biol.* **6:** 3575–3581.

Buratowski, S., S. Hahn, P.A. Sharp, and L. Guarente. 1988. Function of a yeast TATA element-binding protein in a mammalian transcription system. *Nature* **334:** 37–42.

Carlson, M. 1987. Regulation of sugar utilization in *Saccharomyces* species. *J. Bacteriol.* **169:** 4873–4877.

Cavallini, B., J. Huet, J.-L. Plassat, A. Sentenac, J.-M. Egly, and P. Chambon. 1988. A yeast activity can substitute for the HeLa cell TATA box factor. *Nature* **334:** 77–80.

Cavallini, B., I. Faus, H. Matthes, J.M. Chipoulet, B. Winsor, J.M. Egly, and P. Chambon. 1989. Cloning of the gene encoding the yeast protein BTF-1Y, which can substitute for the human TATA box-binding factor. *Proc. Natl. Acad. Sci.* **86:** 9803–9807.

Chaleff, D.T. and G.R. Fink. 1980. Genetic events associated with an insertion mutation in yeast. *Cell* **21:** 227–237.

Chambers, A., J.S. Tsang, C. Stanway, A.J. Kingsman, and S.M. Kingsman. 1989. Transcriptional control of the *Saccharomyces cerevisiae PGK* gene by RAP1. *Mol. Cell. Biol.* **9:** 5516–5524.

Clark-Adams, C.D. and F. Winston. 1987. The *SPT6* gene is essential for growth and is required for δ-mediated transcription in *Saccharomyces cerevisiae. Mol. Cell. Biol.* **7:** 679–686.

Clark-Adams, C.D., D. Norris, M.A. Osley, J.S. Fassler, and F. Winston. 1988. Changes in histone gene dosage alter transcription in yeast. *Genes Dev.* **2:** 150–159.

Coney, L.R. and G.S. Roeder. 1988. Control of yeast gene expression by transposable elements: Maximum expression requires a functional Ty activator sequence and a defective Ty promoter. *Mol. Cell Biol.* **8:** 4009–4017.

Davison, B.L., J. Egly, E.R. Mulvihill, and P. Chambon. 1983. Formation of stable preinitiation complexes between eukaryotic class B transcription factors and promoter sequences. *Nature* **301:** 680–686.

Denis, C.L. and T. Malvar. 1990. The CCR4 gene from *Saccharomyces cerevisiae* is required for both nonfermentative and *spt*-mediated gene expression. *Genetics* **124:** 283–291.

Earnshaw, W.C. 1987. Anionic regions in nuclear proteins. *J. Cell Biol.* **105:** 1479–1482.

Eisenmann, D.M., C. Dollard, and F. Winston. 1989. *SPT15*, the gene encoding the yeast TATA binding factor TFIID, is required for normal transcription initiation *in vivo. Cell* **58:** 1183–1191.

Errede, B., M. Company, J.D. Ferchak, C.A. Hutchison, and W.S. Yarnell. 1985. Activation regions in a yeast transposon have homology to mating type control sequences and to mammalian enhancers. *Proc. Natl. Acad. Sci.* **82:** 5423–5427.

Errede, B., T.S. Cardillo, F. Sherman, E. Dubois, J. Deschamps, and J.M. Wiame. 1980. Mating signals control expression of mutations resulting from insertion of a transposable repetitive element adjacent to diverse yeast genes. *Cell* **22:** 427–436.

Farabaugh, P.J. and G.R. Fink. 1980. Insertion of the eukaryotic transposable element Ty1 creates a 5-base pair duplication. *Nature* **286:** 352–356.

Farabaugh, P., X.B. Liao, M. Belcourt, H. Zhao, J. Kapakos, and J. Clare. 1989. Enhancer and silencerlike sites within the transcribed portion of a Ty2 transposable element of *Saccharomyces cerevisiae. Mol. Cell. Biol.* **9:** 4824–4834.

Fassler, J.S. and F. Winston. 1988. Isolation and analysis of a novel class of suppressor of Ty insertion mutations in *Saccharomyces cerevisiae. Genetics* **118:** 203–212.

———. 1989. The *Saccharomyces cerevisiae SPT13/GAL11* gene has both positive and negative regulatory roles in transcription. *Mol. Cell. Biol.* **9:** 5602–5609.

Fikes, J.D., D.M. Becker, F. Winston, and L. Guarente. 1990. Striking conservation of TFIID in *Schizosaccharomyces pombe* and *Saccharomyces cerevisiae*. *Nature* **346:** 291–294.

Fischer, J.A., E. Giniger, T. Maniatis, and M. Ptashne. 1988. *GAL4* activates transcription in *Drosophila*. *Nature* **332:** 853–856.

Floor, E. 1970. Interaction of morphogenetic genes of bacteriophage T4. *J. Mol. Biol.* **47:** 293–306.

Fulton, A.M., P.D. Rathjen, S.M. Kingsman, and A.J. Kingsman. 1988. Upstream and downstream transcriptional control signals in the yeast retrotransposon, Ty. *Nucleic Acids Res.* **16:** 5439–5458.

Gasch, A., A. Hoffman, M. Horikoshi, R.G. Roeder, and N.H. Chua. 1990. *Arabidopsis thaliana* contains two genes for TFIID. *Nature* **346:** 390–394.

Grunstein, M. 1990. Histone function in transcription. *Annu. Rev. Cell. Biol.* **6:** 643–678.

Guarente, L. 1987. Regulatory proteins in yeast. *Annu. Rev. Genet.* **21:** 425–452.

Hahn, S., S. Buratowski, P.A. Sharp, and L. Guarente. 1989a. Isolation of the gene encoding the yeast TATA-binding protein TFIID: A gene identical to the *SPT15* suppressor of Ty element insertions. *Cell* **58:** 1173–1181.

————. 1989b. Yeast TATA-binding protein TFIID binds to TATA elements with both consensus and nonconsensus DNA sequences. *Proc. Natl. Acad. Sci.* **86:** 5718–5722.

Han, M. and M. Grunstein. 1988. Nucleosome loss activates yeast downstream promoters in vivo. *Cell* **55:** 1137–1145.

Han, M., M. Chang, U.-J. Kim, and M. Grunstein. 1987. Histone H2B repression causes cell-cycle-specific arrest in yeast: Effects on chromosomal segregation, replication, and transcription. *Cell* **48:** 589–597.

Happel, A.M., M.S. Swanson, and F. Winston. 1991. The *SNF2, SNF5* and *SNF6* genes are required for Ty transcription in *Saccharomyces cerevisiae*. *Genetics* **128:** 69–77.

Hayes, T.S., R. Deuring, B. Robertson, M. Prout, and M.T. Fuller. 1989. Interacting proteins identified by genetic interactions: A missense mutation in α-tubulin fails to complement alleles of the testis-specific α-tubulin gene of *Drosophila melanogaster*. *Mol. Cell. Biol.* **9:** 875–884.

Herskowitz, I. and Y. Oshima. 1981. Control of cell type in *Saccharomyces cerevisiae*: Mating type and mating-type interconversion. In *The molecular biology of the yeast Saccharomyces: Life cycle and inheritance* (ed. J.N. Strathern et al.), pp. 181–209. Cold Spring Harbor Laboratory, Cold Spring Harbor, New York.

Himmelfarb, H.J., J. Pearlberg, D.H. Last, and M. Ptashne. 1990. GAL11P: A yeast mutation that potentiates the effect of weak GAL4-derived activators. *Cell* **63:** 1299–1309.

Hinnebusch, A.G. 1988. Mechanisms of gene regulation in the general control of amino acid biosynthesis in *Saccharomyces cerevisiae*. *Microbiol. Rev.* **52:** 248–273.

Hirschhorn, J.N. and F. Winston. 1988. *SPT3* is required for normal levels of a-factor and α-factor expression in *Saccharomyces cerevisiae*. *Mol. Cell. Biol.* **8:** 4608–4615.

Hirschman, J.E., K.J. Durbin, and F. Winston. 1988. Genetic evidence for promoter competition in *Saccharomyces cerevisiae*. *Mol. Cell. Biol.* **8:** 4608–4615.

Hoey, T., B.D. Dynlacht, M.G. Peterson, B.F. Pugh, and R. Tjian. 1990. Isolation and characterization of the *Drosophila* gene encoding the TATA box binding protein, TFIID. *Cell* **61:** 1179–1186.

Hoffman, A., E. Sinn, T. Yamamoto, J. Wang, A. Roy, M. Horikoshi, and R.G. Roeder. 1990. Highly conserved core domain and unique N terminus with presumptive regulatory motifs in a human TATA factor (TFIID). *Nature* **346:** 387–390.

Horikoshi, M., C.K. Wang, H. Fujii, J.A. Cromlish, P.A. Weil, and R.G. Roeder. 1989a.

Purification of yeast TATA box-binding protein that exhibits human transcription factor IID activity. *Proc. Natl. Acad. Sci.* **86:** 4843–4847.

————. 1989b. Cloning and structure of a yeast gene encoding a general transcription initiation factor TFIID that binds to the TATA box. *Nature* **341:** 299–303.

Johnston, M. 1987. A model fungal gene regulatory mechanism: The *GAL* genes of *Saccharomyces cerevisiae. Microbiol. Rev.* **51:** 458–476.

Kakidani, H. and M. Ptashne. 1988. *GAL4* activates gene expression in mammalian cells. *Cell* **52:** 161–167.

Kao, C.C., P.M. Lieberman, M.C. Schmidt, Q. Zhou, R. Pei, and A.J. Berk. 1990. Cloning of a transcriptionally active human TATA binding factor. *Science* **248:** 1646–1650.

Kleinschmidt, J.A., E. Fortkamp, G. Krohne, H. Zentgraf, and W.W. Franke. 1985. Coexistence of two different types of soluble histone complexes in nuclei of *Xenopus laevis* oocytes. *J. Biol. Chem.* **260:** 1166–1176.

Lapeyre, B., H. Bourbon, and F. Amalric. 1987. Nucleolin, the major nucleolar protein of growing eukaryotic cells: An unusual protein structure revealed by the nucleotide sequence. *Proc. Natl. Acad. Sci.* **84:** 1472–1476.

Lech, K., K. Anderson, and R. Brent. 1988. DNA-bound Fos proteins activate transcription in yeast. *Cell* **52:** 179–184.

Liao, X.B., J.J. Clare, and P.J. Farabaugh. 1987. The upstream activation site of a Ty2 element of yeast is necessary but not sufficient to promote maximal transcription of the element. *Proc. Natl. Acad. Sci.* **84:** 8520–8524.

Ma, J., E. Przibilla, J. Hu, L. Bogorad, and M. Ptashne. 1988. Yeast activators stimulate plant gene expression. *Nature* **334:** 631–633.

Mathis, D., P. Oudet, and P. Chambon. 1980. Structure of transcribing chromatin. *Prog. Nucleic Acid. Res. Mol. Biol.* **24:** 1–55.

Meeks-Wagner, D. and L.H. Hartwell. 1986. Normal stoichiometry of histone dimer sets is necessary for high fidelity of mitotic chromosome transmission. *Cell* **44:** 53–63.

Metzger, D., J.H. White, and P. Chambon. 1988. The human oestrogen receptor functions in yeast. *Nature* **334:** 31–36.

Muhich, M.L., C.T. Iida, M. Horikoshi, R.G. Roeder, and C.S. Parker. 1990. cDNA clone encoding *Drosophila* transcription factor TFIID. *Proc. Natl. Acad. Sci.* **87:** 9148–9152.

Nasmyth, K. and D. Shore. 1987. Transcriptional regulation in the yeast life cycle. *Science* **237:** 1162–1170.

Natsoulis, G., C. Dollard, F. Winston, and J.D. Boeke. 1991. The products of the *SPT10* and *SPT21* genes of *Saccharomyces cerevisiae* increase the amplitude of transcriptional regulation at a large number of unlinked loci. *New Biol.* **3:** 1249–1259.

Neigeborn, L., J.L. Celenza, and M. Carlson. 1987. *SSN20* is an essential gene with mutant alleles that suppress defects in *SUC2* transcription in *Saccharomyces cerevisiae. Mol. Cell. Biol.* **7:** 672–678.

Neigeborn, L., K. Rubin, and M. Carlson. 1986. Suppressors of *snf2* mutations restore invertase derepression and cause temperature-sensitive lethality in yeast. *Genetics* **112:** 741–753.

Nishizawa, M., Y. Suzuki, Y. Nogi, K. Matsumoto, and T. Fukasawa. 1990. Yeast Gal11 protein mediates the transcriptional activation signal of two different transacting factors, Gal4 and general regulatory factor I/repressor/activator site binding protein 1/translation upstream factor. *Proc. Natl. Acad. Sci.* **87:** 5373–5377.

Nogi, Y. and T. Fukasawa. 1980. A novel mutation that affects utilization of galactose in *Saccharomyces cerevisiae. Curr. Genet.* **2:** 115–120.

Norris, D. and M.A. Osley. 1987. The two gene pairs encoding H2A and H2B play different roles in the *Saccharomyces cerevisiae* life cycle. *Mol. Cell. Biol.* **7:** 3473–3481.

Norris, D., B. Dunn, and M.A. Osley. 1988. The effect of histone gene deletions on chromatin structure in *Saccharomyces cerevisiae. Science* **242:** 759–761.

Pederson, D.S., F. Thoma, and R.T. Simpson. 1986. Core particle, fiber, and transcriptionally active chromatin structure. *Annu. Rev. Cell. Biol.* **2:** 117–147.

Peterson, M.G., N. Tanese, B.F. Pugh, and R. Tjian. 1990. Functional domains and upstream activation properties of a cloned human TATA binding protein. *Science* **248:** 1625–1630.

Roeder, G.S. and G.R. Fink. 1982. Movement of yeast transposable elements by gene conversion. *Proc. Natl. Acad. Sci.* **79:** 5621–5625.

Roeder, G.S., A.B. Rose, and R.E. Perlman. 1985. Transposable element sequences involved in the enhancement of yeast gene expression. *Proc. Natl. Acad. Sci.* **82:** 5428–5432.

Sawadogo, M. and R.G. Roeder. 1985. Factors involved in specific transcription by human RNA polymerase II: Analysis by a rapid and quantitative in vitro assay. *Proc. Natl. Acad. Sci.* **82:** 4394–4398.

Sawadogo, M. and A. Sentenac. 1990. RNA polymerase B (II) and general transcription factors. *Annu. Rev. Biochem.* **59:** 711–754.

Schena, M. and K. Yamamoto. 1988. Mammalian glucocorticoid receptor derivatives enhance transcription in yeast. *Science* **241:** 965–967.

Schmidt, M.C., C.C. Kao, R. Pei, and A.J. Berk. 1989. Yeast TATA-box transcription factor gene. *Proc. Natl. Acad. Sci.* **86:** 7785–7789.

Shore, D. and K. Nasmyth 1987. Purification and cloning of a DNA binding protein from yeast that binds to both silencer and activator elements. *Cell* **51:** 721–732.

Silverman, S.J. and G.R. Fink. 1984. Effects of Ty insertions on *HIS4* transcription in *Saccharomyces cerevisiae. Mol. Cell. Biol.* **4:** 1246–1251.

Simchen, G., F. Winston, C.A. Styles, and G.R. Fink. 1984. Ty-mediated gene expression of the *LYS2* and *HIS4* gene of *Saccharomyces cerevisiae* is controlled by the same *SPT* genes. *Proc. Natl. Acad. Sci.* **81:** 2431–2434.

Stearns, T. and D. Botstein. 1988. Unlinked noncomplementation: Isolation of new conditional-lethal mutations in each of the tubulin genes of *Saccharomyces cerevisiae. Genetics* **119:** 249–260.

Sternberg, N. 1976 A genetic analysis of bacteriophage λ head assembly. *Virology* **71:** 568–582.

Suzuki, Y., Y. Nogi, A. Abe, and T. Fukasawa. 1988. GAL11 protein, an auxiliary transcription activator for genes encoding galactose-metabolizing enzymes in *Saccharomyces cerevisiae. Mol. Cell. Biol.* **8:** 4991–4999.

Swanson, M.S., M. Carlson, and F. Winston. 1990. *SPT6*, an essential gene that affects transcription in *Saccharomyces cerevisiae,* encodes a nuclear protein with an extremely acidic amino terminus. *Mol. Cell. Biol.* **10:** 4935–4941.

Swanson, M.S., E.A. Malone, and F. Winston. 1991. *SPT5*, an essential gene important for normal transcription in *Saccharomyces cerevisiae,* encodes an acidic nuclear protein with a carboxy-terminal repeat. *Mol. Cell. Biol.* **11:** 3009–3019.

Van Dyke, M.W., R.G. Roeder, and M. Sawadogo. 1988. Physical analysis of transcription preinitiation complex assembly on a class II gene promoter. *Science* **241:** 1335–1338.

Webster, N., J.R. Jin, S. Green, M. Hollis, and P. Chambon. 1988. The yeast UAS_G is a transcriptional enhancer in human HeLa cells in the presence of the GAL4 *trans*-activator. *Cell* **52:** 169–178.

Williamson, V.M., E.T. Young, and M. Ciriacy. 1981. Transposable elements associated with constitutive expression of yeast alcohol dehydrogenase II. *Cell* **23:** 605–614.

Winston, F. and P.L. Minehart. 1986. Analysis of the yeast *SPT3* gene and identification of its product, a positive regulator of Ty transcription. *Nucleic Acids Res.* **14:** 6885-6900.

Winston, F., K.J. Durbin, and G.R. Fink. 1984a. The *SPT3* gene is required for normal transcription of Ty elements in *S. cerevisiae. Cell* **39:** 675-682.

Winston, F., D.T. Chaleff, B. Valent, and G.R. Fink. 1984b. Mutations affecting Ty-mediated expression of the HIS4 gene of *Saccharomyces cerevisiae. Genetics* **107:** 179-197.

Winston, F., C. Dollard, E.A. Malone, J. Clare, J.G. Kapakos, P. Farabaugh, and P.L. Minehart. 1987. Three genes are required for *trans*-activation of Ty transcription in yeast. *Genetics* **115:** 649-656.

Workman, J.L. and R.G. Roeder. 1987. Binding of transcription factor TFIID to the major late promoter during *in vitro* nucleosome assembly potentiates subsequent initiation by RNA polymerase II. *Cell* **51:** 813-822.

Workman, J.L., R.G. Roeder, and R.E. Kingston. 1990. An instream transcription factor. USF (MLTF), facilitates the formation of preinitiation complexes during in vitro chromatin assembly. *EMBO J.* **9:** 1299-1308.

Woychik, N.A. and R.A. Young. 1990. RNA polymerase II subunit structure and function. *Trends Biochem. Sci.* **15:** 347-351.

48

Histones: Regulators of Transcription in Yeast

Michael Grunstein, Linda K. Durrin, Randall K. Mann,
Grace Fisher-Adams, and Lianna M. Johnson
Molecular Biology Institute and
Department of Biology
University of California
Los Angeles, California 90024

OVERVIEW

Histones fold DNA and block initiation of transcription in vitro. Recent evidence suggests that they also regulate transcription in the living cell (*Saccharomyces cerevisiae*). We describe genetic studies of yeast histones that show that nucleosome loss is not merely a result, but also a cause, of transcription initiation in vivo. This suggests a model in which activator proteins must first stimulate nucleosome displacement or a change in nucleosome structure prior to full activation of the preinitiation complex. However, the nucleosome is more than just a general repressor of initiation. Core histones contain basic, flexible amino-terminal tails that have a number of unique regulatory functions. For example, different domains at the histone H4 amino terminus are responsible for repression of the yeast silent mating loci (*HML* and *HMR*) and for activation of a number of regulated genes, including *GAL1* and *PHO5*. The extreme evolutionary conservation of this histone suggests similar functions in other, more complex, eukaryotes.

INTRODUCTION

The positively charged histone proteins allow the folding of a long, negatively charged DNA polymer in a confined nuclear compartment. Aside from this reasonably well understood structural role, the question arises as to whether histones also have a regulatory role, influencing functions dependent on the folding of DNA. Such functions might include chromosomal segregation during mitosis and meiosis, replication, and transcription. This chapter concentrates largely on the approaches our laboratory has taken to the problem of histone function using the unique genetic and biochemical manipulations possible in the budding yeast, *S. cerevisiae*.

Nucleosome Structure

The *nucleosome core particle* contains a histone *octamer* (two molecules each of histones H2A, H2B, H3, and H4) and 146 bp of DNA wrapped approximately 1.8 turns around the octamer. Each of the four core histones contains two highly distinct domains, an extended hydrophilic amino-terminal "tail" containing a number of positively charged amino acids and a globular, hydrophobic carboxyl terminus having a high α-helix content. The amino-terminal tails are the sites of most of the post-translational histone modifications, including acetylation, methylation, and phosphorylation. A molecule of histone H1 interacts with the oc-tamer and linker DNA located between core particles to form the *chromatosome*, condensing approximately two full turns of DNA around the octamer (Simpson 1978; Thoma et al. 1979; Richmond et al. 1984). In the chromatosome, approximately 164–166 bp of DNA are packaged as opposed to 146 bp in the core particle (for review, see McGhee and Felsenfeld 1980; see van Holde 1988). Both histone H1 and the hydrophilic amino-terminal tails are believed to be required for the transition of chromatin from the extended "beads-on-a-string" 10-nm fiber to the folded solenoidal 30-nm diameter fiber that is believed to represent inactive chromatin (Allan et al. 1982). The hydrophobic carboxy-terminal regions are involved in both the histone-histone and histone-DNA interactions that allow nucleosome assembly and stability in vitro (McGhee and Felsenfeld 1980; van Holde 1988).

Biochemical Clues to Nucleosome/Histone Function

There have been a variety of largely abstract clues to the function of nucleosomes in the areas of chromosome segregation, replication, and transcription. Nucleosomal involvement in DNA folding suggests a pos-sible requirement for histones in the proper segregation of the highly folded chromosomal structures. Early studies showed that conditions that block protein (and therefore histone) synthesis do not inhibit DNA replication, arguing that new histone synthesis is not required for ongo-ing replication (Hereford and Hartwell 1973). Most of the clues regard-ing nucleosomal function have been in the area of histone/DNA interac-tions. These findings suggest that the nucleosome is a unit of genetic repression. For example, nucleosomes can in certain instances be located in fixed position with respect to specific DNA sequences (i.e., these

nucleosomes are said to be positioned). Nucleosome positioning can occur as the result of octamer preference for specific bent-DNA sequences
or repulsion by homopolymeric sequences or Z-DNA (for review, see
Garner and Felsenfeld 1987; Travers 1987) or by exclusion from certain
sequences containing tightly bound proteins (Thoma and Simpson 1985;
Thoma 1986; Fedor et al. 1988; Kornberg and Stryer 1988). Positioned
nucleosomes can prevent transcription initiation in vitro. Nucleosomes
positioned on a promoter sequence or present at a certain critical density
will prevent access to basal transcription factors and RNA polymerase
(Knezetic and Luse 1986; Lorch et al. 1987). However, nucleosomes will
not inhibit transcription initiation if the basal factors, in particular the
TFIID complex (the TATA element binding complex), are allowed to
first bind the promoter (Matsui 1987; Workman and Roeder 1987;
Knezetic et al. 1988).

Two other observations have suggested the involvement of histones in
repressing gene expression. First, an altered H1 interaction may be involved in repression. For example, the active somatic 5S genes in
somatic *Xenopus laevis* cells appear to be depleted of H1 as compared to
the inactive oocyte 5S genes (Schlissel and Brown 1984; Wolffe and
Brown 1988). However, studies of other genes have shown the presence
of H1 on active genes (Ericsson et al. 1990), and it may instead be the
case that there is an altered H1/linker DNA interaction on active genes
(Weintraub 1984) resulting in preferential H1 loss from these regions
during experimental manipulation. Second, histone hyperacetylation, in
particular highly acetylated levels of H3 and H4, may cause unfolding of
the 30-nm fiber (Annunziato et al. 1988) and has been strongly correlated
with elevated levels of transcription (Allfrey 1977; Chahal et al. 1980;
Vavra et al. 1982; Prior et al. 1983; Waterborg and Matthews 1984;
Johnson et al. 1987; Hebbes et al. 1988).

Since positioned octamers can repress transcription initiation in vitro,
does this occur also in the living cell? If so, how is the equilibrium between basal transcription factors and nucleosomes surrounding the
TATA box and initiation site altered to allow initiation? Do these mechanisms somehow employ histone modification? Nucleosomes contain
four different proteins with different rates of evolution. Of these, H3 and
H4 are nearly invariant between widely divergent species. Do these
histones harbor transcription-specific functions that differ from those of
the more divergent constituents of the nucleosome? Histones H1, H2A,
H2B, and H3 also contain isoform variants that are developmentally
regulated in higher eukaryotes. The sites of variation are often in the
hydrophilic, multiply modified amino termini. Do the amino termini, by
virtue of these variations and modifications, regulate the reversible

histone/DNA or histone/protein interactions that determine cell-cycle-specific nucleosomal functions? To answer these and related questions, we have concentrated our efforts on a genetic and biochemical analysis of histone function in yeast.

YEAST NUCLEOSOME FUNCTION

Is Histone H1 Present?

An acid-urea gel profile of the yeast histones is shown in Figure 1. Shown are the two subtypes of H2B (H2B1 and H2B2), which differ by four amino acids at their amino termini (Wallis et al. 1980), and the two H2A subtypes, H2A1 and H2A2, which differ by the inverted positioning of two amino acids at their carboxyl termini (Choe et al. 1982). No subtypes have been found for histones H3 and H4 in yeast. Each of the histones is encoded by two different genes as shown in Figure 1. However, the duplicated H3 genes encode the same primary amino acid sequence. Likewise, the nucleotide sequence differences in the two H4 genes are also silent with respect to their encoded products. The yeast histone genes are organized into a total of four genetically unlinked loci as shown. The linked histone genes are transcribed divergently from a common upstream element of approximately 700–800 bp (Hereford et al. 1979; Smith and Andresson 1983; Smith and Murray 1983).

The histone H1-like protein shown in Figure 1 is of the size and charge expected for H1 and copurifies with the other histones. However,

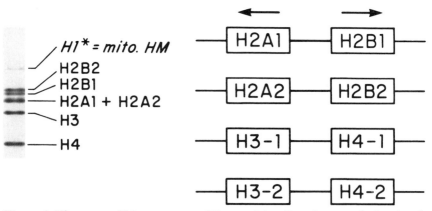

Figure 1 Histones and histone genes of *S. cerevisiae*. Proteins were isolated and electrophoresed on acid-urea polyacrylamide gels as described previously by Certa et al. (1984). H2A1 and H2B1, H2A2 and H2B2, H3-1 and H4-1, and H3-2 and H4-2 histones are coded for by the four unlinked divergently transcribed genes shown.

our biochemical analysis of this protein and antibodies raised against it have been used to show that this H1-like protein is in fact the mitochondrial DNA-binding protein HM (Certa et al. 1984). H1 may be present in yeast but may be difficult to isolate, perhaps due to its low abundance or rapid proteolysis. Alternatively, yeast may not contain histone H1. Evidence favoring the presence of H1 in yeast has been reported by Lowary and Widom (1989). These investigators found that partially purified yeast chromatin can undergo a cation-dependent folding into 30-nm fibers as determined by dynamic light scattering, electron microscopy, and X-ray diffraction. Such in vitro condensation of chromatin from higher eukaryotic organisms has previously been shown to require histone H1 (van Holde 1988). However, it has not been excluded that factors other than H1 facilitate this transition in yeast chromatin.

Is it possible that yeast has no need for H1? Histone H1 has been associated with folding the 30-nm fiber and has been implicated in facilitating genetic repression in higher eukaryotes. However, relative to more complex eukaryotes, much more of the yeast genome is hyperacetylated (Nelson 1982) and transcriptionally active (Davidson 1976; Hereford and Rosbash 1977). Moreover, most of the yeast genome is DNase-I-sensitive, suggesting a generally unfolded yeast chromosomal conformation (Lohr and Hereford 1979). Chromatosome-sized DNA fragments (164–166 bp), which are generated by DNase I digestion only in the presence of H1, have not been found in yeast (Szent-Gyorgyi and Isenberg 1983). Nucleosomes are spaced only 160–165 bp apart in yeast, leaving barely enough room to allow the chromatosomal 10 bp on either end of the nucleosomal 146 bp. Furthermore, yeast nucleosomes allow considerably more thermal untwisting of DNA than do nucleosomes on either chicken erythrocyte or SV40 chromatin (Morse et al. 1987; Lutter 1989). Since H1 interacts with internucleosomal DNA (van Holde 1988) and may constrain the linker, the latter observations raise the possibility that yeast nucleosomal flexibility may reflect the absence of H1. Such data, and the apparent lack of H1 in yeast histone preparations, both argue that yeast may lack H1.

Histone Subtypes Are Not Essential for Growth

To approach the problem of core histone function, we first asked whether the histone H2A and H2B subtypes were required for viability. By replacing each of the H2A and H2B subtypes separately with gene copies containing frameshift mutations, it was shown that yeast does not require histone subtypes for growth and completion of any part of the life cycle.

Furthermore, either H2A subtype could interact functionally in vivo with either H2B subtype (Kolodrubetz et al. 1982). However, deletion of one of the two histone gene copies can slow the growth rate (Rykowski et al. 1981; Kolodrubetz et al. 1982). This may reflect changes in the rate of histone mRNA synthesis (Norris and Osley 1987) or possible nonlethal effects on chromatin assembly (Norris et al. 1988). Gene disruption studies have also shown that yeast can survive with single H3 or H4 genes (Kayne et al. 1988; Smith and Stirling 1988; R. Mann and M. Grunstein, unpubl.). However, inactivation of both gene copies for any of the core histones results in lethality (Rykowski et al. 1981; Kolodrubetz et al. 1982; Kim et al. 1988; Smith and Stirling 1988; R. Mann and M. Grunstein, unpubl.). This observation allowed us to investigate the biochemical and cell cycle phenotypes resulting from histone absence. By pursuing the genetic function of histone proteins in yeast, we have hoped to address their various biological functions.

New Nucleosome Synthesis Is Essential for Chromosomal Segregation but Not for a Full Round of DNA Replication

A yeast strain (MHY102) was constructed lacking both chromosomal H2B genes and containing a single episomal histone H2B gene whose promoter was replaced by the *GAL10* promoter (Han et al. 1987). Similar methods were used to construct a strain (UKY403) containing a sole H4 gene under *GAL1* control (Kim et al. 1988). These strains allow histone H2B (or H4) mRNA synthesis to be activated in galactose or to be repressed by glucose media. Glucose treatment of either strain led to highly synchronous G_2 arrest and a block in chromosomal segregation to the bud, as determined by DAPI staining and flow cytometry. This phenomenon was especially evident when yeast cells were presynchronized in G_1 with α-factor mating pheromone.

Although histone mRNA synthesis is dependent on DNA synthesis, the opposite is not true. A full round of DNA synthesis occurred at an apparently unimpeded rate after histone mRNA synthesis was repressed. As expected, this 2N quantity of DNA contained an approximately 1N complement of nucleosomes, as judged by superhelical density measurements of plasmids harbored in these strains. Nucleosome loss was further confirmed by micrococcal nuclease digestion studies and indirect end-labeling experiments designed to detect nuclease-sensitive linker DNA between nucleosomes (Han et al. 1987; Kim et al. 1988). We concluded that loss of approximately half the normal nucleosomal complement completely blocks chromosomal segregation but allows a full round of

DNA synthesis. These results extend those of Meeks-Wagner and Hartwell (1986), who showed that changes in either histone H2A-H2B or H3-H4 gene copy number resulted in increased chromosome loss.

Histone synthesis is essential for mitosis; however, it appears unlikely that the lethal defect resulting from nucleosome depletion would occur this late in the cell cycle. For example, most nucleosome assembly occurs during the period of DNA replication in S phase. Nucleosome assembly occurs on nascent DNA just behind the replication fork (McKnight and Miller 1977). Therefore, it seems reasonable that altered chromatin formed in S phase upon glucose treatment (i.e., nucleosome loss) would be primarily responsible for lethality, resulting eventually in aborted chromosomal segregation. That this is likely the case was shown by releasing UKY403 cells from exposure to α-factor and glucose. By removing cells at various stages of the cell cycle, as they progressed from G_1 to their arrest point in G_2, and plating them on galactose, the stage at which lethality was first evident could be pinpointed. Most lethality was evident as the cells exited from G_1 and passed through S phase. Therefore, the lethality resulting from nucleosome loss manifests itself mainly in S phase during the period of nucleosome assembly. The altered chromatin formed is likely the cause of the block in chromosomal segregation in G_2. However, as with any genetic experiment, it is difficult to exclude the possibility that cellular events, *resulting from* altered chromatin, block chromosomal segregation.

Nucleosome Loss Activates Transcription of Otherwise Repressed Genes

Nucleosomes are present on genes transcribed by all three classes of RNA polymerase (I, II, and III). In vitro studies have suggested that nucleosomes repress initiation of genes transcribed by RNA polymerases II and III (van Holde 1988). We wanted to address this same issue in vivo by altering nucleosomal density and phasing. Nucleosome loss, obtained by repressing histone H4 synthesis, exhibited little effect on the synthesis of 25S and 18S ribosomal RNAs (the products of RNA polymerase I), and H4 depletion did not affect the synthesis of either 5S or tRNAs, the products of RNA polymerase III (Kim et al. 1988). Since these RNAs are transcribed continuously at high rates in yeast, it may be argued, however, that nucleosomes are already displaced or lost at the promoter sequences of their encoding genes.

Regulated yeast genes transcribed by RNA polymerase II contain enhancer-like, upstream activator sequences (UAS). These UAS elements function in an orientation-independent manner, at variable distance from their cognate coding sequence. UAS elements bind activator proteins that mediate transcription initiation via interactions with the preinitiation complex, possibly through adapter proteins (Berger et al. 1990; Kelleher et al. 1990; Pugh and Tjian 1990). The preinitiation complex, which contains basal transcription factors and RNA polymerase II, binds at the TATA element located just upstream of the site of transcription initiation. Basal factors and RNA polymerase II allow a moderate level of accurate transcription in vitro, even in the absence of the UAS elements and their cognate activator proteins. TFIID, the protein complex that recognizes the TATA element, is especially important in formation of the preinitiation complex. Its binding in vitro is a prerequisite for the subsequent formation of the preinitiation complex.

To analyze the effect of nucleosome loss on this mechanism, we examined both ongoing and repressed mRNA synthesis. Steady-state mRNA levels of yeast genes active in amino acid metabolism (*HIS3, HIS4, ARG4,* and *TRP1*) were examined. At best, only minor differences were found in the mRNA levels of these already active genes after H4 mRNA repression (Kim et al. 1988). An examination of uninduced mRNA levels produced by *regulated* genes initially yielded conflicting results. For example, the uninduced, steady-state level of *PHO5* mRNA was increased considerably following H4 depletion of the repressed *PHO5* gene, suggesting that nucleosomes, which are positioned on the TATA element (Almer and Horz 1986), were repressing transcription. In contrast, the uninduced level of *CUP1* mRNA was not noticeably increased after nucleosome loss (Kim et al. 1988; Han et al. 1988). However, we now have evidence to suggest that activation of *CUP1* by nucleosome loss may be obscured by posttranscriptional degradation of a high basal level of *CUP1* mRNA synthesis (Durrin et al. 1992). In fact, as described below, nucleosome loss activates the initiation of all five regulated promoters examined to date.

When the promoters for the *PHO5, CYC1,* and *GAL1* genes were fused to the *Escherichia coli* β-galactosidase (*lacZ*) reporter gene and introduced into yeast cells on episomal plasmids, it was observed that nucleosome loss activates transcription of each of these promoters. Perhaps, surprisingly, activation of transcription by nucleosome loss did not require the UAS element of any of these genes. In contrast, the TATA element was always essential. Levels of activation by nucleosome loss varied for the different promoter/*lacZ* fusions (ranging from ~2% to ~15% of final inducible levels). These levels represent activation levels of approximately 10- to 100-fold over background and represent minimum activation levels, since nucleosomes are only half depleted (Han and Grunstein 1988). Even the *CUP1* and *HIS3* promoters fused to *lacZ* are activated to high levels by nucleosome loss. Furthermore, similar levels of activation are seen when such constructions are integrated into the genome (Durrin et al. 1992). We conclude from these experiments that nucleosome loss activates transcription initiation of genes that otherwise require the use of specific activating proteins and UAS elements. This may occur by simply providing access to (at least partially) active transcription initiation factors that would otherwise be incapable of associating with the nucleosome-complexed promoter of a regulated gene. Alternatively, nucleosome-loss-induced changes in promoter topology may be energetically favorable for transcription initiation. In either case, these data provide evidence that nucleosomes repress transcription initiation in vivo. Moreover, changes in histone stoichiometry may alter promoter choice from a transposable element inserted next to yeast marker genes (Clark-Adams et al. 1988; for review, see Winston, this volume). These experiments and our own argue strongly that nucleosomes can regulate transcription initiation in living yeast cells.

Chromatin-dependent Activation of Basal Transcription

As outlined in the preceding section, our results show that nucleosome loss activates transcription initiation. To place this result in the context of general regulatory mechanisms, two issues should be emphasized. First, nucleosomes and basal transcription factors of the preinitiation complex compete for access to the TATA promoter element. Nucleosomes can inhibit initiation by basal transcription factors in soluble extracts derived from mammalian cells. However, nucleosomes will not inhibit initiation if the basal initiation factors (in particular TFIID) are allowed to first bind the TATA element (Matsui 1987; Workman and Roeder 1987; Knezetic et al. 1988). Second, basal transcription in vivo occurs at a significantly lower level than that observed in vitro using nuclear extracts lacking nucleosomes (Carthew et al. 1985; Lewis and Manley 1985; Sawadogo and Roeder 1985; Lewin 1990). Moreover, nucleosomes in soluble extracts decrease basal transcription much more so than activated transcription. This is true in experiments using the IE protein of pseudorabies virus, the USF activator protein of the adenovirus major late promoter, and GAL4-VP16 (a fusion of the yeast GAL4 DNA-binding site with the activation domain of the viral activator VP16) (Workman et al. 1988, 1990, 1991).

An important distinction can therefore be made between basal and activated transcription. Basal transcription may be defined as that level of transcription initiation which occurs in vitro upon recognition of the TATA element by the preinitiation complex. Basal transcription is repressed in vivo, most likely by nucleosomes. This repression may be overcome in one of two ways: first, by the action of UAS and the activator proteins that bind to them and, second, by genetically engineered nucleosome depletion.

These arguments raise the possibility that the activator proteins mediate nucleosome displacement from the TATA element. Recent in vitro work has shown that the activator protein VP16 can interact directly with TFIID (Stringer et al. 1990) and with a second basal factor, TFIIB (Lin and Green 1991). Furthermore, there are data showing that an activator can alter the footprint produced by a partially pure mammalian TFIID fraction near the TATA element (Horikoshi et al. 1988). Finally, the VP16 activation domain can prevent nucleosomal repression of initiation in vitro (Workman et al. 1991). Since activators may increase the association rate or stability of TFIID binding (Workman et al. 1990), an altered TFIID interaction mediated through activators might be sufficient to displace nucleosomes from the TATA element. Alternatively, the acidic groups of activator protein domains may interact directly with the highly basic histone proteins, thereby favoring their displacement from DNA. In either case, a *chromatin-dependent activation* step would allow access of a partially active preinitiation complex to the TATA element. However, as described below, there is evidence that some activation of the preinitiation complex by UAS elements and activator proteins can occur even in the absence of nucleosomes in soluble extracts. This suggests that activation cannot be solely dependent on chromatin unfolding. Therefore, a *chromatin-independent activation* step is likely to occur in vivo subsequent to nucleosomal unfolding.

Chromatin-independent Activation of Fully Induced Transcription

Carey et al. (1990) have shown that GAL4-VP16 can activate transcription in HeLa cell nuclear extracts even when the GAL4-binding sites are placed as much as 1.3 kb from the TATA box. Although the levels of activation under such conditions are relatively inefficient as compared to in vivo levels, this may be seen as evidence that some activation is independent of nucleosome structure (since it is unlikely that these extracts assemble nucleosomes). Similarly, GAL4-VP16 can inhibit transcription of genes lacking GAL4-binding sites, presumably by sequestering a factor required for transcription. This finding has been used to suggest that an accessory factor or "coactivator" is mediating the interaction between GAL4-VP16 and the preinitiation complex (Berger et al. 1990; Kelleher et al. 1990). If GAL4-VP16 were to interact solely with histones, the inhibitory effect would be difficult to explain. Activation in the absence of organized chromatin structure has also been observed in experiments involving the activator protein Sp1 (Pugh and Tjian 1990). Therefore, we anticipate that a chromatin-independent component to transcriptional activation accounts for the incremental increase from basal to full induction. This may be mediated through direct or indirect interactions between the activator and TFIID.

In conclusion, our data are most consistent with two levels of activation of regulated genes (Fig. 2). Upon induction, the activator may mediate nucleosome loss from the TATA element by directly or indirectly displacing nucleosomes. This interaction may require the histone H4 amino terminus (see below). This chromatin-dependent activation may allow access to the partially active preinitiation complex, allowing a basal level of transcription. A second chromatin-independent level of activation may then occur in which the activator interacts with TFIID (or other components of the preinitiation complex), leading to the fully induced state. It is likely that the relative contributions of these two steps differ for different UAS and TATA elements (Durrin et al. 1992).

FUNCTION OF THE HISTONE AMINO-TERMINAL TAILS IN YEAST

Large Deletions in the Extended, Hydrophilic Amino-terminal Tails Do Not Eliminate Histone Function

Deletion studies of each of the four core histone genes in yeast have shown that only the hydrophobic carboxy-terminal domains, which are involved in nucleosome assembly and stability, are essential for growth (Wallis et al. 1983; Schuster et al. 1986; Kayne et al. 1988; R. Mann and M. Grunstein, unpubl.). However, genetic studies of the dispensable amino-terminal tails (15–35% of each core histone) have begun to yield interesting insights into their function. Biochemical and biophysical studies have shown that the amino-terminal tails are structurally extended from the nucleosome core, free perhaps to interact reversibly with other nuclear components. Moreover, the tails are the sites of posttranslational modifications. In particular, acetylation of the H3 and H4 tails has been correlated with unfolded transcribed chromatin.

Genetic studies of amino-terminal sequences undertaken by constructing yeast strains that encode truncated and mutated histones suggest unique as well as redundant functions for the tails. The amino termini of all four core histones exhibit different amino acid sequences that for individual histone types are conserved to various extents in evolution. This conservation ranges from a moderate level in the case of the H2B tail, to a high level for H2A, to an almost invariant level or both H3 and H4.

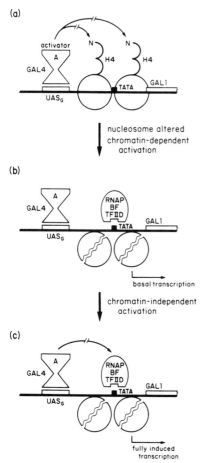

Figure 2 Proposed stages in the activation of a regulated yeast gene. (*a*) → (*b*) Chromatin-dependent activation. The activator bound to the UAS element directly or indirectly mediates nucleosome displacement from the TATA element by way of the histone H4 amino terminus. Nucleosome displacement would cause a partially active preinitiation complex to initiate a basal level of transcription. (*b*) → (*c*) Chromatin-independent activation. The activator directly or indirectly interacts with the TFIID complex to allow full induction.

The varied levels of evolutionary conservation perhaps suggest different functions for each of the core histone amino-terminal tails. However, the dispensability of the tails for all four core histones might also suggest common, perhaps redundant functions. This latter view is supported by the data showing that deletion of the H2A or H2B amino terminus does not prevent growth; however, deletion of both amino-terminal tails in the same cell is highly deleterious. Surprisingly, the presence of either the

H2A or H2B tail is sufficient for growth even when the tails are swapped between the hydrophobic core segments (Schuster et al. 1986). To study the physiological roles of the histone amino termini, our laboratory has analyzed histone acetyltransferase from yeast (Travis et al. 1984), as well as biochemical and cell-cycle-specific phenotypes of histone tail deletions and mutations (see below).

Histone H4 Amino-terminal Deletions Cause Moderate Changes in Chromatin Structure

Deletions in the amino terminus of histone H4 cause increased sensitivity of cellular chromatin to micrococcal nuclease, especially in strains carrying the larger H4 deletions in which residues 4–23 and 4–28 have been deleted. This results in an elongated G_2 phase (Kayne et al. 1988). Nucleosomes do not, however, appear to be generally unstable in these strains. Superhelical density measurements of yeast plasmids have provided a means by which to estimate the number of nucleosomes per episome, since each nucleosome induces one superhelical turn in a covalently closed circular plasmid (Worcel et al. 1981; Wang 1982). The superhelical density of a *TRP1/ARS1* yeast plasmid is unchanged in the H4 amino-terminal deletion (4–28) mutant (Roth et al. 1992; B. Thomsen and M. Grunstein, unpubl.).

Histone H4 Is Specifically Involved in Regulating the Yeast Silent Mating Loci: Identification of Repressor Domains at Residues 16–19 and 21–29

The first example in which we found one of the core histones to be clearly involved in a specific function concerned repression of the silent mating loci. In *S. cerevisiae*, there are three loci on chromosome III (*HMLα*, *MAT* [**a** or α], and *HMR***a**) which encode information that determines mating type (Herskowitz and Oshima 1981). Despite the presence of identical promoter sequences at the silent loci and *MAT* (e.g., *HMLα* and *MATα* or *HMR***a** and *MAT***a**), only the information located at the *MAT* locus is expressed, thereby determining the mating type of the cell (**a**, α, or in the case of a diploid cell, **a**/α). The production of both **a** and α information in the same cell acts to repress haploid functions and prevent further mating. The expression of haploid functions thereby depends on the efficient repression of *HMLα* and *HMR***a**. Repression is dependent on the function of four nonessential repressor proteins, termed Sir1, Sir2, Sir3, and Sir4. These repressors act through the E and I silencer sequences that are present at the boundaries of both silent mating loci (Abraham et al. 1983, 1984; Brand et al. 1985). Surprisingly, although two additional proteins, encoded by *RAP1* and *ABF1*, have been shown to bind to these sites, there is no evidence that Sir proteins bind to silencer sequences (Shore and Nasmyth 1987; Buchman et al. 1988).

Deletions in the amino termini of the H2A and H2B histones had little noticeable effect on mating. Experiments utilizing histone H3 (R. Mann and M. Grunstein, unpubl.) showed that deletion of residues 4–40 at the amino terminus decreased mating by approximately 100-fold. In contrast, deletion of residues 4–19 of histone H4 decreased mating efficiency by approximately 6 orders of magnitude and activated *HMLα* and *HMRa* specifically (Kayne et al. 1988). A deletion that removed residues 4–14 had very little effect on mating and *HMLα/HMRa* derepression. This caused us to focus on residues 15–19 as a site in the H4 protein involved in silencing. This region contains four consecutive basic residues (Lys-Arg-His-Arg). Altering the charge of this basic region specifically activates the silent mating locus *HML* (Johnson et al. 1990; Megee et al. 1990; Park and Szostak 1990). More recently, we have also shown the presence of an adjacent, non-basic domain (residues 21–29) that is also required for repressing the silent mating loci (Johnson et al. 1992).

The involvement of a ubiquitous protein, such as histone H4, in this highly specific function of silencing seems paradoxical. However, we have found that mutations at the amino terminus of Sir3, a repressor specific to the silent mating loci, can suppress single amino acid substitutions of histone H4. Such suppression is not seen in strains that express an H4 variant that is deleted at the amino terminus (Johnson et al. 1990, 1992). Therefore, Sir3 requires the presence of the H4 amino terminus for suppression, and silencing may occur through an interaction between Sir3 and histone H4 (Fig. 3). The specificity for this interaction between silencer DNAs may be provided by other silencer-binding proteins that may interact with a component of the Sir complex (Shore and Nasmyth 1987; Shore et al. 1987; Buchman et al. 1988).

It may be important to note that the deletion which strongly affects silencing (H4 *del4-19* but not H4 *del4-14*) also affects the ability of the yeast α2 operator/repressor complex to position a nucleosome directly adjacent to the operator (Roth et al. 1990, 1992). It will be of special interest to determine whether nucleosome positioning is critical to *HML* and *HMR* repression.

The H4 Amino Terminus Is Also Involved in Gene Activation: An Activation Domain Surrounding the Sites of Acetylation

Acetylation of H4 lysine residues at positions 5, 8, 12, and 16 is correlated with elevated levels oftranscription (Hebbes et al. 1988). These ex-

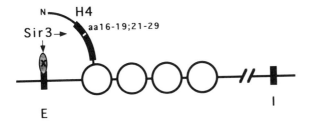

Figure 3 Interaction between H4 and Sir3 to repress the silent mating loci. The histone H4 amino-terminal residues 16–19 and 21–29 are involved in the repression of the yeast silent mating loci *HML* (shown here) and *HMR* by a direct or indirect interaction with the repressor protein Sir3. E and I are the silencer DNA elements, necessary for effective repression of *HML* and *HMR*. Since Sir3 does not appear to recognize the silencer elements themselves, it is proposed that another protein(s) (X) mediates the interaction between Sir3 and E (or I) DNA, thereby providing the specificity for this interaction at the silent mating loci.

periments, coupled with the invariant nature of most of the H4 tail through evolution, argue for other important but nonessential H4 tail functions in the remainder of the amino terminus. We have recently constructed deletions and multiple amino acid substitutions in H4 residues 4–23 (Durrin et al. 1991). Surprisingly, these mutations depress *GAL1* and *PHO5* induction, suggesting that whereas the region at positions 16–19 and 21–29 is involved in repression (of the silent mating loci), the domain at positions 4–23 is involved in gene activation (Fig. 4). Along similar lines, Mary Ann Osley and her colleagues have recently found that the amino termini of H2A and H2B may be involved in autoregulating the synthesis of their encoding mRNAs (Moran et al. 1990; M.A. Osley, pers. comm.). It is possible, therefore, that the H4 amino terminus also possesses this additional, activating role in its own regulation. These overlapping functions of the H4 amino-terminal tail may explain the extremely conserved nature of histone H4.

CONCLUSIONS AND PERSPECTIVES

We have described experiments that suggest a function for the nucleosome as a unit repressing basal transcription initiation of regulated yeast genes. We have also found that the extremely conserved amino-terminal tail of histone H4 has at least two important functions. These include a repressor region (residues 16–19; 21–29) involved in silencing the *HML*α and *HMR*a silent mating loci and an activation domain (resi-

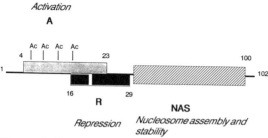

Figure 4 Functional domains of yeast histone H4. Shown is the domain (A) (residues 4–23) containing the acetylated lysine residues (5, 8, 12, and 16) and required for *GAL1* activation (Durrin et al. 1991). (R) Domain containing basic residues 16–19 and 21–29 required for *HML* and *HMR* repression. (NAS) Nucleosome assembly and stability domain (residues 29–100). Strains containing deletions in A or R are viable, whereas deletions in NAS are lethal and have a G_2 arrest phenotype similar to those in which histone H4 synthesis is blocked entirely (Kayne et al. 1988).

dues 4–23) involved in *GAL1* induction. We believe that the conserved nature of histones argues very strongly that nucleosomes repress basal transcription in all eukaryotes and that the H4-specific functions defined herein are applicable to more complex organisms. Although silencing of the mating loci has only been observed in yeast, there are now a number of other eukaryotic genes that are believed to be subject to silencing (Winoto and Baltimore 1989; Alberts and Sternglanz 1990; Baniahmad et al. 1990; Savagner et al. 1990). One interesting case of gene silencing, for which a histone involvement appears likely, concerns heterochromatin in *Drosophila melanogaster*. Position effect variegation in *Drosophila* is caused by the repression of active genes upon their juxtaposition to inactive heterochromatic domains. Moore et al. (1983) have found that deletions resulting in decreased histone gene copy number suppress the inactivation associated with position effect variegation. Biochemical and genetic identification of proteins in yeast that interact with nucleosomal components to allow general initiation, silencing of the mating loci, and promoter activation may very well lead to the identification of similar mechanisms of repression and activation in other eukaryotes.

ACKNOWLEDGMENTS

The experiments from our laboratory described here were funded by U.S. Public Health Service grants from the National Institutes of Health (GM-23674 and GM-42421).

REFERENCES

Abraham, J., K.A. Nasmyth, J.N. Strathern, A.J.S. Klar, and J.B. Hicks. 1984. Regulation of mating-type information in yeast: Negative control requiring sequences both 5' and 3' to the regulated region. *J. Mol. Biol.* **176**: 307–331.

Abraham, J., J. Feldman, K.A. Nasmyth, J.N. Strathern, A.J.S. Klar, J.R. Broach, and J.B. Hicks. 1983. Sites required for position-effect regulation of mating-type information in yeast. *Cold Spring Harbor Symp. Quant. Biol.* **47**: 989–998.

Alberts, B. and R. Sternglanz. 1990. Gene expression: Chromatin contract to silence. *Nature* **344**: 193–194.

Allan, J., N. Harborne, D.C. Rau, and H. Gould. 1982. Participation of core histone "tails" in the stabilization of the chromatin solenoid. *J. Cell. Biol.* **93**: 285–297.

Allfrey, V.G. 1977. Post-synthetic modifications of histone structure: A mechanism for the control of chromosome structure by the modulation of histone-DNA interactions. In *Chromatin and chromosome structure* (ed. H.J. Li and R. Eckhardt), pp. 167–191. Academic Press, New York.

Almer, A. and W. Horz. 1986. Nuclease hypersensitive regions with adjacent positioned nucleosomes mark the gene boundaries of the *PHO5/PHO3* locus in yeast. *EMBO J.* **5**: 2681–2687.

Annunziato, A.T., L.-L.Y. Frado, R.L. Seale, and C.L.F. Woodcock. 1988. Treatment with sodium butyrate inhibits the complete condensation of interphase chromatin. *Chromosoma* **96**: 132–138.

Baniahmad, A., C. Steiner, A.C. Khne, and R. Renkawitz. 1990. Modular structure of a chicken lysozyme silencer: Involvement of an unusual thyroid hormone receptor site. *Cell* **61**: 505–514.

Berger, S.L., W.D. Cress, A. Cress, S.J. Triezenberg, and L. Guarente. 1990. Selective inhibition of activated but not basal transcription by the acidic activation domain of VP16: Evidence for transcriptional adaptors. *Cell* **61**: 1199–1208.

Brand, A.H., L. Breeden, J. Abraham, R. Sternglanz, and K. Nasmyth. 1985. Characterization of a "silencer" in yeast: A DNA sequence with properties opposite to those of a transcriptional enhancer. *Cell* **41**: 41–48.

Buchman, A.R., N.F. Lue, and R.D. Kornberg. 1988. Connections between transcriptional activators, silences, and telomeres as revealed by functional analysis of a yeast DNA-binding protein. *Mol. Cell. Biol.* **8**: 5086–5099.

Carey, M., J. Leatherwood, and M. Ptashne. 1990. A potent GAL4 derivative activates transcription at a distance *in vitro*. *Science* **247**: 710–712.

Carthew, R.W., L.A. Chodosh, and P.A. Sharp. 1985. An RNA polymerase II transcription factor binds to an upstream element in the adenovirus major late promoter. *Cell* **43**: 439–448.

Certa, U., M. Colavito-Shepanski, and M. Grunstein. 1984. Yeast may not contain histone H1: The only known "histone H1-like" protein in *Saccharomyces cerevisiae* is a mitochondrial protein. *Nucleic Acids Res.* **12**: 7975–7985.

Chahal, S.S., H.R. Matthews, and E.M. Bradbury. 1980. Acetylation of histone H4 and its role in chromatin structure and function. *Nature* **287**: 76–79.

Choe, J., D. Kolodrubetz, and M. Grunstein. 1982. The two yeast histone H2A genes encode similar protein subtypes. *Proc. Natl. Acad. Sci.* **79**: 1484–1487.

Clark-Adams, C.D., D. Norris, M.A. Osley, J.S. Fassler, and F. Winston. 1988. Changes in histone gene dosage alter transcription in yeast. *Genes Dev.* **2**: 150–159.

Davidson, E.H. 1976. *Gene activity in early development*, vol. 16. Academic Press, New York.

Durrin, L.K., R.K. Mann, and M. Grunstein. 1992. Nucleosome loss activates CUP1 and HIS3 promoters to fully induced levels in the yeast *Saccharomyces cerevisiae*. *Mol. Cell. Biol.* (in press).

Durrin, L.K., R.K. Mann, P.S. Kayne, and M. Grunstein. 1991. Yeast histone H4 N-terminal sequence is required for promoter activation *in vivo*. *Cell* **65**: 1023–1031.

Ericsson, C., U. Grossbach, B. Bjorkroth, and B. Daneholt. 1990. Presence of histone H1 on an active Balbiani ring gene. *Cell* **60**: 73–83.

Fedor, M.J., N.F. Lue, and R.D. Kornberg. 1988. Statistical positioning of nucleosomes by specific protein-binding to an upstream activating sequence in yeast. *J. Mol. Biol.* **204**: 109–127.

Garner, M.M. and G. Felsenfeld. 1987. Effect of Z-DNA on nucleosome placement. *J. Mol. Biol.* **196**: 581–590.

Han, M. and M. Grunstein. 1988. Nucleosome loss activates yeast downstream promoters *in vivo*. *Cell* **55**: 1137–1145.

Han, M., M. Chang, U.-J. Kim, and M. Grunstein. 1987. Histone H2B repression causes cell-cycle-specific arrest in yeast: Effects on chromosomal segregation, replication, and transcription. *Cell* **48**: 589–597.

Han, M., U.-J. Kim, P.S. Kayne, and M. Grunstein. 1988. Depletion of histone H4 and nucleosomes activates the *PHO5* gene in *Saccharomyces cerevisiae*. *EMBO J.* **7**: 2221–2228.

Hebbes, T.R., A.W. Thorne, and C. Crane-Robinson. 1988. A direct link between core histone acetylation and transcriptionally active chromatin. *EMBO J.* **7**: 1395–1402.

Hereford, L. and L.H. Hartwell. 1973. Roles of protein synthesis in the replication of yeast DNA. *Nat. New Biol.* **244**: 129–131.

Hereford, L. and M. Rosbash. 1977. Number and distribution of polyadenylated RNA sequences in yeast. *Cell* **10**: 453–462.

Hereford, L., K. Fahrner, J. Woolford, and M. Rosbash. 1979. Isolation of yeast genes H2A and H2B. *Cell* **18**: 1261–1271.

Herskowitz, I. and Y. Oshima. 1981. Control of cell type in *Saccharomyces cerevisiae*: Mating type and mating-type interconversion. In *The molecular biology of the yeast Saccharomyces: Life cycle and inheritance* (ed. J.N. Strathern et al.), pp. 181–209. Cold Spring Harbor Laboratory, New York.

Horikoshi, M., T. Hai, Y.-S. Lin, M.R. Green, and R.G. Roeder. 1988. Transcription factor ATF interacts with the TATA factor to facilitate establishment of a preinitiation complex. *Cell* **54**: 1033–1042.

Johnson, E.M., R. Sterner, and V.G. Allfrey. 1987. Altered nucleosomes of active nucleolar chromatin contain accessible histone H3 in its hyperacetylated forms. *J. Biol. Chem.* **262**: 5943–5946.

Johnson, L.M., G. Fisher-Adams, and M. Grunstein. 1992. Identification of a non-basic domain in the histone H4 N-terminus required for repression of the yeast silent mating loci. *EMBO J.* (in press).

Johnson, L.M., P.S. Kayne, E.S. Kahn, and M. Grunstein. 1990. Genetic evidence for an interaction between SIR3 and histone H4 in the repression of the silent mating loci in *Saccharomyces cerevisiae*. *Proc. Natl. Acad. Sci.* **87**: 6286–6290.

Kayne, P.S., U.-J. Kim, M. Han, J.R. Mullen, F. Yoshizaki, and M. Grunstein. 1988. Extremely conserved histone H4 N-terminus is dispensable for growth but essential for repressing the silent mating loci in yeast. *Cell* **55**: 27–39.

Kelleher, R.J., P.M. Flanagan, and R.D. Kornberg. 1990. A novel mediator between activator proteins and the RNA polymerase II transcription apparatus. *Cell* **61**: 1209–1215.

Kim, U.-J., M. Han, P.S. Kayne, and M. Grunstein. 1988. Effects of histone H4 depletion on the cell cycle and transcription of *Saccharomyces cerevisiae*. *EMBO J.* **7:** 2211–2119.

Knezetic, J.A. and D.S. Luse. 1986. The presence of nucleosomes on a DNA template prevents initiation by RNA polymerase II *in vitro*. *Cell* **45:** 95–104.

Knezetic, J.A., G.A. Jacob, and D.S. Luse. 1988. Assembly of RNA polymerase II preinitiation complexes before assembly of nucleosomes allows efficient initiation of transcription on nucleosomal templates. *Mol. Cell. Biol.* **8:** 3114–3121.

Kolodrubetz, D., M.C. Rykowski, and M. Grunstein. 1982. Histone H2A subtypes associate interchangeably *in vivo* with histone H2B subtypes. *Proc. Natl. Acad. Sci.* **79:** 7814–7818.

Kornberg, R.D. and L. Stryer. 1988. Statistical distributions of nucleosomes: Nonrandom locations by a stochastic mechanism. *Nucleic Acids Res.* **16:** 6677–6690.

Lewin, B. 1990. Commitment and activation at Pol II promoters: A tail of protein-protein interactions. *Cell* **61:** 1161–1164.

Lewis, E.D. and J.L. Manley. 1985. Control of adenovirus late promoter expression in two human cell lines. *Mol. Cell. Biol.* **5:** 2433–2442.

Lin, Y.S. and M.R. Green. 1991. Mechanism of action of an acidic transcriptional activator in vitro. *Cell* **64:** 971–991.

Lohr, D. and L. Hereford. 1979. Yeast chromatin is uniformly digested by DNase I. *Proc. Natl. Acad. Sci.* **76:** 4285–4288.

Lorch, Y., J.W. LaPointe, and R.D. Kornberg. 1987. Nucleosomes inhibit the initiation of transcription but allow chain elongation with the displacement of histones. *Cell* **49:** 203.

Lowary, P.T. and J. Widom. 1989. Higher-order structure of *Saccharomyces cerevisiae* chromatin. *Proc. Natl. Acad. Sci.* **86:** 8266–8270.

Lutter, L.C. 1989. Thermal unwinding of simian virus 40 transcription complex DNA. *Proc. Natl. Acad. Sci.* **86:** 8712–8716.

Matsui, T. 1987. Transcription of adenovirus 2 major late and peptide IX genes under conditions of *in vitro* nucleosome assembly. *Mol. Cell. Biol.* **7:** 1401–1408.

McGhee, J.D. and G. Felsenfeld. 1980. Nucleosome structure. *Annu. Rev. Biochem.* **49:** 1115–1156.

McKnight, S.L. and O.L. Miller, Jr. 1977. Electron microscopy analysis of chromatin replication in the cellular blastoderm *Drosophila melanogaster* embryo. *Cell* **12:** 795–804.

Meeks-Wagner, D. and L.H. Hartwell. 1986. Normal stoichiometry of histone dimer sets is necessary for high fidelity of mitotic chromosome transmission. *Cell* **44:** 43–52.

Megee, P.C., B.A. Morgan, B.A. Mittman, and M.M. Smith. 1990. Genetic analysis of histone H4: Essential role of lysines subject to reversible acetylation. *Science* **247:** 841–845.

Moore, G.D., D.A. Sinclair, and T.A. Grigliatti. 1983. Histone gene multiplicity and position effect variegation in *Drosophila melanogaster*. *Genetics* **105:** 327–344.

Moran, L., D. Norris, and M.A. Osley. 1990. A yeast H2A-H2B promoter can be regulated by changes in histone gene copy number. *Genes Dev.* **4:** 752–763.

Morse, R.H., D.S. Pederson, A. Dean, and R.T. Simpson. 1987. Yeast nucleosomes allow thermal untwisting of DNA. *Nucleic Acids Res.* **15:** 10311–10330.

Nelson, D.A. 1982. Histone acetylation in baker's yeast: Maintenance of the hyperacetylated configuration in log phase protoplasts. *J. Biol. Chem.* **257:** 1565–1568.

Norris, D. and M.A. Osley. 1987. The two gene pairs encoding H2A and H2B play different roles in the *Saccharomyces cerevisiae* life cycle. *Mol. Cell. Biol.* **7:** 3473–3481.

Norris, D., B. Dunn, and M.A. Osley. 1988. The effect of histone gene deletions on chromatin structure in *Saccharomyces cerevisiae*. *Science* **242:** 759–761.

Park, E.C. and J. Szostak. 1990. Point mutations in the yeast histone H4 gene prevent silencing of the silent mating locus HML. *Mol. Cell. Biol.* **10:** 4932–4934.

Prior, C.P., C.R. Cantor, E.M. Johnson, V.C. Littau, and V.G. Allfrey. 1983. Reversible changes in nucleosome structure and histone H3 accessibility in transcriptionally active and inactive states of rDNA chromatin. *Cell* **34:** 1033–1042.

Pugh, B.F. and R. Tjian. 1990. Mechanism of transcriptional activation by Sp1: Evidence for coactivators. *Cell* **61:** 1187–1197.

Richmond, T.J., J.T. Finch, B. Rushton, D. Rhodes, and A. Klug. 1984. Structure of the nucleosome core particle of 7Å resolution. *Nature* **311:** 532–537.

Roth, S.Y., A. Dean, and R.T. Simpson. 1990. Yeast α2 repressor positions nucleosomes in TRP1/ARS1 chromatin. *Mol. Cell. Biol.* **10:** 2247–2260.

Roth, S.Y., M. Shimuzu, L. Johnson, M. Grunstein, and R.T. Simpson. 1992. Stable nucleosome positioning and complete repression by the yeast α2 repressor are disrupted by amino-terminal mutations in histone H4. *Genes Dev.* **6:** (in press).

Rykowski, M.C., J.W. Wallis, H. Choe, and M. Grunstein. 1981. Histone H2B subtypes are dispensable during the yeast cell cycle. *Cell* **25:** 477–487.

Savagner, P., T. Miyashita, and Y. Yamada. 1990. Two silencers regulate the tissue-specific expression of the collagen II gene. *J. Biol. Chem.* **265:** 6669–6674.

Sawadogo, M. and R.G. Roeder. 1985. Interaction of a gene-specific transcription factor with the adenovirus major late promoter upstream of the TATA box region. *Cell* **43:** 165–175.

Schlissel, M.S. and D.D. Brown. 1984. The transcriptional regulation of *Xenopus* 5S RNA genes in chromatin: The roles of active stable transcription complexes and histone H1. *Cell* **37:** 903–913.

Schuster, T., M. Han, and M. Grunstein. 1986. Yeast histone H2A and H2B amino termini have interchangeable functions. *Cell* **45:** 445–451.

Shore, D. and K. Nasmyth. 1987. Purification and cloning of a DNA binding protein from yeast that binds to both silencer and activator elements. *Cell* **51:** 721–732.

Shore, D., D.J. Stillman, A.H. Brand, and K.A. Nasmyth. 1987. Identification of silencer binding proteins from yeast: Possible roles in SIR control and DNA replication. *EMBO J.* **6:** 461–467.

Simpson, R.T. 1978. Structure of the chromatosome, a chromatin particle containing 160 bp and all the histones. *Biochemistry* **17:** 5524–5531.

Smith, M.M. and O.S. Andresson. 1983. DNA sequences of yeast H3 and H4 histone genes from two non-allelic gene sets encode identical H3 and H4 proteins. *J. Mol. Biol.* **169:** 663–690.

Smith, M.M. and K. Murray. 1983. Yeast H3 and H4 histone messenger RNAs are transcribed from two non-allelic gene sets. *J. Mol. Biol.* **169:** 641–661.

Smith, M.M. and V.B. Stirling. 1988. Histone H3 and H4 gene deletions in *Saccharomyces cerevisiae*. *J. Cell Biol.* **106:** 557–566.

Stringer, K.F., C.J. Ingles, and J. Greenblatt. 1990. Direct and selective binding of an acidic transcriptional activation domain to the TATA-box factor TFIID. *Nature* **345:** 783–786.

Szent-Gyorgyi, C. and I. Isenberg. 1983. The organization of oligonucleosomes in yeast. *Nucleic Acids Res.* **11:** 3717–3736.

Thoma, F. 1986. Protein-DNA interactions and nuclease-sensitive regions determine nucleosome positions on yeast plasmid chromatin. *J. Mol. Biol.* **190:** 177–190.

Thoma, F. and R.T. Simpson. 1985. Local protein-DNA interactions may determine nucleosome positions on yeast plasmids. *Nature* **315**: 250–252.

Thoma, F., T. Koller, and A. Klug. 1979. Involvement of histone H1 in the organization of the nucleosome and of the salt dependent superstructures of chromatin. *J. Cell Biol.* **83**: 403–427.

Travis, G.H., M. Colavito-Shepanski, and M. Grunstein. 1984. Extensive purification and characterization of chromatin-bound histone acetyltransferase from *Saccharomyces cerevisiae. J. Biol. Chem.* **259**: 14406–14412.

Travers, A.A. 1987. DNA bending and nucleosome positioning. *Trends Biochem. Sci.* **12**: 108–112.

van Holde, K.E. 1988. *Chromatin* (ed. A. Rich). Springer-Verlag, New York.

Vavra, K.J., C.D. Allis, and M.A. Gorovsky. 1982. Regulation of histone acetylation in *Tetrahymena* macro- and micronuclei. *J. Biol. Chem.* **257**: 2591–2598.

Wallis, J.W., L. Hereford, and M. Grunstein. 1980. Histone H2B genes of yeast encode two different proteins. *Cell* **22**: 799–805.

Wallis, J.W., M. Rykowski, and M. Grunstein. 1983. Yeast histone H2B containing large amino terminus deletions can function *in vivo. Cell* **35**: 711–719.

Wang, J.C. 1982. The path of DNA in the nucleosome. *Cell* **29**: 724–726.

Waterborg, J.H. and H.R. Matthews. 1984. Patterns of histone acetylation in *Physarum polycephalum* H2A and H2B acetylation are functionally distinct from H3 and H4 acetylation. *Eur. J. Biochem.* **142**: 329–335.

Weintraub, H. 1984. Histone-H1-dependent chromatin superstructures and the suppression of gene activity. *Cell* **38**: 17–27.

Winoto, A. and D. Baltimore. 1989. $\alpha\beta$ lineage-specific expression of the α T cell receptor gene by nearby silencers. *Cell* **59**: 649–655.

Wolffe, A.P. and D.D. Brown. 1988. Developmental regulation of two 5S ribosomal RNA genes. *Science* **241**: 1626–1632.

Worcel, A., S. Strogatz, and D. Riley. 1981. Structure of chromatin and the linking number of DNA. *Proc. Natl. Acad. Sci.* **78**: 3627–3631.

Workman, J.L. and R.G. Roeder. 1987. Binding of transcription factor TFIID to the major late promoter during *in vitro* nucleosome assembly potentiates subsequent initiation by RNA polymerase II. *Cell* **51**: 1613–1622.

Workman, J.L., R.G. Roeder, and R.E. Kingston. 1990. An upstream transcription factor, USF (MLTF), facilitates the formation of preinitiation complexes during *in vitro* chromatin assembly. *EMBO J.* **9**: 1299–1308.

Workman, J.L., C.A. Taylor, and R.E. Kingston. 1991. Activation domains of stably bound *GAL4* derivatives alleviate repression of promoters by nucleosomes. *Cell* **64**: 533–544.

Workman, J.L., S.M. Abmayr, W.A. Cromlish, and R.G. Roeder. 1988. Transcriptional regulation by the immediate early protein of pseudorabies virus during *in vitro* nucleosome assembly. *Cell* **55**: 211–219.

Cumulative Author Index

Cumulative Subject Index

Hypersynthesis of AraC regulatory
    protein, 647

ICP0, as transcriptional activator,
    707–708
ICP4, as transcriptional activator,
    705–707, 710–712
ICP27, as transcriptional activator, 707
Immunoglobulin
    heavy-chain gene enhancer, 862
    light-chain gene enhancer, 862–863
Inducer for short transcripts (IST), 302
Initiation complex, 220, 227–242,
    329–330. *See also* Transcrip-
    tional initiation
Initiation factors. *See* σ^{70}
Insulin, E boxes and, 862
Integration host factor (IHF), 11, 667
    -induced bend and NIFA, 677–679
    NTRC-mediated activation and,
    678–679
    protein, 969
Interferon
    -β (INF-β) gene regulation, 1193–1215
    consensus sequence binding protein,
    1204
    response sequence, 1197
    -stimulated gene factors, 1202–1203
Intergenic spacer, 315
Interleukin-1 (IL-1), 785
Interleukin-6 (IL-6), 785–786. *See also*
    NF-IL6
IRF-1, 1200–1202
IRF-2, 1202

Jacob, François, early regulatory studies,
    3–7
jun, 797, 812–813, 817, 1048
Jun, 17, 774–776, 838, 882, 1020, 1149
    DNA-binding, 803–806
    effects of cell growth and differentia-
    tion, 815–818
    Fos and cellular transformation,
    818–819
    jun-transforming gene, 812–813
    leucine zipper dimerization, 800–803
    oncogenic transformation, 811–814
    origin, 798–799
    transcriptional regulation, 806–807

in vitro, 808–810
in vivo, 807–808
transcription factor AP-1 and, 799–800
JunB and JunD, 797

Kluyveromyces lactis, 29
Krüppel (Kr), 1238
Krüppel, zinc-binding domain and, 601
Ku antigen, 292

lac, 508, 523
    operator, 636–637, 1261
    promoter, 7, 502, 520–521, 524
    repressor, 7, 470, 546, 629–639, 994,
    1261
    -operator complex, 634–635
lacY, 7
λ late gene operon, 391
λ Q protein, 390–393
λ-repressor, 546
LAP, 1081–1085, 1087
Leader peptide, and transcriptional con-
    trol, 410–411, 415–417, 424,
    431
Leucine zipper, 580, 696, 838, 1023,
    1082, 1155. *See also* bZip
    domain; Coiled coil
    C/EBP as model, 771, 774–778, 800
    dimerization domain, 771, 777, 797,
    800–803
    domains, NMR structure, 590–592
    GCN4 and, 838–841
leu operon, 414–417
LexA, 940, 1008, 1018
    operator, 1023
LF-B1 homeodomain, 559
Ligand screening assay, retinoid recep-
    tors and, 1143–1144
Liver activator protein, 786
lyl-1, 864

Mata1p-Matα2p, 952, 958–959, 961,
    968
MCM1, 937, 975, 1182
    DNA-binding specificity, 984, 992
    as model for SRF function, 895–897,
    984